A Working Guide to Shell-and-Tube Heat Exchangers

ABOUT THE AUTHOR

Stanley Yokell, president of MGT Inc., specializes in tubular heat exchangers, factory management, pressure vessels, and process equipment. He holds a bachelor of chemical engineering degree from New York University. Mr. Yokell is a member of AIChE, ASME, AWS, NSPE, and ASNT; a licensed PE in Colorado, Illinois, and New Jersey; and a member of the Special Working Group on Heat Transfer Equipment, Section VIII, ASME Pressure Vessel Code Committee.

A Working Guide to Shell-and-Tube Heat Exchangers

Stanley Yokell

McGraw-Hill Publishing Company

New York   St. Louis   San Francisco   Auckland   Bogotá
Caracas   Hamburg   Lisbon   London   Madrid   Mexico
Milan   Montreal   New Delhi   Oklahoma City
Paris   San Juan   São Paulo   Singapore
Sydney   Tokyo   Toronto

Library of Congress Cataloging-in-Publication Data

Yokell, Stanley.
   A working guide to shell-and-tube heat exchangers.

   1. Heat exchangers.   I. Title.
TJ263.Y65   1990   621.402′5   89-14028
ISBN 0-07-072281-1

   234567890 DOC/DOC   9543210

ISBN 0-07-072281-1

*The editors for this book were Bob Hauserman, Gail Nalven, and
Beatrice E. Eckes, the designer was Naomi Auerbach, and the
production supervisor was Suzanne Babeuf. This book was set in
Century Schoolbook. It was composed by the McGraw-Hill Publishing
Company Professional & Reference Division composition unit.*

Printed and bound by R. R. Donnelly & Sons Company.

*For more information about other McGraw-Hill materials,
call 1-800-2-MCGRAW in the United States. In other
countries, call your nearest McGraw-Hill office.*

Contents

Contents

Contents   ix

Preface

In 1976 the author was asked to present a lecture on design and fabrication of heat exchangers in the fall lecture series *Practical Aspects of Heat Transfer*, offered jointly by the North Jersey and New Jersey sections of the American Institute of Chemical Engineers. It was specifically to be a detailed review of mechanical design and construction considerations of shell-and-tube heat exchangers. Fools rush in. . . . A lecture was prepared, given, well attended, and well received. The question-and-answer session extended almost until midnight.

Most of the chemical engineers present were well versed in the thermodynamic theory and fluid dynamics of tubular exchangers and the process considerations and requirements that apply. However, it quickly became apparent that they knew little about the mechanical and practical aspects. Remembering the depth of his ignorance when first confronted with heat exchanger problems, the author thought that it would be very helpful to many engineers to have a guidebook.

Some time later, the author agreed to present a 4-day intensive continuing-education course on heat exchangers. Aware that engineering education covers generally the basic knowledge that applies and that such courses had long been offered in the thermodynamics, thermal design, fluid dynamics, and stress analysis of tubular exchangers, he organized one called *Shell-and-Tube Heat Exchangers—Mechanical Aspects*, intended to bridge the gap between theory and practice. It consisted of a series of lectures and a visit to a heat exchanger factory.

The author had assumed that participants would be mostly chemical engineers. He expected them to come from chemical plants, oil refineries, resin and fibers plants, paper mills, steel mills, food- and drug-producing facilities, etc., and hoped that some power plant engineers would attend. Much to his surprise, most were mechanical engineers. A substantial number worked in fossil and nuclear power stations.

Being a believer in the ecumenical nature of engineering, the author had included in the course notes information about power plant heat exchangers, feedwater heaters, and steam generators. Therefore, he quickly adapted the lectures to suit the spectrum of participants. The course was well received and has been given many times in the United States, Canada, and Europe. In response to requests from power generation engineers, Carl F. Andreone and the author organized a similar course devoted to closed feedwater heaters.

This guide includes much that engineers who took part in these courses wanted to know. Although works abound on the stress analysis of heat exchanger components, on the thermodynamics, process, and thermal design, and on the fluid dynamics, few deal with practical requirements. This book is intended as a *working guide* that responds to these needs. It is addressed to mechanical and chemical engineers in the process, refining, food, and power generation industries and to designers, specifiers, purchasers, manufacturers, and maintainers of tubular heat exchangers.

Because engineering students have so much to learn, curricula cannot cover many of the working engineer's needs. Texts are unlikely to deal with such bread-and-butter things as heat exchanger construction, inspection, maintenance and repairs and troubleshooting. This work aims to fill the lack.

The author is indebted to many friends and colleagues for their help and advice. These include the members of the Special Working Group on Heat Transfer Equipment of the ASME Boiler and Pressure Vessel Code Committee. Friends and associates Abe Brothman and Leo J. Marin, who made suggestions and warned that no such work can ever be adequate or complete, have passed on. They cannot be thanked but only remembered.

This book is dedicated to my wife Edith Gersen Yokell, whose patience with the author is boundless.

1

Guide to Describing
Heat Exchangers

Introduction

This chapter discusses the language of shell-and-tube heat exchangers and explains current usage for describing sizes, types, configurations, and installation positions.

Industry practice for shell-and-tube equipment is to use the terms *heat exchanger, tubular exchanger,* and *exchanger* interchangeably without regard to function, and they will be used that way throughout this book. However, *heat exchanger* is also used to describe units that transfer sensible heat from one stream to another in order to conserve energy.

Exchangers are also named to describe their functions. For example, a chiller cools a liquid flowing through one side by transferring some of its heat to a vaporizing refrigerant flowing through the other side, reboilers and vaporizers boil or vaporize a liquid by extracting heat from a hotter fluid, and condensers condense a vapor to a liquid by transferring its latent heat to a colder fluid.

Heat exchangers used in heating, ventilating, air conditioning, and refrigeration, petroleum refining, chemical and petrochemical processing, and general industrial manufacturing are categorized as *process heat exchangers*. Auxiliary shell-and-tube exchangers used in power generation are called *power plant heat exchangers*. Specialized units used to heat boiler feedwater with turbine extraction steam are called *closed feedwater heaters* but may be termed feedwater heaters or simply heaters.

Process heat exchanger nomenclature is based upon the *Standards of the Tubular Exchanger Manufacturers Association (TEMA Standards).*[1] These standards also have systems for describing process exchanger types and for designating sizes and operating positions. With some modifications these systems are used worldwide. American Petroleum Institute (API) Standard 660 incorporates the TEMA nomenclature and terminology by incorporating *TEMA Mechanical Standards*, Class R, by reference.[2]

Similar but somewhat different nomenclature is used in North America by the power generation industry. The Heat Exchange Institute (HEI) has developed standards for power plant heat exchangers (HEI PPS), closed feedwater heaters (HEI CFHS), and steam surface condensers used in power generation.[3-5] The HEI PPS has nomenclature for power plant heat exchangers and its own system for describing types of exchangers, but it has no system for designating sizes. Moreover, there is no HEI CFHS system for describing closed feedwater heater types or sizes.

This chapter provides illustrated guidelines to feedwater heater configurations and reviews current terminology.

Nomenclatures

Figure 1.1, adapted from the *TEMA Standards*, shows cross sections through elevations of schematic drawings of six types of heat exchangers. Figure 1.2, adapted from the HEI PPS, shows cross sections through elevations of schematic drawings of heat exchanger components. The glossary at the end of this chapter defines related terms and expands some of the TEMA and HEI PPS definitions. Figures 1.3 through 1.5 illustrate some frequently used terms.

Designating Size

The *TEMA Standards* size-numbering system is straightforward and simple. It is in general use for process and commercial heat exchangers and is also suitable for designating the sizes of power plant exchangers and feedwater heaters.

In this system, the size number indicates the shell inside diameter (ID) in inches (millimeters), rounded to the nearest integer, and straight tube length (L) in inches (millimeters). For all but kettle-type reboilers, the size number is ID $\times$ L. For kettle-type reboilers, the size number is the port ID through which the bundle enters (ID'), the shell diameter (ID), and the length (L) in the form ID'/ID $\times$ L.

For U-tube exchangers, the straight tube length is the distance from the outermost tubesheet face to the bend line. For straight-tube units, tube length is the length over the outermost tubesheet faces.

Examples of the TEMA size-numbering system

Example 1.1   What is the size number of a straight-tube blowdown cooler that has a 24-in (610-mm) pipe shell, ⅜ in (9.5 mm) thick, and tubes that are 20 ft (6096 mm) long?

answer

English units

Diameter	24 − (2 × ⅜) = 23¼, rounded to the nearest integer = 23
Length	20 × 12 = 240
Size number	23-240

Metric units

Diameter	610 − (2 × 9.5) = 591
Length	6096
Size number	591-6096

Example 1.2   What is the size number of a closed feedwater heater with 24-ft (7315-mm) straight-length U tubes and a 48-in-OD (1219-mm-OD) shell, ½ in (12.7 mm) thick?

answer

English units

Diameter	48 − (2 × ½) = 47
Length	24 × 12 = 288
Size number	47-288

Metric units

Diameter	1219 − (2 × 12.7) = 1193.6, rounded to the nearest integer = 1194
Length	7315
Size number	1194-7315

Example 1.3   What is the size number of a vaporizer with a 24-in-OD × ⅜-in (610-mm-OD × 9.5-mm) bundle nozzle that enters an eccentric conical transition to a 45-in-ID (1143-mm-ID) shell and receives a 16-ft (4877-mm) straight-length U-tube bundle?

answer

English units

Port ID	24 − (2 × ⅜) = 23¼, rounded to the nearest integer = 23
Shell ID	45
Length	16 × 12 = 192
Size number	23/45-192

Metric units

Port ID	610 − (2 × 9.5) = 591
Shell ID	1143
Length	4877
Size number	591/1143-4877

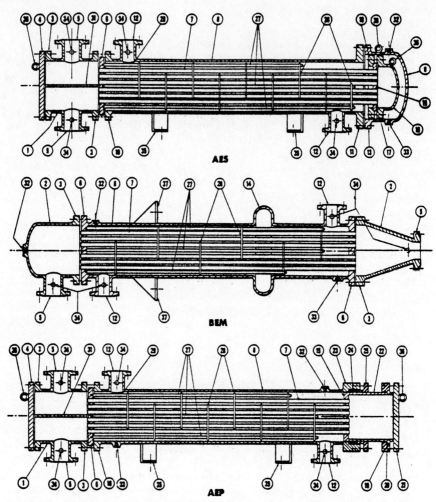

Figure 1.1 TEMA heat exchanger nomenclature. (*Adapted from the* TEMA Standards, *7th ed., by permission of the Tubular Exchanger Manufacturers Association.*)

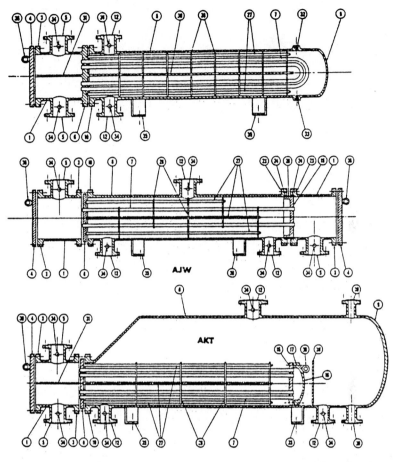

AJW

AKT

1. Stationary head—channel	14. Expansion joint	27. Tie rods and spacers
2. Stationary head—bonnet	15. Floating tubesheet	28. Transverse baffles or
3. Stationary-head flange—	16. Floating-head cover	support plates
channel or bonnet	17. Floating-head flange	29. Impingement baffle
4. Channel cover	18. Floating-head backing	30. Longitudinal baffle
5. Stationary-head nozzle	device	31. Pass partition
6. Stationary tubesheet	19. Split shear ring	32. Vent connection
7. Tubes	20. Slip-on backing flange	33. Drain connection
8. Shell	21. Floating-head cover—	34. Instrument connection
9. Shell cover	external	35. Support saddle
10. Shell flange—stationary-head	22. Floating-tubesheet skirt	36. Lifting lug
end	23. Packingbox flange	37. Support bracket
11. Shell flange—rear-head end	24. Packing	38. Weir
12. Shell nozzle	25. Packing follower ring	39. Liquid-level connection
13. Shell-cover flange	26. Lantern ring	

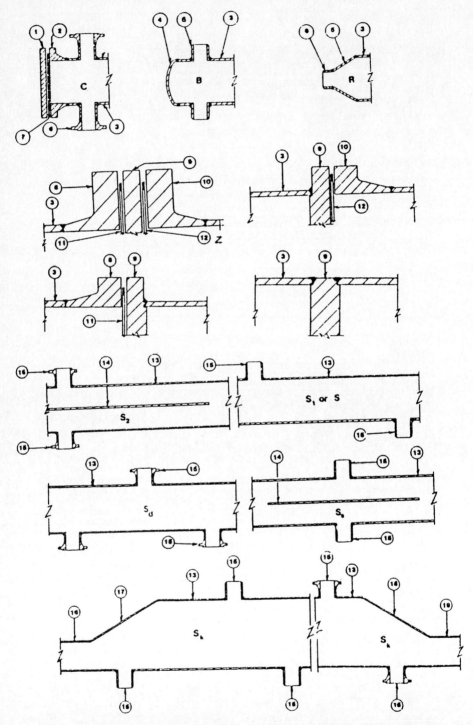

Figure 1.2 HEI heat exchanger nomenclature. (*Adapted from the* HEI Standard for Power Plant Heat Exchangers, *1st ed., by permission of the Heat Exchange Institute.*)

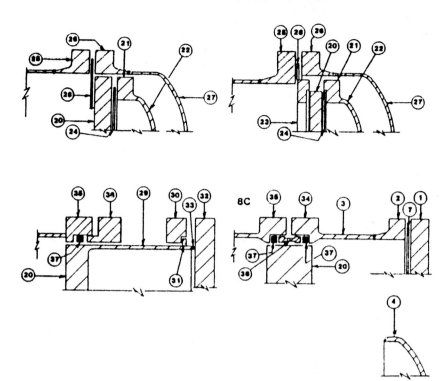

8C

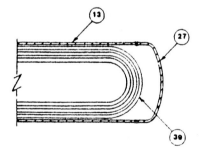

1. Bolted channel cover	14. Shell longitudinal	28. Shell rear gasket
2. Channel-cover flange	baffle	29. Packed floating-head
3 Channel cylinder	15. Shell nozzle	cylinder
4. Integral channel head	(flanged or weld end)	30. Packed floating-head
(bonnet)	16. Shell front exchanger	flange
5. Channel reducer	17. Shell front reducer	31. Split shear ring
6. Channel nozzle	18. Shell rear reducer	32. Packed floating-head
(flanged or weld end)	19. Shell rear cylinder	cover
7. Channel-cover gasket	20. Floating tubesheet	33. Packed floating-head
8. Channel tubesheet	21. Floating-head flange	cover gasket
flange	22. Floating head	34. Channel packing flange
9. Stationary tubesheet	23. Floating-head split	35. Shell packing flange
10. Shell tubesheet flange	backing ring	36. Packing gland
11. Channel tubesheet	24. Floating-head gasket	37. Packing
gasket	25. Shell rear flange	38. Lantern ring
12. Shell tubesheet gasket	26. Shell cover flange	39. Tubes
13. Shell cylinder	27. Shell cover	

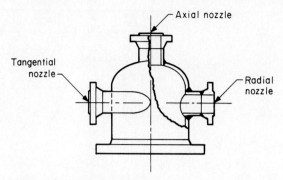

Figure 1.3   Types of nozzles.

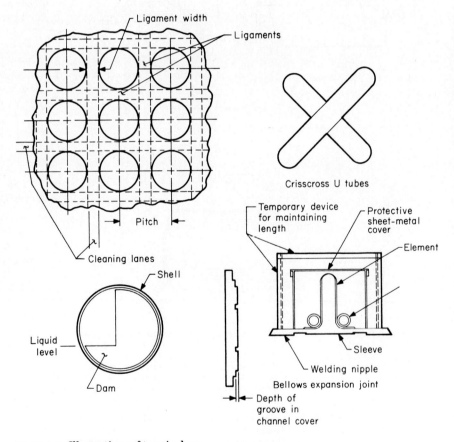

Figure 1.4   Illustrations of terminology.

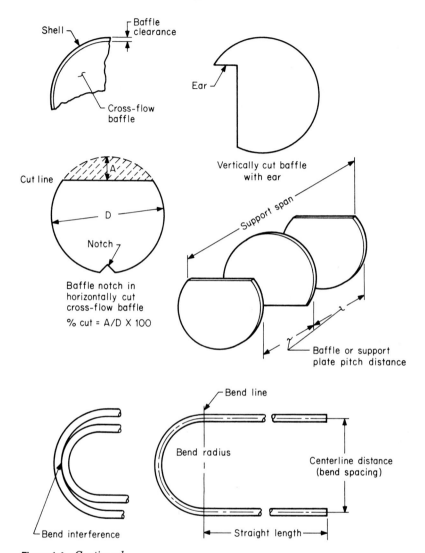

Figure 1-4 *Continued.*

Example 1.4   A fixed-tubesheet phosgene condenser is to be built by using double-tubesheet construction. Face-to-face of the inner tubesheets will be 7 ft 4 in (2235 mm). The gap between the inlet-end tubesheets will be 2 in (50.8 mm). The gap between the outlet-end tubesheets will be 1½ in (38.1 mm). The thickness of the outer tubesheets will be 2⅛ in (54 mm). The tubes are to extend ⅛ in (3.2 mm) beyond the outer tubesheet faces. The shell will be rolled to 33¼-in ID. What will the size number of the unit be?

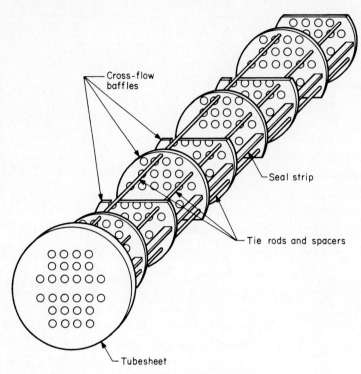

Figure 1.5 Heat exchanger skeleton showing stationary (or front) tubesheet, cross-flow baffles, tie rods and spacers, and seal strips.

answer

English units

Shell ID	33¼, rounded to the nearest integer = 33
Length	7 × 12 + 4 + 2 + 1.5 + 2 × 2.125 = 95.75
Size number	33-96

Metric units

Shell ID	844.6, rounded to the nearest integer = 845
Length	2235 + 50.8 + 38.1 + 2 × 54 = 2431.9, rounded to nearest integer = 2432
Size number	845-243

Describing Exchanger Types

Different systems for indicating exchanger types are recommended by the *TEMA Standards* and the HEI PPS. The TEMA system is used so widely that power station engineers should also be familiar with it.

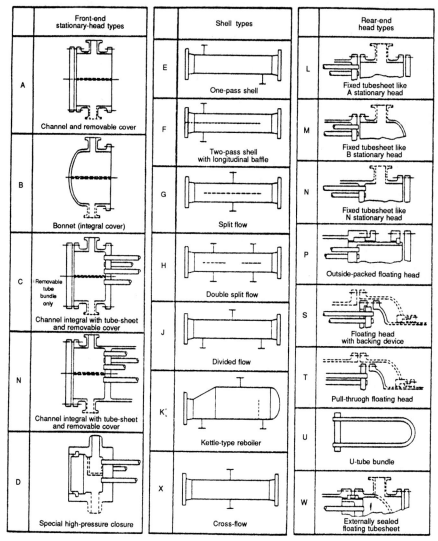

Front-end stationary-head types		Shell types		Rear-end head types	
A	Channel and removable cover	E	One-pass shell	L	Fixed tubesheet like A stationary head
B	Bonnet (integral cover)	F	Two-pass shell with longitudinal baffle	M	Fixed tubesheet like B stationary head
		G	Split flow	N	Fixed tubesheet like N stationary head
C	Removable tube bundle only Channel integral with tube-sheet and removable cover	H	Double split flow	P	Outside-packed floating head
		J	Divided flow	S	Floating head with backing device
N	Channel integral with tube-sheet and removable cover	K	Kettle-type reboiler	T	Pull-thruogh floating head
				U	U-tube bundle
D	Special high-pressure closure	X	Cross-flow	W	Externally sealed floating tubesheet

Figure 1.6 The TEMA expression for designating exchanger types. (*From the* TEMA Standards, *7th ed., by permission of the Tubular Exchanger Manufacturers Association.*)

TEMA system for describing types

The TEMA system (Fig. 1.6) consists of a general expression of these three variables: a front head, shell, and rear head. Constants that indicate component types are substituted for each variable. For the variable *front head*, the constants and their meanings are:

A   Channel with removable cover
B   Bonnet with integral cover

C   Channel integral with the tubesheet and having a removable cover when the tube bundle is removable

N   Channel integral with the tubesheet and having a removable cover when the tube bundle is not removable

D   Special high-pressure closure

For *shell* the constants and their meanings are:

E   One-pass shell
F   Two-pass shell
G   Split flow
H   Double split flow
J   Divided flow
K   Kettle type
X   Cross-flow

Constants to substitute for *rear head* are:

L   Fixed tubesheet like A stationary head
M   Fixed tubesheet like B stationary head
N   Fixed tubesheet like N stationary head
P   Outside-packed floating head
S   Floating head with backing device
T   Pull-through floating bundle
U   U-tube bundle
W   Externally sealed floating tubesheet

Figure 1.6 illustrates and shows how to substitute the constants in the TEMA expression to indicate an exchanger's configuration. The *TEMA Standards* allow manufacturers to use any system to denote special types. Most base special-type designations on the TEMA expressions and the constants listed above whenever they can. Table 1.1 shows the possible configurations that the TEMA expression can indicate with these constants. The italicized types are rarely used.

HEI PPS system for describing types

The HEI system for designating power plant heat exchanger types (Fig. 1.7) employs a five-variable general expression. As in the TEMA system, constants that indicate the configurations of the components are substituted. The HEI PPS general expression is

$$VWS_jYZ$$

The meanings of the variables and the values of the constants are as follows: V stands for the front-head or stationary tubeside closure

TABLE 1.1   Possible TEMA Types

Types in italics are rarely used.

AEL	AEM	*AEN*	AEP	AES	AET	AEU	AEW
AFL	AFM	*AFN*	AFP	AFS	AFT	AFU	AFW
AGL	AGM	*AGN*	AGP	AGS	AGT	AGU	AGW
AHL	AHM	*AHN*	AHP	AHA	AHT	AHU	AHW
AJL	AJM	*AJN*	AJP	AJA	AJT	AJU	AJW
AKL	AKM	*AKN*		AKS	AKT	AKU	
AXL	AXM	*AXM*	AXP	AXS	AXT	AXU	AXW
BEL	BEM	*BEN*	BEP	BES	BET	BEU	BEW
BFL	BFM	*BFN*	BFP	BFS	BFT	BFU	BFW
BGL	BGM	*BGN*	BGP	BGS	BGT	BGU	BGW
BHL	BHM	*BHN*	BHP	BHS	BHT	BHU	BHW
BJL	BJM	*BJN*	BJP	BJS	BJT	BJU	BJW
BKL	BKM	*BKN*		BKS	BKT	BKU	
BXL	BXM	*BXN*	BXP	BXS	BXT	BXU	BXW
			CEP	CES	CET	CEU	CEW
			CFP	CFS	CFT	CEU	CEW
			CGP	CGS	CGT	CGU	CGW
			CHP	CHS	CHT	CHU	CHW
			CJP	CJS	CJT	CJU	CJW
			CKP	CKP	CKT	CKU	CKW
			CXP	CXS	CXT	CXU	CXW
NEL	*NEM*	NEN	*NEP*	*NES*	*NET*	NEU	*NEW*
NFL	*NFM*	NFN	*NFP*	*NFS*	*NFT*	NGU	*NFW*
NGL	*NGM*	NGN	*NGP*	*NGS*	*NGT*	NGU	*NGW*
NJL	*NJM*	NJN	*NJP*	*NJS*	*NJT*	NJU	*NJW*
NKL	*NKM*	NKN		*NKS*	NKT	NKU	
DED				DES	DET	DEU	
DFD				DFS	DFT	DFU	
DGD				DGS	DGT	DGU	
DHD				DHS	DHT	DHU	
DJD				DJS	DJT	DJU	
DKD				*DKS*	*DKT*	DKU	
DXD				DXS	DXT	DXU	

type. To specify the closure type, substitute the constant B, C, or R with these meanings:

B   Integral channel cover (bonnet)

C   Bolted channel cover (cover)

R   Channel reducer (reducer)

W stands for the front tubesheet arrangement. To specify the front tubesheet arrangement, substitute the number 1, 2, 3, or 4 for W as follows:

1   For a bolted tubesheet, gasketed on both sides

2   For a tubesheet integral with the channel (welded) and bolted to the shell

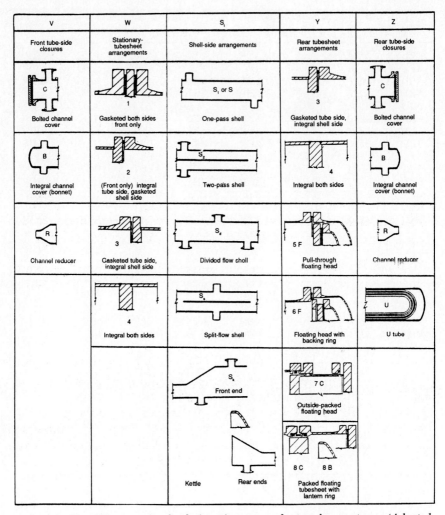

V	W	S_j	Y	Z
Front tube-side closures	Stationary-tubesheet arrangements	Shell-side arrangements	Rear tubesheet arrangements	Rear tube-side closures
C 1 Bolted channel cover	Gasketed both sides front only	S_1 or S One-pass shell	3 Gasketed tube side, integral shell side	C Bolted channel cover
B Integral channel cover (bonnet)	2 (Front only) integral tube side, gasketed shell side	S_2 Two-pass shell	4 Integral both sides	B Integral channel cover (bonnet)
R Channel reducer	3 Gasketed tube side, integral shell side	S_d Divided flow choll	5 F Pull-through floating head	R Channel reducer
	4 Integral both sides	S_s Split-flow shell	6 F Floating head with backing ring	U U tube
		S_k Front end Kettle Rear ends	7 C Outside-packed floating head 8 C 8 B Packed floating tubesheet with lantern ring	

Figure 1.7   The HEI expression for designating power plant exchanger types. (*Adapted from the* HEI Standard for Power Plant Heat Exchangers, *1st ed., by permission of the Heat Exchange Institute.*)

3   For a tubesheet integral with the shell and bolted to the channel

4   For a tubesheet integral with both sides (welded)

S_j denotes the kind of shell. To specify shell construction, substitute a number or letter for subscript j as follows:

1   For one-pass; 2 for two-pass, etc.

d   For divided flow

k   For kettle

s   For split flow

Y represents the rear tubesheet arrangement for straight-tube units. The rear tubesheet arrangement parameters are:

1	Same as for W
2	Same as for W
3	Same as for W
4	Same as for W
5	Pull-through floating head
6	Floating head with backing ring
7	Tubesheet used with an outside-packed floating head
8	Packed floating tubesheet

Z stands for the rear tubeside closure. Substitute constants B, C, R, F, or U to specify the rear tubeside closure. The constants mean:

B	Same as for V
C	Same as for V
R	Same as for V
F	Floating head
U	U tube

Figure 1.7 illustrates and shows how to use the HEI PPS constants to indicate an exchanger's configuration. Table 1.2 compares some HEI and TEMA designations.

The HEI PPS expression conveys a great deal of information. For example, R4S3R describes a single-pass shell, single-pass tubeside fixed-tubesheet exchanger, built for axial inlet and outlet tubeside flow, that has conical reducer bonnets, with the inlet bonnet welded to the inlet tubesheet and the outlet bonnet welded to the rear tubesheet.

Position

Process and power plant heat exchangers may operate with their axial centerlines vertical, horizontal, or at some angle in between. Closed feedwater heaters operate either vertically or horizontally. Neither the TEMA nor the HEI PPS system has an operating-position designator, but it is customary to indicate horizontal positions with H and vertical positions with V. For pitched units, indicate the degrees pitched off the horizontal with HP__° or off the vertical with (V__°).

Practices for Closed Feedwater Heaters

The HEI closed feedwater heater standards (CFHS) do not offer guidelines for describing size or type. The TEMA system can be used to indicate size, but to describe the type it is necessary to specify:

TABLE 1.2   HEI versus TEMA Standard Parts Nomenclature

HEI nomenclature	TEMA nomenclature
Bolted channel cover	Channel cover
Channel cover flange	Stationary head flange—channel or bonnet
Channel cylinder	Stationary head channel
Integral head (bonnet)	Stationary head—bonnet
Channel reducer	Stationary head—bonnet
Channel nozzle (flanged/weld end)	Stationary head nozzle
Channel cover gasket	Channel cover gasket
Channel tubesheet flange	Stationary head flange—channel or bonnet
Shell tubesheet flange	Shell flange—stationary end
Channel tubesheet gasket	
Shell tubesheet gasket	
Shell cylinder	Shell
Shell longitudinal baffle	Longitudinal baffle
Shell nozzle (flanged/weld end)	Shell nozzle
Shell front cylinder	
Shell front reducer	
Shell rear reducer (like front shell rear cylinder)	
Floating tubesheet	Floating tubesheet
Floating head flange	Floating head flange
Floating head	Floating head cover
Floating head split backing ring	Floating head backing device
Floating head gasket	
Shell rear flange	Shell flange rear head end
Shell cover flange	Shell cover flange
Shell cover	Shell cover
Shell rear gasket	
Packed floating head cylinder	Floating tubesheet skirt
Packed floating head flange	Slip-on backing flange
Packed floating head cover	Floating head cover—external
Packed floating head cover gasket	
Channel packing flange	Packing box
Shell packing flange	Packing box
Packing	Packing
Lantern ring	Lantern ring
Tubes	Tubes
....	Expansion joint
....	Tie rods and spacers
....	Transverse baffles or support plates
....	Impingement plate
....	Pass partition
....	Vent connection
....	Drain connection
....	Instrument connection
....	Support saddle
....	Lifting lug
....	Weir

1. Channels and closures
2. Manway that provides access to the tube ends
3. Pass-partition type
4. Steam-side zone arrangements
5. Bundle construction
6. Installation position
7. Miscellaneous details

Describing channels and manways

The HEI CFHS designate channels as *full-diameter access* or *manway access*, each of which has several configurations. The channel configuration affects pass-partition construction and feedwater nozzle positions.

Figures 1.8 through 1.10 illustrate schematically customary usages for describing full-diameter access designs in U-tube-bundle heaters. The usages also apply to fixed-tubesheet and floating-head types. Figures 1.8 and 1.9 illustrate gasketed channel-cover configurations. The construction shown in Fig. 1.8 is similar to a combination TEMA N for the tubesheet and cover attachments and TEMA D for the pass-

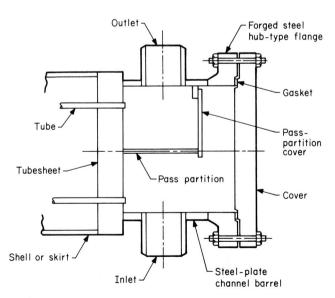

Figure 1.8 Full-opening bolted and gasketed channel cover with a separate pass-partition cover. (*Adapted from the* HEI Standards for Closed Feedwater Heaters, *4th ed., by permission of the Heat Exchange Institute.*)

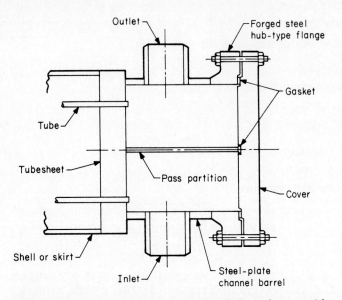

Figure 1.9 Full-opening bolted and gasketed channel cover with pass-partition groove in the channel cover. (*Adapted from the* HEI Standards for Closed Feedwater Heaters, *4th ed., by permission of the Heat Exchange Institute.*)

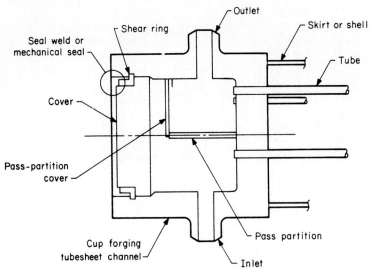

Figure 1.10 Shear-member load-bearing closure.

partition closure. That of Fig. 1.9 is like TEMA N, and Fig. 1.10 is like the TEMA special high-pressure closure designation D.

Figure 1.8 is termed a full-opening bolted and gasketed channel cover with a separate pass-partition cover. The alternative described in Fig. 1.9 is termed a full-opening bolted and gasketed channel cover with a pass-partition groove in the channel cover. Describe the closed feedwater heater channel as a shear-member load-bearing closure.

Figures 1.11 through 1.15 illustrate manway access channel constructions. The configuration shown in Fig. 1.11 is called a hemihead low-pressure manway access channel. It has no barrel section, and the feedwater connections therefore enter at an angle of approximately 30° with the tubesheet face. Figure 1.12 illustrates a similar construction for higher pressures. Here a hemispherical head is welded to a lip that is integral with the tubesheet on the feedwater side. The lip is not long enough to accept radial feedwater nozzles, which also enter at an angle. This configuration is called a hemihead high-pressure manway access channel.

Figure 1.13 is an alternative in which the lip is long enough for the feedwater connections to enter radially. It is called an alternative high-pressure hemihead manway access channel with radial feedwater connections. A variation in which the end closure is an inverted flange welded to the lip, as shown in Fig. 1.14, is called a combination tubesheet and channel barrel with inverted flange, high-pressure manway access channel. The corresponding low-pressure heater alternative described in Fig. 1.15 has a rolled-plate barrel welded to the tubesheet and an elliptical-head end closure. It is called an elliptical-head low-pressure manway access channel.

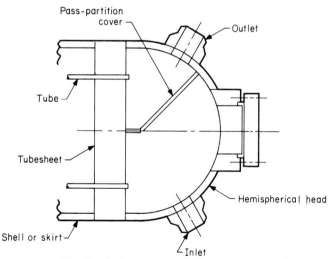

Figure 1.11 Hemihead low-pressure manway access channel. (*Adapted from the* HEI Standards for Closed Feedwater Heaters, *4th ed., by permission of the Heat Exchange Institute.*)

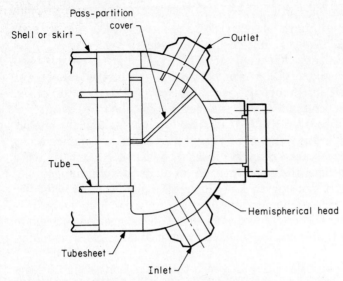

Figure 1.12 Hemihead high-pressure manway access channel. (*Adapted from the* HEI Standards for Closed Feedwater Heaters, *4th ed., by permission of the Heat Exchange Institute.*)

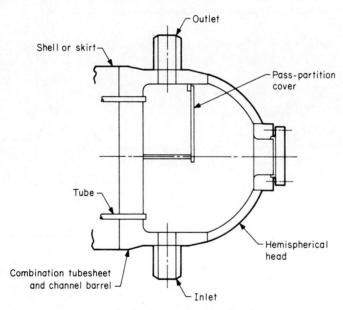

Figure 1.13 Alternative high-pressure hemihead manway access channel. (*Adapted from the* HEI Standards for Closed Feedwater Heaters, *4th ed., by permission of the Heat Exchange Institute.*)

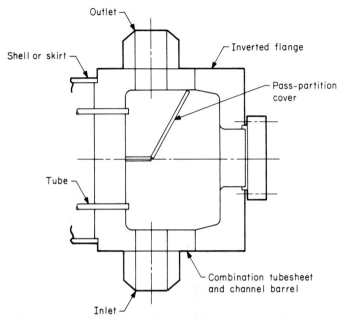

Figure 1.14   Cup forging combination tubesheet and channel barrel with inverted-flange high-pressure manway access channel. (*Adapted from the* HEI Standards for Closed Feedwater Heaters, *4th ed., by permission of the Heat Exchange Institute.*)

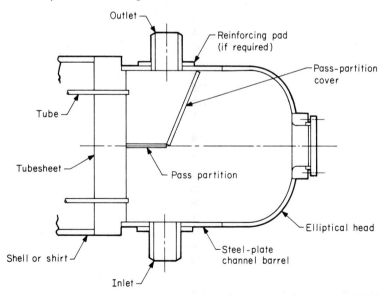

Figure 1.15   Elliptical-head low-pressure manway access channel. (*Adapted from the* HEI Standards for Closed Feedwater Heaters, *4th ed., by permission of the Heat Exchange Institute.*)

Manway types are illustrated in Figs. 1.16 through 1.18. Describe the one shown in Fig. 1.16 as an external-bolted-cover manway; describe the manway shown in Fig. 1.17 as an external-gasketed, bolted-cover type; and call the one depicted in Fig. 1.18 an internal-pressure-sealing-cover manway.

Zones, tube supports, and baffles

The turbine extraction steam supplied to a closed feedwater heater may be superheated or saturated. Condensate may exit the heater at its saturation temperature or be subcooled by the incoming feedwater. The choices are governed by the overall balance of the plant (BOP).

The region of the shell in which the tubes are allocated to condens-

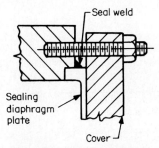

Figure 1.16 External-bolted-cover manway with sealing diaphragm. (*Adapted from the* HEI Standards for Closed Feedwater Heaters, *4th ed., by permission of the Heat Exchange Institute.*)

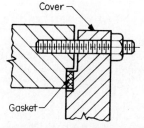

Figure 1.17 External-gasketed, bolted-cover manway. (*Adapted from the* HEI Standards for Closed Feedwater Heaters, *4th ed., by permission of the Heat Exchange Institute.*)

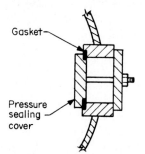

Figure 1.18 Internal-pressure-sealing cover. (*Adapted from the* HEI Standards for Closed Feedwater Heaters, *4th ed., by permission of the Heat Exchange Institute.*)

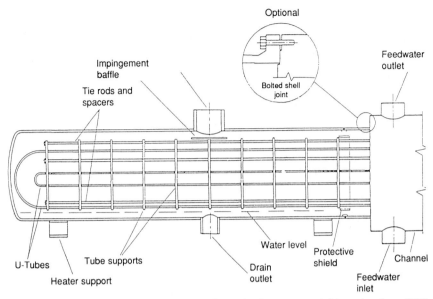

Figure 1.19 Schematic arrangement of a single-zone straight-condensing CFH. (*Adapted from the* HEI Standards for Closed Feedwater Heaters, *4th ed., by permission of the Heat Exchange Institute.*)

ing steam is called the *condensing zone.* When the steam supply is superheated, it enters the shell through an enclosure around the part of the tube bundle that shrouds the region from the condensing zone. This region is called the *desuperheating zone.* When feedwater subcools the condensate, it does so in surface enclosed in a *subcooling zone.*

Closed feedwater heaters in which saturated steam enters and condensate leaves at its saturation temperature are straight-condensing single-zone units (Fig. 1.19). Their bundles are constructed with either semisupports or full-circle supports. When full circles are used, the shell is made larger than the supports to allow for steam passage and distribution. Spiders and skid bars align the full-circle supports with the shell. In straight-condensing units the drains outlet is located at the bottom of the shell.

When a closed feedwater heater receives superheated steam and discharges saturated steam, it is termed a two-zone desuperheating and condensing unit. As shown schematically in Fig. 1.20, the shrouded desuperheating region is located at the outlet end of the outlet-tube pass. Desuperheating zones are fitted with single-segmental, double-segmental, triple-segmental, disk-and-doughnut, or proprietary baffle systems.

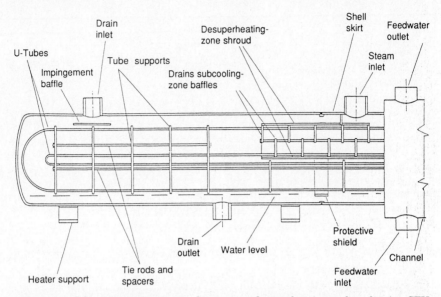

Figure 1.20   Schematic arrangement of a two-zone desuperheating and condensing CFH. (*Adapted from the* HEI Standards for Closed Feedwater Heaters, *4th ed., by permission of the Heat Exchange Institute.*)

To avoid erosion the steam side of the tube must remain dry. Therefore, a set minimum amount of superheat must be available.

When steam enters saturated and is discharged subcooled, the heater is a two-zone closed condensing and subcooling feedwater heater. The enclosed section of tubes in which subcooling takes place is called the subcooling-zone or drains cooler. The structure that surrounds the tubes is called the subcooling-zone enclosure. If part of the length of all the tubes in the feedwater inlet pass is surrounded by the subcooling-zone enclosure, the cooler is termed a full-pass, partial-length drains cooler (Fig. 1.21). If part of the inlet-pass tube count is enclosed for its full length, it is termed a partial-pass, full-length drains cooler.

The subcooling zone is designed as a liquid-to-liquid heat exchanger. Therefore, the tubes are fitted with a baffle system to enhance the shellside heat transfer coefficient and provide protection against shell-flow-induced tube vibration.

The drains outlet is located in the drains cooler above the liquid level in the condensing zone. The inlet to the drains cooler is a pipe, called a snorkel or a snorkel pickup, that extends below the liquid level in the condensing zone. The snorkel is placed at the end away from the front-end tubesheet. Flow velocity into the subcooling zone should be no greater than 1.5 ft/s (0.5 m/s) to avoid tube erosion. To

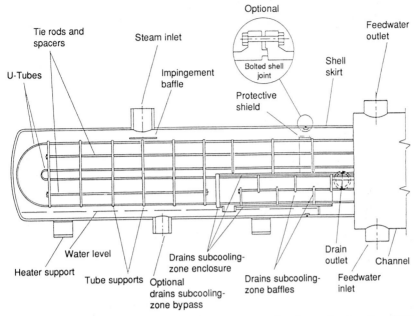

Tie rods and spacers

U-Tubes

Steam inlet

Optional

Impingement baffle

Bolted shell joint

Protective shield

Shell skirt

Feedwater outlet

Water level

Heater support

Tube supports

Drains subcooling-zone enclosure

Optional drains subcooling-zone bypass

Drains subcooling-zone baffles

Drain outlet

Feedwater inlet

Channel

Figure 1.21   Schematic arrangement of a two-zone condensing and subcooling CFH. (*Adapted from the* HEI Standards for Closed Feedwater Heaters, *4th ed., by permission of the Heat Exchange Institute.*)

provide operating flexibility, a drains subcooling-zone bypass may be located in the bottom of the shell.

When a unit receives superheated steam and discharges subcooled condensate, it is called a three-zone closed feedwater heater. Figure 1.22 shows such a unit schematically, while Fig. 1.23 provides a more detailed description and names the various parts.

Most closed feedwater heaters are built with U-tube bundles, but some are made with pull-through floating heads or fixed tubesheets. The latter are used for small heaters or as external subcoolers. Bundle construction is customarily described by using the TEMA designations.

Closed feedwater heater installation positions

Installation positions for closed feedwater heaters are illustrated in Figs. 1.24 and 1.25. The heaters may be installed horizontally on a floor of a power station (Fig. 1.24, upper sketch), vertically in structural steel, or, to save space, horizontally in the neck of a surface condenser (Fig. 1.24, lower sketch). The latter heater may fit entirely within the condenser, or its return end may protrude into an enclosure

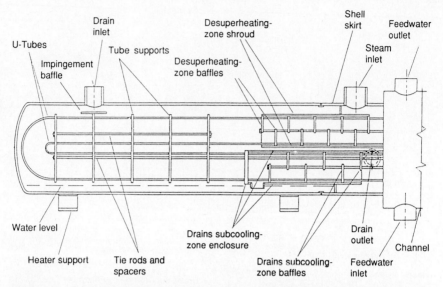

Figure 1.22 Schematic arrangement of a three-zone desuperheating, condensing, and subcooling CFH. (*Adapted from the* HEI Standards for Closed Feedwater Heaters, *4th ed., by permission of the Heat Exchange Institute.*)

built onto the neck. The vernacular expression for this structure is "doghouse."

Describe vertical units (Fig. 1.25) as head up when the channel is at the top and head down when it is at the bottom. Describe horizontal heaters in condenser necks as horizontal neck-mounted units. When two units are mounted in a condenser neck, they may be called twin neck-mounted heaters.

Feedwater piping to heaters is most often welded directly to the channel nozzles, but it may be bolted to flanged connections in small low-pressure units. It is much thicker than extraction-steam piping because the feedwater is at a much higher pressure. For the same reason, the channel barrel is much thicker than the heater shell. Therefore, feedwater heaters are usually disassembled for maintenance by pulling the shell and leaving the channel and bundle in place. An exception is made when heaters are located in condenser necks where there is insufficient working room and access to steam piping is difficult.

To describe a unit completely, specify how the piping is connected.

Miscellaneous construction details

Some details that have not been discussed are illustrated in Fig. 1.23. The BOP (balance of plant) usually requires recovering heat from the

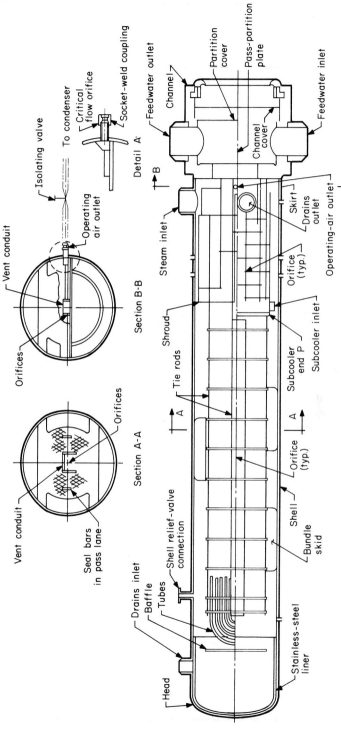

Figure 1.23 Typical three-zone high-pressure heater showing the vent conduit and other details. (*Reproduced from "Achieving Highly Reliable Feedwater Heaters," by Carl F. Andreone and Robert J. Bell, ASME Paper 82-JPGC/Pwr-8, by permission of the ASME.*)

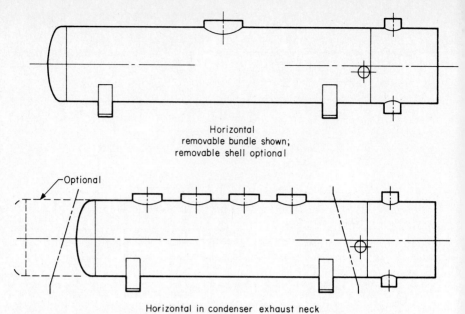

Horizontal
removable bundle shown;
removable shell optional

Horizontal in condenser exhaust neck

Figure 1.24 Horizontal closed feedwater heater installations. (*Adapted from the* HEI Standards for Closed Feedwater Heaters, *4th ed., by permission of the Heat Exchange Institute.*)

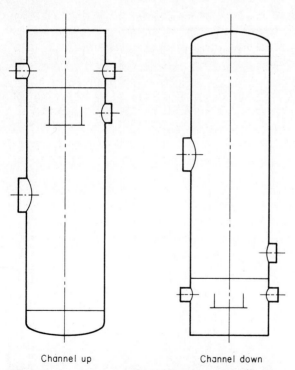

Channel up   Channel down

Figure 1.25 Horizontal closed feedwater heater installations. (*Adapted from the* HEI Standards for Closed Feedwater Heaters, *4th ed., by permission of the Heat Exchange Institute.*)

drains. Therefore, the drains are led into the condensing zone through a drains inlet. Since drains flash when they cascade from higher-pressure to lower-pressure heaters, protection must be provided against shell erosion where the drains enter. This protection may consist of solid or strainer-type impact plates in the body of the shell, but it is better practice to lead flashing drains into a stainless-steel-lined or stainless-steel-clad flash chamber behind the tubes as shown.

Venting is one of the most important requirements of closed feedwater heater operation. The devices used for continuous venting are called continuous or operating vents. Heater manufacturers employ various schemes for continuous venting. Properly to meter the noncondensible flow, they install orifices either in the internal vent collection channel or pipe or in the outlet of the vent collection device.

At startup, the shell is so full of noncondensibles that the operating vents cannot handle the flow. Therefore, a startup vent, or bypass vent around the continuous vent system, is provided.

In Figs. 1.19 through 1.23, a short shell skirt is shown welded between the tubesheet and the rest of the shell. This is the common modern practice. To gain access to the shell side of the bundle, the shell is burned or otherwise cut at the line of the weld of the skirt to the shell, called the cut line. Positioned under the cut line is a protective shield to prevent damage to the tubes by the parting process. The option of constructing the shell with a flanged joint is seldom used.

Some closed feedwater heaters are built with spacer bars instead of tie rods or tie rods and spacers. These units have tube supports that are made smaller than the shell to provide annular steam distribution space. Spiders align the supports with the shell, and skid bars are installed on the spiders along the bottom and around the periphery of full-circle tube supports.

Large bundles are fitted with internal rollers to accommodate differential movement between the bundle and the shell and to facilitate assembly and disassembly. Saddle supports on horizontal heaters may also be fitted with rollers or wheels to permit axial movement. The wheels, wheel supports, and bearings may be designed to permit wheeling the heater into place.

Glossary

Alonizing Proprietary process for diffusing aluminum into steel surfaces, such as those of tubes. The alonized surfaces are suitable for high temperatures and are resistant to hydrogen sulfide, sulfur dioxide, and various other sulfur compounds.

Antiswirl baffle X-shaped baffle placed in the shell outlet nozzle to reduce exit-stream turbulence.

ASME The American Society of Mechanical Engineers.

ASME Boiler and Pressure Vessel Code Boiler and pressure vessel safety code of the ASME (*ASME Code*).

The *ASME Code* has sections with rules for specific types of boiler and pressure vessel construction and sections with general rules applied by reference in the construction rules. The construction sections that apply to shell-and-tube heat exchangers are Section VIII, Division 1, for most units; Section VIII, Division 2, for exchangers that operate at very high pressures, or which undergo severe cycling, or which have unusual configurations; Section I or Section VIII, Division 1, for unfired steam generators; and Section III for units in nuclear service in the primary loop. The division of Section III to which nuclear units must conform depends upon their positions in the loop. In addition, several mandatory and nonmandatory appendixes apply. Sections that the construction rules apply by reference are Section II, "Materials Specifications"; Section V, "Nondestructive Examination"; and Section IX, "Welding and Brazing Qualifications."

Editions of the *ASME Code* are published at three-year intervals. Before the 1986 edition Addenda were published twice a year. Beginning with 1986, Addenda have been published annually. Code cases, which deal with rules for materials, design, and construction that are not incorporated within the main body of rules and Addenda, are issued for limited periods and are discontinued, reaffirmed, or incorporated into the rules.

Axial nozzle Inlet or outlet connection in the head of a heat exchanger that is aligned with the tube axis. (See Fig. 1.3.)

Baffle One of a series of drilled or perforated plates, slightly smaller than the shell ID, located between the front and rear tubesheets or between the stationary tubesheet and the return end through which the tubes pass. The functions of baffles are to direct the flow of the fluid in the shell and to support the tubes. (See also ANTISWIRL BAFFLE; DAM BAFFLE; DISK-AND-DOUGHNUT BAFFLE; DOUBLE-SEGMENTAL BAFFLES; EGG-CRATE BAFFLE; LAMAFLEX BAFFLE; LONGITUDINAL BAFFLE; ORIFICE BAFFLE; SINGLE-SEGMENTAL BAFFLES; TRIPLE-SEGMENTAL CUTS.)

Baffle bypassing Leakage between the baffle OD and the shell ID.

Baffle clearance Space between the design ID of the shell (in closed feedwater heaters, the zone enclosure ID) and the baffle or support-plate OD (also called the transverse support clearance). The *TEMA Standards* have tables of recommended clearances between the shell design ID and the baffle OD for various shell sizes.

Baffle cut Fraction of a segmental baffle or support plate that is cut off to allow passage of the shellside fluid, expressed as a percent of the shell or closed feedwater heater zone ID. Cuts may be single-segmental, double-segmental, or triple-segmental. (See Fig. 1.4; see also PERCENT CUTOFF.)

Baffle ear   Horizontally projecting uncut portion of a baffle at the end of the cut line of a vertically cut segmental baffle. Baffles are provided with ears (1) to receive tie rods, (2) to prevent vapor bypassing in a horizontal condenser when tubes have been omitted from the layout to accommodate impingement protection, and (3) to provide a dam to maintain a liquid level in the subcooling zone of a horizontal process condenser-subcooler that condenses on the shellside. (See Fig. 1.4; see also DAM BAFFLE.)

Baffle-edge distance   Distance between the outermost-tube-hole OD and the baffle OD.

Baffle-hole clearance   Baffle-hole or support-hole diameter minus the tube OD.

Baffle notch   Drainage notch in the bottom of a segmental baffle that has a horizontally cut-off upper sector. Baffle notches are not required for nonviscous fluids because the drainage space between the baffles and shell is adequate. (See Fig. 1.4.)

Baffle pitch   Center-to-center distance between adjacent baffles or tube supports.

Baffle spacers   Spools of pipe or tubing between adjacent baffles to maintain baffle spacing and alignment. The spacers are slid over tie rods that run from the rear face of the front or stationary tubesheet to a point just beyond the last baffle. (See Fig. 1.5.)

Baffle spacing   Distance between adjacent segmental baffles. The baffle spacing is equal to the baffle pitch minus one-half of the baffle thicknesses of the adjacent baffles.

Baffle span   See SUPPORT SPAN.

Bare tubes   Heat exchanger tubes with smooth inside and outside surfaces.

Bayonet   Pair of concentric tubes connected to separate tubesheets at the inlet end of an exchanger. The outer tube has the far end sealed to form an annular return. Bayonets extend either into heat exchanger shells or directly into tanks. The principal heat transfer surface is the outer tube. The inner tube serves as a conduit to lead fluid into the annulus. Bayonets are used in tank suction heaters, vertical vacuum column condensers, and vertical vaporizers.

Beaded end   Expanded tube-to-tubesheet connection in which tube ends that extend beyond the outer face of the tubesheet are beaded over. Beading enhances the strength and tightness of the joint. It may be combined with welding the tubes to the tubesheet.

Bellows expansion joint   Thin-walled expansion joint with a flexible element no thicker than ⅛ in (3.18 mm). The element consists of one or more corrugations shaped like a U, V, omega, toroid, or similar configuration. Corrugation roots may be fitted with root rings to prevent blowout under pressure and to distribute deflections equally between multiple corrugations. Bellows expansion joints are characterized by relatively low spring rates and high cycle lives. The deformations when the joint deflects may be elastic but are usually inelastic.

Bend interference Metal-to-metal contact between U bends in the same plane. Construction in which there is bend interference is unacceptable. (See Fig. 1.4.)

Bend line Point of tangency of the straight-leg centerline to the bend radius of a U tube. (See Fig. 1.4.)

Bend radius Radius of the centerline of a U-tube bend. The bend radius is half the bend spacing. (See BEND SPACING; see also Fig. 1.4.)

Bend spacing Center-to-center distance between the legs of a U tube. (See Fig. 1.4.)

Bend tangent See BEND LINE.

Bend tangent line See BEND LINE.

Bent tube Straight tube with a small bow created by forming the tube to an arc height approximately 2½ percent of the tube length. Bent tubes are used in water evaporators to remove scale buildup by shocking the hot tubes with cold water. They may also be used to accommodate differential thermal expansion between tubes within a bundle and between the bundle of tubes and the shell. (See also SHOCK TUBE.)

Bimetallic tube Tube made by inserting a tube of one metal into a second tube of another metal with a close fit, then drawing the pair together to create an interference fit between the inner and outer tubes. A short length of outer tube is pared away at the tube end and replaced by a ferrule of inner-tube material in order to present only inner-tube metal to the channel side of the tubesheet. Bimetallic tubes with a metallurgical bond between the inner and outer tubes have been produced experimentally by explosively cladding and reduction-drawing a hollow, but they are not commercially available.

Blowdown (1) Connection in an evaporator for removing accumulations of solids, sludge, and scum by partial draining during operation; (2) continuously bleeding liquid from the bottom of a boiler, evaporator, vaporizer, or kettle-type reboiler.

Bolster Structural or fabricated plate spacer set between stacked heat exchangers or heat exchanger shells to maintain a desired separation. Spool pieces are installed between connecting pipe nozzles.

Bolt spacing Bolt-circle circumference of a flange divided by the number of equally spaced bolts.

Bull plug Round or hexagonal bar-stock or forged pipe plug 2½ to 3 in (63 to 76 mm) long.

Bullet See TUBE GUIDE.

Bundle See TUBE BUNDLE.

Bundle entrance area Unrestricted flow area for shellside fluid to enter a bundle from the inlet connection. (See also SHELL ENTRANCE AREA.)

Bundle entrance velocity   Average linear velocity of the fluid entering the space between the tubes and the shell.

Bundle exit area   Unrestricted area for shellside fluid to leave a bundle to the outlet connection. (See also SHELL EXIT AREA.)

Bundle exit velocity   Average linear velocity of the fluid leaving the space between the tubes and the shell (or zone enclosure).

Bundle-in-column reboiler   Reboiler in which the tube bundle is inserted into a horizontal nozzle at the bottom of a vertical column. The bundle may be U-tube or floating-head.

Bundle in tank   U-tube or floating-tube bundle inserted directly into a tank for heating or cooling.

Bundle tracks   See RAILS.

Calandria   Fixed-tubesheet vertical tube bundle that has its top tubesheet bolted to the bottom flange of an evaporator vapor body. A channel may be bolted or welded to the bottom tubesheet and a cover bolted to the channel, or a bonnet may be bolted directly to the body. Calandria are characterized by low height-to-diameter ratios.

Capacitance   Volume of water in a closed feedwater heater required for successful drain control valve operation. Drain control valves operate successfully when they respond to load changes without causing the liquid level to drop so low that the drain-cooling-zone inlet is exposed to erosive steam-water mixtures.

Cascading drains   Any water that enters a closed feedwater heater shell from higher-pressure sources.

Catchall   Cyclone type of accessory installed on an evaporator vapor outlet to remove entrained liquids. Droplets that collect on the cylindrical surfaces under the influence of centrifugal force drain back to the evaporator.

Channel down   (1) Position of a channel when it is at the bottom of a vertical closed feedwater heater; (2) position of a channel when it is at the bottom of a vertical multipass process heat exchanger that has an even number of tube passes.

Channel up   (1) Position of a channel when it is at the top of a vertical closed feedwater heater; (2) position of a channel when it is at the top of a vertical multipass process heat exchanger that has an even number of tube passes.

Circumferentially finned tube   Finned tube that has the fins perpendicular to the tube axis or on a helical pitch. (See EXTENDED-SURFACE TUBE.)

Cleaning lane   Space between adjacent rows of tubes in removable-bundle heat exchangers large enough to permit cleaning devices to enter. Cleaning lanes are provided by arranging the tubes on a square pitch or on a spread triangular pitch.

Cleaning turbine   Air-, hydraulic-, or electric-powered tool for cleaning inside heat exchanger and boiler tubes. It consists of a drive motor, a flexible drive cable or hose, and a head. Heads may be arrangements of blades on hubs, modified drill bits, burrs, or brushes. Cleaning-turbine heads may be constructed to allow water to flow through passageways to wash away deposits removed by turbining. Cleaning turbines are sometimes adapted for cleaning tube exteriors when there are cleaning lanes.

Cleanout Access opening for cleaning out scale and sludge from the bottom of an evaporator, kettle reboiler, or vaporizer.

Closed feedwater heater Shell-and-tube heat exchanger used for heating boiler feedwater or reheating condensate. The feedwater or condensate flows in the tubes. Turbine extraction steam enters and its condensate leaves the shell.

Code See ASME BOILER AND PRESSURE VESSEL CODE.

Condensate level See LIQUID LEVEL.

Condensing zone Portion of a closed feedwater heater tube bundle in which boiler feedwater is heated by saturated turbine extraction steam.

Confined joint Flanged joint in which the gasket is retained in a recess (female flange) that receives the raised face of a mating male flange.

Connection protector Device used to protect machined surfaces or threads of heat exchanger connections during shipping and handling. Flanged connections may be protected with gasketed metal, wood, or composition disks bolted to the flange. Screwed connections may be protected with pipe caps, plugs, or plastic inserts or caps.

Continuous vent Connection and collection device in the shell of a closed feedwater heater for continuously collecting and removing noncondensibles from extraction steam. Continuous vents should be capable of passing at least ½ percent of the steam to prevent noncondensibles from accumulating, thereby causing capacity loss and corrosion. They should be bypassed during startup to allow for rapid purging of inerts.

Conventional double tubesheet Double tubesheet in which each tubesheet of the pair is an individual plate or forging. (See DOUBLE TUBESHEET.)

Core Device (core buster or film breaker) inserted in a tube for its full length to constrict the cross-sectional flow area by forming an annular flow channel.

Core buster Colloquial term for core.

Core tube Core made by sealing one end of a tube with a diameter smaller than that of the exchanger tube and flattening the sealed end so that it fits tightly into the entrance of the exchanger tube. (See also CORE.)

Crisscross U tubes Arrangement of the innermost rows of a U-tube bundle in which the plane of the bends is rotated alternately clockwise and counterclockwise. The bends rotated in one direction pass behind the bends rotated in the other. (See Fig. 1.4 and Chap. 5.)

Cross-flow baffle See BAFFLE.

Crossover area Flow area in a pass compartment measured in the plane perpendicular to the tubesheet. The minimum recommended crossover area for units in severe service is 1.3 times the flow area of the tubes in the tube pass. For less severe services, the flow area may be smaller but never less than the flow area of the tubes in the pass.

Cut line (1) Line on which segments of segmental cross-flow baffles or semisupport plates are cut; (2) circumferential line at which the shell skirt is severed from the shell of a closed feedwater heater to permit the bundle to be removed.

Dam baffle Vertically cut segmental baffle with a bottom ear. The ear dams the condensate flow to provide a liquid level in the bottom of a horizontal process condenser-subcooler. (See Fig. 1.1.)

Davit Inverted L-shaped structure used for handling channels, bonnets, and covers. The davit may be fabricated from structural elements, or it may be a round bar or pipe bent on a radius to provide horizontal and vertical legs. The vertical member or leg fits into a socket in a bracket welded to the shell. An eyebolt, set vertically into the end of the horizontal leg, is directly connected or hooked to the part to be handled. Alternatively, the eyebolt or hook may be connected to a carriage fitting that rolls between stops along the horizontal member.

Demister blanket Pad of knitted wire mesh placed below the vapor outlet of a vaporizer or evaporator. The purpose of the demister blanket is to separate entrained droplets from the outgoing vapor stream.

Demister pad See Demister blanket.

Descaling tube See Bent tube.

Depth of groove In confined-joint construction, the depth of the groove milled into tubesheets and/or channel covers to receive gasket ribs and pass partitions.

Design maximum working pressure Pressure for which a vessel is structurally designed. [See Maximum allowable working pressure (MAWP).]

Desuperheating zone That part of a closed feedwater heater's outlet-tube pass that is reserved for transferring sensible heat to feedwater from superheated extraction steam.

Desuperheating-zone shroud Enclosure surrounding the tubes of the outlet pass at the outlet end of a closed feedwater heater that is designed to be supplied with superheated steam. The shroud is so constructed that superheated steam enters near the inlet end, then flows through a baffle system suitable for sensible-heat transfer. Enough superheat must reside in the exiting steam to keep the tubes dry at the zone exit.

Diaphragm Thin disk of metal continuously welded to the channel flange face of a single-pass heat exchanger. The diaphragm, which takes the place of a gasket, is backed up against positive tubeside pressure by the channel cover. Diaphragms are used when even small leaks cannot be tolerated.

Disk-and-doughnut baffle Baffle system in which the center is removed from a full circle and located one baffle pitch away from the remaining annulus. The center is the disk; the annulus is the doughnut. The baffle span is two pitches long.

Disengaging space   Untubed space above the uppermost row of a horizontal vaporizer to allow for separation of entrained droplets of liquid.

Dismantling clearance   (1) Clearance required at the stationary end of a removable-bundle process heat exchanger to permit bundle removal; (2) clearance required at the front end of a fixed-tubesheet heat exchanger to permit tube removal; (3) clearance required at the return end of a closed feedwater heater to permit shell removal.

Distributor belt   Enlarged section of a shell into which the shell inlet connection enters. The bundle is wrapped with a 360° impingement baffle under the enlarged section. The impingement baffle may have several large holes offset from the inlet nozzle to provide access for the incoming fluid, or it may be perforated by smaller holes except under the nozzle. An alternative is to allow space for flow between the end of the impingement protection cylinder and one end of the enlarged section.

Double effect   Evaporator that consists of two (usually) identical units in which heat of condensation of the vapor generated by evaporation in the first unit (effect) is used to vaporize the material in the second unit (effect). Despite the superficial resemblance, double-effect operation is not analogous to operating a heat exchanger of two shells in series. (See also MULTIPLE EFFECT; TRIPLE EFFECT.)

Double grooves   Two annular grooves machined into the holes of a tubesheet, provided to enhance the strength and tightness of expanded tube-to-tubesheet joints. The standard TEMA and HEI configuration is two grooves $\frac{1}{64}$ in deep × $\frac{1}{8}$ in wide (0.40 mm deep × 3.18 mm wide). Only one groove, more than two grooves, and configurations other than the TEMA ones have been used. Wider grooves are desirable when tubes are to be hydroexpanded.

Double-segmental baffles   Cross-flow baffle system that consists of alternating A-section and B-section segmental baffles. A sections are opposite sectors of a circle; B segments are sections of a circle that remain after opposite sectors have been cut off.

Double tubesheet   Two tubesheets at the tube ends, of which the outer face of the outer tubesheet is exposed only to the tubeside fluid and the inner face of the inner tubesheet is exposed only to the shellside fluid. Conventional double tubesheets are independent plates or forgings separated by a discrete air gap. The gap may be sealed by a peripheral shroud, or the outer edges of the tubesheets may be welded to each other or to a spacer cylinder. Integral double tubesheets consist of a single plate or forging into which annular grooves, approximately $\frac{1}{8}$ to $\frac{1}{4}$ in (approximately 3.2 to 6.4 mm) wide, are cored into the tube holes until adjacent grooves intersect. This creates two separate tubesheets, joined at the peripheral undrilled edges and by metal not removed in coring out the annular grooves. (See Chap. 3.)

Downtake   Centrally located tube or pipe that connects the top of the upper tubesheet to the bottom of the lower tubesheet of a calandria vertical-tube evaporator. The downtake allows cooler liquid to circulate to the bottom of the tubes. The downtake cross-sectional flow area ranges from 50 to 100 percent of the total tube cross-sectional flow area.

Drainage pitch (1) Angle at which a horizontal straight-tube unit is set to ensure full drainage (usually 3 to 5°); (2) angle at which a horizontal U-tube unit is set to raise the U bend above the front end to ensure full drainage (usually 3 to 5°).

Drains subcooling zone See SUBCOOLING ZONE.

Dry pipe Perforated horizontal pipe located above the upper tube row of a horizontal steam generator. A vertical length of pipe connects the dry pipe to the steam outlet nozzle. The dry pipe's function is to vaporize any drops of water in the outlet steam. Flow of the steam through the perforations reduces the pressure between the steam space and outlet nozzle, causing the droplets to vaporize.

Drying surface Tube area at the top of an evaporator or vaporizer used to provide a small amount of superheat to the vapor to ensure that it is dry.

Drying tubes Tubes at the top of a horizontal evaporator or vaporizer bundle used to provide drying surface.

Dual bank (1) Arrangement of tubes, partitions, and nozzles in a surface condenser in which each of the two halves of the tube count may be operated independently; (2) arrangement of tubes, partitions, and connections in a refrigeration system condenser in which each of the two halves of the tube count may be operated independently.

Dual-gauge tube Tube in which the wall of the region to be bent into a U tube is two gauges thicker than in the rest of the tube. The extra thickness is added to the OD; therefore there is no change in cross-sectional flow area. Bending a tube stretches the metal beyond the neutral line (bend radius centerline) and compresses it at the inner part of the bend. Some flattening occurs, which causes the bend region cross section to become ovoid. The extra thickness in the section to be bent allows the minimum thickness in the bent portion to be at least equal to the minimum thickness in the rest of the tube. Because the severity of thinning and deformation depends, among other things, upon the bend radius, it is customary either to require dual-gauge tubes or tubes that are two gauges thicker than the rest for the inner two rows of the tubes of a U-tube bundle. When thicker-walled tubes are provided, the reduction in the flow cross section is ordinarily neglected. Dual-gauge tubes are usually available only in nonferrous material.

Dummy tube Tube that is not used for transporting fluids but occupies space in a tube bundle. Dummy tubes are installed to prevent fluid bypassing around or through a bundle. They are usually welded to the inside face of the front or stationary tubesheet and end a short distance in front of the rear tubesheet or U bend. (See also SEALING DEVICE.)

Effect Term for a complete evaporator module that is analogous to a heat exchanger shell. Evaporators are described as single, double, triple, and multiple effect.

Effective surface Surface that is active in transferring heat. In straight-tube units, effective surface is the tube surface area between the inner faces of the innermost tubesheets. In U-tube units, the bend surface is not usually considered to be effective. Therefore, U-tube effective surface is bounded by the inner face of the innermost tubesheet and the bend line. Drying surface is usually excluded from reported effective surface. Except in process condenser-subcoolers and closed feedwater heaters with subcooling zones, surface flooded by condensate is not considered to be effective.

Egg-crate baffle   Tube support or baffle in which a grid or grating of inter-locked flat bars arranged to provide square or triangular openings is con-tained within a circular band. The tubes pass through the openings in the grid.

Enhanced-surface tube   (1) Tube in which the walls have been deformed or shaped on a pattern that increases turbulence in the fluid stream; (2) tube in which the surface has been treated to permit high flux rates in boiling.

Equalizer connections   In a closed feedwater heater, connections provided for installing pipelines to equalize the pressure between the top and bottom of liquid-level controllers and gauge glasses. The function of equalizer lines is to avoid false readings due to siphoning.

Expanded-tube joint   Heat exchanger tube-to-tubesheet connection made by expanding the tube into the tube hole. The tube is deformed elastically or plastically until it makes contact with the hole. Expanding-force application is continued, enlarging the tube and hole until the tube metal approaches its plastic limit. The hole may deform elastically or plastically, but when expand-ing force is released, it must recover more than the tube to create an interfer-ence fit between the tube and the hole. The magnitude of the interference and the fit pressure it generates depend upon the relative yield strengths of the tubesheet and tubes and other metal properties, the tube's diameter-to-thickness ratio, and the maximum expanding force applied. The methods used to expand tubes into tubesheets are roller expanding, hydraulic expand-ing (hydroexpanding), and near-contact explosive expanding (high-energy ex-panding). Expanded-only joints comprise a large majority of process and power plant heat exchanger tube-to-tubesheet joints. They are frequently used on low-pressure closed feedwater heaters but are not suitable for high-temperature service or for services requiring a very high degree of tightness. Tubes may also be expanded when the primary tube-to-tubesheet connection is made by welding the tubes to the front face of the tubesheet. This is done to seal the crevice between the tube and the hole, to isolate the welded joint from vibration, and to stiffen the tubesheet if contact between tube and hole can be maintained under all conditions of loading.

Explosive cladding   Metallurgically bonding two metals by causing the clad-ding metal to collide with the base metal by means of the shock wave gener-ated by an explosion. The explosion generates a progressive collision front be-tween the parts. The energy of the progressive collision melts the surfaces that make contact. A molten jet of metal oxides, surface impurities, and met-als is expelled from the collision. The surfaces bond to each other in a sinusoidal interface. The bond achieved is a true metallurgical bond whether or not the pair of metals is capable of solution in each other. The process is used to bond metallurgically pairs of dissimilar metals such as aluminum and steel, and titanium and austenitic stainless steel. Explosive cladding is fre-quently used to face process tubesheets with corrosion-resistant alloys.

Extended-surface tube   Tube in which the bare surface of the outer or inner wall has been extended by adding metal projections. The added metal may be in the form of (1) continuous or discontinuous longitudinal high fins, (2) transverse helical or annular high fins, (3) continuous thread-shaped low fins, and (4) pegs or studs. High fins extend beyond the bare tube surface; low fins do not. Longitudinal and transverse high fins may be attached by shrink fitting, fitting them into scored grooves and holding them there by peening the upset groove metal against the fin, or by resistance welding. Longitudinal high fins that are welded to the tube are first formed into a channel shape to permit the web of the channel to be welded to the tube. Low fins are formed from bare tubes without adding metal. The fin OD is the same as or slightly less than the bare-tube OD. Therefore, tubesheet and baffle drilling is the same for low-fin and bare tubes.

Ferrule   (1) Short cylinder of inner tube material of a bimetallic tube that fits the tube end where the outer tube material has been peeled away. The end of the tube presents only inner tube material to the tubeside tubesheet face when the tube is expanded into the tubesheet. (2) Threaded sleeve fitted over the end of the tube of a packed tube joint. The ferrule acts as a packing-gland follower to compress the packing in the tube hole. (3) Sleeve of tube material inserted between a tube and an oversized hole to enable a tight expanded joint to be made. (4) Thin sleeve of material used in bridging the damaged tube area in sleeving.

Field tube   Bayonet.

Film breaker   See CORE.

Fixed-tubesheet exchanger   Straight-tube exchanger in which a tubesheet is fastened to each end of the shell; also called a stationary-tubesheet exchanger.

Flange-edge distance   Distance between the bolt-circle diameter (BC) and the OD of a bolting flange [½(OD − BC)].

Flanged-and-flued-head expansion joint   Thick-walled expansion joint fabricated from a pair of flat flanged heads with centrally located flued-out holes. The ID of the flue holes is equal to or slightly larger than the shell ID. The straight flanges of the flat heads are butt-welded to form a single corrugation joint.

Flanged-only-head expansion joint   Thick-walled expansion joint fabricated from a pair of flat flanged heads with centrally located holes. The flat heads are butt-welded to each other and welded to the shell at the hole locations.

Flared-end joint   Tube-to-tubesheet connection in which tightness and strength are enhanced by flaring extended tube ends. The outer edges of the holes may be relieved in preparation for tube flaring.

Flared nozzle   Nozzle in which the entrance line diameter is increased to a larger diameter where the connection pierces the shell. Flared nozzles are used (1) to reduce pressure loss in vapors entering condenser shells and (2) to enable installing impingement plates without eliminating tubes at the shell inlet.

Flat face   Flange facing in which the gasket sealing surface is in the same plane as the rest of the flange face; also called plain face.

Floating head   Floating tubesheet and its attached floating cover.

Floating-head cover   Return or outlet cover attached to a floating tubesheet.

Floating head with backing device   Floating head in which reaction for bolts or clamps used to hold the cover to the tubesheet is provided by a backing ring behind the tubesheet. The most frequently used backing device designs are (1) a split backing ring that fits behind the tubesheet and that has an ID smaller than the tubesheet OD and (2) a solid backing ring that has an ID slightly larger than the tubesheet OD and that bears against a split shear ring inserted into a groove in the tubesheet rim. The OD of the backing device is larger than the shell diameter. Therefore, the shell cover must be larger than the shell to permit it to fit over the backing device. The shell flange at the cover end and the shell-cover flange have matching ODs and bolt circles (BCs), but the shell flange ID is smaller than the shell-cover flange ID.

Full-circle supports   Tube supports that are full circles drilled to receive all the tubes, tie rods, etc.

Fusion-weld cladding   Integral cladding method in which a base metal is faced by fusion-welding metal to it. It is commonly used on the channel side of forged-steel high-pressure heat exchangers, such as high-pressure closed feedwater heaters, to provide a homogeneous base for tube-to-tubesheet welding.

Gasket   Member placed between mating surfaces to effect a seal by flowing into the irregularities in the surface when the member is compressed.

Gland   Cylinder that fits into a packingbox and bears against the outermost ring of packing to compress it. Most glands are made with an integral bolting flange. Studs, threaded into the packingbox body, pass through bolt holes in the flange of the gland. Nuts are mounted on the studs to drive the gland against the packing.

Groove   See DEPTH OF GROOVE; DOUBLE GROOVES; TUBE-HOLE GROOVES.

Gross surface   Total outside tube surface including surface contained in the tubesheets and U bends.

Hole count   Number of tube holes in one tubesheet. In U-tube bundles the hole count is twice the tube count. (See also TUBE COUNT.)

Holtec Non-Segmental Baffles (formerly called Tweeners)   Proprietary tube support–baffle system that consists of folded and formed sections. Flow is generally axial, and the pressure drop is low. Therefore, spans can be short enough to minimize the prospects of flow-induced tube vibration damage.

Honeycomb   See INTEGRAL DOUBLE TUBESHEET.

Horizontal cut   Segments of cross-flow baffles cut off alternately at the top of one baffle and the bottom of the adjacent baffle to direct stream flow up and down over the tubes. (See Fig. 1.4; see also VERTICAL CUT.)

Hot well   Sump at the bottom of a horizontal vacuum condenser for collecting condensate. (See also SUMP.)

Hydraulic lance   Hydraulic tube-cleaning tool consisting of a hollow rod, somewhat longer than the tube length, fitted at its front end with a nozzle that enters the tube. High-pressure water is pumped through the lance to clean deposits from the inner tube surface as the lance is moved through the tube. The nozzle orifices are designed to suit the nature of the deposit. When hydraulic lances are manually operated, the operator walks with the lance to feed it into the tube. This has given rise to the name *walk lance*. Automatically fed lances are safer and more effective.

Hydroexpanding   Expanding tubes into tubesheet by applying hydraulic pressure directly inside the tubes. The tube wall is not crushed, and the small amount of wall reduction that takes place is due only to the increase in tube diameter. Instead of extruding as in roller expanding, the tube end becomes shorter.

HydroSwage   Trademark of Haskel Incorporated for a system and equipment for hydroexpanding.

Impact plate   Metal plate (also called an impingement baffle or impingement plate) located between the shell inlet nozzle and the tube bundle to prevent fluid from the inlet nozzle from impinging directly on the tubes.

Impingement baffle   See IMPACT PLATE.

Impingement plate   See IMPACT PLATE.

Inclined position   Arrangement of a straight-tube process condenser, condensing in the tubes, in which the axial centerline is between 0 and 90° relative to the horizontal.

Inert-gas blanketing   Purging a unit of air with inert gas, then filling it with inert gas as it is shut down. Inert-gas blanketing is used (1) to prolong the life of closed feedwater heaters that operate on peaking (intermittent) service, (2) to exclude air when shutting down process heat exchangers through which highly flammable or explosive substances flow, and (3) to prevent stored units from corroding.

Inside surface   Tube heat transfer area based upon the ID of the tubes. The inside surface is used in heat transfer calculations for extended-surface tubes.

Insulated pass partition   A shellside pass partition that is made of two layers of metal separated by an air gap and is sealed at all four edges. Insulated pass partitions are used to reduce thermal leakage between the passes of a two-pass shell heat exchanger.

Insurance plugging   Practice of plugging tubes that have not leaked that surround tubes that have. It is intended to avoid risking a subsequent leak in tubes that have not leaked but which may have been eroded by impinging fluid from tubes that are known to have leaked. Insurance plugging is costly in terms of its effect on a unit's capacity. Therefore, it is better practice to eddy-current-scan the tubes that surround leakers to find out if they have been damaged.

Integral cladding   Application of one metal to another so as to metallurgically bond their surfaces. Integral cladding is done by (1) rolling the two plates together in a plate-reducing mill, (2) depositing cladding metal on the

base-metal surface by fusion welding, and (3) explosive cladding. (See also Ex-
PLOSIVE CLADDING; FUSION-WELD CLADDING; ROLL CLADDING.)

Integral double tubesheet Double tubesheet made by machining annular
intersecting grooves (honeycomb) into the tube holes at the midpoint of the
thickness of a single-tube plate. (See also DOUBLE TUBESHEET.)

Intermediate nozzle Nozzle that connects shell to shell or channel to channel
of shells arranged in series.

Jet thermocompressor Steam-jet ejector used to increase the pressure of
steam evolved in a process. (See also THERMOCOMPRESSOR EVAPORATOR.)

Lamaflex baffle Shell pass-partition baffle in which the seal of the baffle to
the shell wall consists of thin metal layered longitudinal strips attached to the
baffle. The strips may be attached by riveting, by continuous-resistance welding, or by spot-welding them to the underlying pass partition. When the bundle is inserted into the shell, the strips bend elastically to remain in tight contact with the shell wall, thereby effecting a seal. The lamaflex baffle must be
installed so that higher pressure is on the concave side to avoid leakage. (See
also LONGITUDINAL BAFFLE.)

Lantern ring Metal cylinder equal in ID and OD to the packing in a packed
floating head. The lantern ring is placed between two sets of packing rings. It
is drilled with radial holes to permit leakage through either set of packing
rings to drain to the atmosphere.

Lap-joint flange Flange that fits loosely around a cylinder and bears against
a gasket sealing ring integral with the cylinder end. Lap-joint flanges may be
used with channel barrels, shell or cover cylinders, or nozzle-neck lap-joint
stub ends. (See also STUB END.)

Layout See MIXED LAYOUT; PIE LAYOUT; QUADRANT LAYOUT; RIBBON LAYOUT.

Ligament Metal in a tubesheet between adjacent tube holes.

Ligament width Width of a ligament, equal to the tube pitch distance minus
the tube-hole diameter.

Liquid level Level of the condensate surface in a closed feedwater heater. Although the liquid level is usually shown schematically as a flat surface, it is
higher at the condensate inlet end than at the outlet. The surface configuration is irregular between the inlet and the outlet.

Liquid-level equalizer line Pipeline, external to a closed feedwater heater,
that connects the bottom of the shell level connection in the condensate region
to the top of the shell level connection in the condensing zone. Its purpose is to
preclude condensate siphoning.

Lollypop See SWING BOLT.

Long baffle See LONGITUDINAL BAFFLE.

Longitudinal baffle Shellside pass partition. Longitudinal, or long, baffles
may be sealed to the shell of a nonremovable-bundle exchanger by (1) continuous or discontinuous internal welds, (2) plug or slot welds that pierce the
shell, or (3) making the shell in two halves with the longitudinal baffle welded
between them. In removable-bundle equipment, the baffle is made part of the

bundle skeleton. It may be sealed to the shell by packing or by using metal-to-metal sealing strips sprung against the shell wall. (See also LAMAFLEX BAFFLE.)

Longitudinal baffle seal   Means used to prevent fluid bypassing between the shell and edges of the shell pass partitions.

Longitudinal fins   Fins arranged parallel with the longitudinal axis of extended-surface tubes.

Loop seal   External inverted U-shaped pipe loop in the condensate outlet of a condenser-subcooler, for maintaining a liquid level in the subcooling zone. The top of the loop is vented or connected to the condensing zone by a tie line to prevent siphoning.

Loose cladding   See LOOSE LINING.

Loose lining   Lining (cladding) of corrosion-resistant metal that is not integrally bonded to the backing material. Loose linings may be held in place by plug or slot welds or be resistance-welded to the backing material.

Low-fin tube   Circumferentially finned tube in which the fin diameter is equal to or slightly less than the bare-tube diameter. Low-fin tubes must be bare at their ends for a distance somewhat greater than the tubesheet thickness. Therefore, the mill must furnish them cut to length. Low-fin tubes may also be obtained bare where they are to be bent into U tubes. They are mechanically interchangeable with bare tubes of the same diameter.

Lug   (1) Mechanical projection forming part of a breech-lock type of channel closure; (2) one of two or more supports welded to the shell of a vertically mounted unit.

Lug support   See SUPPORT BRACKET.

Maximum allowable working pressure (MAWP)   As defined in the *ASME Code*, the maximum pressure permissible at the top of the shell and at the top of the channel in their normal operating positions at the operating temperatures specified for the pressures. The MAWP is the pressure stamped on the nameplate for each side of the unit and is the pressure setting of at least one pressure-relief device on each side. To provide a suitable margin between the operating pressure and the primary safety-relief-device setting, it is good practice to set the MAWP higher than the operating pressure. Each industry has its own standards. Typical in the process industries is to set the MAWP to at least 110 percent of the operating pressure but at not less than the operating pressure plus 15 lb/in^2 (10,340 Pa) for pressures up to 1000 lb/in^2 (6895 kPa). For closed feedwater heaters, recommended MAWP settings are at least 115 percent of operation pressure but not less than operating pressure plus 15 lb/in^2 (10,340 Pa) for pressures up to 1000 lb/in^2 (6895 kPa) and at least 115 percent of the operating pressure above 1000 lb/in^2 (6895 kPa).

Minimum-bend radius   Minimum centerline radius to which a U tube may be bent without flattening by more than 10 percent or becoming crimped. The attainable minimum-bend radius is a function of the tube wall thickness, tube diameter, and metal properties. Typical minimum-bend radii in the process industries are 1.5 to 2 tube diameters. The minimum recommended in the HEI CFHS is 1.5 tube diameters.

Mixed layout   Tubesheet layout in which flow is partially ribbon and partially quadrant. (See also PIE LAYOUT; QUADRANT LAYOUT; RIBBON LAYOUT.)

Multinozzle heater   Single-zone closed feedwater heater in which steam enters the shell through nozzles located on either side of the thermal centerline. (See THERMAL CENTERLINE.)

Multiple effect   Evaporator consisting of two or more (usually) identical modules or effects. Vapor generated in the first effect is fed to the condensing side of the tubes in the second effect to supply its heat of vaporization. Vapor from the second effect is then fed to the condensing side of the next effect to provide its heat of vaporization and so on. The pressures in the vapor bodies decrease from effect to effect. Although multiple-effect evaporator operation appears superficially to be similar to series heat exchanger operation, it is not analogous. (See also DOUBLE EFFECT; TRIPLE EFFECT.)

Multiple-inlet steam nozzles   See MULTINOZZLE HEATER.

Multisegmental cuts   Cuts of segmental cross-flow baffles that divide a full circle into three or more parallel segments. The baffles produced by double-segmental cuts consist of a pair of equal-width segments cut off on parallel chords separated by one baffle pitch from a central portion that remains after two equal-width segments have been cut off a full circle on parallel chords. Outer two-piece baffles and inner one-piece baffles alternate, with their projections overlapping. Triple-segmental baffles consist of regularly alternating outer, intermediate, and inner pieces with overlapping edges.

Multitube exchanger   Exchanger in which the shell consists of two legs joined by a fixed or removable-end cover. U-bent tubes are inserted with one leg of each U bend in each shell leg before the shell cover is closed. The tube ends may be joined to a separate tubesheet with a bonnet at each shell-leg stationary end, or one rectangular tubesheet and an elongated two-pass bonnet may be used. Multitube exchangers may be arranged for true countercurrent or cocurrent flows.

Nests   Acronym for *n*eoteric *e*ndo*s*tratiformed *t*ube *s*upports. Nests is a proprietary patented concept that has the advantage of full tube supports and low pressure drop.

No tubes in window (NTIW)   Construction in which each tube passes through each cross-flow baffle. To accomplish this, tubes that would pass through the plane of a baffle where a segment has been cut off are excluded from the layout. (See WINDOW.)

Nozzle   Flanged pipe connection to a heat exchanger or a pressure vessel; also used to describe pipe connections that have their ends beveled for field welding. (See also AXIAL NOZZLE; FLARED NOZZLE; INTERMEDIATE NOZZLE; OFFSET NOZZLE; RADIAL NOZZLE; TANGENTIAL NOZZLE; WELD-END NOZZLE.)

Nozzle entrance velocity   Average linear velocity of the fluid in the inlet or inlets to the shell.

Nozzle losses   Pressure losses in a fluid due to friction created as the fluid expands from the inlet nozzle to the bundle and contracts when it enters the outlet nozzle.

Nubbin   Narrow raised portion of the gasket surface of a flange face that is too thick or wide enough to be considered a tongue. The function of the nubbin is to apply high unit force to the central part of the gasket while permitting some compression in the remainder.

O-ring gasket   Ring gasket in which the cross section is circular. O-ring gaskets are most often used in self-energizing closures.

Offset bend lines   Arrangement of U tubes in a bundle in which the bend lines of successive rows are offset axially by a constant amount. The straight lengths of successive rows are thereby increased by a constant increment. The axial distance between successive bends is the sum of the pitch distance and the increment.

Offset nozzle   Nozzle with its centerline located in a plane parallel with a plane that passes through a unit's axial centerline and in which the distance between the parallel planes is less than the maximum possible. (See also TAN-GENTIAL NOZZLE.)

Operating pressure   Pressure for which a side of a unit is thermally designed and rated.

Orifice baffle   Full-circle flow baffle in which the tube holes are substantially larger than the tube ODs. The area of the annuli formed between the tube ODs and the hole IDs is approximately equivalent to that which would be provided if 25 percent cut segmental cross-flow baffles were used. Flow in the shell of a unit fitted with orifice baffles is essentially axial.

Outer tube center   Diameter of the circle on which is located the center of the tube farthest from the center of the tubesheet.

Outer tube limit   Diameter of the circle that circumscribes the tubes farthest from the center of the tubesheet.

Outside tube surface   Tube surface based upon the tube OD.

Packed floating head   Floating tubesheet sealed to the shell by packing. In some versions, the floating-end cover and the shell cover are one and the same. They are sealed to the tubesheet with packing separated by a lantern ring.

Packed joint   Tube-to-tubesheet connection in which the tubesheet holes are enlarged and tapped for approximately three-fourths of their depth. Packing is compressed in the annular spaces between the tubes and holes by ferrules screwed into the tapped holes. This seals the tubes to the tubesheets.

Packing gland   See GLAND.

Packing ring   Ring of fibrous or elastomeric material inserted between the tubesheet and the packingbox of a packed floating-head unit. The packing is compressed by a gland to seal the floating tubesheet to the shell. Usually the packing is square, but chevron rings may be used.

Packingbox   Enlarged portion of the shell or cover machined to receive packing; also known as a stuffing box.

Pass   (1) Group of tubes manifolded together in the tubesheet that receives the full flow from the inlet; (2) one transit of fluid through the straight tube length in a tube pass.

Pass-partition bypassing   Flow between a pass partition and a channel cover or between a pass partition and a tubesheet. In bolted assemblies, pass-partition bypassing may be due to cover or tubesheet deflection under the influence of tubeside pressure. For units designed to the TEMA or HEI PPS, the small amount of pass-partition bypassing due to deflection probably does not materially affect thermal performance. However, if the tubeside fluid is at high pressure or is erosive or corrosive, pass-partition bypassing may lead to erosion-corrosion in the region of the pass partition.

Pass-partition cover   Sheet-metal or thin-plate cover of the outlet pass compartment of a two-pass tubeside unit. When a pass-partition cover is used, the channel cover is sealed to the channel flange by a ring gasket without a rib or by a welded-on diaphragm. The seal of the pass-partition cover to the outlet pass compartment needs only to resist the differential pressure between the inlet and the outlet to the tubes. When a pass-partition cover is used, the channel cover need not be rigid to seal the gasket rib to the pass partitions because channel-cover deflection cannot cause pass-partition bypassing.

Pass-partition grooves   Grooves milled into tubesheets and channel covers to accept gasket pass-partition ribs when confined joint construction is used.

Percent cutoff   Height of the segment cut off a segmental cross-flow baffle expressed as a percent of shell ID. (See Fig. 1.4; see also BAFFLE CUT.)

Pie layout   Tubesheet layout similar to a quadrant layout but with more than four tube passes. (See QUADRANT LAYOUT.)

Pigtail   Loop of pipe or round bar welded to the top of a cover to provide a handling ring.

Pipe shell   (1) Heat exchanger shell made of standard pipe as opposed to one made of rolled and welded plate; (2) term applied to a heat exchanger when the shell is made of standard pipe.

Pitch pattern   Arrangement of tubes that pierce the tubesheets' baffles and supports. Typical pitch patterns are (1) square, with shell flow entering the bundle perpendicularly to the pitch line; (2) rotated square, with shell flow entering the bundle at the intersection of perpendicular pitch lines; (3) triangular, with shell flow entering the bundle parallel with the base of the equilateral triangle on which the tubes are arranged; (4) triangular, with shell flow entering the bundle at the apex of the equilateral triangle on which the tubes are arranged; and (5) diamond.

Plain face   See FLAT FACE.

Plate shell   (1) Heat exchanger shell cylinder made by rolling a plate into a cylinder and welding the long seam. Rolled-plate shells are used for units that have diameters larger than standard pipe sizes or when standard pipe construction is more costly than fabricating a shell. (2) Heat exchanger that is larger than a standard-pipe-size unit.

Plug.   See TUBE PLUG.

Plug map   Tubesheet layout marked to show the locations of plugged tubes in the tube field. Plug maps should also show the axial positions of leaks, the radial orientation of failures, and the dates of plugging. (See also TUBE FAILURE PROFILE.)

Plug welding   Fusion welding of an applied loose lining to a backing surface on a pattern of holes perforated through the lining.

Pull-through floating head   Floating tubesheet and bolted cover that fit entirely within the shell.

Quadrant layout   Four-pass tubesheet layout in which each pass occupies one quadrant of the tubesheet.

Radial nozzle   Nozzle that has its centerline located in a plane that passes through the axial centerline of the unit. Radial nozzles may be pitched axially or perpendicularly to the axial centerline. (See Fig. 1.4.)

Radial pitch   Tube pitch pattern in a cross-flow condenser in which the tubes are laid out on arcs that have a common origin in the bottom of the condenser. The space between the tubes decreases in successive arcs as the origin is approached.

Rails   Guides in a removable-bundle heat exchanger, kettle-type reboiler, or closed feedwater heater for aligning and supporting removable bundles. The rails may be made from structural angles, flat bars, or other structural shapes. The bundle support plates may be notched to slide on the rails. Rails may also be used as roll bars on which rollers fastened to the bundle roll. (See also SKID BARS.)

Ribbon layout   Tubesheet layout in which each pass partition is parallel with a common centerline. Inlet and outlet nozzles are on opposite sides of the channel.

Rod end   See SWING BOLT.

Roll cladding   Cladding a baseplate with a cladding metal by placing the layer of cladding metal on the base metal, then simultaneously reducing the combined thickness in a plate-reducing mill. When the cladder and the baseplate are compatible, a metallurgical bond is created that is capable of withstanding shearing and bending without parting.

Rolled-plate shell   See PLATE SHELL.

Rolled-tube joint   Expanded tube-to-tubesheet connection in which the expanding is done by a tube roller. The roller consists of a slotted cage that contains three or more hardened rolls and a tapered mandrel that fits between them. The tube roller is inserted into the tube and is rotated by a power source that turns the tapered mandrel and thrusts it forward. The mandrel simultaneously rotates the rolls in a direction counter to its rotational direction and forces them against the tube wall. As the rolls bear upon the tube wall, they first force it outward until it makes contact with the hole. To this point tube expansion may be elastic or plastic. After contact, continued rolling stretches both tube and tubesheet. Tubesheet deformation may be fully elastic or fully plastic or may verge from plastic to elastic. However, in order to obtain a seal the tube must deform plastically after contact. When the roller is withdrawn, the tube hole must recover more than the tube. The high unit force of the rolls on the tube exceeds the tube metal's plastic limit, causing some wall reduction and axial extrusion. The residual stresses in the tube wall due to tube crushing resist tube recovery and help maintain the joint tight and strong.

Roller expanding   Process of making rolled tube joints. (See also Tube rolling.)

Root rings   Round bars, pipes, or cast rings fitted into the roots of adjacent corrugations of bellows expansion joints. Root rings reinforce the roots of the corrugations against internal pressure and maintain equal distances between corrugation crowns.

Rubber expanding   Expanding tubes into tubesheets by axially compressing a cylindrical elastomeric plug inserted into the tube end. When the plug is compressed, it bulges, forcing the tube against the hole.

Sacrificial anode   Replaceable metal wasting plate affixed to the internal part of an exchanger that is lower on the electromotive-force scale. The preferential corrosion sacrifices the anode, thereby protecting the exchanger part.

Saddle   See Support saddle.

Seal strip   Longitudinal metal strip that traverses the length of a tube bundle, placed so as to prevent fluid bypassing around or through the bundle. (See also Sealing device.)

Sealing device   Device installed in a tube bundle to prevent fluid bypassing around or through the bundle. Sealing devices may be dummy tubes, seal strips, tie rods and spacers, or a combination of these parts.

Self-energizing closure   Channel-cover closure in which hydrostatic force due to operating pressure is used to push a self-energizing gasket into the space to be sealed.

Semicircular baffle   Cross-flow baffle from which a segment measuring approximately 45 percent of the diameter is cut off.

Semisupport   Tube support plate from which a segment measuring approximately 45 percent of the diameter is cut off.

Separator   Internal drum in the vapor space of a power plant evaporator in the way of the vapor outlet. Its function is to separate droplets of water entrained in the vapor stream and return the collected liquid to the boiling pool.

Shell   (1) One complete heat exchanger; (2) one heat exchanger module in a group of modules connected in series or in parallel; (3) that part of a heat exchanger of closed feedwater heater into which the bundle is inserted; (4) pipe or rolled-plate cylinder from which a shell is fabricated.

Shell cover   Rear head of the shell of a U-tube or floating-head heat exchanger.

Shell entrance area   Unrestricted area for flow between the shell inlet and the bundle.

Shell exit area   Unrestricted area for flow between the bundle and the shell exit.

Shell plate   Rolled plate from which a shell cylinder is fabricated.

Shell skirt   Short length of shell cylinder behind the stationary tubesheet or stationary-end shell flange. The shell skirt is constructed integrally with or welded to the shell or (less frequently) flanged and bolted to a mating shell flange. It is customary to install shell skirts in U-tube closed feedwater heaters to facilitate disassembly by parting the skirt from the shell. If a shell skirt is integral with the shell, it is parted at a predetermined cut or burn line. A thin, wide metal band is set in place under this line to protect the tubes, shrouding, or baffles when the skirt is parted from the shell to enable the unit to be disassembled. When the bundle and the shell are reassembled, the protective band is used as a backing ring that remains in place, and the rejoining weld is then in the category of a single-butt weld from the outside.

Shellside pressure drop   Pressure loss through the shell of a heat exchanger, excluding static losses. Permissible shellside pressure drops in process heat exchangers are determined by process requirements and the economics of operation. The suggested limits in closed feedwater heaters are 30 percent of the differential pressure between stages and no more than 5 lb/in^2 (34.5 kPa) in any one zone. When there are appreciable line losses and static head between stages, these limits may be reduced. (See also TUBESIDE PRESSURE DROP.)

Shim   Adjusting plate between the matching saddles of stacked units.

Shock tube   (1) Tube that is prebent to a bow to withstand the thermal impact of cyclical or sudden high-temperature heating and chilling. Shock tubes are used in regenerative heat recuperators. (2) Bowed tube of a boiler feedwater evaporator that is designed to be shocked with cold water to crack off scale. (See also BENT TUBE.)

Shoes   Flat bars installed on the horizontal edges of notches in the support plates or baffles of removable-bundle units. The shoes ride on slide rails. This reduces friction during thermal expansion and contraction and facilitates bundle removal. (See also SKID BARS.)

Shoulder bolt   Stud bolt with an annular shoulder approximately halfway along its length. The cross section of the shoulder may be rectangular, or the shoulder may taper from a perpendicular face to the stud-bolt diameter. Shoulder bolts are used in removable-bundle exchangers when the stationary tubesheet is extended as a flange. Their function is to maintain the tubesheet connection to the shell flange when the channel is removed. When shoulder bolts are used, the tubesheet bolt hole is recessed to receive the rectangular shoulder or chamfered to receive the tapered shoulder so that it is positioned just below the tubesheet face. It is customary to install shoulder bolts in one-quarter of the bolt holes. However, half or all of the bolts may be shoulder bolts.

Single effect   Evaporator unit that consists of one assembly of heating element and vapor body (effect).

Single-inlet steam nozzle   Steam inlet nozzle that enters the shell of a closed feedwater heater at the plane of the thermal centerline and through which all the extraction steam enters. (See THERMAL CENTERLINE.)

Single-segmental baffles   Cross-flow baffles in which sectors of adjacent baffle circles are cut off alternately side to side or top to bottom, leaving behind baffle segments that direct the fluid up and down or side to side across the tubes.

Skid bars   Pairs of parallel thick rectangular bars, fastened about two-thirds of the shell diameter apart, to a heavy bundle's baffles or tube supports. The skid bars ride on the shell, permitting inserting and pulling the bundle without damaging the baffles or supports.

Snap ring   Machined square or rectangular ring with one cut across its cross section. The ring fits into a groove on the periphery of the floating tubesheet or a floating head with backing device. The snap ring is sprung apart to permit sliding it over the tubesheet. It then springs into the groove, providing a shear ring for reaction to the clamping device.

Spacers   See BAFFLE SPACERS.

Split flange   Lap-joint flange cut on a diameter between pairs of bolt holes. Split flanges are usually ring flanges, thicker than solid rings. They may be used in pairs with the split lines 90° apart.

Split ring   Floating-head backing device consisting of a split bolting flange.

Split shear ring   Two-part machined rectangular ring used as a shear ring in a floating head. The ID of the split shear ring is approximately that of the depth of a rectangular groove machined into the periphery of the floating tubesheet. The OD extends far enough to permit a backing ring to bear against the side of the split ring. The backing-ring ID is slightly larger than the tubesheet OD, which permits it to clear. The floating-head cover flange bolts to the backing ring. (See also SNAP RING.)

Spread pitch   Tubesheet drilling pitch greater than 1¼ times the tube diameter.

Spring washer   Conically shaped washer installed under the nut of a bolting-flange stud bolt to ensure that enough tension will remain in the bolt to keep the gasket tight under varying temperature and pressure regimes.

Stacked shells   Horizontal heat exchanger shells mounted one upon the other. The bottom supports of the next upper shell bolt to mating supports on the preceding lower shell.

Standpipe   Vertical extension of the liquid-return connection of a kettle-type reboiler. The standpipe extends above the level of the highest tube to ensure that the bundle is always fully immersed.

Startup vent   Vent connections in the shell of a feedwater heater or condenser that bypass the operating vents during startup to effect rapid removal of noncondensibles present before startup.

Stationary-tubesheet exchanger   See FIXED-TUBESHEET EXCHANGER.

Steam chest   Shellside of the tubular portion of a vertical-tube calandria-type evaporator.

Steam distribution zone   Untubed region under the inlet nozzle of a horizontal closed feedwater heater.

String   See TRAIN.

Stub end   End of a nozzle or cylinder turned over to form an integral annular ring that serves as a gasket surface. A loose flange (lap-joint flange) fits over the cylindrical part of the stub end and bears against the back of the lap. The OD of the annular ring may be as small as the gasket OD or as large as the lap-joint flange OD. Stub ends may be fabricated by (1) welding an annular ring to the end of a pipe or cylinder and machining as required, (2) forging integrally and machining, and (3) bending over the end of a cylinder or pipe and facing the gasket surface.

Stuffing box   See PACKINGBOX.

Subcooling zone   (1) In a process condenser-subcooler, the region of tubes flooded to subcool the condensate; (2) in a closed feedwater heater, the portion of the tube surface enclosed by a drains subcooling-zone enclosure.

Subcooling-zone enclosure   Enclosure in a closed feedwater heater around the inlet-pass tubes, into which condensate and drains from the condensing zone are fed. The surface contained within the subcooling-zone enclosure acts as a condensate-feedwater heat exchanger in which the condensate and drains surrender heat to incoming feedwater. In horizontal heaters, the subcooling zone can be split-pass, full-tube-length, or full-pass short-tube-length. Subcooling-zone enclosures of split-pass types envelope a fraction of the tubes in the inlet pass for their full length; in full-pass short-tube-length heaters, they surround all the tubes in the inlet pass for a short length behind the tubesheet at the inlet end.

Sump   Auxiliary portion of a condenser shell for the purpose of accumulating condensate. Sumps may be horizontal or vertical. Horizontal sumps may be integral with the shell and extend for part or all of the shell length. (See also HOT WELL.)

Support bracket   Bracket for supporting a heat exchanger vertically or horizontally. Brackets may consist of loose saddles or a framework for horizontal units or loose lugs that bear against rings on the shells of vertical exchangers. They are usually loose, whereas saddles and lugs are welded.

Support lug   See LUG.

Support ring   Plate or bar ring joined to the shell of a vertical heat exchanger and used to support it in a structure. The ring is stiffened by lugs or gussets.

Support saddle   Structural or fabricated support for supporting a horizontal unit. Support saddles are usually installed in pairs, but very long units may have intermediate saddles. The stationary or front-end saddle is usually fixed by bolting to the structure on which it rests. The other saddle or saddles are free to move axially to accommodate shell length changes due to temperature variations.

Support span   Distance traversed by a tube between support points. When full-circle supports are used, the support span is equal to the support pitch. When segmental baffles or semisupports are used, the support span is two semisupport or baffle pitches.

Swing bolt   Bolt (rod end) shaped roughly like a lollypop. The flattened head is drilled to receive a hinge pin that fits into holes in pairs of parallel lugs welded to the channel. The threaded shank of the bolt swings into bolting slots in the channel cover or into pairs of parallel lugs welded to the cover. Standard hexagonal, wing, or loop nuts are threaded to the straight end. When swing-bolt construction is used, the cover can be opened and closed more quickly than with stud-bolt and hexagonal-nut construction. Covers fastened with swing bolts are either hinged or hung from davits.

Tangential nozzle   Connection with its centerline in a plane parallel with a plane passing through the axial centerline of the exchanger and in which the distance between the parallel planes is at the maximum. (See Fig. 1.3.) Tangential nozzles may be rotated within their plane of entry. They may also enter the dish of a bonnet. (See also OFFSET NOZZLE.)

Taper plug   Tube plug machined from a round bar to provide a locking taper when driven into a tube end (included angle of approximately 5°). Taper plugs are installed to seal off leaking tubes. (See also TUBE PLUG.)

Test flange   Loose ring flange used to seal the tubesheet of a removable-bundle exchanger to the shell with tube ends exposed during hydrostatic testing. The tubesheet is sandwiched between the gasketed shell flange and the test flange. Test flanges are also used with fixed-tubesheet units in which the tubesheets are neither welded nor bolted to the shell.

Test gland   Device used in place of a bonnet to seal the floating tubesheet to the shell during hydrostatic testing of an externally sealed, packed floating head. The tube ends at the floating end are exposed.

Test ring and gland   Device used to seal the floating tubesheet to the shell during hydrostatic testing of a pull-through floating head or a floating head with backing device. The front face of the test ring is machined and drilled to make a gasketed, bolted joint with the shell flange at the cover end. The back of the test ring is constructed as a packingbox to receive a gland that compresses packing against the OD of the floating tubesheet. When a test ring and gland are used during hydrostatic testing, the tube ends in the floating tubesheet are exposed.

Thermal centerline   Point along a non-desuperheating-zone closed feedwater heater tube bundle where steam flow is distributed equally in both directions.

Thermocompressor evaporator   Evaporator in which vapor rising from the boiling liquid is compressed in an external compressor and routed to the steam chest; also called a vapor-compression still. The mechanical work of compression raises the vapor pressure and temperature. An auxiliary heat source is required to initiate vaporization. Auxiliary heat may be provided by electric heaters or by line steam supplied to the steam chest. After startup, the auxiliary source is shut down and energy for continuous vaporization is supplied by the compressor.

Thick-walled expansion joint   Heat exchanger shell expansion joints more than ⅛ in (3.18 mm) thick. They are characterized by higher spring rates and (usually) lower cycle lives than thin-walled (bellows) expansion joints of the same diameter designed for identical pressures. (See also BELLOWS EXPANSION

JOINT; FLANGED-AND-FLUED-HEAD EXPANSION JOINT; FLANGED-ONLY-HEAD EXPANSION JOINT.)

Tie rods Round bars that pierce the cross-flow baffles or tube supports and are attached to the stationary tubesheet at one end and to the last baffle or tube support at the other. Usually, baffle spacers are mounted on the tie rods to space and align the baffles and supports. In some units, the baffles are welded directly to the tie rods. (See Fig. 1.5.)

Tongue-and-groove joint Confined joint construction in which a gasket is confined in a groove and compressed by a tongue that fits the groove.

Torpedo See TUBE GUIDE.

Total surface See GROSS SURFACE.

Train Group of closed feedwater heaters connected in series on the feedwater side. Two or more trains may be arranged in parallel. The words *train* and *string* are used interchangeably.

Transverse fins Fins arranged perpendicularly to the tube axis of finned tubes.

Transverse support clearance See BAFFLE CLEARANCE.

Triple effect Evaporator system in which, to make the most efficient use of energy, primary steam is fed to the heating element of the first effect (evaporator); lower-pressure steam, generated by vaporization of water in the first-effect body, is fed to the heating element of the second effect (evaporator); and lower-pressure steam generated in the second-effect body is fed to the heating element of the third effect. The pressures in the vapor bodies are progressively lower.

Triple-segmental cuts Segmental cross-flow baffle system that consists of cyclically repeating arrangements of two A segments, two B segments, one C segment, and two B segments (ABCBABCBABCB..., etc.). The A segments are equal sectors of a full circle that together occupy somewhat more than 40 percent of the shell diameter. The B segments are made from a full circle by cutting off equal parallel outer sectors and an inner segment that has sides parallel to the bases of the sectors. Two B segments also occupy a little more than 40 percent of the shell diameter. The C segments are full circles from which sectors have been cut off on parallel chords. A single C segment takes up a little more than 40 percent of the shell diameter. The segment edges overlap to permit tie rods and spacers to support and align adjacent baffles. Triple-segmental baffles remove very little energy from the shell stream. The main flow direction is axial. Use of these baffles results in minimal pressure loss and in freedom from vibration problems. (See also MULTISEGMENTAL CUTS.)

Tube bundle (1) In a removable-bundle heat exchanger, the assembly of tubesheet or tubesheets, baffles and/or supports, tie rods and spacers, tubes, and any other appurtenances not connected to the shell; (2) in a fixed-tubesheet exchanger, the part of the unit that extends from outer tubesheet face to outer tubesheet face.

Tube count Number of tubes in a tube bundle. For U-tube heat exchangers, the tube count is half of the hole count. (See also HOLE COUNT.)

Tube failure profile Record of the dates and locations of tube failures in a unit. It also shows the axial position and orientation of the failures. The profile may consist of a plug map and accompanying notes that detail failure positions and types of failures. Tube failure profiles are desirable for maintenance, repair, and replacement planning. They may also indicate where design and operating deficiencies require correction or where additional protection must be provided within the structure to prevent continuing deterioration and failures.

Tube guide Device that has a bullet-shaped head (called a torpedo) with the same diameter as the tube OD and a twisted, short brush-and-spring tail that fits snugly into the tube end. Tube guides protect the tube ends and guide the tubes through the tubesheet and baffle holes as they are loaded into the bundle. When a tube has penetrated the hole at the far end, the guide is removed and reused.

Tube-hole grooves One or more annular grooves in the holes of a tubesheet. Tube-hole grooves are used to enhance strength and tightness when tubes are expanded into tubesheets.

Tube-joint temperature Temperature of the tube-to-tubesheet joint. In process and power plant heat exchangers, the tube-joint temperature is estimated from the design heat transfer calculations. For the purpose of establishing temperature limits of expanded-only joints in closed feedwater heaters, the tube-joint temperature is considered to be the outlet feedwater temperature at the design-point conditions.

Tube lane See Cleaning lane.

Tube metal temperature Highest tube metal temperature calculated by considering the relative heat transfer coefficients on both sides of a tube.

Tube pitch pattern See Pitch pattern.

Tube plug Plug for sealing the end of a tube when there is a leak in the tube wall. Common types are (1) single-piece metal or fiber taper plugs with a locking taper angle, (2) two-piece plugs in which the inner piece is a taper plug that fits into a matching taper inside the outer piece, (3) two-piece extension plugs for sealing the far end of a tube that is inaccessible, (4) thimble-shaped plugs that are roller-expanded or hydraulically expanded into the tube ends, (5) explosive plugs, and (6) welded plugs. Welded plugs vary from a length of round bar press-fitted into the tube (or tube hole when the tube end is cut away) and fusion-welded with a filet weld to the surrounding structure to shapes designed to prevent impurities from the back face of the tubesheet and the space between the tube end and hole from contaminating the weld. Plugs may also be explosively welded to the tube end or hole. Proprietary types are commercially available. The tightness of nonwelded plugs depends upon friction between the tube and the plug. Taper plugs make line contact before they are driven but deform the tube to provide some surface for friction. The required interfacial-fit pressure between the taper plug and the tube is high because the surface available for friction is small. Two-piece, thimble, and explosive-expanded plugs provide greater contact areas than one-piece taper plugs. Therefore, they require less interfacial pressure to seal. Two-piece plugs may have their exterior barrels serrated to enable them to cut through the scale of deposits that cannot be readily removed before plugging.

Tube ribbons   Twisted strips of metal inserted in tubes to increase turbulence.

Tube rolling   Expanding tubes into tubesheets by roller expanding.

Tube-thinning allowance   Excess tube wall thickness allowed for the thinning of a U bend at its outer radius. The TEMA minimum tube wall thickness before bending is

$$t_0 = t_1(1 + d_0/4R) \tag{1.1}$$

where t_0 = original wall thickness
t_1 = minimum *ASME Code* straight tube thickness
d_0 = tube OD
R = mean bend radius

In the HEI standards, the minimum wall thickness before bending is

$$t = \frac{Pd(1 + d/4R)}{2S + 0.8P} \tag{1.2}$$

where t = original tube wall thickness before bending
d = outside tube diameter
P = design pressure
R = mean bend radius
S = allowable tube design stress at the temperature that corresponds with the shell design pressure

Thinning should not exceed 17 percent of the nominal wall thickness. Flattening at the bend should not exceed 10 percent of the nominal tube OD.

Tubeside pressure drop   Pressure loss through tubes, tubeside connections, and pass turnarounds. (See also SHELLSIDE PRESSURE DROP.)

Tweeners   See HOLTEC NON-SEGMENTAL BAFFLES.

U-bend exchanger   Exchanger made with U-bend tubes (U tubes). Except when there are more than two passes, horizontal U-bend exchanger bundles are preferably built with the bends in the vertical plane to take full advantage of the flexibility of the bent ends. For example, if steam is being generated in the shellside of a U-tube unit, low water level that exposes upper tube rows can create a far more severe differential-thermal-expansion problem in bundles with tubes bent in the horizontal plane than in the vertical. Whenever possible, vertical U-bend exchangers are arranged to operate head down to permit the tubes to drain.

Unbalanced pass count   Arrangement in which there are more tubes in one pass than in another. Unbalance should be limited to 5 percent of the average of the pass tube counts.

Unit   Heat exchanger consisting of one or more shells. Shells in a unit may be arranged in series, in parallel, or in series-parallel flow combinations.

Vapor belt   Cylindrical enlargement of the shell concentric with the shell cylinder of a process condenser. The vapor belt (vapor bustle or vapor distribution belt) is somewhat longer than the width of the vapor inlet nozzle. The enlargement permits incoming vapor to distribute itself to the tubes. When the vapor belt extends for substantially the full shell length, the flow characteristics approach cross-flow.

Vapor bustle   See VAPOR BELT.

Vapor-compression still   See THERMOCOMPRESSOR EVAPORATOR.

Vapor distribution belt   See VAPOR BELT.

Vertical cut   Vertically cut segmental support plate or cross-flow baffle in a horizontal unit.

Wall clearance   Clearance between the OD of cross-flow baffles or tube supports and the shell or zone enclosure ID.

Wasting plate   Plate intended to be preferentially eroded or corroded. (See SACRIFICIAL ANODE.)

Water box   Channel of a steam surface condenser.

Weep hole   (1) Small hole drilled in the cover plate to indicate when there is leakage in an applied lining; (2) small tapped hole in a doubler plate or reinforcement fully sealed to a pressure part used as a leak indicator and vents; (3) small hole drilled through a pass partition to permit full drainage of the compartment.

Weir   Transverse plate behind the tube bundle in a kettle reboiler. The top of the weir is located above the level of the highest tube. When the weir is sealed to the shell to enclose the bundle in a hydraulically tight trough, it is an overflow weir. When the seal is interrupted at the bottom by an open space, it is an underflow weir. Overflow weirs are used with viscous liquids. Liquid that is not vaporized flows over or under the weir to the compartment behind it. The compartment empties to the column bottom or recirculating pump. The weir provides a calming zone for instrumentation and level control.

Weld-end nozzle   Connection with the end beveled or otherwise prepared for welding to the connecting pipe.

Window   Distance between a baffle or tube support cut line and the shell; in a closed feedwater heater desuperheating or condensing zone, the distance between the cut line and the zone enclosure.

Wire drawing   Erosion due to high-pressure fluid on one side of a tubesheet passing between the tube and the hole into a low-pressure space on the other side. An example is leakage of feedwater between a tube and the tubesheet. (See also WORMHOLING.)

Wormholing   Spiral or curved grooves on the tube and tube-hole surfaces, similar in appearance to holes made in wood by worms. The holes are initiated at the high-pressure side of the tubesheet and penetrate axially. Wormholing may become so severe that the ligaments between adjacent tubes are penetrated.

References

1. *Standards of the Tubular Exchanger Manufacturers Association*, 7th ed., The Tubular Exchanger Manufacturers Association, Tarrytown, N.Y., 1989.
2. *Shell-and-Tube Heat Exchangers for General Refinery Services*, API Standard 660, 4th ed., The American Petroleum Institute, Washington, September 1982.
3. *Standard for Power Plant Heat Exchangers*, 1st ed., The Heat Exchange Institute, Cleveland, 1980; Addendum 1, 1984.
4. *Standards for Closed Feedwater Heaters*, 4th ed., The Heat Exchange Institute, Cleveland, August 1984.
5. *Standard for Steam Surface Condensers*, 8th ed., The Heat Exchange Institute, Cleveland, 1984.

Chapter

2

Guide to Heat Exchanger Tubing

Introduction

The tubes are the essential element of a shell-and-tube heat exchanger. The rest of the structure serves only to direct flow into or around the tubes. This chapter discusses the elements of tubing specifications for heat exchangers built to the *ASME Code*; how seamless and welded tubes are manufactured and tested; the meanings of minimum wall, nominal wall, and average wall and the distinctions between them; U-tube bending; bimetallic tubing; and tubing with extended and enhanced surfaces.[1]

Tubing Specifications

When specifying heat exchanger tubing, it is not sufficient to use a general type designation or trade name. To specify or order tubing properly, require it to conform with the specification for the type and grade of tubing found in the construction code that applies.

In North America, most heat exchangers are built to the *ASME Code* rules. Section II, "Materials Specifications," has specifications for heat exchanger and condenser tubing that, with some exceptions, are identical with ASTM specifications. Table 2.1 lists *ASME Code* specification numbers for ferrous heat exchanger tubing; Table 2.2 lists the *ASME Code* specification numbers for nonferrous tubing.

TABLE 2.1   Specifications for Ferrous Tubing Used in Heat Exchangers

1986 Edition, *ASME Boiler and Pressure Vessel Code*, Section II, "Material Specifications"

Type of tube	Specification number
All Ferrous Tubing	
Carbon steel, ferritic alloy, and austenitic alloy steel tubes—general requirements	SA-450
Seamless Ferrous Tubing	
Seamless cold-drawn low-carbon steel heat exchanger and condenser tubes	SA-179
Seamless cold-drawn intermediate-alloy steel heat exchanger and condenser tubes	SA-199
Seamless ferritic and austenitic alloy steel boiler, superheater, and heat exchanger tubes	SA-213
Welded Ferrous Tubing	
Electric-resistance-welded carbon steel heat exchanger and condenser tubes	SA-214
Welded austenitic steel boiler, superheater, heat exchanger, and condenser tubes	SA-249
Welded carbon and alloy steel tubes for low-temperature service	SA-334
Electric-resistance-welded carbon steel feedwater heater tubes	SA-557
Welded austenitic stainless-steel feedwater heater tubes	SA-688

Each specification may apply to several types, alloys, or grades. Specifications for tubing not found in the body of the code may be permitted by code cases.* If a specification is not listed, an interpretation may be requested from the code secretary to determine if it can be used in *ASME Code* construction. A discussion of the elements of typical heat exchanger tubing specifications follows.

Scope

The scope of tubing specifications sets forth the types, grades, and size range of tubing and service for which it is intended. When the specification permits sizes outside the specified range, the scope may limit the applicability of specific requirements. It also calls attention to optional supplementary requirements that the purchaser may specify. Some scope statements say whether or not the specification includes seamless or welded tubes or both.

Applicable documents

Tubing specifications list documents that apply by reference. Examples of such reference documents are ASTM Standard SA-450, "Spec-

---

*The *ASME Code* and code cases are discussed in Chap. 8.

TABLE 2.2   Specifications for Nonferrous Tubing Used in Heat Exchangers

1986 Edition, *ASME Boiler and Pressure Vessel Code*, Section II, "Material Specifications"

Type of tube	Specification number
Aluminum and Aluminum Alloys	
Aluminum-alloy drawn seamless tubes for condensers and heat exchangers	SB-234
Copper and Copper Alloys	
Seamless copper tubes	SB-75
Copper and copper-alloy seamless condenser tubes and ferrule stock	SB-111
Copper and copper-alloy seamless condenser and heat exchanger tubes with integral fins	SB-359
U-bend seamless copper and copper-alloy heat exchanger and condenser tubes	SB-395
Welded copper and copper-alloy heat exchanger tubes	SB-543
Nickel and Nickel Alloys	
Seamless nickel and nickel-alloy condenser and heat exchanger tubes	SB-163
UNS N08028 seamless tubes	SB-688
Supplementary requirements for nickel-alloy seamless pipe and tube for nuclear applications	SB-513
Welded chromium-nickel-iron-molybdenum-copper-columbium stabilized alloy tubes	SB-468
Welded nickel-iron-chromium alloy tubes	SB-515
Welded nickel-alloy tubes	SB-626
UNS N08904	SB-674
UNS N08366 welded tube	SB-677
Titanium and Titanium Alloys	
Seamless and welded titanium and titanium-alloy tubes for condensers and heat exchangers	SB-363
Zirconium and Zirconium Alloys	
Seamless and welded zirconium and zirconium-alloy tubes for condensers and heat exchangers	SB-523

ification for General Requirements for Carbon, Ferritic Alloy and Austenitic Steel Tubes," and A-762, "Practice for Detecting Susceptibility to Intergranular Attack in Ferritic Stainless Steels."

Terminology

Some tubing specifications have a section that defines terminology. An example is the definition of a heat exchanger tube quoted from ASME "Specification for Aluminum-Alloy Drawn Seamless Tubes for Condensers and Heat Exchangers," SB-234:

A tube for use in which fluid inside the tube will be heated or cooled by fluid outside the tube. The term is usually not applied to coiled tube or to tube used in refrigerators or radiators.

General requirements

ASME Code specifications for most ferrous and nonferrous tubing require compliance with ASME specification SA-450, which lists general requirements such as:

1. Responsibility for quality assurance
2. Leak testing
3. General quality
4. Certification

Others include equivalent requirements in the body of the text such as cladding thickness for aluminum tubes of one alloy coated with another alloy.

Ordering information

Tubing specifications state what the purchase order must include to describe the material completely. Typically, the purchase order must have the following information:

1. Specification number
2. Quantity (feet, meters, or number of lengths)
3. Length (specific or random)
4. Name of material (seamless or welded tubes)
5. Type and grade
6. Size and nominal wall thickness for nominal-wall specifications or minimum thickness for minimum-wall specifications
7. Optional requirements (heat or product analysis, hydrostatic or eddy-current test, etc.)
8. Special requirements

Process

The requirements for raw-material manufacture are specified under the heading "Process." A process specification may require the raw steel to be produced by the electric-furnace, open-hearth, basic-oxygen method. Most specifications also permit the purchaser to approve an alternative primary process.

The specification defines what constitutes a heat when secondary melting is used. If the purchase order states specific melting requirements, the material manufacturer must provide the reports specified in the general requirement for melting.

Manufacture

This element indicates whether tubes are to be made seamless or by automatic welding of formed strip. For automatic welding, the specification may state whether or not filler metal is to be added and the type of welding to be performed. Typical automatic welding processes are gas-tungsten arc welding (GTAW), electric-resistance welding (ERW), and electric-induction welding (EIW). Requirements may be specified for working the weld or parent metal in welded-tubing specifications.

Heat treatment

An element of tubing specifications is a listing of requirements for heat treatment, stress relief, and normalization. This element also lists conditions for optional heat treatments and those that may be negotiated between the buyer and the producer.

The reason for heat treating may simply be to assure uniform properties, as in titanium tubing, or it may be to provide maximum corrosion resistance after welding and sizing, as in austenitic stainless-steel tubes.

Hardness and strength are also adjusted by heat treatment. For many nonferrous materials, it is necessary not only to specify the basic material or alloy but also to specify the temper. For example, aluminum alloys 1060, 3003, Alclad 3003, 5052, and 5454 are supplied in a strain-hardened temper to meet the specified tensile and yield strengths. Alloy 6061 is supplied either in the heat-treated temper (T-4) or the heat-treated-and-aged temper (T-6). The T-4 temper is more workable, and after forming work has been completed, the alloy may be aged to the T-6 temper.

Care must be taken when using T-6 temper tubes for welded-only tube-to-tubesheet joints. The heat of welding may reduce the strength of the tube (and perhaps the tubesheet) to the strength of T-4 temper. Straightening tubing after production also induces strain hardening. Therefore, it may be necessary to heat-treat afterward to relieve the stresses due to straightening.

Several nonferrous tube specifications provide for annealing the tube ends only. The purpose is to take advantage of the high strength of the unannealed body of the tube and at the same time have more ductile metal available for tube expanding at the annealed tube end. Tube-end working produced by expanding is assumed to bring tube-end strength up to the level of the rest of the tube. When tube-end annealing is specified, the tube manufacturer is required to perform an expanding test.

Chemical requirements

Raw-material chemistry is usually prescribed in tables. The specification may also state which analysis methods must be used to determine that the chemistry conforms with the specified analysis.

Heat analysis

The specification for heat analysis requires the manufacturer to determine the percentages of elements in the raw material and states the conditions for sampling and reporting.

Product analysis

Product analysis requires further testing to determine the chemical composition of a tube sample to make sure that it conforms with the chemical requirements of the specification. Product analysis specifications lay down conditions for acceptance or rejection and retesting when a sample fails.

Requirements for performing product analysis may be mandatory or optional, depending upon the specification. When they are optional, the purchaser must specify the requirement on the purchase order to have product analysis done. The tubing specification lists the product analysis specifications whether optional or required.

Tensile requirements

The tube mill must test specimens to show that the tubes conform with the tensile properties tabulated in the specification. Always insist that tensile testing be done after all other operations have been completed. If work-hardenable tubing is tensile-tested before it is roller-straightened, the results will not reflect conditions after straightening. Straightening may increase tube yield strength so much that a tight rolled joint cannot be produced unless the tube ends have first been annealed.

For expanded tube-to-tubesheet joints, it is important to understand that acceptance criteria are *minimum* values for yield and tensile strength and *maximum* values for hardness. Therefore, instead of using specified values of minimum yield and maximum hardness, use actual mill-test report values to establish rolling torque or hydro-expanding pressure.

Wide variations within the permissible range can seriously affect expanded tube-to-tubesheet joint quality. Table 2.3 illustrates how tube and tubesheet yield strengths can vary within permissible limits. The data in the table were taken from actual mill-test reports of SB-75 annealed seamless copper tubing and SA-285 Grade C steel plate used for the tubesheets. The specified minimum yield strength of the tubes is 9 ksi (62,050 kPa), and the specified minimum yield strength of the plate is 24 ksi (165,470 kPa). The next stronger temper of seamless copper tubing to SB-75 is light-drawn with a specified minimum yield of 30 ksi (206,800 kPa). Therefore, the yield strength of the annealed copper tubing may vary from the minimum of 9 ksi to just under 30 ksi (62,500 to 206,800 kPa). Rolling torque settings based upon spec-

TABLE 2.3   Variations of Yield Strength for SB-75 Annealed Copper Tubes and SA-285-C Plates

Plate number	Yield strength, ksi	Tube lot	Yield strength, ksi
1	38.9	1	16.5*
2	37.7	2	11.9
3	36.1	3	12.2
4	35.9	4	12.2
5	38.4	5	13.3
6	35.8	6	12.4
7	37.8	7	12.8
8	37.4	8	12.8
9	36.4	9	12.3
10	35.4	10	13.6
11	39.5	11	13.8
12	31.5†	12	12.8
13	33.1	13	12.6
14	35.2	14	12.3
15	36.3	15	12.6
16	34.8	16	12.3
17	36.1	17	11.7†
18	36.1	18	12.3
19	40.7*	19	15.7
20	34.4	20	14.2
Mean	36.8		13.02

*Highest value.
†Lowest value.

imen joints made from the lowest-yield-strength tubes would not produce tight joints with the highest-yield-strength tubes.

Hardness requirements

Tube hardness must not exceed the hardness number listed in the tube product specification. Hardness should be tested after all other operations have been completed.

Mechanical tests

Each tubing specification lists required mechanical tests. They may include:

1. Tension tests
2. Flaring test (for seamless tubes)
3. Flange test (for welded tubes)
4. Hardness test
5. Reverse-flattening test (for welded tubes)
6. Hydrostatic or nondestructive electric test

Other tests and examinations

Depending upon the specifications, examinations and testing may be required to determine uniformity and size of metal grain structure, completeness of recrystallization after annealing, corrosion resistance to certain environments, and the ability of the tube to be expanded. Some of these tests are:

1. Microscopical examination
2. Grain size determination
3. Expansion test
4. Impact test (for tubes used in low-temperature service)
5. Chemical tests for detecting susceptibility of intergranular corrosion of ferritic steels
6. Mercurous nitrate test for some copper alloys
7. Nitric acid test for austenitic stainless steels
8. Ferric sulfate or sulfuric acid test for austenitic stainless steels

Forming operations

A typical statement in a tubing specification about forming might read as follows:

All tubes, when properly manipulated, shall be able to withstand all forging, welding, and bending operations necessary for application without developing defects.

Permissible variations in dimensions

Variations in outside diameter, wall thickness, and length are restricted to tabulated values. Here are some permissible variations tabulated in general specification SA-450.

Before bending or otherwise forming, seamless cold drawn and welded tubes may be no thinner than the minimum thickness. Seamless cold drawn tubes 1½ inches (38.1 mm) OD and smaller may be as much as 20% thicker. Larger seamless tubes may be 22% over the minimum wall thickness.

Welded tubes ordered to minimum thickness may be 18% thicker than the minimum. The outside diameter of welded and cold drawn seamless tubes may be 0.0004 inches (0.010 mm) larger or smaller when the tubes are under one inch (25.4 mm) ODs, 0.006 inches (0.15 mm) larger or smaller when the tubes are one inch to one and one half inches (25.4 mm to 38.1 mm) inclusive outside diameter, 0.008 inches (0.20 mm) larger or smaller for tubes over 1½ inches and less than 2 inches (larger than 38.1 mm and less than 50.8 mm) OD and 0.010 inches (0.254 mm) larger or smaller for tubes 2 inches up to but not including 2½ inches (50.8 mm up to but not including 63.5 mm) OD.

Tubes with very thin walls are apt to become out of round during final annealing and straightening. The *ASME Code* defines thin-walled tubes as all tubes 0.020 in (0.508 mm) thick or thinner and as tubes with walls equal to 2 percent of the diameter for tubes 2 in (50.8 mm) or less and 3 percent of the diameter for larger tubes. This is a different definition from that customarily used in stress analysis.

The diameter tolerances quoted above apply only to the mean of the maximum and minimum diametral measurements at any cross section. They are not sufficient to provide for the additional ovality anticipated in manufacturing thin-walled tubes. For such tubes the difference in extreme outside-diameter measurements is limited to 0.020 in (0.51 mm) for tubes 1 in (25.4 mm) in diameter and smaller and 2 percent of the diameter for tubes 2 in (50.8 mm) or less and 3 percent of the diameter for tubes larger than 2 in (50.8 mm).

Finish

The specifications contain finish requirements such as smooth, burr-free ends and freedom from injurious defects. Finish is extremely important in achieving tight, trouble-free tube-to-tubesheet joints.

If the tube edge is ragged, the tube may split during expansion.

Burrs on tube ends may score the tube holes when the tubes are set into the tubesheets. If the expanding tool knocks the burrs off, the scraps of metal may damage the expander or get between the tube and the hole. This will make it impossible to produce a tight joint. If the joint is made by welding, burrs may cause porosity and cracks in the weld.

Heat-treating tubes may cause surface scale buildup and discoloration. The specifications describe the required surface finish after final heat treatment. Descaling is required for ferritic tubes, but a light oxide coating is permitted. Austenitic steel tubes must be pickled and passivated or bright-annealed. Discoloration due to induction heat treating of U bends after bending is acceptable.

Aluminum tubes must be clean, but discoloration due to heat treatment is not considered to be objectionable. Copper and copper-alloy tubes that are stress-relieved or annealed must be clean, but they may have a superficial dull iridescent film on the inside and outside surfaces. Cold-drawn copper and copper-alloy tubes may be coated with drawing lubricant.

Annealed nickel and nickel copper should have a dull matte finish. Stress-relieved nickel and nickel-copper tubes should have a thin, light to medium-dark surface. Nickel-chromium-iron, nickel-iron-chromium, and nickel-iron-chromium-molybdenum-copper alloys with an annealed and ground outside diameter may have a bright interior finish if the tubes are annealed in a protective atmosphere. Otherwise, the inside must be descaled.

Marking

The general specifications include marking requirements. These comprise manufacturer, diameter, wall thickness, specification number and type, and heat number. For example, ¾-in OD by 18-BWG welded stainless-steel Type 316 tubes manufactured in conformity with specification SA-249 may be marked "Manufacturer .75 inch OD × 0.049 inch Avg SA-249 TP316, heat number xxxxxxx" at regular intervals along each length of tubing, where the manufacturer's name is substituted for "Manufacturer" and the heat number is substituted for "xxxxxxx."

Supplementary requirements

Supplementary requirements are criteria that apply only when they are stated on the purchase order. Here are three examples: (1) If the purchase order specifies air-underwater testing, the supplementary requirements specification gives minimum requirements for performing the test and the acceptance criteria. (2) If the purchase order specifies heat-treating austenitic stainless-steel tubes to the stress-relieved, annealed condition, the supplementary requirements specify the heat treatment. (3) If the order calls for tubes, ordinarily purchased to nominal-wall thickness, to be minimum-wall, the supplementary requirements specify that the manufacturer must meet the minimum-wall requirements of the general specification.

Minimum Wall, Nominal Wall, and Average Wall

Welded tube wall thicknesses vary when strip thicknesses are not uniform. Seamless tube wall thicknesses vary when the holes in hollow ingots, pierced billets, or extruded-bar hollows, used for drawing, are not concentric and when, in drawing tubes, there are die clearance irregularities that cause wall-thickness variations. Depending upon how deviations from theoretical dimensions are dealt with, tubing is described as minimum-, nominal-, and average-wall.

Some *ASME Code* tubing specifications are for minimum-wall tubes; others, for nominal-wall tubes. The *TEMA Standards** state, "Wall thickness tolerance shall be specified as either minimum or average." This can be very confusing if the meanings of nominal-, minimum-, and average-wall are not fully understood.

Minimum-wall tubes are tubes in which the least thickness of the tube wall is the thickness specified in the purchase order. *ASME Code* specifications SA-213 for seamless tubing and SA-214 for welded tubing are examples of minimum-wall specifications. The mill must fill an order for 1-in-OD (25.4-mm-OD) 16-BWG tubes to one of these specifications with tubes at least 0.065 in (1.65 mm) thick. SA-213 tubing produced to satisfy the specification could be as much as 20 percent thicker, or 0.0780 in (1.98 mm) thick, and SA-214 tubes could be as much as 18 percent thicker, or 0.0767 in (1.95 mm) thick.

According to earlier TEMA editions, one could order tubes to a minimum-wall specification and add the words, "except average-wall." Ordering tubing that is made to a minimum-wall specification to average-wall tolerances, as permitted in the current edition, implies that the tubes are being ordered one gauge thinner than minimum-wall tubes of the same gauge. However, the tube manufac

---

*See Table RCB-2.21 of the *Standards of the Tubular Exchanger Manufacturers Association*, 7th ed., 1989.

turer will not guarantee that the minimum thickness of tubing ordered to average-wall thickness is the minimum thickness of the next thinner gauge.

Nominal-wall tubes are tubes in which the *ASME Code* tubing specification permits the thickness to be greater or less than the specified wall thickness by a stated percentage. *ASME Code* specification SA-249 for welded stainless-steel tubing for heat exchangers and condensers is a nominal-wall specification that permits wall thickness to vary 10 percent from the nominal.

The thickness of 1-in-OD (25.4-mm-OD) by 16-BWG SA-249 tubing may be as little as 0.0585 in (1.49 mm) or as much as 0.075 in (1.91 mm). However, if the purchase order specifies minimum-wall tubing to SA-249, the mill will start with strip thick enough to ensure that the minimum thickness is 0.065 in (1.65 mm). It will sample and examine appropriately to make sure that the tubing is not thinner than 0.065 in (1.65 mm).

For *ASME Code* purposes, the tube wall thickness calculated to withstand pressure is the minimum thickness that may be used (excluding any allowance for corrosion or erosion). Therefore, if a 1-in-OD (25.4-mm-OD) tube were required to be 0.065 in (1.65 mm) thick to withstand pressure, the nominal thickness of an SA-249 tube would have to be 0.0722 in (1.83 mm), which corresponds to 15 BWG.

Under the same constraint, SA-213 and SA-214 tubing would also have to be a minimum thickness of 0.065 in (1.65 mm). Tubes that would provide the required 0.065-in (1.65-mm) minimum thickness, which were made to specification SA-213, except average-wall, could vary from 0.065 in (1.65 mm) to 0.0780 in (1.98 mm), or 20 percent thicker. SA-214, except average-wall, tubing could vary from 0.065 in (1.65 mm) to 0.0767 in (1.95 mm), or 18 percent thicker. To satisfy *ASME Code* required minimum thickness, 14-BWG average-wall, which is 0.083 in (2.11 mm), would be required, since 15-BWG tubes are only 0.072 in (1.83 mm) thick.

Therefore, when specifying tubing for high-pressure heat exchangers, indicate that only minimum-wall is acceptable for tubes made to minimum-wall specifications. Show a thickness at least 10 percent greater than the calculated required thickness for tubes made to a nominal-wall specification.

Manufacturing Processes

Heat exchanger and condenser tubes are made either seamlessly or by forming strip into a cylinder and welding the open seam. Seamless heat exchanger tubes are cold-drawn. Welded tubes may be cold-drawn or be rounded and sized by ring dies. For some materials welded tubes that are not cold-drawn must have the weld and adjacent metal worked to achieve an acceptable grain structure.

From the point at which final tube size is attained, the steps in manufacturing seamless and welded tubes are essentially alike. The generalized descriptions that follow are broken down into operations performed to produce seamless tubes, those done to manufacture welded tubes, and those common to both. Note that operations and sequences vary with the tube material, type, and manufacturer.

Manufacture of seamless tubing

The raw material for producing seamless tubes is a hollow ingot, a pierced billet, or a solid bar extruded into a cylinder that is sized by cold reducing with ring or split dies and subsequently annealed. The raw cylinders are called tube shells or hollows. (Welded tubes made for subsequent cold drawing to size are also called hollows.) The hollow may be further extruded or reduced to a size suitable for cold drawing, or it may be directly cold-drawn to the required thickness and diameter.

Cold drawing reduces the tube diameter and wall. In cold drawing, either a plug or a rod mandrel is inserted into the tube, and the end is then pointed and lubricated. The tube is passed, pointed end first, through a die or dies.

Plug mandrels remain stationary relative to the drawing die and float relative to the inside of the tube. Therefore, they are also referred to as floating mandrels. In plug drawing, the diameter and the wall thickness are sized in one operation.

Rod mandrels move with the tube. Therefore, the operation is called bar or rod drawing. After the mandrel has been inserted, the hollow is drawn in a drawbench. Three operations are needed to rod-draw. First the tube wall is fixed, next the tube is expanded to release the mandrel, and finally the tube is sunk (the diameter is sized by pulling the tube through a sizing die without a mandrel).

To draw the tube without generating excessive heat or scoring inner and outer surfaces, lubricant must be provided. Variations in the die clearances and ductility of the hollows may cause variances in the wall thickness, diameter, and roundness (ovality) of the tubes.

Depending upon the material properties, it may be necessary to use various intermediate heat treatments during tube drawing and finishing. The tube may have to be partially drawn and annealed to restore ductility in several steps to completion. However, the material is cold before each drawing step, which is why the process is called cold drawing. In contrast, hot-finished tubing, which is not used in heat exchangers, comes directly from a hot-extrusion press without further size and wall reduction.

Manufacture of welded tubing

The raw material from which welded tubing is produced is strip selected to meet the chemical and physical requirements specified for the finished tubing. Strip thickness, width, and edge condition are carefully controlled. Special cleanliness requirements are established to reduce the possibility of contamination by manufacturing, handling, and packaging.

The strip is fed from a continuous roll to a forming and welding machine like that pictured in Fig. 2.1. It has a series of vertical and horizontal forming rolls that continuously bend the strip into a round open-seamed tube. The edges to be welded must be clean and aligned exactly as they pass under a welding torch that automatically welds them together. Precise control of diameter and roundness are not necessary because the tube is sized and cold-worked after welding. Figure 2.2 is a closeup photograph of the forming rolls, showing the feed for inert-gas backing.

Austenitic stainless steel, high alloys, titanium, and exotic metals.   The welding process for high-alloy tubes is gas-tungsten arc welding

Figure 2.1 Forming and welding high-alloy tubes. (*Carpenter Technology, Reading, Pennsylvania.*)

Figure 2.2 Closeup of tube forming showing inert-gas backing feed. (*Carpenter Technology, Reading, Pennsylvania.*)

(GTAW) with no filler metal. Horizontal rolls apply pressure to support the weld metal until it solidifies.

These welding procedure variables must be tightly controlled to make sure that a uniform, fully penetrated, uncontaminated, crack-free weld suitable for cold working is produced: weld arc voltage and current flow; torch position relative to the welding rolls; angle between the open-seam edges; position of the torch relative to the pressure rolls; weld arc shielding-gas mixture and flow rate; composition, flow, and pressure of backing gas fed to the underside of the weld; and rate at which the open-seamed tube passes under the stationary welding head (speed of welding).

To size the diameter and wall and to obtain a suitable weld metal structure, the welds must be cold-worked. This may be done by drawing and sizing the tubes in a drawbench, or the welds may be bead-conditioned by swaging or cold rolling and the tubes subsequently sized by sizing rolls on the welding machine.

Of these processes, cold drawing provides the most cold work, reduces the weld-bead crown more, and yields a finer weld grain structure than the bead-conditioning processes, which work only the weld. Therefore, it is more likely to reveal any defects in the tube. Because drawing produces a low bead profile, cold-drawn tubes damage tube-expanding equipment less than tubes that are swaged or cold-rolled.

The chief disadvantage of cold drawing is that it is more expensive than the alternatives. Also, if lubrication is inadequate, the tubes may be longitudinally scored by mandrel or die galling. If the lubricant is not completely removed after drawing, heat treating may carburize the tubes. This impairs the corrosion resistance of austenitic steel surfaces.

To swage the weld, a stationary plug is inserted into the tube, and the outside weld surface is hammered with dies. Bead conditioning by swaging may be done on the welding machine or in a separate operation after the tubing has been removed.

The weld bead is cold-rolled by special rolls fitted to the welding machine after the welding head. An internal plug mandrel with close-fitting rolls that conform with the tube ID is inserted into the tube. The weld bead is then worked between the rolls on the machine and in the tube.

Carbon steel. Carbon steel welded tubes are made in similar equipment. However, the machine is fitted with forge rolls that tightly squeeze the open-seamed cylinder edges together. The welding process is high-frequency electric-resistance welding (ERW). Since the flash that forms on the inside and outside surfaces of the weld contains impurities, it is removed to leave the weld flush. Welding speed is much faster than in the GTAW process used with austenitic stainless steel, high alloys, titanium, etc.

Nonferrous metals. Tubes of copper-bearing alloys are produced much like those of carbon steel. However, welding is done by the high-frequency electric-induction process (EIW) at a speed comparable with ERW.

ASME Code specification SB-543 covers welded copper and a variety of welded copper-alloy heat exchanger tubes that may be produced in these forms: as-welded, with internal and external flash removed; welded, with internal and external flash removed and annealed to produce a grain size appropriate to the specified temper; welded, with internal and external flash removed and cold-drawn to the specified size and temper; and fully finished. Fully finished tubes are welded tubes with internal and external flash removed that have been cold-drawn, annealed, and redrawn when necessary to the specified temper. Except for the drawn forms, the tubes are ring-die-sized.

Common manufacturing steps

After basic manufacturing, additional operations are required before the tubing is ready for shipment to the exchanger manufacturer. Among the manufacturing steps common to seamless and welded tubes are degreasing, heat treatment, nondestructive testing and examination for quality control, cutting to size, destructive testing to determine mechanical properties, formability testing, straightening, surface treatment, and packaging.

Degreasing. The tenacious lubricants required for drawing, cold working, and sizing must be removed before heat treatment. This is accomplished by solvent degreasing and detergent washing followed by water rinsing.

Heat treatment. The purposes of heat-treating tubes are (1) to restore corrosion resistance or to produce optimum corrosion resistance in weld and parent metal, (2) to relieve stresses that result from forming and welding, or (3) to temper the material to a specified hardness. Austenitic stainless-steel tubes must be annealed after welding and cold working to redissolve complex carbides precipitated during cooling of the weld. To maintain the carbides in solution, the tubes must be quenched to black rapidly from the heat-treating temperature. They are also heat-treated to reduce hardness and residual stress due to forming, welding, and cold working and to achieve uniformity in the composition of the weld and parent metal. Here, some weld metal recrystallization also takes place.

Carbon steel and low-alloy tubes are heat-treated primarily to reduce hardness and residual forming and welding stresses. Copper-bearing and aluminum-alloy tubes are heat-treated to relieve forming stresses and subsequently to produce required hardness and strength.

Depending upon the material and purpose of heat treatment, the hot tubes may be slowly cooled or rapidly quenched. To quench the tubes, they may be spray-cooled externally, air-blast-cooled, cooled by circulating air through the tubes and spray quenching outside, or immersed in water. Air-blast cooling or air-blast cooling supplemented by water spraying is used on smaller sizes and thinner gauges.

When tubes are heat-treated by being passed through an induction coil or in a continuous-roller furnace, no attempt is made to exclude air. This produces on the surfaces a tight oxide film that must be substantially removed by descaling.

Austenitic stainless steels are descaled and passivated in solutions of nitric and hydrofluoric acid, which leave an etched, white matte finish on the surface. In addition, the mixed-acid solution preferentially attacks regions that have become carburized or in which carbides have precipitated, and it dissolves tight films of metal on the surface that result from drawing and may hide underlying defects.

The acid bath acts much like a fluid penetrant in that it is retained by very tight cracks and similar flaws. Therefore, acid descaling of open-annealed austenitic tubes enhances quality control. Because thorough subsequent washing to remove all traces of pickling and passivating liquor is essential, mills use several cold- and hot-water washes.

The principal impediments to acid pickling and passivating are the inability to dispose of spent liquor economically without damaging the environment and the hazard to health that the acids present. For these reasons, many mills now bright-anneal the tubes in closed furnaces that have controlled atmospheres of hydrogen or cracked ammonia.

Bright annealing preserves the surface finish developed in cold working. Improperly controlled, bright annealing in a cracked-ammonia atmosphere can cause nitriding. If the ammonia is not dry enough, stainless-steel tubes may develop a hard-to-remove green chromium oxide coating.

Bright-annealed tubes cannot be directly quenched in the retort. Therefore, a jacketed cooling chamber is used. However, quench cooling in the chamber may not be rapid enough to avoid precipitating complex carbides in austenitic stainless steels, with consequent loss of corrosion resistance. To remove contaminants, it may be necessary to pickle the tubes. However, the acid treatment is not as intensive as in oxide scale removal and does not disclose hidden defects.

Nondestructive examinations. Tube mills do nondestructive tests and examinations dictated by the specifications. Requirements for additional nondestructive tests may be negotiated between the buyer and the mill. In addition to leaks and visible gross defects, nondestructive testing may disclose dings, straightener marks, loose ID bead and cutting chips, scratches, steel-die stamps, chattered flash trim, stop marks, and tube-reducer ripple. Although no defects are desirable, some may not be injurious; others can be repaired to make an acceptable tube. ASME specification SA-450 regards any of the listed defects that are deeper than 0.004 in (0.10 mm) or greater than 12½ percent of the tube wall thickness as unacceptable.

The most frequently used nondestructive examinations are eddy-

Figure 2.3 Continuous eddy-current testing. (*Carpenter Technology, Reading, Pennsylvania.*)

current testing, water-submerged-air testing, and hydrostatic testing. Other nondestructive means available at most mills are ultrasonic testing and flux-leakage examination. Each kind of examination has its place. Continuous eddy-current examination (Fig. 2.3) discloses significant discontinuities of the short, abrupt type. Ultrasonic examination may disclose longitudinal discontinuities but may not reveal discontinuities with a circumferential orientation or short, deep defects. Flux-leakage examination is useful in searching for significant longitudinal and transverse discontinuities in ferritic materials.

Hydrostatic testing can disclose a defect only if it penetrates the tube wall. It may not expose such defects if the edges of the opening are tightly pressed together. Furthermore, very small openings are hard to detect hydrostatically. Therefore, probably the most effective way to uncover penetrating defects is by water-submerged-air testing, illustrated in Fig. 2.4. There is a reasonable chance that most defects will be found in tubes that are eddy-current-examined and water-submerged-air-tested. For tubes in critical services, consider additional requirements such as ultrasonic examination.

Radiography and fluid-penetrant examinations are also available but are seldom used. Radiographic examination can detect flaws in

Figure   2.4 Water-submerged-air testing. (*Carpenter Technology, Reading, Pennsylvania.*)

relatively thick-walled hollows, but it is not very discriminating in thin-walled tubes. Fluid-penetrant examination of exteriors may disclose surface cracks, but it is not a cost-effective quality assurance tool for this purpose.

Straightening.   Tubes that come off the mill are not straight enough to install through the tubesheets, baffles, and supports. Therefore, they are straightened by passing them through crossed straightening rolls. The work of the rolls on the tubes increases their hardness. Austenitic tubes that are severely strain-hardened by straightening may have to be heat-treated again. Nonferrous tubes are usually annealed after straightening to relieve the straightening stresses and to adjust the temper to conform with the specification.

Cutting to length.   The length of seamless tube that can be produced from a hollow cannot be precisely determined. The length produced from a strip by welding is too great to be handled economically or to ship in one piece. Mills use a flying rotary abrasive saw (Fig. 2.5) to cut tubes to length. As the saw cuts, it travels with the tube at the same speed as it emerges from the mill.

The cut is always to an exact length. If tubes are ordered to random lengths, the exact length will lie between the upper and lower lengths permitted by random cutting. The mill will then adjust the cut lengths to get the maximum number of pieces out of the strip or drawn tube, but all the pieces will be the same length.

In the United States, the tubes of straight-tube exchangers are customarily chosen to be 8, 10, 12, 16, 20, or 24 ft (approximately 2.44, 3.05, 3.66, 4.88, 6.10, or 7.32 m) long. Depending upon market conditions, exchanger shops may find it economical to inventory tubes of a length such as 40 ft ¾ in (about 12.2 m) from which they can cut tubes to size with the least wastage. Shops that follow this practice must protect the tubes from damage and control their storage to make sure that the material remaining in inventory is properly tracked and documented.

At other times, exchanger manufacturers find it advantageous to buy tubes cut and deburred at the mill in exact quantities plus a small

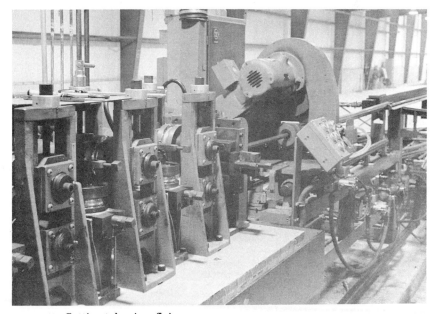

Figure 2.5   Cutting tubes in a flying saw.

percentage of spares. This "hand-to-mouth" purchasing can be combined with "just-in-time" scheduling so that the tubes arrive just when the bundle is ready for tubing. This avoids tying up space and working capital. However, when the general level of orders in the heat exchanger industry is high, hand-to-mouth purchasing may cause production delays and mills are unable to cooperate with just-in-time scheduling.

In boom times in the industry, exchanger buyers and their expediters find it easier to track and inspect tubes produced specifically for their equipment.

Tubes for U-tube bundles must be long enough to allow the ends to be trimmed. The allowance for trim is usually 1 in (25.4 mm). The tubes are cut to lengths that are appropriate for each row of U tubes. The required length is twice the straight-leg length plus the arc length at the neutral line (centerline bend radius) plus the amount allowed for trimming.

One or more tubes of the longest length are cut to replace any tubes damaged in bending or which do not meet the subsequent leak test. Alternatively, spares of the largest bend radius are ordered and rebent and trimmed if a smaller-radius tube must be replaced.

The longest U tube that can be made depends upon the maximum tube length that the mill can supply. Some manufacturers of feedwater heater and surface condenser tubing can furnish tubes as long as 150 ft (45.72 m). This permits the fabrication of U-tube bundles of approximately 70-ft (21.34-m) straight length.

Some exchanger manufacturers have successfully butt-welded tubes to achieve lengths that mills were unable or unwilling to supply. However, this extreme measure should be avoided. The *Standards for Closed Feedwater Heaters* of the Heat Exchange Institute recommend against extending tube length by butt welding.[2] When extending tubes in this way is unavoidable, the welding procedure and nondestructive examinations must be selected with great care.

Once the author found it necessary to provide tubes approximately twice as long as could then be obtained from a mill. The tubes were to be used for a pair of U-tube heat exchangers designed for 1500 lb/in^2 at 700°F (10,349 kPa at 371°C). The tubing was ¾-in OD by 0.049-in (approximately 19-mm-OD by 1.24-mm) average-wall seamless nickel copper. Each leg of the U tubes was extended successfully by butt welding. Consumable inserts, argon-gas purging and backup inside the tubes, and GTAW manual welding were used. The joints were fluid-penetrant-examined and radiographed, and the tubes were hydrostatically tested to 2000 lb/in^2 (13,790 kPa).

Destructive testing.   Tube manufacturers destructively test representative samples to determine the mechanical properties of the finished product. Mill samples are most often taken during manufacture. If random lengths are being produced, ends shorter than the random-length range are used for the test specimens.

The mechanical properties tested are yield strength, tensile strength, and hardness. Carbon steel and low-alloy tubes for use in low-temperature service are also impact-tested to assess their capacity to resist low-temperature embrittlement. It may be necessary to negotiate with the mill the temperature at which it will conduct the test to demonstrate that the tubing is suitable for the design temperature.

The ability of tubes to undergo operations used in heat exchanger production must also be tested at the mill. The tests used to demonstrate suitability are flattening, reverse flattening, flaring, flanging, and expansion. The required tests and the acceptance criteria are listed in the applicable tubing specification.

The *flattening test*, which indicates ductility and soundness, consists of flattening a specimen cold between two parallel plates. For welded tubes, the weld is set 90° from the direction in which force is applied. The specimen is considered to be sufficiently ductile if there are no cracks or breaks (with some exceptions permitted for thin-walled tubes) when the parallel plates are a distance apart determined by a formula. The formula takes into account wall thickness, tube diameter, and deformation per unit length.

To test soundness, the plates are further closed until the specimen breaks or opposite walls of the tube meet. Evidence of laminated or unsound material or of incomplete welding is cause for rejection.

The *reverse-flattening test* is used to determine that sound welds have been produced. The specimen is split longitudinally 90° on either side of the weld. It is opened and flattened with the weld at the point of maximum bending. To be acceptable, there must be no evidence of cracks or lack of penetration or of overlaps resulting from removing weld flash.

The purpose of the *flaring test* is to prove that the tube ends can be flared without tearing, an important tube-to-tubesheet joint consideration. A tapered flaring tool with a 60° included angle is inserted into the end of the tube. It is forced in until the flared mouth has been expanded a specified percent of the inside diameter, related to the ratio of tube ID to OD. The tube ends must not crack or show imperfections rejectable under the specifications.

The *flange test* is an alternative to the flaring test. The tube must be capable of being flanged over by an amount specified for the given tube product.

The *expansion test* is used to show that nonferrous tubes can be expanded without cracking or rupture visible to the naked eye. The amount of expansion of the OD is related to tube OD, thickness, and material properties. The test is carried out when required by the tube product specification.

Surface conditioning. Mills customarily protect carbon steel and low-alloy tubes from corroding during storage and shipment by coating them with oil or grease. Ordinarily heat exchanger manufacturers remove the coating only from enough of the tube ends to make sure that they can make a sound tube-to-tubesheet connection. If the coating is not removed, there is a reasonable assurance that the tubes will not corrode excessively during hydrostatic testing or in the period before the exchanger is installed and first operated. Water washing is not adequate to remove these coatings, and precleaning and pretreatment are suggested before putting such exchangers into operation.

Some mills are equipped to polish stainless-steel tubes, but they shun the operation because it does not lend itself to production flow and examination. Therefore, when a purchaser requires tubes to be polished, it is likely that the mill will subcontract the work.

Depending upon the material, heat exchanger tubes may be mechanically polished inside, outside, or both. Available finishes vary from 100 grit to 360 grit, or finish numbers varying from 4 to 7. Tubes may also be electropolished. Finish acceptability is negotiated by the polisher and the user.

For most services, there is no advantage to polishing. However, tubes of units used in producing foods and drugs may have to be polished to conform with a governing sanitary code. It may also be advantageous to polish tubes when the fluid to be handled has a propensity to coat or stick to the walls. For this purpose, electropolishing may be more economical than mechanical polishing.

Packaging. Mills package tubes in wooden boxes, paperboard boxes, paperboard tubes, and in steel-strapped burlap wrapping. They may even ship truckload quantities unpackaged.

For transocean shipments, the container or packaging should be lined with a waterproof vapor barrier. Austenitic stainless-steel tubes shipped by sea should be plugged on each end with tight-fitting plastic stoppers and wrapped in tightly sealed vapor-barrier material to reduce the possibility of subsequent stress-corrosion cracking due to the presence of chloride ions in the atmosphere.

Some residues of chemicals used to treat wood and to manufacture paperboard packing remain in boxes and containers. When they become wet, residual chemicals leached onto the tube surfaces may cause corrosion. Therefore, tubes should be removed from shipping containers that have been soaked through. Otherwise, it is preferable not to open the containers until the tubes are to be loaded into the bundle.

U tubes bent at the mill are most often shipped in wooden boxes with internal separations that hold tubes of each bend radius firmly. The separations are arranged so that workers can start by removing the smallest-bend-radius tubes from a box and install them and progress to the largest-bend-radius tubes in the same order as they are loaded into the bundle. U tubes that are not boxed are grouped by bend radius and tied or taped together.

Bimetallic Tubes

Bimetallic, or dual, tubes consist of an inner tube of one metal in intimate contact with an outer tube of another. Installing bimetallic tubes permits building a heat exchanger with the best metal for resisting corrosion on each side of the tubes. To join the tubes to the tubesheet, outer tube material is peeled off at the tube end for a distance equal to the thickness of the tubesheet. As shown in Fig. 2.6, a ferrule of inner tube material of the same OD as the outer tube is press-fitted onto the inner tube to take the place of pared-away outer tube metal. Bimetallic tubes are otherwise like single-metal tubes and can be finned to extend the effective surface.

Current technology for producing bimetallic tubes is to draw loose-fitting inner and outer tubes simultaneously in a drawbench to produce an interference fit between the tubes. Because the tube surfaces are not free of oxides, there is some resistance to heat flow across the interface. Annealing after dual-tube drawing relieves some of the residual stresses required to maintain the interference fit and may even result in loss of the bond.

If a bimetallic tube is bent into a U tube and the bent area is subsequently annealed, the bond in that region is probably loosened.

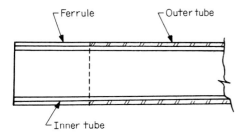

Figure 2.6 End of a bimetallic tube showing the ferrule.

Figure 2.7 Experimental explosively clad and drawn bimetallic tube produced by Explosive Fabricators of Louisville, Colorado. (*Photograph courtesy of MGT Inc., Boulder, Colorado.*)

However, the surface area in U bends is usually excluded from the effective surface, and the additional resistance in the U bends is unimportant. Finning work-hardens tubes, and U tubes made from finned dual tubes therefore are heat-treated in the U-bend region to prevent cracking due to excessive hardness.

Figure 2.7 shows an experimental bimetallic tube in which the inner and outer tubes are fused to each other. The raw materials consisted of relatively large-diameter, short, heavy-wall inner and outer pipes explosively welded together to form hollows for drawing. The pipe thicknesses were chosen to produce the desired inner and outer thicknesses after welding and drawing. A fusion bond is desirable because (1) it presents less resistance to heat transfer than a mechanical bond and (2) it will not separate under the most severe heat treatment or mechanical deformation. The technology may become important in the future.

U-Tube Bending

Bending tubes into U shapes or hairpins is essentially a manual process. Figure 2.8 shows how it is done. The tube is arranged so that one leg is fixed and the other is bent around a fixed wheel-shaped die by a matching movable die. The die rims are machined to the tube radius plus a small amount of die clearance. The part of the tube within the dies is completely encircled. The radius of the fixed die wheel determines the bend radius of the tube. Therefore, a different fixed die is

Figure 2.8 Bending U tubes. (*Atlas Industrial Manufacturing Company, Inc., Clifton, New Jersey.*)

needed for each U-tube row. The fit and hardness of the dies and the lubricant used affect the quality of the bends.

Bending affects the tube in these ways: (1) The fibers beyond the neutral line (bend centerline) are stretched and the inner fibers compressed, (2) outer-fiber stretching is accompanied by tube-wall thinning and strain hardening, (3) compression at the inside of the bend tends to crimp the tube, and (4) the tube tends to flatten in the bent region.

The minimum radius to which a tube can be bent without excessive flattening, crimping, and wall thinning depends upon its diameter, thickness, spread between yield and ultimate strengths, modulus of elasticity, hardness, and strain-hardening characteristics.

Strain hardening is of special concern in materials that work-harden rapidly and in low-finned tubes. Such materials may not be capable of being bent to radii small enough to be suitable for U-tube bundle construction. Intermediate heat treatment may be used to relieve the bending stresses, or the bending may be done hot. However, both processes are costly and therefore are seldom used. Some manufacturers of tantalum U bends get around the problem by cutting out the required degrees of arc of a large-radius bend and joining the legs as shown in Fig. 2.9.

TEMA and HEI standards for U-tube bundles and U tubes do not completely address U-tube bending. The following summarizes their requirements and tolerances and recommends supplementary tolerances that manufacturers can meet.

U-tube requirements and tolerances

The TEMA mechanical standards do not have quantitative tolerances for bend spacing. Here are their qualitative requirements:

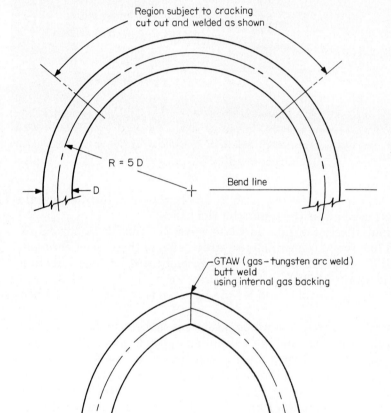

Figure 2.9 Partially U-bent tantalum tubes, cut and welded.

1. Center-to-center dimensions between parallel legs must be such that the tubes can be inserted into the baffle assembly without damage.

2. Bend interference (metal-to-metal contact between tubes in the same plane) is prohibited.

3. The assembly of bends must have a "workmanlike" appearance.

Whether or not an assembly of bends is workmanlike is subjective. Nevertheless, people experienced in heat exchanger construction have little difficulty in distinguishing between a U-tube bundle in which the work has been well executed and one that is unacceptable.

The TEMA standard requires flattening to be no more than 10 percent of the tube OD; i.e., the difference between the major and minor diameters may not be greater than 10 percent of the specified OD. Thinning due to stretching of the outer fibers is deemed to be normal. When the bends are formed from relatively non-work-hardening metals of appropriate temper, the standards recommend limiting thinning to 17 percent of the original wall thickness. The previous edition of the *TEMA Standards* permitted no crimping in the bend region. Although this prohibition is not in the seventh edition, crimping is not usually an acceptable condition.

Equation (2.1) is used to calculate the minimum tube wall thickness before bending.

$$t_0 = t_1(1 + d_0/4R) \qquad (2.1)$$

where d_0 = tube OD
  R = mean bend radius (centerline bend radius)
  t_0 = minimum thickness before bending
  t_1 = calculated minimum tube wall thickness for the straight tube using *ASME Code* calculation rules

The manufacturer may supply more than one thickness of tubes or dual-gauge tubes in a bundle. It is a common practice either to make two or more of the inner tube rows two gauges thicker than the rest or to provide dual-gauge tubes that are two gauges thicker in the bend portion.

Dual-gauge tubes (Fig. 2.10) are made by thickening the tube wall midway between the ends of the tube for a distance slightly more than the arc length of the bend. All the increase is on the outside, and there is a very gradual transition from the nominal OD to the OD at the thicker portion. (There is no change in the tube ID.) Because the en-

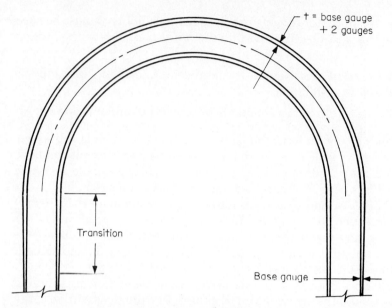

Figure 2.10   Dual-gauge tubes at the U-bend region.

larged OD is confined to the U-bend region, there is no difficulty in loading tubes through the transverse baffles or into the tubesheets.

Not all tube manufacturers produce dual-gauge tubes. Those that do can usually also furnish tube with walls thickened at the ends. Dual-gauge tubes are supplied principally in nonferrous metals and are not readily available in all materials.

For exchangers built to the *HEI Standard for Power Plant Heat Exchangers* (HEI PPS) and for closed feedwater heaters, the minimum thickness before bending is calculated by Eq. (2.2).[3]

$$t_0 = Pd_0(1 + d_0/4R)/(2S + 0.8P) \qquad (2.2)$$

where d_0 = tube OD

P = pressure

R = mean bend radius (centerline bend radius)

S = *ASME Code* allowable tube stress at the design temperature

t_0 = minimum thickness before bending

This standard states that, for materials of a suitable temper that do not severely work-harden, the minimum tube wall thickness of the smallest-bend-radius tubes may not be less after bending than 83 percent of the wall thickness before bending. To meet this requirement, the innermost rows may have to be dual-gauge or thicker than the tubes in the remaining rows.

When the tube metal has low ductility or work-hardens rapidly, it is usually necessary to heat-treat the bent region after bending because of embrittlement or sensitization to corrosive atmospheres. The user and the manufacturer should confer about such conditions and agree on the heat treatment to be performed.

The heat required for stress relief is most frequently created by resistance to an electric current circulated through the bend and approximately 12 in (300 mm) of the straight legs. The possibility of carbide precipitation in the transition zone between the cold legs and the heat-treated bend should be considered when the tubes are made of unstabilized austenitic material.

Recommended supplementary requirements and tolerances*

The following recommendations, based upon procedure specifications and tolerances in use at tube mills, can generally be met by tube benders proficient in the art.

Before bending, straight tubes should be eddy-current-tested and air-submerged-water-tested and be segregated by length or bend radii. Those that are to be bent into small radii may have to be supported by an internal mandrel to avoid crimping. To determine the need for a support mandrel, a sample bend must be made.

If the tube crimps, an internal nylon or aluminum bronze mandrel is required. Any mandrel lubricant that remains after bending must be cleaned away by blowing a close-fitting plug soaked in a volatile, chloride-ion-free solvent through the tube. (Despite its hazards, acetone may be used for this purpose.) The preferred propellant for blowing the plug through the tubes is dry inert gas. However, dry, oil-free compressed air may be used.

Bend-die lubricant for austenitic stainless steels or other materials subject to stress-corrosion cracking in the presence of chlorides should have a maximum chloride-ion content of 50 parts per million (ppm). All lubricant must be removed by washing with chloride-free solvent, and the tubes subsequently blown dry with inert gas or dry, oil-free compressed air.

Finished U tubes should be packed so that normal handling and transportation do not cause damage. They should be so arranged that they can be removed progressively from the smallest to the largest

---

*See also the tolerances and supplementary requirements of specification SA-688 of Section II, "Materials Specifications," of the *ASME Code*.

bend radius. Before loading, boxes should be lined with inert plastic sheeting or vapor-barrier material.

Figure 2.11 illustrates recommended tolerances for bend dimensions, deviation of the bend from plane, leg length, leg-to-leg length difference, and end squareness. The inside diameter of the bend is not permitted to vary from the drawing dimension by more than $1/16$ in (1.6 mm) for U bends with centers greater than 10 in (254 mm) or 0.040 in (1.02 mm) for U bends with pitches of 10 in (254 mm) or less.

The maximum permissible deviation from the plane of the bend, measured from the point of tangency to the end of the U, is $1/16$ in (1.6 mm). After final cutting, the leg length from the point of tangency to the U may not be less than the specified length but may be longer. The overtolerances are $1/8$ in (3.2 mm) for tubes 20 ft (6 m) long or less, $5/32$ in (4 mm) for tubes over 20 ft up to 30 ft (over 6 m up to 9 m) inclusive, and $3/16$ in (4.8 mm) for longer tubes.

When the bend radius is 10 in (254 mm) or less, leg-to-leg difference may be a maximum of $1/32$ in (0.8 mm). For bend radii greater than 10 in (254 mm) but no greater than 20 in (508 mm), leg-to-leg difference may be a maximum of $1/16$ in (1.6 mm). For bend radii greater than 20 in (508 mm), the maximum permissible difference is $3/32$ in (2.4 mm).

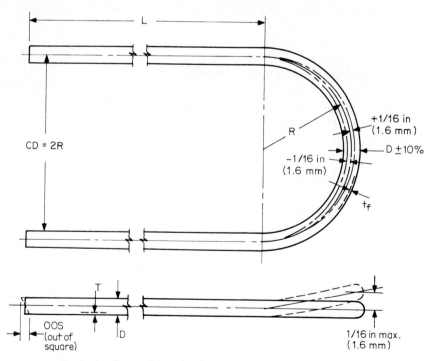

Figure 2.11   U-tube bending and length tolerances.

Tube-end squareness tolerances are 0.010 in (0.25 mm) for tubes of ⅝-in (15.9-mm) OD and smaller and 0.016 in (0.41 mm) for larger tubes.

Bending practice

Typical bending practice is as follows. Before bending, the tubes are eddy-current- and water-submerged-air-tested. Appropriate dies are selected for the radii to which the tubes are to be bent.

If there is no history of bending the tube diameter, thickness and specified material to the smaller radii, internal mandrels, and lubricant are provided. Trial pieces with legs about 2 ft (0.6 m) long are test-bent to the smallest radii without the mandrels to determine if mandrels are needed.

The specimens are inspected for crimping and measured for flattening. If they are crimped, another test bend is made by using the nylon or aluminum bronze mandrel to support the tube wall. For each radius, a test bend must be produced that shows no crimping and is not flattened beyond the tolerance. When success is achieved, the specimen is cut and the wall is measured to determine thinning. If wall thinning is excessive, the tube gauge may be increased.

After the test specimens have been accepted, production bending is started by setting a stop on the leg of the tube to fix a length that includes the bend. The stop is adjusted to provide approximately equal leg lengths after bending. The arm of the bender is brought around to make the bend. When the bend is completed, the die is released and the tube inspected for excessive flattening, dents, and crimping. These deficiencies are cause for rejection. The tube is then removed from the bending machine, and the legs checked for overall length and leg-to-leg matching lengths.

Supporting mandrels are inspected periodically. After a mandrel has been used, a plug soaked with a chloride-ion-free volatile solvent (usually acetone) is blown through the tubes, which are then dried with oil-free clean dry air.

If stress relieving is required, the tube is placed at the stress-relieving position and a pressure fitting is clamped to the end of each leg. Copper clamps secure the U bend and about 12 in (305 mm) of each leg in the jaws of a resistance-stress reliever.

Simultaneously, nitrogen is fed through the pressure fittings into the tube to purge it of air. When the purge cycle is complete, current is applied to heat the tube. The current cycle is timed to give the specified temperature, which is checked at intervals with a hand-held pyrometer. The bend is not held for any specified time at temperature. All heating and cooling takes place in air. When the current cycle ends, high-speed fans rapidly cool the tube OD below 700°F (approximately 370°C).

After heat treating, the tube is inspected for arc burns or other damage and conformity to the specified tolerances. Tubes that have been damaged, which can be successfully repaired to conform with the specifications, are accepted for shipment.

Availability, Cost, and Reliability of Welded and Seamless Tubes

Pressure vessel codes may have specifications for both welded and seamless tubes of some materials. However, only one or the other may be produced commercially. There is no *ASME Code* specification for welded aluminum heat exchanger tubing, and this tubing is made only by a seamless process.

For identical diameter, wall thickness, and materials of construction, seamless tubes may cost approximately 10 to 50 percent more than welded ones. When tubing cost is a small fraction of total exchanger cost, the price advantage of welded tubes may be insignificant, as in a small all-carbon-steel exchanger. However, when the cost of the tubes is a substantial fraction of total exchanger cost, for example, in a large exchanger tubed with stainless-steel tubes, the price difference between welded and seamless tubes is usually significant.

If welded and seamless tubes were equally reliable and corrosion-resistant, one would always use the less costly welded tubes. To choose between them, it is necessary to balance the degree of reliability needed for the service against the cost difference. Most welded tubing is reliable enough. Therefore, the market share of welded tubing has far outstripped that of seamless.

Some questions to ask when comparing the reliability of welded and seamless tubes are:

1. Is there a difference in corrosion rates between seamless and welded tubes made of the same metal?

2. Do welded tubes leak more frequently than seamless tubes?

3. Is there a difference in the rate of failure resulting from flow conditions, i.e., failures from erosion or vibration?

4. Are there more failures at tube-to-tubesheet joints with welded or with seamless tubes?

For the most part, the answer to all of these questions is no. Corrosion rates and mechanical properties for welded and seamless austenitic stainless-steel and high-nickel-alloy tubing have been found to be about the same.[4,5] As experience is gained with welded ferritic and dual stainless steels, it is likely that a similar situation will be found. However, for critical service such as corrosive environments and high-pressure, high-temperature conditions, evaluate reliability by substantial testing.

Pressure vessel codes reduce the allowable stresses of welded tubes to account for weld joint efficiency. Therefore, seamless tubes are advantageous for high internal design pressure and temperature. They may also be more suitable for exchangers in which lethal material flows in the shellside or tubeside. Under present *ASME Code* rules for lethal-service construction, these alternatives are permitted when the lethal fluid flows through one side: (1) Use seamless tubes and construct for lethal service only on the side through which the lethal material is to flow, (2) use welded tubes with their seams fully radiographed in accordance with *ASME Code* requirements and construct for lethal service on the one side only, and (3) use unradiographed welded tubes and construct for lethal service on both sides. The implication of the third choice is that all piping and equipment downstream of both sides must be suitable for handling the lethal material. Usually the most economical choice is seamless tubes.

Extended- and Enhanced-Surface Tubes

Extended-surface tubes are tubes in which the effective surface has been increased over that provided by bare tubes. Enhanced-surface tubes do not increase effective surface but make more efficient use of bare tube surface.

Extended surfaces

The most common way to extend heat exchanger tube surface is to fin the outside tube surface. Finned tubes are made by forming fins from the bare-tube material in low and high configurations (integrally finned tubes) or by applying fins by various means in the shape of perpendicular disks, helices, and longitudinal straight strips. The tube ends are left bare for a distance slightly longer than the tubesheet thickness as shown for integral low-fin tubes in Fig. 2.12. Finned tubes must always be ordered to exact length with the amount of bare end specified.

Integrally finned tubes. Integral finning is achieved by deforming the outside of the tube into helical fins. If, after forming, the fin OD is

Figure 2.12 Low-fin tube showing the bare end. (*Carpenter Technology, Reading, Pennsylvania.*)

slightly smaller than the bare-tube OD, the tubes are called low-fin tubes. The thickness at the root between the fins is approximately two gauges less than the bare tube.

Tubesheet and baffle or support-plate drilling are the same for bare tubes and low-fin tubes. Therefore, bundles originally tubed with bare tubes can be retubed with low-fin tubes. However, because the tube wall available to resist internal pressure is reduced at the root of the fin, it may be necessary to start with a thicker tube. Furthermore, if the original bare-tube thickness included some allowance for corrosion, the starting thickness must be increased to achieve the same allowance on the fin-tube replacement. Increasing the wall reduces the tube ID and the cross-sectional flow area. As a result, it increases pressure drop through the tubes.

Tubes of some soft metals integrally finned with fins that extend beyond the bare-tube OD are called integrally high-fin tubes. The tube centers must be far enough apart to permit some clearance between the fins of adjacent tubes. Baffle and support-plate holes are larger for high-fin tubes than for bare tubes. Consequently a bundle tubed with bare tubes cannot be retubed with high-fin tubes.

The deformation of the tube metal into fins produces residual stresses. Fin tubes can be obtained as finned or be heat-treated after finning to relieve residual stresses. When tube vibration is a consideration and for cyclical operation, it is well worth paying the extra cost for heat treatment.

Austenitic stainless steels, which are subject to stress-corrosion cracking in some environments, generally require stress relief. Ferritic-alloy tubes are generally not sensitive to stress-corrosion cracking and therefore are not usually stress-relieved after finning.

An integrally finned tube which is to be U-bent should be stress-relieved before bending. Alternatively, the tube may be ordered with the part that is to be bent unfinned. It is also possible to obtain tubes finned for part of the length. Thus, when it is advantageous in the thermal design of a U tube to have one finned leg and one bare leg, the tubes can be obtained to suit. For applications where it is desirable to have tubes bare where they pass through cross-flow baffles, integrally finned tubes can be obtained with the finning interrupted to leave bare lands at the baffle locations.

Integral exterior tube finning was first done on copper and copper-alloy condenser tubes, which are soft relative to steels. However, tube manufacturers have since succeeded in overcoming the problems of finning harder materials. Integrally low-finned tubes are now generally available in most materials used in shell-and-tube heat exchangers. These include the whole range of austenitic stainless steels, low-alloy chromium-iron steels, ferritic steels, nickel-copper, nickel, and high-nickel alloys, and alloys of titanium and zirconium.

Depending upon the tube metal, diameter, and wall thickness and the manufacturer's tooling, low integrally finned tubes are available in 9, 11, 16, 19, 26, 28, 30, 32, and 40 fins per inch (approximately 354, 433, 630, 748, 1024, 1102, 1181, 1260, and 1574 fins per meter). High integrally finned tubes are produced mostly in copper, copper alloys, and other soft, ductile materials such as aluminum. They are available in configurations of 5, 7, 9, and 11 fins per inch (approximately 197, 275, 354, and 433 fins per meter).

Some nonferrous tubes can be obtained with integral low fins on the interior surface in addition to the fins formed on the outside. The pitch of the internal fins is usually longer than that of the external fins.

Applied high fins. High fins are also applied to bare tubes by shrink fitting, welding, brazing, soldering, and setting thin strips into grooves scored into the tube followed by swaging the metal upset by grooving against the strip to hold it tightly in place. Fins applied by shrinking or swaging can be made of a more conductive metal than that of the underlying tube. This permits, for example, shrinking aluminum high fins onto steel tubes to improve the combined heat transfer characteristics. When fins are applied by soldering or brazing, the operating range must be within suitable temperature limits.

The number of applied high fins per unit length is not standardized. Applied transverse high fins may be annular disks or continuous helices. Longitudinal high fins may be applied by mechanical bonding or welding. In the mechanical process, the underlying tube is scored to provide channels into which thin strips are forced (Fig. 2.13). The metal upset in scoring is swaged against the strips to form a tight bond. To apply longitudinal fins by welding, a thin strip is continu-

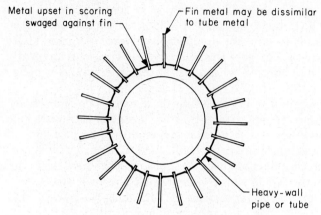

Figure 2.13   Mechanically bonded longitudinal-fin tubes.

ously roll-formed into channels and resistance-welded to the underlying tube (Fig. 2.14).

Transverse and longitudinal applied high fins may be interrupted to increase turbulence by making cuts in the fins perpendicular to the tube and bending the cut edges to form tabs.

The outside heat transfer surface may also be extended by applying fins of other geometric configurations such as stars and rectangles arranged transversely to the tubes. Pegs, spines, and blades cast into tubes found in furnace economizers are not used in shell-and-tube equipment.

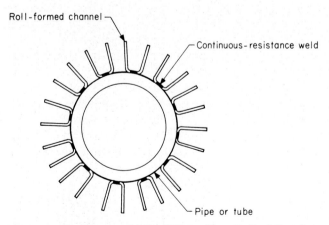

Figure 2.14   Resistance-welded, roll-formed longitudinal-fin tube.

The effects of fin parameters on heat transfer rates and fluid friction have been examined mathematically. However, thermal designers customarily use correlations of experimentally obtained data for heat transfer calculations. Many such correlations are available in the open literature and in manufacturers' publications. Most have been adjusted to fit within the calculation scheme ordinarily used for bare tubes.

The parameters that differ for fin tubes in comparison with bare tubes are outside surface area per unit of length, ratio of outside surface to inside surface, effective clearance between adjacent tubes and equivalent diameters used in calculating hydraulic characteristics on the shellside, and shellside friction factors.

The effectiveness of increasing the surface by adding fins depends upon the number per unit length of tube, shape, height, and thickness. A unit of finned surface is less effective in transferring heat than one of bare surface. In addition, there is a difference in temperature between the film of fluid in contact with the crown of the fin and that in contact with the root, which reduces the effectiveness of the surface added by finning. However, the ratio of finned surface to bare surface in a unit length of tubing is so great that the loss of effectiveness is more than compensated for. For example, the unit external surface of a typical ¾-in-OD (19-mm-OD) tube with 19 fins per inch (748 fins per meter) is 3 times that of a bare tube of the same OD.

The loss of effectiveness is accounted for in thermal calculations by means of a weighted fin efficiency. Plots of weighted fin efficiency versus effective shellside heat transfer coefficient are available in the literature and from fin-tube manufacturers for various metals.

The effective clearance between bare tubes in a tube field is fixed at the tube pitch minus the tube diameter. However, for finned tubes the clearance may be as small as the pitch minus the fin crown diameter or as large as the pitch minus the fin root diameter. Effective clearance and equivalent diameter may be estimated from the number of fins per unit length, fin thickness, and root diameter. Most manufacturers publish tables of effective and equivalent diameters for various tube diameters, fin configurations, and tube pitches.

Finning increases resistance to fluid flow across the finned surface. This factor must be considered in shellside pressure-drop calculations. Plots of the variation of shellside friction factor with Reynolds number are also available from most manufacturers.

Consider using fin-tube construction under the following conditions:

1. The tubeside film coefficient of a bare-tube unit is more than 2½ times the shellside coefficient.

2. Shellside fouling is severe, and the tubeside fouling factor is a maximum of 0.0015 (h · ft^2 · °F)/Btu [0.2642 (m^2 · °C)/kW].

3. A gas or vapor is heated or cooled in the shell, and the tubeside fluid is water or condensing steam.

When total shellside bare-tube film resistance is several times greater than total tubeside resistance, fin tubes can be substituted for bare tubes to raise the product of shellside conductance and surface area to approximately the product of tubeside conductance and surface area.

Fin tubes are more costly per unit length than bare tubes. To justify their use, the sum of the amortized initial cost and lifetime operating costs must be less for an exchanger tubed with fin tubes than for one in which the tubes are bare. A true comparison must be based upon thermal designs of both types of exchanger for a set of identical conditions.

Customarily the bare-tube thermal design precedes the fin-tube design to permit examining the relationship between the shellside and tubeside film coefficients of heat transfer and to discern the differences in pressure drops. Exchanger prices and installation costs are estimated to establish the initial cost.

With somewhat less precision, costs of maintenance over the anticipated life of the exchanger can be estimated for each type. Generally the labor of tube plugging or retubing is the same per tube for bare and finned surfaces. The time required to clean the outside depends upon the nature of the fouling.

Despite numerous studies and large amounts of information in the literature, fouling is still an unresolved problem in heat exchanger design and operation. The following simplistic discussion is offered to explain why fin tubes should be considered when shellside fouling is severe.

Foulants dissolved in process fluids deposit in molecular layers at rates related to tube metal condition and surface temperature. Figure 2.15 is a picture of a heavily fouled low-fin-tube bundle. Figure 2.16 is a closeup view of fouled tubes in a different bundle. As the photographs show, the deposits on the low-fin tubes follow the contours of the fins and do not bridge the fins. Therefore, the reduction in heat transfer rates due to fouling is related only to the thickness of the coating and not to blinding of the fins.

As a layer of foulant forms on a surface, fluid shear tends to wipe it off. If the axial shear strength of the bond between the foulant and the

Figure 2.15 Fouling follows the contour of low-fin tubes. (*High Performance Tube Inc., Union, New Jersey.*)

Figure 2.16 Closeup of fouled low-fin tubes showing fouling following fin contours. (*High Performance Tube Inc., Union, New Jersey.*)

surface is greater than the axial fluid force per unit of surface, the layer adheres to the tube and provides a surface for deposition of another layer. Successive layers deposit by the same mechanism and in extreme cases may plug the total flow area. Depending upon the relative values of bond strength and fluid shear, depositions may take one of the following courses: Layers may accrete uniformly with the passage of time, the rate of accretion may increase as the unit operates, or buildup may slow down and even stop.

In operation, at any plane perpendicular to the tube there is a temperature gradient between the fluid bulk temperatures. The heat flux between the fluid bulk temperatures is equal to the temperature gradient divided by the sum of the individual resistances to heat transfer between the two temperatures. The fraction of temperature gradient attributable to fouling is directly proportional to its contribution to total resistance. Temperatures along the tube also vary with the heat transferred.

The thermal coefficients of expansion of foulant and tube metal are generally far apart. In clean fin tubes, the temperature at the crown is different from that at the root. The temperature of deposits on the crown is also different from that of deposits on the root. As fouling increases, the metal surface temperatures at root and crown change, as do the temperatures at the inner and outer surfaces of each layer of foulant. In addition, the average tube metal temperature changes, causing minute changes in fin spacing.

The combination of these differences in metal and foulant layer temperatures with the difference in thermal coefficients of expansion between the metal and the foulant causes thermal stresses in the foulant. If the stresses are high enough, the foulant flakes off, probably because the thermal and mechanical stresses crack the layers and the bond between the foulant and the tube surface. The well-known effect of thermal stress on scale is taken advantage of to descale makeup-water evaporators by steam-heating the shellside with the tubes empty, then rapidly chilling the tubes.

Layers that flake are hydraulically flushed off and carried away by the shellside fluid. The rate of buildup on fin tubes therefore appears to be of the third sort described above. Figure 2.17 is a photograph of a fouled bundle in which a low-fin tube has been installed in a nest of bare tubes to show the difference in fouling buildup.

If fouling deposits as shown in Fig. 2.16, it usually takes less time to clean the unit hydraulically than if the tubes are bare. Fouling does not appear to adhere as tightly to finned surfaces as to bare surfaces, and because of the threadlike configuration hydraulic cleaning seems to be more effective in peeling off layers.

Figure 2.17 Difference in fouling between bare and low-fin tubes. (*High Performance Tube Inc., Union, New Jersey.*)

Enhanced surfaces

Inner and outer tube surfaces may be enhanced by metallurgically bonding metal coatings 5 to 15 mils (0.127 to 0.371 mm) thick to the underlying bare tube surfaces. The coatings are porous metal or have a microscopic netlike configuration. Surfaces enhanced by coating are said to improve boiling heat transfer film coefficients as much as tenfold.[6]

The coated tubes are available in a variety of alloys with the coating applied to either or both surfaces. Coating may be supplemented on the hot side by fluting or finning to improve the hot-side film coefficient. The bond of the metal film to the tube is strong enough to remain intact throughout heat exchanger construction and assembly. Tubesheet and baffle-hole drilling are the same as for bare tubes. Therefore, existing equipment may be retubed with enhanced-surface tubes.

In boiling on bare tube surfaces, the maximum heat flux is limited by the ability of the surface to form nuclei for bubble initiation. Bubble generation occurs from random pits and scratches. If bubbles do not form rapidly enough, the surface may be blanketed by vapor as the bubbles expand. Treating the surface with a porous or reticular coating creates many stable bubble nucleation sites. The metal matrix has high thermal conductivity, high microsurface area, and many contact points within the layer.

Although enhancement was originally developed for refrigeration systems that used ethylene, propane, propylene, R-12, and R-22, it has been applied in conventional reboiler use, mostly in horizontal kettle-type reboilers and thermosiphons or in vertical thermosiphon reboilers.

Other types of enhancement consist of deforming the tube with helical indentations or corrugations.[7] Developed for steam surface condenser use, they have been employed to advantage in keel coolers and in desalting plants. Tests made in a steam surface condenser to compare bare tubes with this kind of enhanced-surface tubing indicate that condensing film coefficients 30 to 40 percent higher than those of bare tubes are attainable and that fouling rates and cleanability are similar.

In condensing, the grooves on the outside surface improve condensate drainage, thereby enhancing the condensing coefficient. Enhancing the tubeside improves sensible-heat transfer by increasing turbulence. Because increased turbulence is accompanied by increased pressure drop, several configurations are available to permit balancing the improvement in heat transfer rate against the increase in pressure loss.

These tubes also fit into standard baffle and tube holes. They are available in a variety of nonferrous and ferrous alloys.

Suggested Reading

The following are suggested for readers interested in sources of additional information about heat exchanger tubing.

Caruso, L.: "Copper Alloys in Shell and Tube Heat Exchangers," *Proc. Second Annu. Symp. Shell-and-Tube Heat Exchangers*, Houston, Sept. 14–16, 1981.

Covington, L. D., and I. A. Franson: "Application of Titanium to Oil Refinery Environments," *Proc. 42d Midyear Meet.*, Refining Dept., American Petroleum Institute, 1977.

Deverell, H. E., I. A. Franson, and T. J. Nichol: "Fabrication Requirements for High Purity Ferritic Stainless Alloys Related to Heat Exchanger Tube Bundles," *Proc. Second Annu. Symp. Shell-and-Tube Heat Exchangers*, Houston, Sept. 14–16, 1981.

Doughty, S. E.: "Chloride Contamination of Tubing," *Power Eng.*, September 1969.

———: "Annealing Stainless Tubes for Best Corrosion Resistance, *Power Eng.*, March 1979.

Ferguson, C. S.: "Nondestructive Test Methods of Specialty Metals Production," *Nat. Fall Conf. American Society for Nondestructive Testing*, Detroit, Oct. 21–24, 1974; available from Huntington Alloys, Inc., Huntington, W.Va.

Gadbut, J.: *The Manufacturing of Nickel Alloys*, Huntington Alloys, Inc., Huntington, W.Va.

Hoxie, E. C.: "The Application of Austenitic Stainless Steels and High Nickel Alloys for Shell and Tube Heat Exchangers," *Proc. Second Annu. Symp. Shell-and-Tube Heat Exchangers*, Houston, Sept. 14–16, 1981.

Kurtz, H. D.: "Quality Assurance at the Tube Mill," *Proc. Second Annu. Symp. Shell-Tube Heat Exchangers*, Houston, Sept. 14–16, 1981.

McCue, D. M.: "Titanium Tubes Cut Costs Even in Average Water," *Electr. World*, Feb. 15, 1975.

"New Heat-Exchange Units Rely on Enhanced Transfer," *Chem. Eng.*, Feb. 25, 1980, p. 44.

References

1. *ASME Boiler and Pressure Vessel Code*, 1989 ed., American Society of Mechanical Engineers, New York. (New editions are published at 3-year intervals.)
2. *Standards for Closed Feedwater Heaters*, 4th ed., The Heat Exchange Institute, Cleveland, August 1984.
3. *Standard for Power Plant Heat Exchangers*, 1st ed., The Heat Exchange Institute, Cleveland, 1980; Addendum 1, 1984.
4. R. E. Smallwood, "Heat Exchanger Tubing Reliability," *Mater. Perform.*, vol. 16, no. 2, February 1977, p. 33.
5. R. B. Leonard, F. G. Hodge, and D. A. Junker, "Corrosion and Mechanical Behavior of Nickel-Base Alloy Tubing," *Corrosion '76, NACE*, Pap. 151, Mar. 22–26, 1976.
6. *Advanced Heat Transfer Technology with High Flux Tubing*, Publ. F-063 87-0117 10/79 5M, Union Carbide Engineering Products and Processes, Tonawanda, N.Y.
7. W. E. Sartor, "Extended and Enhanced Tube Surfaces to Improve Heat Transfer," *Proc. Second Annu. Shell-and-Tube Heat Exchangers*, Houston, Sept. 14–16, 1981; Library of Congress Catalog No. 82-72486, ISBN 0-87170-145-6, SAN 204-7586.

Chapter

3

Tubesheets

Introduction

Heat exchanger tubesheets are thicker than the channel and the shell
and usually are more massive than body and channel flanges. Their
raw-material and manufacturing costs make them one of the most important components of the prices of exchangers. The mechanical design of tubesheets may be complicated and more expensive than that
of any other part.

This chapter examines tubesheet functions, constructions, and materials, discusses what to consider in designing tubesheets, and suggests
analysis methods to use. It recommends when to choose double-tubesheet
construction and describes how double-tubesheet exchangers are manufactured and used.

Functions

A tubesheet and attached channel, bonnet, or return cover form a
chamber through which the tubeside fluids flow. Connecting the
tubesheet to the shell creates a chamber through which the shellside
fluids flow. When the mating parts are attached by bolting, the
tubesheet serves as a bolting flange.

Like the tubes, a tubesheet is a physical barrier to the mixing of the
shellside and tubeside fluids. In multipass tubeside flow, the
tubesheet functions as a manifold plate for the tubes in each pass. Together with the pass partitions, it also acts to seal flow between pass
compartments.

If a catastrophic tubesheet failure would subject the channel or shell
to higher-than-design pressure, the tubesheet is a primary pressure
part. However, if the failure would relieve pressure from the high-
pressure into the low-pressure side without exceeding the low-

pressure-side design conditions, the tubesheet is a secondary pressure part.

Construction Configurations and Confinements

The following is a guide to construction configurations and confinements. Note that some figures used to illustrate the text show loose-ring flanges and others hub flanges, but this is only for convenience. Constructions may be loose-ring, lap-joint with lap rings welded to the barrels, integral-ring, or hub flanges.

Figures 3.1 and 3.3 through 3.5 depict various arrangements. The gaskets between the tubesheets and the parts with which they mate may be unconfined as in the plain-face and raised-face options, they may be fully confined as in the TEMA standard confinement shown in the sketches or in a tongue-and-groove arrangement, or the ring part of the gaskets may be confined peripherally without separate pass-partition retainage.[1]

Each confinement may be used with any of the joint configurations. However, unconfined construction should not be used for gaskets that tend to creep. Unconfined plain and raised faces are suitable for moderate tubeside pressures and temperatures when there is a modest pressure drop between passes. The typical design pressure range for unconfined gasket joints is atmospheric to 150 lb/in^2 (1035 kPa) at temperatures below 300°F (about 150°C).

Least expensive are the plain-face and alternative plain-face options. A disadvantage of plain faces is that the gaskets may have to be taped or pasted in place to permit assembly because gaskets optimal for the flange design usually are not self-centering. With raised faces, wide gaskets can be centered between the stud bolts because the raised-face width limits the effective gasket width.

In an alternative plain-face construction, the tubesheet is machined only in way of the gasket. This confinement is suitable for low-cost multipass units in noncritical services. It can be used both for tubesheets of single-pass exchangers and for return-end tubesheets of two-pass equipment.

The TEMA standard confinement and the tongue-and-groove alternative are desirable for these conditions:

1. Design pressures higher than 150 psig (1035 kPa)

2. Full-vacuum service

3. Temperatures above 300°F (150°C)

4. Gasket yield values greater than 2200 lb/in^2 (15,170 kPa)

5. Gaskets that tend to creep

To produce these confinements, grooves to accommodate the gasket ribs are end-milled into the tubesheets. End milling is done after facing the gasket-ring contact surfaces. To do so, the tubesheet must be removed from the lathe or boring mill and set up for end milling. This time-consuming process makes the TEMA standard and the tongue-and-groove alternative the most expensive confinements.

The less expensive rabbet confinement is suitable for use at the return end of two-pass units with TEMA or tongue-and-groove confinements at the stationary tubesheet and for single or multipass exchangers when the pass-to-pass pressure drop is small.

Tubesheets of fixed-tubesheet exchangers

Figure 3.1 depicts fixed-tubesheet exchanger tubesheets that are extended as bolting flanges. Of the various configurations, these are the most complicated to analyze. They are also the most frequently used. The channel flanges and the extended part of the tubesheet bend when they are bolted up. When confinement is plain-face, the bending may permit the flange and tubesheet rims to make contact before the

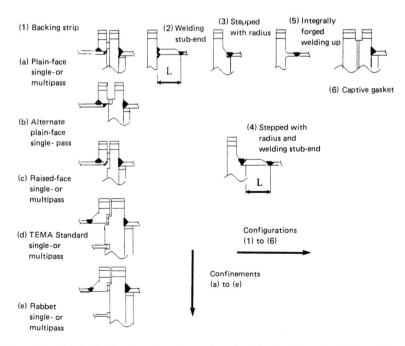

Figure 3.1   Fixed-tubesheet constructions when the tubesheet is extended as a flange.

gasket yields enough to make a tight joint. This can happen even when the bolting, flange, and tubesheet design stresses are within the pressure safety code's allowable limits.

Therefore, limit after-bolt-up flange and tubesheet bending to bending that allows a clearance between the rims of at least half the gasket thickness. As a rough rule of thumb, do not use plain-face construction when the gaskets are less than $3/32$ in (2.4 mm) thick and have yield values greater than about 2200 lb/in^2 (15,170 kPa).

For these exchangers, flatness across the gasket surfaces determines how closely the actual flange-to-tubesheet joint approximates the theoretical design. The principal causes of out-of-flatness are weld shrinkage at the shell-to-tubesheet joint and expanding tubes into the tubesheet holes. To determine flatness, measure between the center of the tubesheet and the outside edge of the gasket surface. Figure 3.2 shows some effects of tubesheet out-of-flatness on fixed tubesheets extended as bolting flanges.

Ideally, the shell-to-tubesheet joint would be stress-relieved after welding and the gasket surfaces machined after tube expanding. Such practices would add to an exchanger's cost and might be impractical

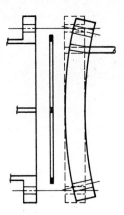

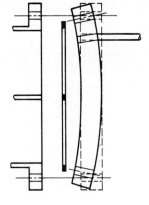

Convex tubesheet bowing

    Bolts overstressed

    Bolts may bend

    Pinch of gasket ring shifted inward

    Center (or inner) ribs crushed

    Tubes may be loosened

    Tube-to-tubesheet weld overstressed

    Channel flange bent or overstressed

Concave tubesheet bowing

    Bolts overstressed

    Bolts may bend

    Pinch of gasket ring shifted outward

    Center rib of gasket may not be compressed

    Tubes may be loosened

    Tube-to-tubesheet weld overstressed

    Channel flange bent or overstressed

Figure 3.2 Effects of out-of-flatness on fixed tubesheets.

for many heat exchanger shops. Although Section 2 of the *TEMA Standards* has tolerances that apply to tubesheet diameter and thickness, depth of groove for gasket retention, and pass-partition groove width, it has none for tubesheet out-of-flatness.

Shops can reasonably be expected to limit out-of-flatness across the tubesheet face to 0.375 percent of the tubesheet diameter after fabrication. For single-pass units and for return-end tubesheets of two-pass units, 0.5 percent is probably tolerable. To apply out-of-flatness tolerances, include them in bid and purchase specifications. Specific flatness tolerances may have to be negotiated with the manufacturer.

To quantify analytically how out-of-flatness affects joint tightness and stress in the parts requires considering many factors. Among them are tubesheet slope at the gasket surface, shift of the gasket line of action, effects of gasket ribs, gasket dimensions and properties, and tubesheet and mating-flange flexibilities.

Flatness tolerances at peripheral gasket surfaces may have to be considerably tighter to prevent leakage to the atmosphere and must be more stringent for vacuum operation. API Standard 660's standard requirements for gasket contact surfaces other than nozzle flange facings is $\frac{1}{32}$ in (0.8 mm) as measured by a straightedge; for special applications such as high-pressure, high-temperature, or hydrogen service they are much more restrictive (see Table 3.1).[2] The standard requires measuring the girth-flange flatness tolerance after the flange is attached to the component cylinder or the cover following any postweld heat treatment and measuring tubesheet gasket contact surfaces after the tube-to-tubesheet joints are expanded or welded.

The simplest and least costly way to join the tubesheet to the shell is shown in configuration 1 of Fig. 3.1. A disadvantage is that the backing strip, which remains in place, may contribute to crevice corrosion. Another unfavorable feature is that, to provide adequate weld strength, the cover pass of the half-V single butt weld must be rela-

TABLE 3.1   Flatness Tolerance on Peripheral Gasket Contact Surfaces*

Nominal exchanger diameter		Tolerance	
in	mm	in	mm
≥ 15	≥ 381	0.003	0.08
< 15–30	< 381–762	0.006	0.15
< 30–45	< 762–1143	0.008	0.23
< 45	1143	0.012	0.30

*Based on API Standard 660, Table 1.

NOTES: 1. Girth-flange flatness tolerance shall be measured after the flange is attached to the component cylinder or the cover after any postweld heat treatment.

2. The flatness of tubesheet gasket contact surfaces shall be measured after the tube-to-tubesheet joints are expanded or welded.

tively wide. On cooling, shrinkage of the wide weld pulls the extended part of the tubesheet. In response, the tubesheet bends, causing the tubesheet face to bow.

Good shop practice is to minimize the weld shrinkage caused by bending by providing a heatsink and restraining the tubesheet as the weld cools. Tightly bolting a preconstructed mating channel, channel cover, or bonnet to the tubesheet without an intervening gasket before making the closing shell-to-tubesheet weld usually provides sufficient restraint.

Configurations 2 through 5 of Fig. 3.1 provide access for full-penetration butt welding. They eliminate a backing strip and reduce tubesheet bending due to tubesheet-to-shell welding. Providing forged lips or stub ends welded to the tubesheet before final machining minimizes weld shrinkage caused by postweld tubesheet bending. The effects of tube expanding after joining the tubesheets to the shell are the same as in configuration 1.

Another function of integrally forged welding lips and welded-on stub ends is to make sure that the shell thickness is adequate to approximate a fixed support for the tubesheet under bending loads. Design methods for fixed tubesheets constructed to be integral with the shell assume that the shell provides fixed support for the tubesheet. If the shell is not strong enough, the tubesheet support may be more nearly free. This condition may be an unsuspected cause of repeated leaks in tube-to-tubesheet joints located on or near a common tube center radius.

Lacking fixed support, the tubesheet periphery and attached shell rotate when the tubesheet bends under load. The whole corner is highly stressed, and shell bending may be plastic. These effects are usually not noticeable when the exchanger operates noncyclically. However, when the operation is cyclical, the shell-to-tubesheet weld and the shell in the vicinity of the attachment may crack from fatigue.

Connections that penetrate the shell close to the back of the tubesheet create discontinuities. Because these connections are usually small and close to the tubesheet, they are difficult to fit and weld to the shell. Therefore, leaks in their welds to the shell are often attributed to inadequate joining. But it is far more likely that the failures are the result of fatigue in the nozzle weld and adjacent shell.

Mechanical designers should always investigate the shell's capability of providing fixed support for the tubesheet. When the shell thickness is inadequate for this purpose but is otherwise satisfactory, consider providing a thicker welding stub or an integrally forged lip on the tubesheet. Alternatively, the end section of the shell may be made thicker or reinforced. The lip, welding stub, or increased shell thickness should be at least 3 in (76.1 mm) long but no less than $3rt$, where r is the mean radius of the shell and t is the shell thickness.

When option 3 of Fig. 3.1 is used, tubesheet bending due to bolt loads affects the peripheral tubes less than with the other options because the part extended as a flange bends more readily than the main portion of the tubesheet. Option 4 of Fig. 3.1 combines this advantage with a thick welding stub for tubesheet support and affords the shop the ability to machine the tubesheet before welding it to the shell.

Figure 3.3 illustrates some fixed-tubesheet constructions in which

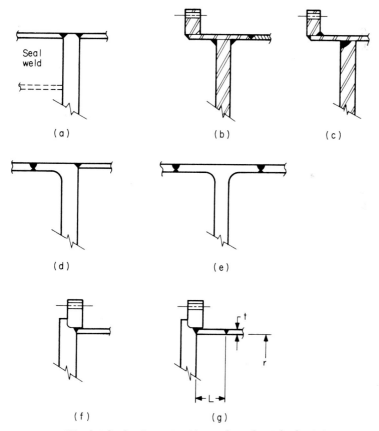

Figure 3.3 Fixed tubesheet constructions when the tubesheet is not extended as a flange. (*a*) Butt-welded on both sides. (*b*) Filet-welded on both sides. (*c*) Filet-welded on one side. (*d*) Forged lip on high-pressure side, butt-welded on low-pressure side. (*e*) Forged lip on both sides. (*f*) Tubesheet extended as a lap with loose backing flange behind the tubesheet. (*g*) Tubesheet welded to a stub and extended as a lap with loose backing flange.

the tubesheet is not extended as a flange. Both the shell and the channel barrel are made integral with the tubesheet in constructions *a* through *e*. Mechanical designers should investigate tubesheet support and bending in both channel and shell for these configurations.

If the tube bundle is fabricated and installed in the shell before the channels and pass partitions are joined to the tubesheet, the layout can contain about the same number of tubes as when the tubesheet is extended as a flange. However, the heat of welding may relieve locked-in stresses needed for expanded-joint strength and tightness. It may also be impractical to repair peripheral tube-to-tubesheet joints and those next to pass partitions because of inadequate clearance for repair equipment.

Manufacturers customarily use lower tube counts when channels are integral with the tubesheets than when they are bolted on. Reducing the tube count increases the shell size for a given count. It also creates open spaces between the shell and peripheral tubes and behind the pass partitions. To close the open spaces, place seal strips, dummy tubes, or extra tie rods and spacers in the bundle.

The forged lips illustrated in Fig. 3.3*d* and *e* are relatively thick because the construction is used for high-pressure designs and larger diameters. To reduce stress concentration, the tubesheet-to-lip transition radius should be at least 3 times the finished barrel thickness exclusive of corrosion allowance.

To minimize the cost of large-diameter, thick high-alloy or exotic-metal tubesheets, consider the lap-joint construction shown in Fig. 3.3*f* and *g*. It can be used with any of the confinements described in Fig. 3.1. Additional benefits are that (1) channel-to-tubesheet bolt-hole alignment is simplified and (2) the bending load that bolting up applies to the tubesheet is reduced because the backing flange bends and rotates somewhat.

Removable-bundle tubesheets

Figure 3.4 illustrates some typical constructions of stationary-end tubesheets of removable-bundle exchangers. Sketches 1(*a*) through 1(*e*) show through-bolt construction. Sketch 2 shows the tubesheet tapped for through stud bolts. These designs have the advantages of (1) permitting tightness testing of either side of the bundle without using a separate ring flange to hold the tubesheet in place, (2) facilitating bundle alignment, especially when the gaskets are unconfined, and (3) permitting the channel to be removed without breaking the tubesheet-to-shell-flange seal. In through-bolt construction, this is accomplished by making every fourth bolt a shoulder bolt. In tapped tubesheet hole construction, the channel-to-tubesheet seal remains in-

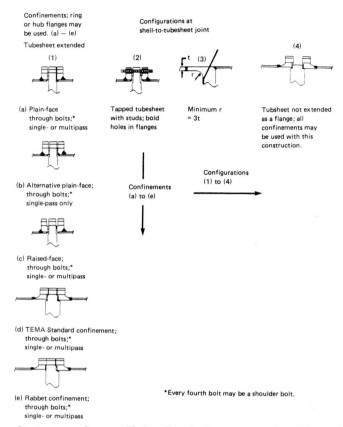

Confinements; ring
or hub flanges may
be used. (a) — (e)

Tubesheet extended

Configurations at
shell-to-tubesheet joint

(1)

(a) Plain-face
through bolts;*
single- or multipass

(2)

(a) Tapped tubesheet
with studs; bold
holes in flanges

(3)

Minimum r
= 3t

(4)

Tubsheet not extended
as a flange; all
confinements may
be used with this
construction.

(b) Alternative plain-face;
through bolts;*
single-pass only

Confinements
(a) to (e)

Configurations
(1) to (4)

(c) Raised-face;
through bolts;*
single- or multipass

(d) TEMA Standard confinement;
through bolts;*
single- or multipass

(e) Rabbet confinement;
through bolts;*
single- or multipass

*Every fourth bolt may be a shoulder bolt.

Figure 3.4 Stationary-end removable-bundle tubesheet constructions. Ring or hub flanges may be used (*a*) through (*e*) when tubesheet is extended.

tact when the bundle is removed from the shell, and the shell-to-tubesheet seal remains unbroken when the channel is removed.

These benefits must be traded off against the higher cost of labor and materials for stationary-tubesheet configurations in which the tubesheet is not extended. Maintenance for tapped tubesheet stud-bolt construction is far more difficult than with through-bolt construction. Here is why.

To remove the channel, the holes in the channel flange must be in alignment with the studs in the tubesheet. Until the channel flange clears the studs, it must remain parallel with the outer tubesheet face. Similarly, to pull the bundle, the shell flange holes and studs must be in alignment and the inner tubesheet face parallel with the shell flange until the studs clear.

In shop assembly, the stud bolts are lubricated and free of rust. It is a simple matter first to align the tubesheet, channel, and shell and then to insert the stud bolts through the bolt holes in one of the mating flanges, thread them into the tapped holes in the tubesheet, and continue to screw them in until they come out through the bolt holes in the other mating flange.

Field assembly and disassembly are inherently harder because the studs are already in place. The work is tedious enough when the stud bolts are accurately spaced on the design bolt circle and perpendicular to the tubesheet. Small displacements in stud-bolt positions markedly increase the difficulty. Any bending that produces a set in the tubesheet and flanges adds to the problem because it rotates the stud bolts out of perpendicular. Furthermore, after even a short period of operation the stud bolts may seize in the tapped holes. On completion of disassembly it is likely that the bolt threads will have been so badly damaged that the bolts must be replaced.

When the tubesheet is not extended, a test flange that mates with the channel and shell flanges is needed to test either side of the bundle with the other side exposed. Assembly and disassembly are somewhat more troublesome than for extended-tubesheet configurations. Nevertheless, the large majority of removable-bundle stationary tubesheets are made this way.

The forged integral tubesheet and channel barrel with lip construction of sketch 3 of Fig. 3.4 are typical in high-pressure closed feedwater heaters and similar high-pressure equipment. Although this configuration is used most frequently with U-tube construction, such stationary tubesheets have been employed with pull-through floating-head (TEMA Type T) and backing-ring-device (TEMA Type S) floating-tubesheet units. It has the advantage of eliminating a set of costly shell and channel flanges, bolts, and gaskets.

A generous transition radius is required where the tubesheet joins the lip. This produces considerable distance between the outer-tube-limit (OTL) circle and the shell. The distance is not disadvantageous in feedwater heaters because it provides steam distribution space. When the shellside fluid is a liquid, however, install seal strips or other devices to prevent fluid bypassing.

The floating-tubesheet constructions shown in Fig. 3.5 can be used in both single-pass and multipass construction. Except for the configuration illustrated in Fig. 3.5f, the gasket between the return cover and the tubesheet may be confined or unconfined. Less frequently used are floating tubesheets to which the return cover is welded and multiple floating tubesheets in which each return pass of a multipass unit has a separate tubesheet. Multiple floating tubesheets accommodate differential pass expansion when there is a large tubeside temperature range.

In producing floating tubesheets, the manufacturer must make sure

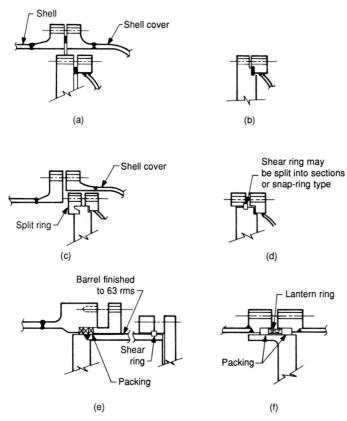

Figure 3.5 Removable-bundle construction at the floating end. (*a*) Pull-through floating-head plain-face construction. (*b*) Pull-through floating-head confined-joint construction. (*c*) Split-backing-ring floating-head confined-joint construction. (*d*) Shear-ring floating-head confined-joint construction. (*e*) Outside-packed floating head. (*f*) Lantern-ring floating head.

that after tube joining there is enough clearance between the tubesheet OD and the shell to permit bundle insertion and withdrawal without applying excessive force.

Shell-cover flanged joints must be placed so as to allow wrench and hand room for access to the heavy hexagonal nuts behind the inner tubesheet face that are threaded onto the stud bolts. Frequently, insufficient space is allowed for convenient maintenance because (1) it is desired to keep the floating-head assembly as close as possible to the rearmost tube support and (2) the length of tubing aft of the shell nozzle is not very effective in transferring heat. As a rule of thumb, position the shell-cover flange face 2½ to 3 heavy-hexagonal-nut thicknesses forward of the inner floating-tubesheet face.

Floating tubesheets of pull-through units are extended as bolting flanges for fastening the return cover. Their design and manufacture are straightforward. Here are some of the considerations.

To accommodate the pull-through feature, the shell is made larger for a given tube count than for units made with backing devices. Therefore, for the same tube surface TEMA Type T stationary tubesheets are larger and thicker than TEMA Type S tubesheets. Since stationary and floating tubesheets are usually made equally thick, floating TEMA T tubesheets are also larger and thicker than floating TEMA S tubesheets. Therefore, it is economical to design them with the smallest feasible bolting-flange extensions.

For this purpose, use the smallest bolt diameter consistent with maintenance requirements and the corrosive environment. Collateral benefits of using small bolts are that (1) it minimizes the lever arm between the bolt-circle and gasket-load line of action, thereby minimizing the bending moment that bolting applies to the tubesheet and return cover flange, (2) it minimizes bending between the bolt holes (scalloping), and (3) it provides a tighter joint.

The *TEMA Standards* state only that internal bolting must be suitable for the mechanical design and be made of a material as corrosion-resistant as the material of the shell interior. Bolts smaller than ⅝ in (16 mm) may not be suitable for the services where most TEMA T units are used. In choosing corrosion-resistant bolt material, be cognizant of the allowable bolt stresses and the tendency of the threads of high-alloy metals to gall.

The width of the extended ring of tubesheet may be reduced somewhat by tapping the tubesheet bolt holes and using socket-head cap screws. However, it is harder to assemble the return cover to the tubesheet with socket-head cap screws because the cover-flange bolt holes must be smaller than for through bolts. If the tubesheet takes a set after the exchanger has been in operation, the tapped holes rotate out of perpendicular. This may impede disassembling the return cover from and reassembling it to the tubesheet.

Backing devices frequently used to join return covers to TEMA S floating tubesheets are schematically shown in Fig. 3.5c and d. Clamp mechanisms may be used to simplify assembly and maintenance and to reduce the size of the shell cover needed to accommodate the floating head. The clamps may be multiple split clamps, multiple forked-edge clamps, C clamps, or variations on these types.

The hand-in-glove tapered-alignment feature of the split backing ring shown in Fig. 3.5c is not a structural requirement. However, it facilitates assembling the floating head and prevents the split ring from bending.

Sectional and snap-ring shear rings illustrated in Fig. 3.5d must fit neatly into the peripheral groove in the tubesheet. The backing ring that bears against the shear ring must closely fit the tubesheet OD. Otherwise, the joint may not remain tight because the shear ring and the backing flange may bend.

The tubesheets and attached barrels of TEMA P outside-packed floating heads sketched in Fig. 3.5e and lantern-ring TEMA Type W floating heads illustrated in Fig. 3.5f must be round. The finish of the region under the packing must be at least as fine as 63 root mean square (rms) to enable the packing to seal. Therefore, the rough outside diameter and barrel thickness of the weldment or casting must be large enough to allow for machining.

The stuffing-box ID is made smaller than the shell ID, as shown in the sketches, to make it possible to push the bundle into the shell and pull it out without damaging the fine tubesheet finish. Before pulling or inserting a packed floating bundle, wrap the tubesheet and barrel in a thin, close-fitting cylinder of aluminum to protect the finish.

Bolt up the gland follower without cocking so that it compresses the packing just enough to allow some dripping. Packing-gland follower nuts pulled up tightly enough to seal completely against shell leakage cause the packing to brake floating-tubesheet movement. Under too much compression, as the packing hardens with age, it may axially score the sealing surface.

TEMA P units can be used for single- and multipass tubeside flow. For single-pass flow, provision must be made for expansion between the tubeside outlet and the connection to the piping. Type W construction is suitable only for single-pass tubeside flow. In these units, one must keep the floating-end cover in alignment to avoid excessive tubeside leakage. The purposes of the lantern gland are to provide bearing surfaces for the packing on both sides and to allow for packing lubrication. It may be designed to accept grease under pressure to minimize leakage. Different packing materials may be used on each side of the lantern ring, but they must be equally compressible.

Design Considerations

Compliance with the *ASME Boiler and Pressure Vessel Code* and other pressure safety codes requires stress in parts containing pressurized fluids not to exceed prescribed limits.[3] However, a tubesheet that satisfies a code's safety requirements may be unsatisfactory for a heat exchanger's operation. It may bend so much, without exceeding the allowable stresses, that expanded tube-to-tubesheet joints cannot remain tight or that the welds of tubes welded to the tubesheets are overstressed. Excessive bending may also cause pass-partition bypassing and leaks in the flanged joints of tubesheets to shells and channels.

These are some of the factors that must be considered in the tubesheet stress analysis:

1. Tubesheet, tube, and shell metal temperatures under the various loadings
2. Tube pitch pattern
3. Layout of the tube field
4. Number of tubes (tube count)
5. Limits of the tube field [In circular tubesheets, the limit is defined by the outer-tube-limit (OTL) circle.]
6. How the tubes are joined to the tubesheets
7. How the channel and shell support the tubesheets
8. Channel and shell thicknesses

Detailed stress analysis is not within the scope of this work. Following is a guide to suitable methods.*

Use an interaction analysis based upon classical axisymmetric shell-and-plate theory for exchangers that (1) are fully tubed, (2) are constructed with cylindrical shells and channels, (3) will operate in steady-state service, and (4) will have a moderate combination of design conditions and sizes.[4–15] The analyses of the listed references use as a model a perforated plate with an unperforated rim. For cyclical service, consider also the need for fatigue analysis.

Use a numerical method such as elastic or elastic-plastic finite-element analysis when any of these conditions exist: (1) The pressure on either side exceeds 3000 lb/in^2 (20,700 kPa), (2) the product of internal pressure and the diameter is greater than 60,000 lb/in (10.51 MN/m), (3) the service is highly fluctuating or cyclical, (4) the tubesheet is not fully tubed, and (5) there are unusual or irregular attachments to the tubesheet.

Except for differential-pressure design, investigate removable-bundle exchanger tubesheets for the absolute pressures applied independently on each side of the tubesheet. In fixed-tubesheet exchangers, investigate the tubesheets for absolute pressures applied

---

*Most heat exchanger tubesheets will be adequate if they are designed in accordance with the seventh edition of the *TEMA Standards* previously referred to. Nonmandatory Appendix AA of the 1986 edition of the *ASME Code* also has methods for designing some types of tubesheets. Calculation methods for additional types are in work. At some future date, Appendix AA rules will probably be made mandatory.

independently of each other and applied at the same time. After selecting a tubesheet thick enough to withstand the design conditions, investigate the stresses produced by hydrostatic testing.

In differential-pressure design, the pressure parts exposed to both fluids are designed for the difference in their operating pressures. Factors to evaluate in choosing this option are operating circumstances, safety requirements, and economics.

Operating circumstances that favor differential-pressure design are (1) a common source of supply of the shellside and tubeside fluids, (2) shellside and tubeside operating pressures in the range of 1000 lb/in^2 (6900 kPa) and above, (3) pressure in one side that varies directly with pressure in the other, and (4) capability of measuring and controlling the differential pressure.

Safety considerations are (1) startup procedures and pressurization sequence, (2) shutdown procedures and depressurization sequence, (3) effects of upsets and pressure excursion, and (4) ability to relieve excess pressure in the higher-pressure side to the lower-pressure side.

Designing for differential pressure reduces the required thicknesses of tubesheets and tubes, but there is no difference in channels and shells between exchangers designed for differential pressure and those designed for pressure applied independently.

The cost factors to evaluate are:

1. The fraction of exchanger cost represented by the tubes and fabricated tubesheets

2. The effect of reducing tube wall thickness on the cost of the tubes and of joining them to the tubesheets

3. The costs of drilling, machining, and assembling the thinner tubesheets required for differential-pressure design compared with those for the thicker conventional-design tubesheets

4. The relative handling and fitting costs of the two designs

5. The number of shells in the unit

6. The cost of additional safety precautions required for differential-pressure design

7. The increase in design engineering cost

8. The cost of operator training for differential-pressure operation

9. Additional operating costs

Tubesheet metal temperatures

Temperature distribution in heat exchanger tubesheets and the embedded tubes is complex. It varies with the fluid regimes on each side, tube and shell pass arrangements, and tubeside inlet and outlet temperatures. For thick tubesheets, consider finite-element analysis because it provides very close assessments of tubesheet and tube-wall metal temperatures. This kind of analysis is especially recommended for quadrant-layout multipass exchangers with a large temperature difference between the tubeside inlet and outlet.

For quick estimates that are reasonably close to reality when the shellside and tubeside film coefficients are not too far apart, use the method devised by Gardener.[16] Here is a brief summary that assumes use of consistent units.

To estimate the metal temperatures of the untubed part of the tubesheet faces exposed to the fluids use Eqs. (3.1) and (3.2). In this region, it is reasonable to assume that the metal temperature varies linearly through the tubesheet thickness.

$$T_0 = T_t + \frac{(T_s - T_t)}{1 + \dfrac{h_t}{h_s}\left(\dfrac{1}{1 + h_t/h_m}\right)} \tag{3.1}$$

$$T_L = T_t + \frac{(T_s - T_t)}{(1 + h_t/h_m) + h_t/h_s} \tag{3.2}$$

In these and subsequent equations:

h_m = metal conductance (equal to L/k, L being metal thickness and k metal thermal conductivity)
h_s = shellside film coefficient of heat transfer
h_t = tubeside film coefficient of heat transfer
T_L = tubesheet tubeside-face metal temperature
T_0 = tubesheet shellside-face metal temperature
T_s = shellside fluid temperature
T_t = tubeside fluid temperature

Following is a procedure for calculating tubesheet metal temperatures in the region circumscribed by the OTL. It assumes that (1) the ligament between adjacent tubes is so thin relative to its length that there is a negligible temperature gradient over any cross section normal to its length, (2) the tube and tubesheet thermal conductivities are identical, (3) the tubeside film coefficient of heat transfer is the same on the tubeside tubesheet face as inside the tubes, and the shellside coefficient is the same on the shellside tubesheet face as outside the tubes, and (4) the tubesheet area through which heat flows on the shellside includes the tube-wall cross-sectional area. Note that the third assumption may not be justified in a given exchanger.

Referring to Fig. 3.6,

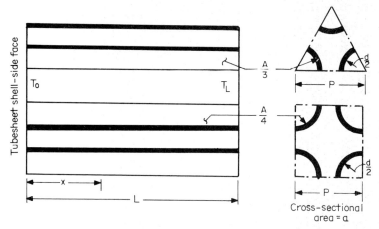

Figure 3.6 Tubesheet face temperatures and thickness, cross-sectional areas a, and inside tube heat transfer surfaces A for triangular and square pitches, for estimating tubesheet metal temperatures.

A = inside surface area of the tubes that bound a ligament

$A = \pi dL$ for square layouts

$A = \pi dL/2$ for triangular layouts

a = associated cross-sectional area of the ligament and bounding tubes

For a square pitch arrangement, $a = P^2 - (\pi/4)d^2$

For tubes set on triangular pitch, $a = 0.433P^2 - (\pi/8)d^2$

d = inside diameter of the tubes in the heat exchanger

$$K = \sqrt{(A/a)(h_t/h_m)} = \sqrt{(A/a)(h_t L/k)} \qquad (3.3)$$

x = depth of tubesheet measured from the shellside face

P = distance between tube centers (pitch distance)

T_{av} = average metal temperature of tubesheet

ϕ = fin effectiveness of tubesheet ligament (These calculations treat the ligament as a fin on the tube. The fin effectiveness is the ratio of heat transferred through the tube and fin to the heat transferred through the base area of the tube if the fin were not present.)

Here is the sequence of calculation:

1. Calculate areas A and a.

2. Calculate constant K from Eq. (3.3).

3. Calculate the fin effectiveness ϕ from Eq. (3.4).

$$\phi = (A/aK)\left[\frac{1 + (A/aK)\tanh K}{A/aK + \tanh K}\right] \qquad (3.4)$$

4. Use Eq. (3.5) to estimate the metal temperature T at any point x from the shellside face toward the tubeside face.

$$T = T_t + (T_s - T_t)\left[\frac{\cosh K(x/L) - (Ka/A)\Phi \sinh K(x/L)}{1 + \Phi(h_t/h_s)}\right] \quad (3.5)$$

5. Calculate constant F from Eq. (3.6).

$$F = \frac{1}{\cosh K + K(a/A)\sinh K} \quad (3.6)$$

6. Find the highest metal temperature. When the hotter fluid is in the shell, use Eq. (3.7). When the hotter fluid is in the tubes, use Eq. (3.8).

$$T_0 = T_t + \frac{(T_s - T_t)}{1 + \Phi(h_t/h_s)} \quad (3.7)$$

$$T_L = T_t + \frac{F(T_s - T_t)}{1 + \Phi(h_t/h_s)} \quad (3.8)$$

7. Calculate the average tubesheet metal temperature from Eq. (3.9).

$$T_{av} = T_t + (T_s - T_t)\frac{(\phi - F)}{(A/a)[1 + \phi(h_t/h_s)]} \quad (3.9)$$

Except when A/a and h_t/h_m are very small, the following approximations may be used in place of Eqs. (3.7), (3.8), and (3.9).

$$T_0 = T_t + (T_s - T_t)(aK/A)(h_s/h_t) \quad (3.10)$$

$$T_0 = T_t + (T_s - T_t)(aK/A)(h_s/h_t)$$

$$T_L = T_t \quad (3.11)$$

$$T_{av} = T_t + (T_s - T_t)(a/A)(h_s/h_t) \quad (3.12)$$

These equations indicate that, except for a thin section near the shellside tubesheet face in which there is a steep temperature gradient, the average metal temperature is close to the tubeside fluid temperature. Therefore, in the tubes, tubesheet, and tube-to-tubesheet joint, presumably only peak thermal stresses are created in the thin layer.

More recently, Singh and Holtz demonstrated that the temperature gradient may be more gradual.[17] They point out that, for high-shellside–low-tubeside heat transfer coefficients, the more gradual temperature gradient may cause the tubesheet to bow and the tube-to-tubesheet connections to leak.

Their method involves so many computations that use of a programmable calculator or personal computer is suggested. It is a good design and analysis tool that provides for different tube and tubesheet thermal conductivities and for film coefficients of heat transfer calculated at the tubesheet faces. (Recall that the Gardener method assumes that the tubeside film coefficient is identical with that in the tubes and that the shellside film coefficient is identical with that in the shell.) However, correlations for calculating the actual film coefficients on the tubesheet faces are not ordinarily available to the mechanical designer. (In the sample problems of their work, Singh and Holtz made the same assumptions as Gardener.)

Tubesheet Drilling[18]

The quality and precision of tubesheet drilling depend upon the drilling machine, the drilling-machine controls, and the drill that the machine drives. The tubesheet material and thickness determine the kind of drilling machine and drill required and the sharpening angle, rotational speed, and feed rate. If the drilling machine is controlled manually, the tubesheet must be laid out by hand and center-punched (Fig. 3.7). This makes the layer-out's skill in locating the holes and the drill operator's adeptness in setting the drill point into the center-punched positions factors in determining quality.

Until the development of more precise machines, only radial drill presses were used to drill tubesheets individually, together, or stacked with baffles to a total metal thickness of 8 to 10 in (203 to 254 mm) as shown in Fig. 3.8. Despite the availability of other kinds of drilling machines, they are still often adequate and economical to use. Radial drills consist of a C-shaped assembly of horizontal base, vertical column, and horizontal cantilevered arm that can be rotated or swung on the column. The drilling spindle can be positioned anywhere along the arm. These movement capabilities permit drilling at any position within the swing of the machine.

The drill-press base is machined and the assembly fitted with great exactness to ensure that the column and the spindle are parallel with each other and perpendicular to the base. Fitted to the base and held by T bolts in channel slots is a precision-machined boxlike structure or table upon which the part to be drilled is mounted and dogged down. The base contains a coolant-lubricant reservoir and circulating pump piped to feed to the entry point of the drill. This fluid returns to the reservoir through a strainer after it has been captured in channels or grooves cast into the base.

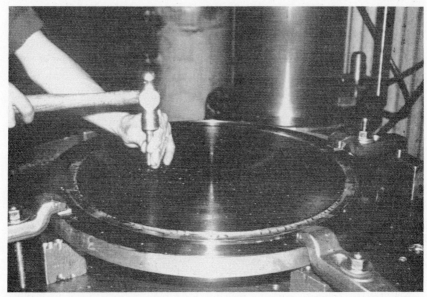

Figure 3.7 Manual tubesheet layout prior to drilling. (*Atlas Industrial Manufacturing Company, Inc., Clifton, New Jersey.*)

Figure 3.8 Stack-drilling tubesheets and baffles on a radial drill. (*Atlas Industrial Manufacturing Company, Inc., Clifton, New Jersey.*)

Reaction to the drill pressure bends the cantilevered radial-drill arms and columns and rotates them within the limits of the support bearing clearances. Consequently the centerline of the drill deviates from parallel with the centerline of the column. The divergence depends upon the flexural rigidity of the parts and their fit to the bearings. As a result of the rotations and deflections, the drill does not penetrate the tubesheet perpendicularly. The centerline of the hole where the drill emerges may be offset from the centerline of the hole at its entry site. The difference is called drill drift. The *TEMA Standards* have tolerances for drill drift.

The moment created by reaction to the drill varies linearly with the distance between the column and spindle centerlines. The deflection of the arm varies as the cube of this distance. For a given moment, the deflection of the column varies as the square of the distance between the base and the vertical position of the arm. Therefore, drill drift is much greater in holes farthest from the column than in those that are nearest. For this reason, skilled machinists try to set the table and tubesheet as close as possible to the column.

If, instead of being mounted on an arm cantilevered off a single column, the drilling spindle is set on a rigid structure supported by columns, drill drift can be substantially reduced and drill-drift variation across the tubesheet can be practically eliminated. The metal thickness that such a machine can penetrate is also somewhat greater than that of a radial drill press. Tubesheets or tubesheets and baffles can be stack-drilled as in radial drills. The spindle movement of these machines is on perpendicular axes. Therefore, all hole locations are on cartesian coordinates.

Instead of a base fastened to the columns, the table may be separate from the support of the drill and driving mechanism; both structures are precisely aligned and rigid. In one make, the spindle position is fixed and the table moves to set hole-drilling positions at the spindle location. Because the spindle moves on x–y lines, drilling patterns can be duplicated along the table. Therefore, several identical tubesheets can be set up at one time and drilled in one operation.

To eliminate manually laying out tubesheets and baffles, reduce the required level of skill, and shorten drilling times, some radial drills and virtually all beam-and-post machines are fitted with numerical controls.

Multiple spindles have also been used. Large, relatively thin tubesheets, such as those of surface condensers, may be drilled on machines with well over 100 spindles. With such machines, possible alignment problems may be avoided by using drill bushings to guide the drill points into the proper locations.

The bits used in the machines discussed to this point are twist drills made of materials suited to the drilling condition. These are the most common drilling tools. However, they are relatively long, slender columns, unstable because of their fluted shape. Tool pressure tends to bow the drill. If the sharpening angles are not uniform at the flute ends, the drill will waver within the hole during rotation under load. This produces runout. Therefore, twist drills are not suitable for drilling holes with length-to-diameter ratios much greater than 10. The practical maximum hole diameter is about 2 in (50.8 mm). Depending upon the machine that uses the twist drill, a smaller pilot hole may have to be drilled before drilling holes much larger than about 1 in (25.4 mm).

Twist drills may be manufactured with hollow cores that permit lubricant and coolant to be fed to the drill point. Coolant may also be sprayed onto the work surface. These drills remove metal from the hole in long spirals or chips. The chips must be removed from the region of the drill and hole because otherwise they may score the hole. When drilling is done vertically, the spiral chips tend to drape themselves about the drill and spindle. Therefore, radial-drill operators pull the emerging spiral chips away from the drill with a hooked-end reach rod.

Beam-and-post machines can be constructed with the drill vertical or horizontal. In the horizontal position, when the drills are appropriately sharpened, the chips are predisposed to break and fall. This makes it possible to use an automatic chip-removal elevator.

Hollow Lahr drills are commonly used to drill thicker tubesheets. The drives have very rigid, horizontal spindles supported by beams and posts. Their rotational speed and their feed rate and position indexing are numerically controlled. Their powerful driving mechanisms permit them to exert enormous tool pressure (which may also be controlled) on the tubesheet. Properly sharpened, the drills are self-aligning and produce small chips that quickly fall from the drill. In addition to intensive spray cooling, coolant-lubricant flows to the drill end through the hollow interior. The practical limit of the ratio of hole depth to diameter is about 40.

The thickest of tubesheets, such as those of large high-pressure feedwater heaters, may be drilled on numerically controlled, sturdy, rigid gun drills. These are self-aligning drills that core the holes in one pass with very little runout. (They are called gun drills because they were developed for drilling gun barrels.) Gun drills can be used to drill the tubesheets of just about any heat exchanger configuration. The depth to which they can drill is limited only by the ability of the drill to resist torsion. The hole-diameter limit of gun drills is about 1 in (25.4 mm).

Very-high-quality precision drilling can be achieved with BTA (Boring-Trepanning Association) drilling, which is increasing in popularity. BTA drilling uses single-edge cutting tools and has internal chip removal. It requires high-pressure lubricant-coolant, which flows toward the work in an annular passage in the tool shank and forces chips out through its hollow interior. Although BTA drilling can be done with a variety of machine tools (engine lathes, turret lathes, vertical and horizontal boring mills, radial drills, and precision boring machines), for deep-hole drilling single-purpose deep-hole machines should be used to achieve the high performance needed for tubesheet work.

Double Tubesheets

No known method of joining tubes to tubesheets completely eliminates the possibility of leakage. Where mixing of shellside and tubeside fluids cannot be tolerated, consider using double tubesheets to eliminate mixing due to leaks through the tube-to-tubesheet joints. Although double tubesheets will not reduce the leakage, they will prevent the fluid on one side from leaking into the fluid on the other. Two designs are available: the "conventional" double tubesheet and the integral double tubesheet.

Conventional double-tubesheet construction

The conventional double-tubesheet exchanger has two tubesheets at each end of the tubes. Ordinarily, adjacent tubesheets are joined to each other only by the tubes, as shown in Figs. 3.9, 3.10, and 3.11a. Shrouding, illustrated in Fig. 3.11b and c, may be used to seal the gap between adjacent tubesheets so that any material that leaks into the gap may be collected. Alternatively, the sealed gap can be filled with an inert substance at a pressure higher than either the shellside or the tubeside pressure. This permits leakage to be detected by metering pressure or flow of the inert substance or by monitoring the composition of the outlet shellside and tubeside streams for concentrations of the inert fluid. After a leak has been found, if inert fluid in the process stream is acceptable, operation may be continued until it is convenient to make a repair.

The shellside tubesheet of a conventional double-tubesheet U-tube unit may be constructed with any of the attachments used for removable-bundle construction; the shellside tubesheets of fixed-tubesheet units are welded to the shell. The tubeside tubesheets may be bolted or welded to the channel. In the typical construction shown in Fig. 3.11a, the channel-side tubesheet is similar to a floating tubesheet. If it is connected to the shellside tubesheet by a shell used

Figure 3.9 Gap between conventional double tubesheets. (*Atlas Industrial Manufacturing Company, Inc., Clifton, New Jersey.*)

Figure 3.10 Conventional double-tubesheet fixed-tubesheet heat exchanger. (*Atlas Industrial Manufacturing Company, Inc., Clifton, New Jersey.*)

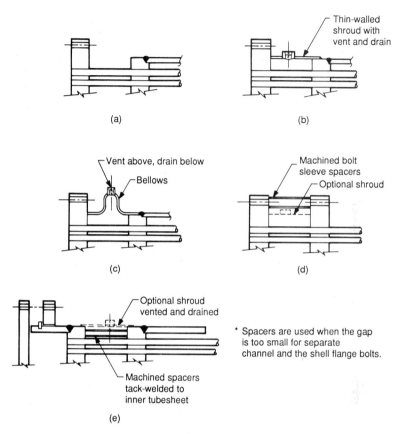

Figure 3.11 Conventional double-tubesheet constructions. (*a*) Fixed tubesheet with open gap. (*b*) Fixed tubesheet; light-gauge vented and drained shroud around gap. (*c*) Fixed tubesheet with bellows in light-gauge shroud; vent and drain in bellows. (*d*) Stationary-end removable-bundle preferred construction. (*e*) Packed floating-head end.

as a shroud, it is similar to a fixed tubesheet. Therefore, the effects of differential expansion between the connecting shell and the tubes between the two tubesheets must be considered in design. Alternatively, the shroud may be designed with an expansion bellows as shown in Fig. 3.11*c*.

Tube-to-tubesheet joint leaktightness is affected by how conventional double-tubesheet exchangers are manufactured. The highest-quality tubesheets and baffles or tube supports are produced by individually drilling each tubesheet and baffle or tube support on a numerically controlled drill of the multiple-column-and-beam type. Because such machines deflect very little under load, the holes in the tubesheets and baffles or support plates are perpendicular to their faces. The numerical control assures that tube holes in the tubesheets and baffles or supports that occupy the same position in the tube field will register within the precision of the drilling machine's tolerances.

If the tubesheets or baffles or combinations of tubesheets and baffles are stacked for drilling, some precision in registering holes at the same position in the tubesheets, baffles, and supports is lost. This is so because the drill drifts as it penetrates the stack.

Drill drift is greater when radial drilling machines are used than with the multiple-column-and-beam type. The reason is that drill pressure bends the cantilevered radial-drill arms and columns. These parts also rotate somewhat in their support bearings—the amount depends upon the fit of the parts to the bearings and the wear that has occurred. If the tubesheets and baffles are laid out manually (Fig. 3.7) and drilled in a manually controlled radial drill, the chances of a mismatch in the positions of holes in adjacent parts increase enormously. The skills of the layout worker and the radial-drill operator and the conditions of lighting under which they work become critical factors.

At assembly, hole-to-hole positions in adjacent tubesheets may also be displaced if the tubesheets' main centerlines are not maintained congruently. Severe problems may also be created if adjacent tubesheets are not set parallel with each other. For these reasons, it is essential for a purchaser to review with the manufacturer the equipment and techniques to be used for drilling and assembling conventional double-tubesheet exchangers.

Following are some guidelines for shops to assure proper assembly.

1. Machine opposed adjacent tubesheet faces flat and perpendicular to the tube (and bolt) holes. The machined surfaces should extend from just outside the OTL to the tubesheet periphery.

2. Prepare spacers precisely machined to the specified gap distance between the tubesheets.

3. Carefully mark the quarter points on the tubesheet rims.

4. Align the quarter points on both tubesheets of each pair.

5. Clamp the aligned tubesheets over the machined peripheral spacers. Keep the clamps in place until all tubing, tube joining, and tubesheet-to-shell-and-channel assembly are complete. Alignment may also be maintained by bolts as shown in Fig. 3.11d or by tack-welding the spacers in place as shown in Fig. 3.11e.

6. Machine a round bar for a length somewhat longer than the distance between the outer faces of the adjacent tubesheets to a diameter 0.002 in (0.051 mm) less than the recommended TEMA standard drilled hole size plus 0.000 in (0.00 mm) minus the TEMA permitted hole undertolerance as a gauge to make sure that the tubes will freely

enter the tubesheet holes of both tubesheets. Leave an unmachined length convenient for a handle. Before tubing the unit, check randomly selected tube holes in each quadrant of the layout for free entrance of the gauge.

For example, if an exchanger is to be built with 3-in-thick (76.2-mm-thick) conventional double tubesheets, separated by a 2-in (50.8-mm) gap and the tubes are ¾ in (19 mm), a convenient bar would be 1-in diameter by 12 in long (approximately 25.4 by 305 mm). The machined length would be about 8½ in (216 mm). The machined diameter for TEMA standard-fit holes would be a maximum of 0.753 in and a minimum of 0.751 in (a maximum of 19.13 mm and a minimum of 19.08 mm).

Displaced holes in closely spaced adjacent double tubesheets impose bending and shearing forces on the tubes and tubesheet ligaments. The consequent tube and ligament distortions may make it impossible to produce tight expanded joints. The outer tubesheet joints can be made tight by welding, but the problem remains at the inner tubesheet, where the joints can be made only by the process of expanding.

In choosing conventional double-tubesheet design, first estimate the tubesheet metal temperatures for the anticipated most severe conditions of startup, shutdown, operation, or upset. Then consider the effects of the difference between the radial expansions of the inner and outer tubesheets. Here is why.

If the plates are allowed to move freely, the holes away from the center of the tubesheet undergoing the greater expansion will be progressively displaced from the holes in the other plate. The largest displacement will occur in the peripheral holes. However, the tubes resist the movement, undergoing shear and bending stresses and applying loads to the ligaments. If the adjacent tubesheets are restrained peripherally, as by being tightly bolted or welded together, they will bow perpendicularly to the exchanger length. This is also resisted by the tubes through the tube-to-tubesheet connections.

The tube-to-tubesheet joints must remain tight, and the tubes must not be unreasonably stressed. When the gap between the tubesheets is small, the interaction between the tubes, tubesheets, and edge restraint is complex. The effect of shellside tube supports or baffles close to the shellside tubesheet must also be considered for a complete analysis. Small misalignments of the tubesheets and close tube supports may invalidate the stress analysis. When the spacings are large, modest misalignments may be tolerated.

To set an appropriate gap between the tubesheets, it is necessary to examine the complete system of thermal and pressure loads and the geometry of the assembly. A widely used simple method for setting the gap is a special case of more complex analyses.[19] It makes these assumptions: (1) The tube is a guided cantilever beam, (2) the tubesheets are rigid, (3) all movements due to thermal expansion are in the plane of the tubesheets, (4) there is no edge restraint, (5) pressure loads may be neglected, (6) the tubesheets are far enough apart so that shear of the tube is negligible, and (7) the effect of the first baffle or tube support is insignificant.

Equations (3.13) and (3.14) are used to estimate a suitable space between the tubesheets.

$$\delta = (OTL/2)\,[\alpha_h(T_h - RT) - \alpha_c(T_c - RT)] \qquad (3.13)$$

$$G = \sqrt{(1.5E_t d\delta)/\sigma_a} \qquad (3.14)$$

where d = tube outside diameter, in (mm)
$\quad E_t$ = Young's modulus for the tube, lb/in^2 (Pa)
$\quad G$ = gap between adjacent faces of the tubesheet pair, in (mm)
$\quad$ OTL = previously defined outer tube limit, in (mm)
$\quad$ RT = room temperature (the temperature at which the exchanger is assembled), °F (°C)
$\quad T_c$ = temperature of the colder tubesheet, °F (°C)
$\quad T_h$ = temperature of the hotter tubesheet, °F (°C)
$\quad \alpha_c$ = thermal coefficient of expansion of the colder tubesheet between assembly temperature RT and temperature T_c, in/(in · °F) [mm/(mm · °C)]
$\quad \alpha_h$ = thermal coefficient of expansion of the hotter tubesheet between assembly temperature RT and temperature T_h, in/(in · °F) [mm/(mm · °C)]
$\quad \delta$ = free differential in-plane movement, in (mm)
$\quad \sigma_a$ = allowable stress in the tubes, lb/in^2 (Pa)

This method does not offer a complete design analysis. Other factors include interaction effects of the tubesheets and the first support in the shell, tubesheet flexibility, edge restraint, and shear in the tubes.[20–23]

Despite its flaws, the simple calculation outlined above is widely used because in most cases it sets the gaps conservatively. It is generally unsatisfactory for large units with expensive tubing and cases in which the permissible pressure drop is very small. Some precautions should be followed: (1) Do not arbitrarily select a smaller gap without performing an interaction analysis, (2) consider the gaps between the tubesheets in the thermal design and pressure-drop calculations, and (3) expand the tubes into the inner tubesheets before joining them to the outer ones.

For analysis, use the methods of Refs. 21 and 22. The latter includes a program suitable for use with a personal computer. Use numerical analysis for large double-tubesheet equipment such as power station steam surface condensers and for critical services.

In performing thermal design calculations, note that the effective heat transfer surface is limited to the surface between the inner faces of the innermost tubesheets. However, tubing in the gap and in the four tubesheets that is lost to heat transfer contributes to pressure drop in the tubes.

Specially designed tools are used to expand the tubes into the tubesheets separated by a gap. The process is basically the same as for very thick single-tubesheet construction.

Double tubesheets have been designed with small gaps and edge restraints. In some constructions the edges are restrained by a thick-walled cylinder welded to the tubesheet outside the OTL. In others, forged lips on facing tubesheets are welded to each other. These constructions must be examined for the effects of edge restraint, tubesheet flexibility, and shear and bending in the tubes and tubesheets. Inability of the tubes and tubesheets to withstand the thermal loads in such tubesheets manifests itself as leaks in tube-to-tubesheet connections, tube stress-corrosion cracking, and fatigue failures in tubes and ligaments.

Integral double tubesheets

A different type of double tubesheet, shown in Fig. 3.12, is made from a single plate or forging.* The original patentee called them Letect tubesheets. Various other names have been used, but the designation *integral double tubesheet*, used in Ref. 19, is now almost universal.

In this design, a single tubesheet is drilled to the desired pattern. Then annular grooves are machined into the tube holes about midway between the faces to a depth such that adjacent ones break through the ligaments into each other. Thus two separate tubesheets are created that are joined integrally to each other between adjacent tubes, at pass-partition lanes (if any), and beyond the outer tube limit. Figure 3.13 is a photograph of a partially sectioned model with tubes in place. Figure 3.14 is a photograph of a model without tubes.

With this construction, the drill-drift, alignment, and assembly problems discussed for conventional double tubesheets are eliminated.

Heat is conducted through the metal in the tube walls, through the ligaments that join the halves of the tubesheet, and through the pe-

---

*U.S. Patent 1,987,891.

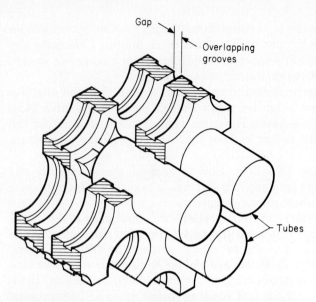

Figure 3.12   Schematic of integral double-tubesheet construction.

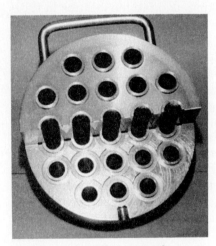

Figure 3.13 Partially sectioned model of an integral double tubesheet with tubes in place. (*Atlas Industrial Manufacturing Company, Inc., Clifton, New Jersey.*)

Figure 3.14 Model of an integral double tubesheet showing hole drilling and ligament breakthrough. (*MGT Inc., Boulder, Colorado.*)

ripheral section of the tubesheet. There is a temperature gradient between the hot and cold faces of the tubesheet in contrast with conventional double tubesheets, which have discrete hot and cold tubesheets adjacent to each other. Forces that result from differential expansion between the hot and cold faces are restrained by the integral ligaments, the tubes, and the rim that extends from the OTL to the periphery.

Integral double tubesheets are usually made to the same thickness as single tubesheets plus the width of the groove. Therefore, the effective heat transfer surface is but slightly reduced from that of single-tubesheet construction, and frictional resistance to fluid flow is the same.

Manufacturers use various groove widths and locations between the faces. The grooves are usually positioned midway between the faces to straddle the neutral bending line. If the process fluids are clean and not viscous, the grooves may be as narrow as can be conveniently produced by available tooling. Groove width in double-tubesheet steam surface condensers for power generation is usually ⅛ in (3.2 mm). Grooves in process heat exchangers are customarily ¼ in (6.35 mm).

Producing the grooves is hard on the tools. The cutting edge must be lubricated and cooled, and chips must be removed. If the tubesheet material work-hardens readily, extreme care must be used in cutting the gap. Consequently integral double tubesheets are usually limited to relatively free-machining materials.

It is generally less costly to manufacture heat exchangers with integral double tubesheets than with conventional double tubesheets for sizes larger than 18-in (457-mm) pipe.

Tubesheet Materials

Most tubesheets are made from rolled plate or forged ingots. Tubesheets of small production-line units may be cast. Nonmetallic materials and composites of thin metals coated with epoxy resins have been used in small air-conditioning units.

Carbon steel tubesheets less than about 5 in (150 mm) thick are most often burned from plate. Usually high-alloy and nonferrous tubesheets under about 3 in (76 mm) thick are parted from plate by powder burning, plasma-arc cutting, or machining. Thicker tubesheets are machined from forgings.

Within the limits of mill tolerances, as-rolled plates are out of flat and wavy and have a camber. Depending upon how a tubesheet plate is parted from the parent plate, it may have an irregular peripheral surface with unacceptable mechanical properties. For these reasons, specify rough-machining or surface-grinding all tubesheet surfaces to size before drilling and subsequent machining of the gasket surfaces. This is most important for tubesheets mated to bolted-on channels and return covers that have gasketed pass-partition-to-tubesheet closures. Conditioning a tubesheet by hand grinding to remove mill scale, scabs, surface gouges, and other irregularities is not a suitable substitute for machining or surface grinding.

For nonfouling fluids, when the channel barrel is welded to the front of the tubesheet as in TEMA Type C, it may be acceptable to machine only the OD and back face and to condition the front face. TEMA Type N tubesheets may require only conditioning the faces because the channel barrel and the shell are both welded to the tubesheet. However, the peripheral surface must not have been unacceptably damaged in parting the tubesheet from the parent plate and the rough face surfaces must not cause process problems.

Clad tubesheets

Tubesheets may be made from a base metal (most often carbon steel) integrally clad with another metal or metal alloy. Consider using clad tubesheets when:

1. The required parent-metal thickness exceeds the construction code's permissible thickness for the material.

2. Mills do not produce plate of the required metal thickness, and forgings are either too costly or are unavailable.

3. A metal that is resistant to corrosion by the fluid on one side will corrode when subjected to the fluid on the other side.

4. Costly corrosion-resistant metal is required on one side but less expensive metal can serve on the other, and the clad tubesheet is substantially less expensive than the solid one.

5. It is desirable to fusion-weld the tubes to the tubesheet, but the tube and tubesheet metals are incompatible.

6. The granular structure of the tubesheet is not uniform, making it unsuitable for fusion-welding the tubes to the tubesheet.

The savings in material cost for clad tubesheets as compared with solid ones is a function of the market for the material. Some rough guidelines: for tubesheets with ⅜ to ½ in (9.5 to 12.7 mm) of clad metal, the breakpoint for austenitic and ferritic stainless steels is 2 to 2½ in (50.8 to 63.5 mm); for titanium, it is in the range of ¾ to 1 in (19 to 25.4 mm); and for more costly materials it may be even less.

Integral cladding may be applied by fusion welding, roll cladding, or explosive cladding. When the strength of the cladding metal is used together with the base metal to resist pressure, the *ASME Code* (and other pressure vessel safety codes) requires the bond between the two to be examined ultrasonically for discontinuities. However, even when the capacity of the layer of cladding to sustain pressure loads is neglected, consider specifying this requirement for the sake of tube-to-tubesheet joint quality.

Fusion-weld cladding.   Fusion-weld cladding may be applied only when the base metal and the weld deposit are compatible. The most desirable process is gas-tungsten arc welding (GTAW), often called TIG (for tungsten inert-gas). Gas-metal arc welding (GMAW), often called MIG (for metal inert-gas), has been used. However, the GTAW process provides a denser deposit less subject to porosity than that of the GMAW process.

The tubesheet is set up on a motor-driven turntable. The welding is done either semiautomatically or automatically. Weld metal is fed continuously, either from a spool of wire (Figs. 3.15 and 3.16) or from a ribbon of curved strip. The turntable rotation speed and weld metal

Figure 3.15 Tubesheet set up in a turntable prior to wire-cladding gas-tungsten arc welding (fusion-weld cladding). (*Atlas Industrial Manufacturing Company, Inc., Clifton, New Jersey.*)

Figure 3.16 Semiautomatic fusion-weld wire-cladding a tubesheet by gas-tungsten arc welding. (*Atlas Industrial Manufacturing Company, Inc., Clifton, New Jersey.*)

feed rate are coordinated so that the weld bead laid down has a uniform thickness and width.

Some hints for achieving fully fused, porosity-free fusion-weld cladding follow. Prepare the surface by machining off all oxides just before depositing the first weld pass. Scrupulously wash the machined surface several times with a volatile solvent that will not damage the metal. Acetone is often used. Note that acetone is a highly flammable ketone that may harm the health of workers who are excessively exposed, and appropriate precautions must be taken. Between washes and after the last wash, blow-dry the surface with filtered air. Try to complete the work without interruption. If welding is interrupted before a pass is completed, make sure that the workpiece is covered to protect it from foreign matter in the atmosphere and maintained free of moisture until welding is restarted. If work is interrupted long enough for the tubesheet to cool, enclose it in a sealed container together with a bag of desiccant.

Roll cladding.   In the roll-cladding process, a rectangular-plate pack of compatible base and cladding metals is assembled. The pack consists, in order, of (1) a layer of base metal, (2) a layer of cladding metal, (3) a parting compound, (4) a layer of cladding metal, and (5) a layer of base metal. The facing surfaces of cladding and base metal must first be conditioned to remove surface oxides. The edges of the pack are welded together to maintain the relative positions of the components. The pack is then passed back and forth between the rolls of a plate-reducing mill.

As the thickness of the entire pack is reduced, the cladding metal forge-welds to the base metal. When the amount of reduction is appropriate, the pack is parted, the surfaces are conditioned, and the clad plates are heat-treated and cleaned. The tubesheet is then parted from the rectangular plate.

Explosive cladding.   The familiar use of explosively clad metals is in coins that consist of a sandwich of copper alloy between two layers of silver alloy. Figure 3.17 illustrates schematically how explosive cladding is done. A rough outline of the process follows.

The baseplates and cladding plates are conditioned. The cladder is set at a specific standoff distance from the baseplate by metal spacers. A measured layer of granular explosive is set on the cladding plate and detonated. The explosion progressively bends the cladder as it drives it into the base metal.

The pressure generated by the high-energy collision front between

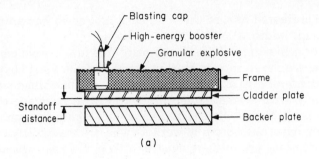

(a)

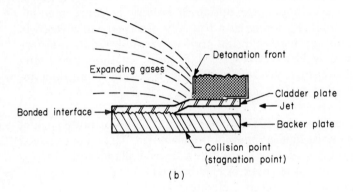

(b)

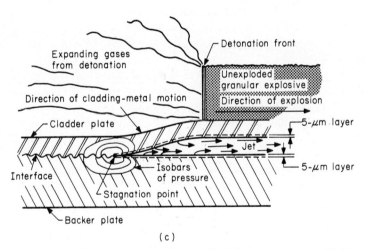

(c)

Figure 3.17 Schematic of the explosive-cladding process. (*a*) Assembly before detonation. (*b*) Assembly during detonation. (*c*) Mechanism for jetting away the 5-μm surface layers.

the cladder and baseplate fluidizes the colliding surfaces. A jet of fluid metal and surface intermetallics is ejected as the impact front travels forward, scouring the surfaces free of impurities. The cladder welds to the backer progressively behind the jet. The shape of the weld is sinusoidal. The clad plate may be converted in a plate-reducing mill when necessary to reduce the overall thickness.

A great advantage of explosion cladding is the wide range of metal pairs that can be metallurgically bonded. Fusion-weld and roll cladding can only be done with metals compatible for fusion or forge welding, but with explosion cladding a large array of base metals and metal alloys can be clad with an equally large assortment of cladders. These include combinations of copper and copper alloys, nickel and nickel alloys, brass, aluminum, platinum, steel, tantalum, titanium, silver, and gold.

A recent innovation developed by Explosive Fabricators, Inc., of Louisville, Colorado, for thick high-pressure tubesheets is explosively to weld multiple layers of fine-grain steel plates to each other to form a thick composite of uniform granular structure. This provides a structure uniform in strength throughout its thickness. Thick forgings, on the other hand, may be weaker in the interior regions than near their surfaces owing to nonuniform granular structure.

Tubesheet vents and drains.   Vertical heat exchangers cannot be fully vented or drained through shellside connections because it is nearly impossible to fabricate connections flush with the tubesheet inner faces. A heel remains on the bottom. The underside of the top tubesheet is blanketed with noncondensibles. For complete venting and draining, provide tubesheet vents and drains shown schematically in Fig. 3.18. A less satisfactory compromise for thin tubesheets is to install snorkels through the shell. Piped connections to hold through the tubesheets for venting and draining are unacceptable because of the difficulty of assembly and disassembly.

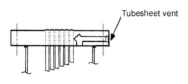

Tubesheet vent

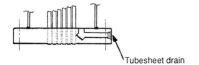

Tubesheet drain

Figure 3.18 Schematic illustration of tubesheet vents and drains in vertical heat exchangers.

References

1. *Standards of the Tubular Exchanger Manufacturers Association*, 7th ed., Tarrytown, N.Y., 1988.
2. *API Standard 660, Shell-and-Tube Heat Exchangers for General Refinery Services*, 4th ed., The American Petroleum Institute, Washington, September 1982.
3. *ASME Boiler and Pressure Vessel Code*, Section VIII, Division 1: *Unfired Pressure Vessels*, 1989 ed., American Society of Mechanical Engineers, New York. (New editions are published at 3-year intervals.)
4. *Standards of the Tubular Exchanger Manufacturers Association*.
5. K. A. Gardener, "Heat-Exchanger Tube-Sheet Design," *J. Appl. Mech.*, vol. 70, 1948, p. 377.
6. K. A. Gardener, "Heat-Exchanger Tube-Sheet Design—2," *J. Appl. Mech.*, vol. 74, 1952, p. 159.
7. K. A. Gardener, "Heat-Exchanger Tube-Sheet Design—III: U-Tube and Bayonet Tube-Sheets," *J. Appl. Mech.*, vol. 27, no. 82, 1960, pp. 25–32.
8. K. G. G. Miller, "The Design of Tubeplates in Heat Exchangers," *Proc. Inst. Mech. Eng. (London)*, vol. 18, p. 215.
9. R. Angehrn and B. Barp, "Calculation of Tube Plates in Heat Exchangers," *Konstruktion (Federal Republic of Germany)*, no. 9, 1971.
10. A. I. Soler, "Tubesheet Design in U-Tube Exchangers Including the Effect of Tube Rotational Restraint," *J. Eng. Ind., Trans. ASME*, vol. 98, no. 4, 1976, pp. 1157–1160.
11. A. I. Soler and J. E. Soehrens, "Design Curves for Stress Analysis of U-Tube Heat Exchanger Tubesheet with Integral Channel and Head," *J. Press. Ves. Technol.*, no. 100, May 1978, p. 221.
12. R. G. Malek, "A New Approach to Exchanger Tubesheet Design," *Hydrocarbon Process.*, January 1977, pp. 163–170.
13. J. P. Gupta and S. Sivasankaran, "Computer Program for Tubesheet Design," *Hydrocarbon Process.*, November 1981.
14. Van Le Ngan, "Required Thickness of Class 1 U-Tube Bolted Tubesheet," ASME Pap. 82-PVP-26, contributed by ASME Pressure Vessel and Piping Division, New York.
15. K. P. Singh and A. I. Soler, *Mechanical Design of Heat Exchangers and Pressure Vessel Components*, Arcturus Publishers, Cherry Hill, N.J., 1984.
16. K. A. Gardener, "Heat Exchanger Tube Sheet Temperatures," *Refiner Nat. Gas. Manuf.*, March 1942.
17. K. P. Singh and M. Holtz, "An Approximate Method for Evaluating the Temperature Field in Tubesheet Ligaments of Tubular Heat Exchangers under Steady State Conditions," *J. Eng. Power*, vol. 104, October 1982.
18. S. Azad and S. Chandrashekar, "BTA Deep-Hole Machining," *Mech. Eng.*, September 1985.
19. S. Yokell, "Double-Tubesheet Heat-Exchanger Design Stops Shell-Tube Leakage," *Chem. Eng.*, May 14, 1973.
20. R. D. Cook, *A Mechanical Analysis of Coupled Tube Sheets*, University Microfilm Inc., Ann Arbor, Mich., 1973.
21. A. I. Soler, "Analysis of Closely Spaced Double Tubesheets under Mechanical and Thermal Loadings," ASME Pap. 77-JPGC-NE-21, September 1977.
22. A. I. Soler, "Tube Stresses Due to In-Plane Thermal Expansion of Tubesheets in Closely Spaced Double Tubesheets," *Int. J. Press. Ves. Piping*, no. 7, 1979.
23. A. I. Soler and K. P. Singh, *Mechanical Design of Heat Exchangers and Pressure Vessel Components*, Arcturus Publishers, Cherry Hill, N.J., 1984, chap. 10.

4

Tube-to-Tubesheet Joints

Introduction

The reliability of a shell-and-tube heat exchanger depends upon the integrity of many parallel tube-to-tubesheet joints, each of which must be virtually free of defects. Therefore, the connection of the tubes to the tubesheets is a critical element.

The part of the tube fastened to the tubesheet is treated more severely than the main body of the tube, and most joint configurations allow only limited nondestructive examination. Accordingly, tube-to-tubesheet connections are frequently the site of failures.

This chapter examines the functions and requirements of tube-to-tubesheet joints, the methods and equipment used in joining, inspection of joints, and failure mechanisms.

Joint Functions and Requirements

To understand the degree of reliability needed, consider the functions of the joints and the consequences of failure. The main function of tube-to-tubesheet joints is to seal the tubes tightly to the tubesheets. A second function may be to create firm contact between the tube and the tubesheet hole when tube metal embedded in the tubesheet is used to increase the plate's ability to resist bending. A third function may be to transfer forces from the tubesheet to the tubes when the tubes stay the tubesheets against pressure-induced loads.

To seal a tube to the tubesheet effectively, a joint must remain tight under test, startup, operating, upset, and shutdown conditions. If a tube is to increase the tubesheet's capability to resist bending, it must remain in fixed contact with the hole under all conditions of tubesheet loading. To enable the tubes to stay straight-tube-exchanger tubesheets, the joints must be strong enough to transfer pressure loads from the tubesheets to the tubes.

The joints must also be able to withstand thermal loads that stem from restrained differential expansion between the shell and tubes of fixed-tubesheet units and between the hot and cold passes of all straight-tube equipment.

Leaking joints may cause:

1. Erosion of the tube ends and tube-hole walls

2. Corrosion of the lower-alloy side

3. Poisoning or fouling of the atmosphere

4. Fire or explosion

5. Tube-wall fouling

6. Catalyst poisoning

7. Product adulteration and degradation

8. Yield reduction

9. Power generation capacity reduction

10. Power outages and plant shutdowns

11. Structural damage to the heat exchanger

When tubes pull or push out under load or break at the tubesheet joint, structural damage to the exchanger may be substantial.

When joint leakage cannot be tolerated, consider using double tubesheets. The extra cost may be justified when (1) the hazard caused by the leak is great and (2) joint failures are more probable than failures in tube bodies.

The required degree of hydraulic tightness depends upon service conditions. Minor leaks in commercial low-pressure water heaters may be tolerated. In these units it is barely significant if a drop of water leaks through a tube joint after a half-hour-long hydrostatic test. To try to reduce the leakage rate below watertightness would hardly be worthwhile.

On the other hand, consider that the maximum permissible chloride ion concentration in steam surface condensers is 0.1 part per million (ppm). A typical brackish condenser cooling-water supply might have a chloride ion concentration of 5×10^{-3} ppm.[1] A surface condenser producing 5000 gal/min (0.315 m^3/s) of condensate could therefore tolerate a total brackish-water leak of approximately 0.1 gal/min (6.3 $\times$ 10^{-6} m^3/s). The number of tubes in a two-pass condenser that could handle the steam load would be approximately 50,000, making the average permissible brackish-water leak through each joint 1×10^{-6} gal/min (6.3 $\times 10^{-11}$ m^3/s). In order to minimize surface-condenser-tube-joint leakage, double tubesheets have been used.

Testing Tube-to-Tubesheet Joints

Tube-to-tubesheet joints are tested to determine their strength and tightness. In examining test results, it is necessary to take into account the fact that pressure, shear-load, and leak tests made on models or mockups indicate only the strength and tightness of the joints in the model. The results may be deceptive because the model tubesheets may barely deflect under pressure whereas full-size tubesheets may undergo substantial deflection. Tests of models and specimens demonstrate only the adequacy of the joining procedure.

Testing joint tightness

One way to assess the quality of tube-to-tubesheet joints is to measure how tight they are. It is reasonable to assume that a measured leak rate below the tolerable service rate provides some assurance that joint quality is acceptable.

Although necessary, it is hard to set permissible operating-condition leak rates realistically because it is seldom possible to measure leak rates of process fluids at operating conditions. With expanded-only joints it is even more difficult because thermal gradients affect their tightness. Consequently operating-condition leak rates may differ considerably from rates measured at leak-test conditions.

Fluids commonly used as media for measuring rates of leakage are air, nitrogen, helium, refrigerant gases, water, and lubricating oils. In setting permissible test leak rates, take into account that the rate of leakage varies directly with the difference between the squares of the pressures on each side of the leak and inversely with fluid viscosity. Table 4.1 lists typical viscosities at standard conditions for the common leak-test media.

After setting acceptable operating-condition leak rates, select tightness-testing methods and acceptance standards that match test-condition tightness with service requirements. The *ASME Boiler and Pressure Vessel Code* (hereafter referred to simply as the *ASME Code*)

TABLE 4.1   Viscosities of Common Fluids Used in Leak Testing

Fluid	Viscosity, poise
Air, nitrogen, helium	1.9×10^{-4}
Refrigerant gases	1.2×10^{-4}
Water	1
Lubricating oils	1×10^{2}

has recommendations in Section V, "Nondestructive Testing," for selecting tightness-testing methods and for setting acceptance standards.[2]
    The following ways to gauge tightness are arranged in a rough or-
der of sensitivity.

1. Visual observation of tube ends during hydrostatic pressure testing

2. Bubble testing

3. Gas-lake testing

4. Helium mass-spectrometer detector-probe-testing sniffer

5. Halogen diode detector-probe-testing sniffer

6. Helium mass-spectrometer tracer-probe technique

7. Helium mass-spectrometer hood method

    The detection system may enhance or decrease the ultimate mea-
suring sensitivity of the detection instruments. For example, the ultimate instrument sensitivity of the mass spectrometer is greater than
that of the halogen diode detector. A system that uses a mass spectrometer to measure the flow of tracer helium gas from the shell into
a tubeside vacuum is far more sensitive than one that uses a halogen
diode sniffer to probe for leaks from the pressurized shell to the atmosphere. However, for probing tube ends for tracer-gas leaks from the
pressurized shell, the halogen diode leak detector is more sensitive to
halogen leaks from an air-halogen mixture than the mass spectrometer is to helium leaks from a mixture of air and helium.
    The *ASME Code*'s Section V accepts only the helium hood method
as quantitative. Table 4.2 lists the acceptable leak rates for halogen
and helium leak-test systems.

TABLE 4.2   Acceptable Leak Rates for Halogen and
Helium Leak-Test Systems

System	Maximum acceptable leak rate, standard cm^3/s
Helium sniffer*	1×10^{-4}
Halogen sniffer*	1×10^{-4}
Helium tracer probe*	1×10^{-5}
Helium hood†	1×10^{-6}

*Considered to be qualitative under the rules of *ASME
Code*, Section V, "Nondestructive Testing."
    †This is the only method that the *ASME Code* accepts as
quantitative.

Visual observation during liquid pressure testing. The purpose of *ASME Code* hydrostatic pressure testing is to stress the structure under controlled conditions to make sure that it is safe to be put into service. For most equipment, joint tightness under *ASME Code* pressure testing is adequate.

Generally the *ASME Code* test pressure is 1½ times the design pressure, adjusted for the difference between allowable stress at design and test temperatures. If there are no visible leaks or structural distortions after at least ½ h on test, the inspector authorized by the *ASME Code* (hereafter called authorized inspector, or AI) accepts the structure as sound. Acceptance means only that the AI observed no leaks at the test site under test conditions. If the exchanger is correctly designed, properly transported, installed without damage, and operated as specified by the manufacturer, the joints will probably remain hydrostatically tight in operation.

Hydrostatic-test temperatures must be high enough to avoid the test's causing brittle failure. The relationship of ductility and thickness of the construction material determines the temperature at which brittle failure may occur. This should always be investigated for exchangers with thick sections because the *ASME Code* specified minimum temperatures may not be high enough when shells, channels, or tubesheets are thick.

The common medium for static pressure testing is water, but *ASME Code* rules permit using alternative inert test fluids. Such fluids might be used because they are more searching than water or because the use of water would create a subsequent hazard. When testing with a liquid might endanger the structure, the rules allow air or inert-gas pressure testing and specify the testing requirements.

Test media should be noncorrosive and free of slime-producing biological substances and suspended solids that may settle. Test water should be filtered and treated with an algicide that will not harm the unit. Do not test austenitic stainless-steel exchangers with water that has a chloride ion concentration high enough to cause stress-corrosion cracking. Most potable water supplies are chlorinated, making it necessary to use demineralized or distilled water for hydrostatic testing.

Each side of the exchanger must be pressure-tested with the other side at atmospheric pressure. Under shellside hydrostatic pressure, leaks through the tube joints are readily visible in the various exchanger configurations because, with the bonnets, channels, or channel covers removed, the tube ends are exposed. When the tubeside is pressure-tested, leakage is directly visible only in removable bundles. However, specific locations of leaking joints deep within the tube field may not be discernible.

To test the shellside, pressurize the shell with the bonnets, channels, or channel covers removed so that the tube ends are exposed and leaks are visible. Test rings are required for removable-bundle units when bonnets or channels are removed.

To test the tubeside, pressurize the channels and tubes. Test removable bundles outside the shell, using test rings to seal the tubesheets to the channels. Test fixed-tubesheet exchangers for overall joint leakage by pressurizing the tubeside and measuring pressure loss over an extended period (usually 24 h). Maintain constant ambient temperature, and make sure that there are no connection leaks to cause false indications.

In addition to pressurizing each side with the other side at atmospheric pressure, the pressure test should include pressurizing both sides simultaneously. Joint leaks cannot be seen under this condition.

The *ASME Code* hydrostatic test is required only for *internal-pressure* testing, but internal-pressure testing of the shell subjects the tubes to *external pressure*. Therefore, before testing the shell, it is necessary to examine the tubes' capability of bearing the test pressure applied to their exteriors.

In filet-welded joints, porosity or inclusions may create hidden partial leak paths. Fluid-penetrant examination and *ASME Code* hydrostatic testing may not disclose the partial paths. For critical services, consider performing a series of hydrostatic tests. This will impose cycles of high stress on the welds that may cause the partial leak paths to be completed.

After static pressure testing proves the exchanger's structural soundness, tube-joint tightness may be further leak-tested. Before further leak testing, drain and thoroughly dry the shell. Section V of the *ASME Code* has information about the leak-testing methods discussed in the following paragraphs.

Bubble testing.   Section V specifies requirements for bubble testing by the direct-pressure and vacuum-box techniques. The direct-pressure technique using bubble solution is the more common. To do this test, fill the shell with inert gas or air at the design pressure. After a pressure soak time of at least 15 min, flow bubble solution over the joints or tube ends, or brush or spray the tube ends and joints with the bubble former. Generally the surfaces must be in the temperature range of 40 to 125°F (approximately 4.5 to 52°C).

The test solution must not break away from the test surfaces or break down rapidly because of air drying or low surface tension. Bubble testing is frequently misnamed air-and-soapy-water testing. Although the bubble-forming solution may be a soap or a detergent, household soaps and detergents are not permissible. Therefore, use a bubble former developed specifically for bubble testing.

Gas-lake testing. Here is how to gas-lake-test. (1) Pressurize the shellside of the heat exchanger with air or nitrogen to the maximum allowable working pressure (MAWP) at room temperature, (2) set the unit vertically and seal a 1- or 2-in-high (25.4- or 50.8-mm-high) ring dam to the tubesheet, (3) fill the tubeside with water to the level of the dam, and (4) observe for air or nitrogen bubbles.

Detector-probe methods. Halogen and helium detector-probe (sniffer) methods are inexpensive compared with helium tracer-probe and hood techniques. They are most often used when an exchanger is to handle lethal or noxious fluids and for ensuring that air-conditioning and refrigeration heat exchangers are not leaking refrigerant gases. Because the helium sniffer leak-testing system is somewhat less sensitive than that of the halogen sniffer system, use halogen leak testing except where the halogen tracer gas can cause corrosion.

The detector, or sniffer, sucks air through a tubular probe into an instrument that is sensitive to small amounts of tracer gas. To use a sniffer, traverse the tube ends with the probe at a distance of approximately $\frac{1}{8}$ in (about 3.2 mm) at a scanning rate predetermined on a standard leak. Also insert the probe into the tube ends for about $\frac{1}{4}$ in (about 6 mm). If the tubes are welded to the tubesheet, you may check the welds by encapsulating each tube end with a funnel connected to the probe.

In the halogen diode instrument, air from the probe passes over a heated platinum element (the anode). The element ionizes halogen gas present in the air, and the ions flow to a collector plate (the cathode). Current, proportional to ion formation rate and flow, is indicated on a meter.

In helium-gas tracer probing, the tracer gas is helium and the portable mass spectrometer replaces the halogen diode detector. The *ASME Code* requires the sniffer to be calibrated against a capillary tracer-gas standard with a leakage rate of 0 to 1×10^{-5} standard cm^3/s before use and again at intervals of not more than 2 h.

Here is a typical halogen sniffer-test procedure.

1. The preferred tracer gas is refrigerant 12, but refrigerants 11, 21, 22, and 114 or methylene chloride may be substituted.

2. Clean and dry the shell. Fill it with a mixture of 10 percent by

volume tracer gas and clean, dry inert gas under the specified pressure. [Typical fill pressures are 30 to 50 lb/in^2 (207 to 345 kPa).] Allow at least 30 min for tracer-gas dispersion.

3. Determine the scanning rate by passing the probe over the leak standard orifice at a rate that detects leakage of 1×10^{-5} standard cm^3/s.

4. Traverse each tube joint, keeping the probe tip within ⅛ in (3.2 mm) of the test surface at the interface of the tubes and tubesheet. Check for cracked tube ends by inserting the probe into each tube end to a minimum depth of ¾ in (19 mm) and holding it there for about 3 s.

When the tubes are too small to allow the probe to enter and too close to each other for effective scanning, use the halogen sniffer in a *bag-test* system. Enclose the channel side of the tubesheet in a plastic bag sealed to the tubesheet periphery. At the end of the soak time, perforate the bag and insert the probe. If there are no leak indications from all the simultaneously encapsulated tube ends, no further probing is required. When there are indications, the region of the leaks can be found by passing the probe back and forth across the tubesheet.

Helium tracer-probe and hood methods.   These methods are used when even very small leaks present a hazard to life and property. The hood technique is used when quantitative leak rates must be determined. Both techniques require precise system calibration. To use these methods for tube-to-tubesheet joint testing, evacuate the shellside and detect leakage of 100 percent helium gas into the evacuated space.

In the tracer-probe method, a stream of helium gas is directed from the probe at each joint. In hood testing the channel side of the tubesheet is enclosed in a hood filled with helium. The instrument then detects the total leakage through all the joints and the tubes into the shell.

Testing joint strength

It is neither convenient nor practical to measure tube-to-tubesheet joint strength directly. Instead, pullout or pushout (shear-load) tests are made on representative specimens. The test specimens are full-size tube-to-tubesheet joints, made in test block models that represent the production tubesheets. The shear-load test subjects the specimens to axial loads until either the tube or the joint fails.

These are reasons to shear-load-test:

1. To investigate the variation of strength with joint design and production parameters
2. To compare joint strengths achieved by various joining methods
3. To establish joint efficiencies for use in determining *ASME Code* allowable joint loads when the tubes stay the tubesheet

For the third purpose, Appendix A to Section VIII of the *ASME Code* has requirements for establishing joint efficiencies. It tabulates two sets of joint efficiency factors that apply to various types of joints, $f_{r(\text{test})}$ and $f_{r(\text{no test})}$. The tabulated values of f_r established by test are maximum values; the values tabulated for joints that are not tested may be used as shown.

Table 4.3 lists the current values to show their magnitudes. In the

TABLE 4.3   Values of f_r^*

Type	Description of joints	$f_{r(\text{test})}$	$f_{r(\text{no test})}$
a	Welded only; depth of weld along the tube equal to or greater than 1.4 times the tube wall thickness	1.00	0.80
b	Welded only; tube wall thickness equal to or less than the depth of weld along the tube; depth of weld along the tube less than 1.4 times the tube wall thickness	0.70	0.55
c	Brazed, examined	1.00	0.80
d	Brazed, not fully examined	0.50	0.40
e	Rolled, welded; depth of weld along tube equal to or greater than 1.4 times the tube wall thickness	1.00	0.80
f	Rolled, two or more grooves, and welded; depth of weld along tube less than 1.4 times the tube wall thickness	0.95	0.75
g	Rolled, single-groove, and welded; depth of weld along tube less than 1.4 times the tube wall thickness	0.85	0.65
h	Rolled, no grooves, and welded; depth of weld along tube less than 1.4 times the tube wall thickness	0.70	0.50
i	Rolled, two or more grooves	0.90	0.70
j	Rolled, single groove	0.80	0.65
k	Rolled, no grooves	0.60	0.50

*These values are for illustrative purposes only. They are restricted by footnotes in Table A-2 of *ASME Code*, Section VIII, Appendix A (or such other number that is assigned when the appendix becomes mandatory). Refer only to the appendix for values of joint efficiency.

ASME Code table, the use of each factor is qualified by one or more restrictions. Therefore, do not use the factors listed here because Table 4.3 lacks these notes.*

The manufacturer may use the lower (no-test) values without performing shear-load tests. The higher values are the maximum permitted when three sets of specimens are tested. They may be increased to a maximum value of 1 if nine sets of specimens are tested. Under some circumstances, listed joint types must be tested. Nine sets of specimens must be tested for all joint types that are not included in the table.

When joint strength is derived primarily from welding or brazing, the test efficiency factor is set to the lower of (1) the tabulated test value or (2) 80 percent of the load at which the test specimen failed, divided by the product of the tube nominal transverse cross-sectional area and tensile strength as shown in Eq. (4.1).

$$\frac{0.8L_{(\text{test})}}{f_{r(\text{test})}} = A_t S_t \qquad (4.1)$$

When joint strength is achieved primarily by tube expanding, efficiency is adjusted by dividing by a factor for the depth of expanding relative to tube diameter and by another factor for differences in the mechanical properties of the tube and tubesheet as shown in Eq. (4.2).

$$\frac{0.8L_{(\text{test})}}{f_{r(\text{test})}} = A_t S_t f_e f_y \qquad (4.2)$$

In these equations,

L_{test} = lowest axial load at which failure of the test specimen occurs, lb (N)

A_t = tube nominal transverse cross-sectional area, in^2 (mm^2)

$f_{r(\text{test})}$ = test efficiency factor

S_t = specified minimum tensile strength of tube material, lb/in^2 (kPa)

f_e = factor for length of expanded portion of the tube

f_y = factor for differences in the mechanical properties of the tubesheet and tube materials

The factor for the expanded depth of tube is 1.0 when tube holes are double-grooved. In ungrooved holes, the expanded-depth-of-tube factor is equal to the lesser of the ratio of the length of the expanded portion

---

*The values of joint efficiency currently tabulated in Appendix A were arbitrarily chosen. Those for expanded joints may not be suitable for some tube-tubesheet metal combinations and for some drilling and joint geometries.

of the tube divided by the tube OD or 1.0. The factor for the differences in the mechanical properties of the tubesheet and tube is the lesser of 1.0 or the ratio of tube yield stress to plate yield stress. When the plate-to-tube-yield-stress ratio is less than 0.6, the appendix requires qualification tests to be performed.

Maximum permissible joint loadings are calculated by multiplying the tube nominal transverse cross-sectional area by the *ASME Code* allowable working stress, the efficiency factors, and (when they apply) the factors for depth of expanding and mechanical properties.

The *ASME Code*'s Appendix A to Section VIII, Division 1, specifies specimen preparation, testing procedures, and acceptance standards for shear-load tests. Specimens consist of tubes joined to a test block that simulates the production tubesheet. Tubesheet and tube materials must be identical for the model and for the production joint. All tubes in the array must be taken from the same heat. For consistency, cut tube specimens from the same length of tubing whenever possible. The test block parameters must match those of the production tubesheet, except that the model tubesheet may be thinner. Tube expansion depth in the model may be less than that to be used in production.

The test block model may be circular, square, or rectangular. It must be drilled on the tube pitch of the tubesheet it represents, with the edges of the simulated tubesheet extending for at least a ligament width beyond the peripheral tubes. The procedure used to prepare specimen joints must be identical with the procedure to be used in production. The tube to be loaded must be located in the geometric center of the tube array and be completely surrounded by at least one row of adjacent tubes.

The *ASME Code* requires manufacturers to have qualified procedures for welded tube-to-tubesheet joints but not for expanded-only joints. Nevertheless, it is prudent to require manufacturers to have on hand certified test reports to support their expanded tube-to-tubesheet joining procedures for joints for which Appendix A requires testing and for those tested to take advantage of efficiency factors higher than those listed in the appendix.

To establish optimum parameters and procedures for tube-to-tubesheet joining it is necessary to test more specimens than the number required to qualify an already-established procedure. Optimization models for these purposes may consist of single tubesheets that contain several sets of specimens. As in the *ASME Code* qualifying tests, each specimen should be surrounded by at least one row of adjacent tubes, and tube materials, diameters, and thicknesses should be identical with those of the proposed production joints. Whenever possible, minimize the effect of varying tube properties by cutting each set of tube coupons from one tube and, in any event, all specimens from one heat of tubes.

Shear-load tests performed at room temperature do not account for the effects of operating temperature on joint strength. When the tube and the plate expand at about the same rate (they have similar thermal coefficients of expansion), welded-joint strength varies with temperature in parallel with the variation of the parent metals and the *ASME Code*'s metal temperature limits apply. When tube and plate thermal expansion coefficients are far apart, welded joints may be subjected to severe shear stress. The effects of temperature on expanded joints are discussed below. The effects of differences in thermal expansion rates must be investigated for each metal pair, tube diameter, and thickness.

Appendix A sets temperature restrictions on the use of tubes as stays when they are joined to tubesheets only by expanding. It provides a basis for setting permissible axial loads based upon shear-load-testing one set of specimens at the proposed operating temperature and a second set, which has been heat-soaked for 24 h, at room temperature. The joint is acceptable if the lowest load at which it fails during testing equals or exceeds the product of the tube nominal transverse cross-sectional area, the tube minimum tensile strength, and the factors for depth of expansion and metal property differences.

In cyclical operation, joints are periodically loaded and unloaded with pressure and thermal loads, and load directions may be reversed. Hence failure may occur well below the point of failure under static load. To examine cycling effects, simulate calculated anticipated peak-cycle loads and deflections on a standard test fixture.

Shear-load and cycle tests disclose the loads that will cause failures in models but not the effects of test and operating conditions on full-scale geometry. A complete design analysis requires considering tubesheet deflection, tubesheet temperature gradients, interpass tube metal temperature differences, and vibration.

How Tube-to-Tubesheet Joints Are Made

Tube-to-tubesheet joints are made in the following ways:

1. Stuffing the space between the tube and hole with packing
2. Sealing the tube to the hole by means of an interference fit, with and without anchoring the tubes to annular grooves in the tube holes
3. Welding or brazing the tubes to the tubesheets
4. Gluing the tubes to the tubesheets

5. Combinations of the first four methods

Packed joints

Figure 4.1 is a sketch of a typical packed joint. At the inner side of the tubesheet, the clearance between the tube and the hole is just large enough to let the tube slide through. The counterbored recess at the outer side of the hole is threaded for approximately half its depth. A slotted, threaded ferrule is used to squeeze packing rings into the chamber. The friction of the compressed packing against the tube and hole surfaces determines the strength and tightness of the joint.

Tubes of packed joints do not contribute to supporting the tubesheets. Their advantages are that (1) they are easy to assemble and disassemble, (2) they allow differential expansion between the tubes and the shell, and (3) they allow differential expansion between tubes within the tube nest. The tradeoff is that either the tubesheet ligaments are narrow or the tube pitch is spread.

The first alternative requires thicker tubesheets to resist pressure loads than would be required with wide ligaments. The second reduces the number of tubes that the shell can contain and may also reduce the shellside thermal coefficient of heat transfer. A further disadvantage is that the packing may dry out in service, becoming stiff and hard, and the ferrules may become frozen, making tube replacement difficult.

More economical and positive methods have largely replaced packed joints. Aside from some small auxiliary exchangers, their principal use today is in vertical, low-pressure fixed-tubesheet heat recuperators and economizers. In this equipment, hot combustion gas, which may be laden with pollutants, flows through the tubes. Cold combustion air flows through the shell. Baffles in the shell direct the air back and forth across the tubes.

Foulants in the gas settle nonuniformly on the tube walls, resulting

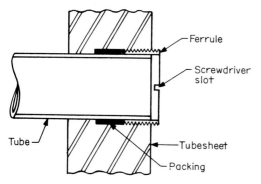

Figure **4.1** Packed tube-to-tube sheet joint. (*Courtesy of* Chemical Engineering.)

in different rates of fouling that may cause the average temperatures of adjacent tubes to be markedly different. If the tubes were to be firmly fastened to both tubesheets, the forces created by the differential expansion could rupture the joints, damage the tubesheets, and buckle or stretch the tubes.

With loosely packed joints in the cold end and welded joints at the hot end, the tubes may expand individually. The arrangement requires combustion air pressure to be somewhat higher than combustion gas pressure and small leaks of combustion air into burnt gas to be acceptable.

The tubes of many heat recuperators are large enough for the ferrules to be designed as stuffing-box gland followers with wrench flats.

Alternatives to packed-end recuperator joints are (1) expanding the lower tube end to sliding contact with the tube hole and (2) making each lower tube-to-tubesheet connection through a bellows expansion joint.

Interference-fit joints

If the perforated tubesheet were to be shrunk onto the tubes, interference between the tubes and hole walls would create interfacial pressure. The hydraulic tightness and strength of the joints would depend upon the following:

1. Interfacial-fit pressure
2. Tube surface area in contact with the hole wall
3. Static coefficient of friction between the tube and hole surfaces
4. Poisson's constant
5. Other properties of the metals

The amount of interference required to produce shrunk-fit joints is very small.[3] For an assumed static coefficient of 0.32, Table 4.4 shows the range of interference required to produce maximum joint strength of thick-walled tubes, expanded into a 1-in-long (25.4-mm-long) sleeve with an OD that approximates the diameter of a circle that would circumscribe the ligaments surrounding a tubesheet hole. For the purposes of the table, the maximum strength is defined as the product of tube cross-sectional area and yield strength.

To determine the feasibility of shrink-fitting tubesheets to tubes consider the following. To permit the tubes to be loaded into position, the tube holes must be drilled larger than the tubes. Using as an example 1¼-in (32-mm) OD × 0.065-in-thick (1.65-mm-thick) austenitic tubes made to ASME specification SA-249, for tubesheets produced to

TABLE 4.4   Interference Required for Maximum Strength of Expanded Tube-to-Tubesheet Joints, Based upon Coefficient of Friction = 0.32

Tube diameter, in	Tube thickness, in	$k = OD/t$	Stainless-stainless	Austenitic-stainless	Titanium 2–Muntz	Copper-stainless	Admiralty stainless
0.625	0.109	5.73	0.00074	0.00094	0.00226	0.00124	0.00062
0.625	0.095	6.57	0.00071	0.00091	0.00218	0.00123	0.00062
0.625	0.083	7.53	0.00069	0.00088	0.00210	0.00122	0.00061
0.625	0.072	8.68	0.00067	0.00085	0.00202	0.00121	0.00061
0.625	0.065	9.61	0.00066	0.00084	0.00197	0.00121	0.00060
0.625	0.058	10.77	0.00064	0.00082	0.00192	0.00120	0.00060
0.625	0.049	12.75	0.00062	0.00080	0.00186	0.00119	0.00060
0.625	0.042	14.88	0.00061	0.00078	0.00180	0.00119	0.00059
0.625	0.035	17.85	0.00059	0.00076	0.00175	0.00118	0.00059
0.75	0.134	5.59	0.00107	0.00136	0.00328	0.00179	0.00090
0.75	0.12	6.25	0.00104	0.00132	0.00318	0.00178	0.00089
0.75	0.109	6.88	0.00102	0.00129	0.00310	0.00177	0.00089
0.75	0.095	7.89	0.00098	0.00125	0.00299	0.00176	0.00088
0.75	0.083	9.03	0.00096	0.00122	0.00289	0.00175	0.00087
0.75	0.072	10.41	0.00093	0.00119	0.00279	0.00173	0.00087
0.75	0.065	11.53	0.00091	0.00117	0.00273	0.00173	0.00086
0.75	0.058	12.93	0.00089	0.00114	0.00266	0.00172	0.00086
0.75	0.049	15.3	0.00087	0.00111	0.00258	0.00171	0.00085
1	0.165	6.06	0.00186	0.00237	0.00570	0.00317	0.00159
1	0.134	7.46	0.00177	0.00226	0.00539	0.00313	0.00157
1	0.12	8.33	0.00173	0.00220	0.00524	0.00312	0.00156
1	0.109	9.17	0.00170	0.00216	0.00511	0.00310	0.00155
1	0.095	10.52	0.00165	0.00211	0.00495	0.00308	0.00154
1	0.083	12.04	0.00161	0.00206	0.00481	0.00306	0.00153
1	0.072	13.88	0.00157	0.00201	0.00467	0.00305	0.00152
1	0.065	15.38	0.00154	0.00198	0.00458	0.00304	0.00152
1.25	0.18	6.94	0.00282	0.00358	0.00858	0.00492	0.00246
1.25	0.165	7.57	0.00276	0.00352	0.00839	0.00489	0.00245
1.25	0.134	9.32	0.00264	0.00337	0.00796	0.00484	0.00242
1.25	0.12	10.41	0.00258	0.00330	0.00775	0.00482	0.00241
1.25	0.109	11.46	0.00254	0.00324	0.00759	0.00480	0.00240
1.25	0.095	13.15	0.00247	0.00317	0.00738	0.00477	0.00239
1.25	0.083	15.06	0.00242	0.00310	0.00719	0.00475	0.00237
1.25	0.065	19.23	0.00234	0.00300	0.00690	0.00471	0.00236
1.5	0.134	11.19	0.00367	0.00469	0.01099	0.00691	0.00346
1.5	0.109	13.76	0.00354	0.00453	0.01053	0.00686	0.00343
1.5	0.083	18.07	0.00340	0.00436	0.01003	0.00680	0.00340
2	0.12	16.66	0.00611	0.00783	0.01808	0.01212	0.00606
2	0.109	18.34	0.00603	0.00773	0.01779	0.01208	0.00604

the *TEMA Standards* the standard-fit hole size is 1.264 in (32.11 mm).[4] Permissible undersize is 0.006 in (0.15 mm); permissible oversize is 0.002 in (0.05 mm) for 96 percent of the tubes and 0.01 in (0.25 mm) for the remainder.

The permissible variation in tube diameter is ± 0.005 in (± 0.127

mm). If the hole diameter is at its maximum tolerance and the tube diameter is at its minimum, there will be a clearance of 0.007 in (0.178 mm), or more than twice the interference required for maximum strength.

Despite attempts to size holes and tube ends to make shrink fitting feasible, it has not been a commercial success.

The practical way to make interference-fit joints is to expand the tubes into holes. Expanding is the most frequently used way to join tubes to tubesheets. It is the standard method used for exchangers built to the *TEMA Standards*. A brief description of how the process works follows. For simplicity it is based upon applying pressure uniformly in the tube ends, although more often than not tubes are not expanded by a uniform-pressure process.

The following terms, assuming consistent units, are used in this discussion:

a	Tube inside radius
b	Tube outside radius
r	Radius to any point in the tube
σ_r	Radial plastic stress
σ_y	Yield stress
σ_{yp}	Tubesheet yield stress
σ_{yt}	Tube yield stress

When a tube is first inserted into a tubesheet hole, there is an initial clearance between the tube's OD and the hole wall. Application of expanding pressure deforms the tube until it makes contact with the hole wall. At this point, the deformation may be fully elastic or fully plastic or vary from plastic at the interior surface to elastic at the exterior surface. With further application of expanding force, the outside of the tube applies pressure to the inside of the hole, deforming the surrounding material.

When the expanding pressure in the tube exceeds $(1/\sqrt{3})\,\sigma_{yt}$, or approximately $0.577\sigma_{yt}$, referred to here as the *elastic limit*, a plastic zone is established that begins at the inner tube wall. If pressure is released, the tube will recover approximately elastically (but not to its original size).

Applying more pressure further deforms the tube; its exterior increases pressure on the surrounding tubesheet metal, causing further deformation. Tubesheet deformation may be fully elastic or be plastic in the region of contact and elastic farther out. Under maximum expanding pressure, equilibrium is established between the expanding and resisting stresses. Upon release of expanding pressure, the tube and the surrounding ring of metal recover. In order to create interference, free recovery of the tubesheet metal must be greater than free recovery of the tube. For the process to work, tube deformation must be fully plastic, although tubesheet deformation may be fully elastic, fully plastic, or plastic in the vicinity of the tube exterior and elastic farther out.

After recovery, the permanently strained assembly has a zone of residual stress that increases from zero at the inside of the tube to a maximum and then declines with increasing radial distance. The residual radial stress component at the tube-plate interface is the interfacial-fit pressure analogous to the pressure created by shrink fitting.

Several analyses of tube expanding have been made.[5-10] Because the residual radial stress at the tube-tubesheet interface (interfacial-fit pressure) is the major determinant of joint strength and hydraulic tightness, the analyses seek to relate the interfacial pressure to the maximum expanding pressure applied. These analyses are based only upon uniform pressure; they disregard cyclical contact stresses, such as occur in tube rolling, and the effects of strain hardening.

The following paraphrases the Goodier and Schoessow analysis (Ref. 5). Their model consists initially of pressure applied in a single hole in an infinitely large plate in which stress in the direction of the tube axis is assumed to be zero. The theory is then extended to account for an inner ring of material that is not initially integral with the plate (i.e., a tube end) and may have different mechanical properties.

A continuous plate represents the situation in which the tube and the tubesheet are of the same material and are in intimate contact. Here plastic deformation begins when expanding pressure exceeds the elastic limit. Elastic and plastic stresses correspond at the boundary between the elastic and plastic zones. The maximum expanding pressure that can be applied is $(2/\sqrt{3})\,\sigma_y$, or approximately 1.155 times the yield stress, called here the *plastic limit*. Attempts to apply higher pressure are defeated because the material at the interior of the hole (or tube ID) begins to extrude. At this limit, the plastic-zone radius is 1.75 times the inside radius of the hole ($1.75a$).

For a tube of any thickness in contact with the hole wall, if the tube and tubesheet yield stresses are equal ($\sigma_{yt} = \sigma_{yp}$), the pressure that the exterior of the tube can apply on the hole wall must be less than the pressure inside the tube. If the plate yield stress is higher than the tube yield stress, the tube plastic-limit stress also sets the limiting expanding pressure. However, stress distribution in the plate surrounding the tube is different, and the distance that the plastic zone extends into the ligament is reduced. When the tubesheet yield stress is twice the tube yield stress, the tubesheet remains elastic.

Expanding pressure is probably seldom applied to the point of fully developing yield in the tubesheet ligaments because the resulting tubesheet distortion may be unacceptable. Furthermore, permanently enlarged holes could make retubing difficult.

A tube yield stress higher than plate yield stress is less favorable for the expanding process. As tube thickness approaches zero, pressure at the outside of the tube approaches the pressure applied inside. When the tube is stronger than the plate, the pressure of a tube of infinitesimal thickness on the ligament will exceed the plate plastic limit. In the extreme, when tube yield stress is twice plate yield stress, expanding pressure equal to the tube *elastic* limit will apply pressure on the ligament equal to twice its *plastic* limit. When the pressure is released, the hole will be permanently enlarged, but the tube will return to its original size, creating additional clearance instead of interference. Therefore, when the plate yield stress is less than the tube yield stress, expanding pressure must be reduced below the tube-yield-stress-limited pressure to avoid exceeding the plate plastic limit.

Goodier and Schoessow's analysis of the residual stress produced by various magnitudes of expanding pressure shows that, to obtain the strongest joint, the highest pressure should be used that (1) will not cause the tube to extrude and (2) will not cause the tubesheet to extrude under the pressure applied by the tube. To meet the first condition, expanding pressure must not exceed the tube plastic limit. To meet the second, the pressure of the tube on the hole wall must not exceed the tubesheet material's plastic limit.

The second condition implies that the maximum pressure that the tubesheet can exert on the outside of the tube is the tubesheet's plastic limit. The tubesheet plastic limit may be expressed in terms of the tube's plastic limit by multiplying the tube plastic limit by the ratio of tubesheet to tube yield stresses, or $(2/\sqrt{3})\, \sigma_{yp} = (2/\sqrt{3})\, \sigma_{yt}\, (\sigma_{yp}/\sigma_{yt})$.

To find the optimal expanding pressures, Goodier and Schoessow selected external pressures on the tube for various ratios of tubesheet to tube yield stresses $(\sigma_{yp}/\sigma_{yt})$ and plotted the plastic stress curve as the ratio of radial plastic stress to tube yield stress (σ_r/σ_{yt}) against the ratio of radius to any point in the tube to its outside radius (a/r). Their curves are reproduced here in modified form as Fig. 4.2.

Each curve begins at the outside of the tube, where the plastic stress is equal to the external pressure on the tube, and ends at the inner limiting radius that corresponds with an internal pressure of $1.155\sigma_{yt}$ (the limit pressure). The plot of inner limiting radii that corresponds with the limit pressure is called here the *limit line*. The terminus of the curves at the limit line establishes the minimum ratio of inside radius to outside radius (a/b) at which the tube plastic-limit pressure

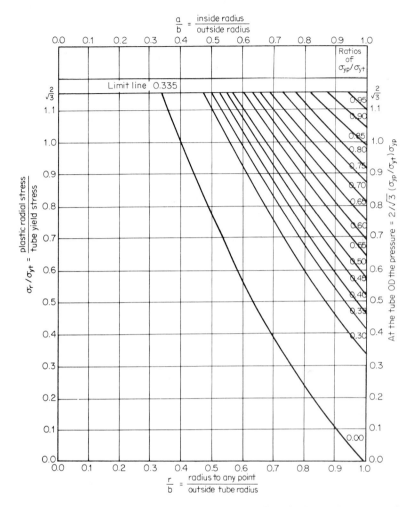

Figure 4.2 Radial plastic stress versus position in the tube for various ratios of plate yield stress to tube yield stress when the external pressure on the tube is equal to the plate plastic limit. The intersections of the curves in the limit line are the maximum ratios of a/b at which expanding pressure of $2/3\sigma_{yt}$ may be applied inside the tube.

can be applied without exceeding the plastic limit in the plate for each ratio of σ_{yt}/σ_{yp}.

A similar curve, plotted for zero plastic stress at the tube exterior and limiting internal pressure, intersects the limit line at a value of a/b of 0.335. This is equivalent to a diameter-to-thickness ratio (d/t) of 3.01. Thicker tubes of any internal radius will have an outer zone of elastic stress and, according to this analysis, cannot be expanded with the hope of achieving autofrettaging. Thus the smallest practical d/t

limit is 3. For ratios that approach this limit, consider welding as the primary joining method. (Despite the theoretical analysis, some tubes with a thickness-to-diameter ratio greater than 3 have been successfully expanded. The purpose of expanding these thick tubes has been to seal the crevice between the tubes and the hole walls after front-face fusion welding.)

According to the Goodier and Schoessow theory, when tube yield stress exceeds plate yield stress, a minimum thickness is required for each tube diameter in order to create an interference fit. However, it should be noted that high-strength tubes with walls thinner than permitted by the theory have been successfully expanded into lower-strength tubesheets as demonstrated by results of these pullout load tests for Sea Cure.*

Specimen joints were made by rolling ⅞-in-OD × 0.029-in-thick (22-mm-OD × 0.74-mm-thick) Sea Cure tubing, with a nominal yield strength of 75,000 lb/in^2 (517,100 kPa), into various commercial-alloy tubesheet specimens. Typical tubesheet metals and their associated nominal yield strengths were: Muntz metal (60 Cu, 40 Zn), 20,000 lb/in^2 (137,900 kPa); mild steel, 30,000 lb/in^2 (206,800 kPa); and stainless-steel Type 316 (16 Cr, 12 Ni, 2 Mo), 30,000 lb/in^2 (206,800 kPa).

Rolling was controlled to produce 6 percent tube-wall reduction. Joint strengths were reported as pullout load divided by tube–hole-surface area in contact, lb/in^2. The reported pullout strengths were approximately 650 lb/in^2 (4480 kPa) for Muntz metal, 875 lb/in^2 (6035 kPa) for steel, and 940 lb/in^2 (6480 kPa) for stainless-steel Type 316.

Generally, in expanded-only joints of thin-walled tubes to tubesheets, higher joint strengths are attained when the tube elastic modulus is equal to or greater than the tubesheet elastic modulus than when the tubesheet elastic modulus is higher than that of the tube.

Tube-expanding methods. Tubes may be expanded into tubesheets by these methods:

1. Rolling the tube ends into the holes with a mechanical tube roller (roller expanding)

2. Exploding charges in the tube ends (explosive expanding)

3. Compressing an elastomer in the tube ends to create radial pressure (rubber expanding)

---

*Sea Cure is a trademark of the Trent Tube Division of Crucible Materials Corp., Troy, Wisconsin.

4. Applying hydraulic pressure directly in the tube end (hydro-expanding)

5. Hydroexpanding until the tube makes firm contact with the hole,followed by roller expanding (hybrid expanding)

Roller expanding.   The tube rollers, shown assembled and disassembled in Figs. 4.3, 4.4, 4.5, and 4.6, consist of a cylindrical cage with three to five (and for special purposes seven) equally spaced longitudinal slots, hardened rolls nested in the slots, and a tapered mandrel that fits between the rolls. The cage's drive end is threaded to receive a thrust collar and locking nut. The axial position of the rolls in the tube is set by adjusting the position of the thrust collar.

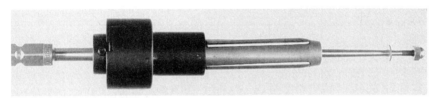

Figure 4.3 Self-feeding three-roll tube expander. (*Airetool Division of Dresser Industries, Springfield, Ohio.*)

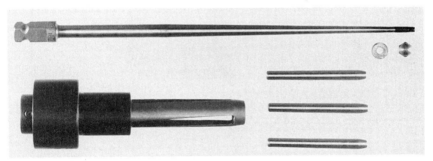

Figure 4.4 Disassembled self-feeding three-roll tube-expanding tool. (*Airetool Division of Dresser Industries, Springfield, Ohio.*)

Figure 4.5 Self-feeding five-roll tube expander. (*Airetool Division of Dresser Industries, Springfield, Ohio.*)

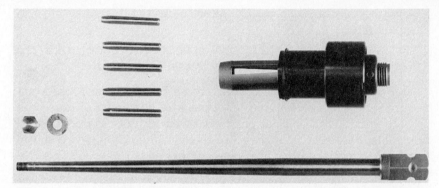

Figure 4.6 Disassembled self-feeding five-roll expanding tool. (*Airetool Division of Dresser Industries, Springfield, Ohio.*)

The tube roller is shown in the tube before expanding in Fig. 4.7. To expand the tube, the rolling tool is lubricated and inserted into the tube end. The mandrel is rotated and pushed forward, driving the rolls outward to bear upon the tube end. Friction between the mandrel and the rolls causes the rolls to turn and rotate the cage.

Before the advent of power-driven rolling, forward thrust was created by hammer blows on the back end of the mandrel. The mandrel was turned between blows by a wrench. In powered rolling, torque is supplied by electric, air, or hydraulic motors.

Usually, some of the input torque of electric and air motor drives is converted to thrust to drive the mandrel axially by setting the cage slots at a small angle with the tool's axis. The tube is pulled against the thrust collar in reaction to the thrust. A disadvantage of this self-feeding arrangement is that soft tubes in hard tubesheets may take an hourglass shape and that hard tubes in soft tubesheets may become barrel-shaped. Either condition reduces the amount of effective tube-

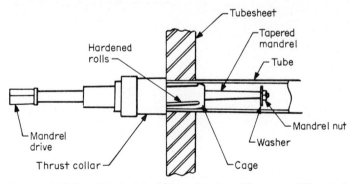

Figure 4.7 Tube roller in tube before cleaning. (*Courtesy of* Chemical Engineering.)

hole contact surface and, consequently, joint strength and tightness. Another disadvantage is that the roll motion becomes a combination of sliding and rolling, which can abrade the tube wall.

Figures 4.8 and 4.9 illustrate hydraulically driven tube-rolling equipment. Unlike self-feeding rollers, the cage slots are aligned with the tool's axis. Hydraulic piston power is used to insert and retract the mandrel.

As the tube expands, before it makes contact with the hole wall, the tube end becomes slightly shorter and thinner owing to the Poisson effect. The volume of the metal in the tube end remains unchanged. After contact, as the surrounding ligaments resist the tube movement, the surface under each roll is slightly depressed. As the rolls ride up the side of the depression, they squeeze the tube wall, applying con-

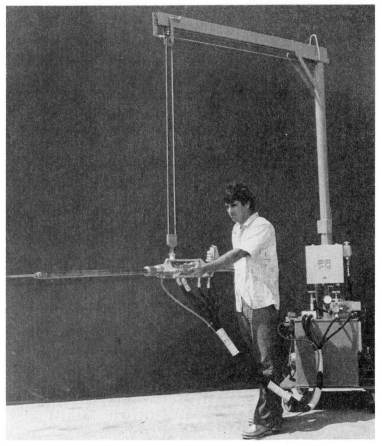

Figure 4.8 Vernon hydraulically driven, hydraulically positioned tube-expanding machine. (*Vernon Tool Company, Ltd., Oceanside, California.*)

Figure 4.9 Vernon hydraulically driven tube roller showing parallel rolls and hydraulically positioned tapered mandrel. (*Vernon Tool Company, Ltd., Oceanside, California; courtesy of* Chemical Engineering.)

tact stresses that exceed the tube metal's plastic limit. This further reduces tube wall thickness and extrudes the tube end.

Wall reduction is the most-often-used criterion of rolling adequacy. Rolled-joint pullout strength increases approximately linearly with percent wall reduction, but rolling must not proceed to the point at which adjacent holes are distorted.

It is not practical to measure the wall thickness of the tube end embedded in the hole to determine the amount of wall reduction. Therefore, wall reduction is estimated by measuring hole and tube dimensions before rolling and tube ID after rolling. Equation (4.3) is used for calculating the percent wall reduction. This calculation does not account for radial ligament deformation. Therefore, it would be more appropriate to call the wall reduction the apparent wall reduction

$$\text{Percent} = \frac{[\text{ID} - (\text{initial ID} + \text{clearance})]100}{2(\text{measured unrolled wall thickness})} \tag{4.3}$$

where
ID = measured tube internal diameter, in (mm)
OD = measured tube outside diameter, in (mm)
clearance = measured tubesheet hole diameter—OD, in (mm)

In order to establish a repeatable procedure, torque input is sensed and controlled.[11,12] The control cuts off power at a preset torque that has been correlated with wall reduction, which in turn has been correlated with strength and tightness tests. Typical wall reductions range from 3 to 12 percent. Torque outputs that produce these reductions are in the range of 1 to 20 ft · lb (approximately 1.4 to 27 MN). Specific tube-wall reduction and torque values depend upon tubing properties and dimensions and must be determined experimentally. As a general rule, consider rejecting expanded joints when wall reductions approach 12 percent.

Rolling torque may also be correlated directly with joint strength. This practice is recommended for high-yield-stress, low-elastic-modulus thin-walled tubes, where the small wall thickness makes wall reduction measurements difficult, as, for example, 1-in-OD × 0.028-in-wall (approximately 25-mm-OD × 0.7-mm-wall) titanium Grade II tubes.

In order to make sure that the torque cutoff point is maintained, rolling-procedure specifications should require output torque calibration with a torque analyzer (dynamometer) every 50 to 100 rollings and every time that the rolling tool is changed.

These factors affect the quality of roller expanding:

1. Cleanliness of the tube, tubesheet, and roller
2. Condition of the cage, rolls, and mandrel
3. Lubrication and cooling
4. Tube and hole dimensions
5. Torque cutoff control monitoring and maintenance
6. Rolling technique
7. Roller rotation speed
8. Number of rolls
9. Angle of rolls relative to the tube axis
10. Shape of the rolls
11. Worker fatigue

For any tube-to-tubesheet joining process to be successful, the parts to be joined and the joining tools must be extremely clean. Here are recommended steps for preparing tubesheets and tube ends for expanding.

1. Wipe the tubesheets and tube ends with lint-free rags.

2. Flush the tubesheets and tube ends with a volatile chloride-ion-free solvent. If acetone is used, take appropriate health and safety precautions.

3. Blow-dry the tube ends and tubesheet with warm, filtered air.

4. Repeat steps 2 and 3 at least 3 times or more often as necessary after inspecting for foreign matter.

Rolling tools should be disassembled and similarly cleaned before using.

The cage should rotate freely against the thrust collar. Slot edges should be smooth. The rolls should be smooth and free of nicks and evidences of flaking. The tapered mandrels must not be bent, nicked, or chipped or unevenly worn. During rolling, the tool and tube surfaces should be lubricated frequently to maintain consistency in the torque being sensed. Despite the lubrication, rolling generates considerable heat that may affect the friction of the parts, hence the torque being sensed. Good practice is to dip the tool into the lubricant frequently between tube rollings and to keep a second tool immersed in lubricant. Change the tool when it becomes uncomfortably hot to the touch.

With appropriate wall reductions or torque settings, full joint strength is developed in an expanded depth of 1½ to 2½ in (38.1 to 63.5 mm). The general practices for strength-expanding depth in North America are as follows. For equipment constructed to TEMA Classes R and B and for power plant heat exchangers, tubes are expanded for the lesser length of 2 in (50.8 mm) or the full tubesheet thickness, minus ⅛ in (3.2 mm); for TEMA Class C exchangers, the minimum strength expansion depth is no less than the least of two tube diameters, 2 in (50.8 mm), or the tubesheet thickness, minus ⅛ in (3.2 mm).

When tubesheets are thicker than 2 in (50.8 mm), it is customary to strength-expand for the depth that produces full joint strength and to contact-expand the remaining tubesheet thickness. The purposes of contact expanding are (1) to seal the crevice between the tube and the hole that would otherwise remain as a source of crevice corrosion; and (2) to reduce the effective size of the tubesheet perforations to that of the tube ID, thereby stiffening the tubesheet.

The pullout strength requirement can be met by using less than the theoretically optimum maximum expanding torque if the product of interfacial pressure, coefficient of friction, and tube–hole-wall contact surface is large enough to provide the requisite joint strength.

An alternative to full-depth rolling in thick tubesheets is to expand for 1 in (25.4 mm) or so from the rear tubesheet face forward and an equal amount from the front face rearward, leaving an unexpanded section in between. This seals the front and back of the tube-to-tubesheet connection without excessively compressing the tube. However, it stiffens the tubesheet only by the fraction of tube length that has been expanded to make firm contact with the hole wall. If the partially expanded joint leaks after a period of operation, in addition to reexpanding the front and back sections that were previously expanded, the unrolled gap may be expanded.

The maximum practical depth for rolling in one step is about 2 in (50.8 mm). Full-depth rolling into thicker tubesheets must be performed in overlapping steps. Because the rolling tool causes axial tube-end extrusion, step rolling should be regressive, starting ⅛ in (3.2 mm) in front of the rear tubesheet face and proceeding outward to allow the extruded end to move out freely through the tube hole. Regressive step rolling is desirable for removable-bundle construction because it facilitates maintaining axial dimensions. In fixed-tubesheet construction, it minimizes the compressive force on the tubes that results from restraining the extrusion.

Equipment is available that automatically performs regressive step rolling. The amount of extrusion that occurs in a rolling step depends upon the length of the rolls. Axial extrusion proceeds from the middle of the roll equally toward the front and rear faces of the tubesheet. Therefore, to minimize locked-in axial stresses in the tube, use relatively short rolls for step rolling.

Tube rolling may have several undesirable effects on tubesheets. Tubes rolled into the second tubesheet of a straight-tube unit by self-feeding tube rollers are stretched before they lock into the holes. (A similar effect may occur as the result of tube-end shortening during hydroexpanding.) The resulting tensile forces in the tubes may cause thin tubesheets to dish inward. However, if tube-end extrusion is substantial, it may cause the tubesheets to dish outward.

Tubesheet dishing may be enhanced by the radial deflection of the ligaments under the pressure of the tubes. Because expanding tends to enlarge the tube holes, tubesheets into which tubes are rolled tend to grow radially. This may be inconsequential in fixed-tubesheet exchangers, but it can cause clearance problems in removable-bundle equipment if the tubesheet OD is not subsequently turned down.

Tubes rolled into the stationary end of U-tube bundles or into the second end of straight-tube exchangers, may twist before enough friction is generated to lock them into the holes. When many tubes twist, the whole tubesheet of a U-tube bundle may rotate. In floating-tubesheet units, the second tubesheet to have its tubes rolled in tends to rotate relative to the first. The rotation may not be apparent in fixed-tubesheet units, but the author has examined floating-head bundles with 15° twists caused by tube rolling. The way to avoid this problem is to set the tube ends before rolling.

If the tubes are not rolled in a proper sequence, tube-end extrusion can cock the tubesheet out of perpendicularity to the bundle axis. For example, if rolling simply proceeds from the top to the bottom tube rows, tube ends may protrude from the upper tubesheet half and be some distance inside the tube holes in the lower half as a result of the cocking.

Because rolling technique is so large a factor in achieving good joint quality in manufacturing and retubing, purchasers should review and discuss the rolling procedure with prospective manufacturers. The procedure should include the cleaning procedure and the rolling sequence. A typical tack-rolling sequence, recommended for minimizing some of the effects of rolling, is shown in Fig. 4.10.

The effects of extrusion and improper rolling technique are intensified in conventional double-tubesheet construction. In constructing these units, extreme care must be taken to maintain adjacent tubesheets parallel and their tube holes aligned. The tubes should be expanded into the inner tubesheets and the joints tightness-tested before expanding the tubes into the outer tubesheets. Here is a recommended manufacturing sequence.

1. Fix the pairs of tubesheets at each end parallel with each other and with the tube holes aligned.

2. Set the pairs of tubesheets at the opposite ends parallel with each other and with the tube holes aligned.

3. Tube the bundle. Follow the specified tube-end and tubesheet cleaning procedure.

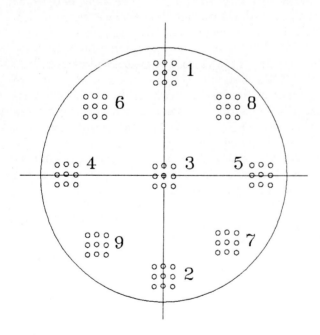

Figure 4.10   Typical tack-rolling sequence.

4. Tack-expand the tubes in the front inner tubesheet in a sequence similar to that shown in Fig. 4.10.

5. Fully expand the tube ends into the front inner tubesheet. Step-roll into thick tubesheets regressively.

6. Repeat steps 4 and 5 at the rear tubesheet.

7. Pressurize the shellside. Inspect for leaks with strong lights and mirrors. Reexpand as necessary.

8. Repeat steps 4 and 5 for the outer tubesheets.

9. Pressurize the gaps if possible. Inspect the tube ends for leaks and reexpand as necessary. If the gaps are open to the atmosphere, pressurize the tubeside. Inspect for leaks behind the outer tubesheets with strong lights and mirrors.

Explosive expanding.   In explosive expanding, a charge is set off in the tube ends. The process is also called near-contact forming, near-explosive expanding, kinetic expanding, and Detnaforming.* It is applied mostly to tubesheets thicker than 2 in (50.8 mm). Important uses are contact-expanding tubes previously strength-welded to the front faces of high-pressure feedwater heaters and making expanded-only joints in low-pressure feedwater heaters.

In kinetic expanding, the tube is the workpiece. The tubesheet and the air gap between the tube and the hole wall make up a forming die. The explosive-charge insert package consists of Primacord contained in a polyethylene cylinder. The insert must be closely fitted into the tube so as to leave no air gap.

The detonation distorts the inside tube surface less severely than rolling and does not damage the tubesheet or distort the ligaments. The rapid diminution of stress waves through the plastic cylinder minimizes shocks to the tubes and ligaments.

The polyethylene cylinder transmits the explosive force to the tube in a controlled way. Polyethylene is used because:

1. Its resiliency accommodates large elastic strains without cracking or bursting and makes it easy to install and remove the inserts.

2. It is cheap and readily available.

3. It is easy to handle.

4. It resists attack by water and most solvents.

5. It is flexible.

---

*Detnaform is a trademark of Foster-Wheeler Energy Corp., Livingston, N.J.

6. It is fairly dense.

7. It melts at a temperature high enough for the process.

8. It does not react with most tube metals.

9. It does not create a cleaning problem after charge detonation.

Pressures generated by an explosion decrease very quickly with distance. Attenuation is especially rapid close to the explosion. This makes it possible to control precisely the tube length to be expanded. This capability permits postweld contact expanding of tubes that have been strength-welded to a tubesheet's front faces. A unique feature is that, with only one explosion, full expansion pressure may be applied in the vicinity of annular grooves and contact-only pressure in the rest of the tube end.[13]

Figure 4.11 is a cross section through part of a tube and tubesheet joined by a front-face weld. It shows the arrangement of Primacord, polyethylene medium wrapper, and air gap for controlled contact expanding of the tube without stressing the weld.

Points of attention in reviewing the explosive-expanding procedure are:

1. How the charge is established

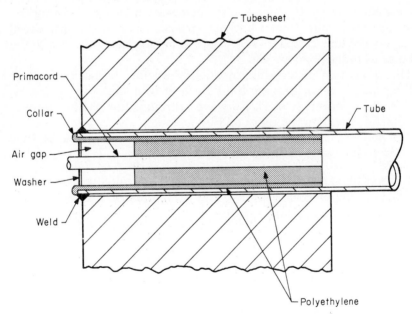

Figure 4.11 Explosive-expanding assembly. (*Courtesy of* Chemical Engineering.)

2. How the connections to the charges are to be made secure and reliable

3. How misfires are to be prevented

4. How misfires that occur are to be corrected

5. How the joints are to be tested

6. How cleanup is to be done after testing

Safety, blast effects, and noise containment must also be considered. Charge size is established by correlation with pullout test results. The selected charge is then set off in unrestrained tubes and the resulting strains measured to verify that adequate tube deformation will take place. Data gathered from these tests should be made available to the exchanger purchaser.

Rubber expanding (compressing an elastomer in the tube end). Hitachi calls its system for creating uniform radial expanding force *rubber expanding* because it is based upon compressing a rubberlike elastomer in the tube ends. Figure 4.12 shows schematically how the Hitachi machine works. The expanding medium is a cylinder of a suitable elastomer. The pressing rod, connected to the hydraulic cylinder,

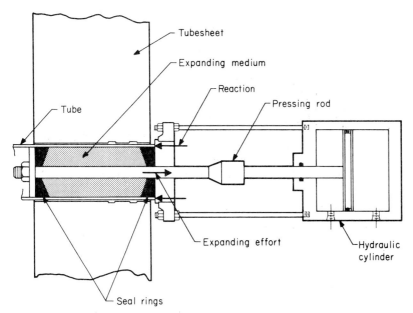

Figure 4.12 Sketch of how Hitachi rubber expanding works. (*Courtesy of* Chemical Engineering.)

passes through the medium. When the hydraulic piston retracts the pressing rod, the medium is compressed and bulges to exert pressure in the tube.

The seal rings at the inner and outer faces of the medium prevent its extruding during compression. The nut and washer on the pressing rod's inner end transfer force from the hydraulic piston to compress the medium. A thrust bushing, seated in the retainer held to the hydraulic cylinder by the tie rods, contains reaction to the axial force.

The degree of expansion is related to the hydraulic cylinder's retracting pressure. The expansion pressure in the tube end cannot be directly measured or controlled. In any plane perpendicular to the tube axis, radial force is uniform. However, its magnitude may vary with axial distance through the medium.

Hydroexpanding.   Hydroexpanding is the process of expanding tubes by applying hydraulic pressure directly in the tube ends.[14–16] There are no high-contact forces to cause the tube-end mashing, extrusion, and thinning produced by roller expanding. As the tube end is stretched radially, it becomes somewhat shorter and thinner while maintaining its original volume.

An illustration of this behavior is provided by the following measurements made before and after hydroexpanding:

Fifty-one ⅝-in-OD × 0.050-in-thick (15.9-mm OD × 1.27-mm-thick) titanium tubes were hydroexpanded into 1.614-in-thick (41-mm-thick) steel tubesheets. Before and after measurements showed constant tube-end volume within the precision of the measurements. Tube-end shortening was approximately 1.33 percent of the embedded length, and tube-wall-thickness reduction was about one percent.

This contrasts with tube-end extrusion and with tube-wall-thickness reductions in the range of 8 to 12 percent that are typical for titanium tubes.

The working fluid used in hydroexpanding is pressurized demineralized or distilled water. Figure 4.13 schematically illustrates how the Haskel HydroSwage* system applies the process. Figure 4.13a shows a section through a tube end positioned in a tube hole in a tubesheet. Figure 4.13b and c shows a tool that Haskel calls the *tube-lock*, inserted into the tube in its extended and retracted positions. Retracting the plunger expands the tube end into firm but not hydraulically tight contact with the tube-hole wall. Figure 4.13d and e depicts the hydraulic mandrel in the tube before and after applying hydraulic pressure. Figure 4.13f is a section through the finished joint.

Figure 4.14 is a picture of the system's main components:

---

*HydroSwage is a trademark of Haskel Incorporated, Burbank, California.

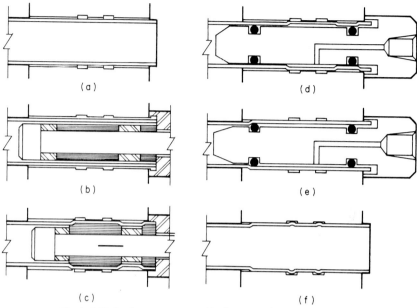

(a)

(b)

(c)

(d)

(e)

(f)

Figure 4.13 Haskel HydroSwage system of hydroexpanding.

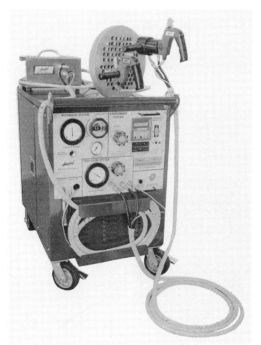

Figure 4.14 Main components of the Haskel HydroSwage system. (*Haskel Incorporated, Burbank, California.*)

1. The power supply
2. The intensifier assembly
3. The tube-lock tool
4. The control gun with attached flexible high-pressure capillary tubing
5. The hydraulic expanding mandrel and adapter
6. The leak-test tool

The power supply operates and controls the system. It has an air-pump-driven hydraulic pump designed for water operation. The hydraulic pump transfers water from a 5-gal (19-L) reservoir to an accumulator that stores 1 gal (3.8 L) of water under a constant pressure of 2000 lb/in^2 (13,790 kPa). The air pump requires a supply of 20 to 25 ft^3/min at 80 to 120 lb/in^2 (34 to 42.5 m^3/h at 550 to 825 kPa).

The pressurized water from the accumulator flows through a regulator to the intensifier pictured in Fig. 4.15. The intensifier increases the water pressure by a constant multiple; so regulating its input pressure sets its output pressure. The output-pressure control tolerance is ±500 lb/in^2 (3450 kPa).

The functions of the tube-lock tool, illustrated in Fig. 4.16, are (1) to adjust the tube-end position to a specified location below, flush with, or above the tubesheet face; (2) to set the tube so that there is no axial movement when the hydraulic mandrel is inserted; and (3) to flare the

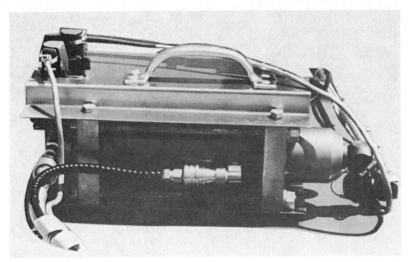

Figure 4.15 HydroSwage intensifier. (*Haskel Incorporated, Burbank, California.*)

Figure 4.16 Tube-lock tool with connected mandrel for fixing tubes in place. Connection is firm but not hydraulically tight. (*Haskel Incorporated, Burbank, California.*)

tube end slightly to facilitate inserting the hydraulic-expanding mandrel. It sets all the tube ends at precisely the same position relative to the outer tubesheet face.

The tube-lock tool's body is a hydraulic cylinder that has a piston to which a mandrel is connected. The mandrel consists of a body, which Haskel calls the anvil, through which a compression rod passes. The anvil bears against the tubesheet in the ligament space. It is recessed to accommodate tube-end protrusion. Tube axial position is set by inserting rings into the recess. Polyurethane segment rings, a steel compression washer, and a nut and steel washer are mounted on the compression rod.

Depressing a pushbutton on the tube-lock tool's handle actuates a solenoid valve. When it opens, water flows into the tool from the accumulator at the system's low-pressure side. This forces the piston to retract, pulling the compression rod with it, thereby forcing the outermost segment against the anvil and compressing the polyurethane segments. Under compression, the segments bulge radially and deform the tube end into firm contact with the hole. The end segment imparts the slight flair that eases inserting the hydroexpanding mandrel.

The tube-lock tool is light enough to be handled easily by one worker, who can set the tubes rapidly. It can be used at the same time that other tubes are being hydroexpanded.

Hydroexpanding is performed by using the control gun shown in

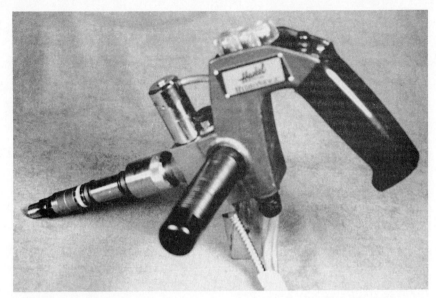

Figure 4.17 Haskel HydroSwage control gun and hydraulic mandrel. (*Haskel Incorporated, Burbank, California.*)

Fig. 4.17. Depressing a button on its handle releases high-pressure water from the intensifier into the high-pressure capillary tubing. The pressurized water travels into the mandrel, which injects it into the tube end. Amber and green signal lights are illuminated to indicate the start and finish of successful expanding. A red signal lights to indicate failure to achieve the preset expanding pressure. When the expanding cycle is complete, the pressure in the tube end is automatically relieved and the water is returned to the reservoir.

The period that pressurized water resides in the tube end (dwell time) is adjustable. This factor accommodates variations in the time it takes the tube-ligament combination to reach equilibrium. Residence time depends upon the dimensions and properties of the tube and tubesheet.

Figure 4.18 is a closeup of HydroSwage hydraulic-expanding mandrels. The end with the spring connects with the control gun. Figure 4.19 shows the HydroSwage mandrel set into a tubesheet that has

Figure 4.18 Hydraulic expanding mandrels. (*Haskel Incorporated, Burbank, California.*)

Figure 4.19 HydroSwage expanding mandrel in a sectioned tubesheet hole. (*Haskel Incorporated, Burbank, California.*)

been sectioned to reveal the positions of the O rings when pressure is applied. Under pressure, the O rings slide up the tapered ramps until they bear against the polyurethane backing rings. The left side of the photograph shows the adapter and collar with the spring fully compressed. The adapter's function is to facilitate connecting and disconnecting the mandrel to the gun. The collar's purposes are to align the mandrel with the tube and to fit it neatly during insertion.

The mandrel has two rubber O rings backed by segmented backup rings for support against the applied pressure. The sealing mechanism accepts a maximum tube ID enlargement of 0.040 in (1.02 mm). Only one application of hydraulic pressure is required for any tubesheet thickness. However, more time and care are required to insert long mandrels for expanding tubes into thick tubesheets and to fill the tube-end space than for thin or moderately thick tubesheets.

The degree of expanding is controlled by controlling the water pressure to the hydroexpanding mandrel. The Goodier and Schoessow work indicates that when the ratio of tubesheet to tube yield stresses is equal to or greater than 1, the expanding pressure should be set to about 115 percent of the actual tube yield stress. It also indicates that when the ratio of plate to tube yield stresses is less than 1, the pressure must be reduced.

For this purpose, Fig. 4.20 provides a simple way to select a suitable hydroexpanding pressure. It is a plot of the ratio of the inside to outside tube radius, a/b, versus the ratio of the plate to tube yield stress, σ_{yp}/σ_{yt}, at which expanding pressure equal to the tube plastic-limit stress may be applied without causing the pressure of the tube on the hole wall to exceed the tubesheet plastic-limit stress.

Note. For all thicknesses, the capability of producing strong expanded joints declines with the ratio of plate to tube yield stress. When the ratio is 0.6 or less, make pullout or pushout and tightness tests to evaluate the capability of any expanding process to produce acceptable joints.

Here is how to use the figure:

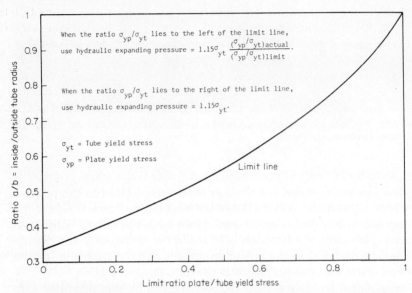

Figure 4.20 Ratio of the inside to outside tube radius versus the plate-to-tube-yield-limit ratio.

1. Calculate the ratio of the inside to outside tube radius, a/b.

2. Enter the figure at the left and move horizontally to the intersection with the curve (limit line).

3. Drop vertically to read the limit ratio of plate to tube yield stresses, σ_{yp}/σ_{yt}. This is the limiting ratio at which expanding pressure of $(2/\sqrt{3})\sigma_{yt}$ can be applied inside the tube without causing excessive plate deformation.

4. Calculate the actual ratio of σ_{yp}/σ_{yt} from mill-test reports of plate and tube yield stresses.

5. If the actual ratio σ_{yp}/σ_{yt} lies to the right of the limit-line value, the appropriate expanding pressure to produce maximum interfacial-fit pressure is $(2/\sqrt{3})\sigma_{yt}$ (= the tube plastic limit). This is the theoretical maximum pressure that can be applied without causing tube extrusion according to the Goodier and Schoessow analysis.

6. If the actual ratio σ_{yp}/σ_{yt} lies to the left of the limit-line value, the appropriate expanding pressure is

$$(2/\sqrt{3})\sigma_{yt}\,\frac{(\sigma_{yp}/\sigma_{yt})_{\text{actual}}}{(\sigma_{yp}/\sigma_{yt})_{\text{limit}}}$$

This reduces the pressure on the inside of the hole to $(2/\sqrt{3})\sigma_{yp}$ (= the plate plastic limit). This is the theoretical maximum pressure that can be applied by the tube exterior on the hole interior without causing tube extrusion according to the Goodier and Schoessow analysis.

The HydroSwage system includes the tube test tool pictured in Fig. 4.21. It is used to test hydraulic tightness in specimen joints and to facilitate adjusting the expanding pressure to that which will produce tight joints. The tool consists of a mandrel threaded at one end with a boss on the other. An O ring seals the mandrel OD to the tube specimen ID, while another O ring seals the boss to the outer tubesheet face at the ligament surrounding the tube.

To use the tool, hydroexpand approximately 6-in-long (152-mm-long) tube coupons from the production heat of tubing into a model of the production tubesheet that has identical physical properties, thickness, and holes. Insert the tool into the tube stub so that the boss and sealing O ring bear against the surrounding ligaments and the threaded end protrudes from the rear of the stub. Run the capture nut onto the mandrel and draw it up snugly. Fill the annular space with pressurized water from the system's low-pressure side, and examine the specimen for leaks at the rear face.

Alternatively, the stub may be hydroexpanded into the production tubesheet. This is feasible because expanding pressures that produce hydraulic tightness do not damage the ligaments. In either case, the specimens may be tested at pressures up to the low-pressure side's limit of 2000 lb/in^2 (13,790 kPa).

If the tube is expanded into the production tubesheet, after the test pull the stub and install the full-length tube. Before doing so, examine

Figure 4.21   HydroSwage tube test tool. (*Haskel Incorporated, Burbank, California; courtesy of* Chemical Engineering.)

the hole surface for axial scoring due to tube pulling and dress as necessary to remove scores.

In a variation of hydroexpanding termed *bladder expanding*, a bladder or bulb filled with pressurized water is inserted into the tube. This method has been used in retubing steam generators to seal the crevice behind front-face primary strength-welded joints. On the basis of a limited number of tests, bladder hydroexpanding appears to be most suitable when the tubesheet's elastic modulus is equal to or greater than that of the tubes.[17]

Tube recovery in hydroexpanding and tube rolling.   The process used in expanding affects tube recovery (springback). Both applying pressure uniformly, as in hydroexpanding, and applying bearing pressure cyclically, as in tube rolling, initially cause tube-end shortening and very modest tube-wall thinning as the tube is stretched outward. Plastic deformation is accompanied by some strain hardening, which resists tube recovery upon unloading.

For tube rolling, however, as resistance to expanding increases, the situation changes, especially after tube-hole contact. To visualize what happens, it helps to think of the tube and the surrounding metal, against which it bears, as a series of concentric shells in intimate contact. As a roll traverses the tube surface, it applies and then releases pressure to the inner surface of the innermost shell against which it bears. At any roll position, the exterior of the innermost shell applies somewhat less pressure to the next shell, and so on until the pressure is fully attenuated.

The magnitude of the pressure that the rolls apply depends upon the pressure applied by the mandrel. The residence time of the applied pressure at any location around the tube surface depends upon the rotational speed of the driver.

Depending upon the tube metal properties and the residence time, the radial stresses in successive shells vary from fully plastic at the innermost shell to fully elastic at some shell farther out. Radial plastic tensile stress at the exterior of the outermost-yielded shell is balanced by elastic compressive stress applied by the successive outer shells. After each passage of the rolls, the radius at which the stresses in inner and outer shells are in balance increases. For practical purposes, the boundary for applying plastic stress is the circle that circumscribes the adjacent ligaments.

As the surface under a roll is unloaded, the plastically deformed shells recover but not to the positions they held before the roll passed.

The initial contact pressure between the roll and the inner shell exceeds the tube metal's plastic limit because the initial contact width (hence the contact surface between roll and tube) is infinitesimally small. This high pressure causes the inner shells to extrude, which increases the tube length more than the initial shrinkage and further reduces the tube wall.

The metal in the extruded inner shells is strain-hardened much more than that in the successive shells, where bearing pressure does not exceed the plastic limit. [Reference 6 has figures (*a* and *b*) that show a difference in metal slip-line patterns between tubes expanded by applying pressure uniformly and by rolling.] This further counters the tendency of the tube to recover after passage of the rolls.

In contrast, when pressure is applied uniformly by hydroexpanding, after tube–hole-wall contact there is additional tube-end shortening and very modest further wall thinning. Springback after plastic tube deformation is resisted only by the uniform strain hardening of the plastically deformed shells.

Because of this difference, when the tube has a low elastic modulus and a high yield strength relative to the tubesheet, joints made in ungrooved tube holes may not be as tight or as strong as rolled joints. Satisfactory strength and tightness can be attained by providing suitable annular tube-hole grooves.

A consequence of tube rolling is that the cyclical loading and unloading of the tube end combined with the thinning that takes place tend to sensitize the tube to fatigue cracking. For this reason five-roll (and sometimes, in large-diameter tubes, seven-roll) expanders are used for expanding fatigue-sensitive, thin-walled, high-strength tubes.

Fatigue and tube-end thinning effects may be minimized by first hydroexpanding the tubes to make firm contact with the hole walls, then rolling at a torque considerably less than would be required for rolling only. This combination is called hybrid expanding.

Hybrid expanding.   In hybrid expanding, the initial hydroexpanding brings the tube into intimate contact with the hole wall in one application of pressure. This results in minimal general tube metal strain hardening. The subsequent working caused by rolling maintains joint strength and tightness without imposing excessive cycles of loading and unloading on the tube.[18,19]

Springback of tube ends after the release of pressure that has been applied uniformly can be measured experimentally. By comparing the springback with the interference required to produce an adequately strong joint, the feasibility of expanding can be assessed. Making such measurements can also help one decide whether to roll, hydroexpand, or hybrid-expand.

Effects of temperature on expanded joints. Frictional characteristics may differ in cold- and hot-expanded joints. An investigation of stainless-steel tubes hydroexpanded into steel tubesheets showed that in cold pullout tests, pullout force increased to a maximum, then dropped as contact surface was reduced due to tube movement. However, in hot tests pullout force varied in a repetitive sawtooth pattern typical of *stick-slip* friction, or galling.[20]

Despite very close or equal tube and plate thermal coefficients of expansion, creep at prolonged high-temperature operation may relieve the locked-in stresses upon which expanded joints depend for strength and tightness. This creep relief can occur within the *ASME Code*'s permitted metal temperatures. Therefore, limit joint operating temperature so that creep stresses are high enough to produce a creep rate low enough to provide long joint life.* Table 4.5 suggests temperature limits for strength-expanded joints with similar tube and tubesheet thermal coefficients of expansion. These arbitrary limits, chosen by considering creep-temperature curves, are based upon average temperature through the tubesheet thickness. When there is a large temperature difference between the tubesheet faces, the limits may not be suitable.

The situation is more complex when there is a substantial difference between the thermal expansion of the tubes and the tubesheet. The

TABLE 4.5 Suggested Temperature Limits for Expanded Tube-to-Tubesheet Joints with Similar Tube and Tubesheet Metals*

Material	Suggested limits	
	°F	°C
Low-carbon steel	700	370
5% Cr, ½% Mo, T-2	900	480
Stainless Type 304	1000	535
Stainless Type 316	1050	565
Stainless Type 347	1050	565
Nickel 200	600	315
Inconel 600	750	400
Incoloy 800	1025	550
Monel 400	750	400

*These suggested temperature limits are the lowest of the following three temperatures: (1) the first temperature at which the yield stress at temperature is no more than 90 percent of the creep stress that will produce 1 percent elongation in 100,000 h, (2) the temperature at which the yield stress–temperature curve exhibits a sharp decline, or (3) the maximum temperature permitted by Section VIII of the *ASME Code*.

---

*This discussion is based upon the author's as yet unpublished paper "Temperature Limits for Expanded Tube-to-Tubesheet Joints."

difference may result from disparate thermal expansion coefficients, differences in tube and tubesheet metal operating temperatures, or both. High thermal stresses may be generated when differential expansion is restrained as metal temperatures change from assembly to operating conditions.

When the tube plate expands more with temperature increase than the tubes, the interfacial pressure declines. The resulting loss of strength may be readily calculated. But when the tube expands more rapidly with temperature than the tubesheet, the situation is more complex. Here, there is a redistribution of stresses in the tube end and surrounding tubesheet metal. If the room-temperature expansion produced the theoretical maximum interfacial pressure between the tube and the hole wall, the effect of increasing temperature will be similar to that of overexpanding: the joint may become weaker at the operating temperature. For the purposes of the *ASME Code*'s Appendix A, the weakening is acceptable if the pullout strength at temperature is not reduced below the value that will permit the tubes to stay the tubesheets.

Pressure generated by thermal loading may be great enough to permanently set the tube end and ligaments. Expanded joints heated to and beyond this point may become so weak that after cooling the tubes may be pulled out by hand. An analysis and a computer model of expanded tube-to-tubesheet joints have been made to simulate temperature effects on joints made by uniform-pressure expanding.[21] They may be capable of being used to generate a curve of estimated pullout strength versus temperature and thus to establish a suitable temperature limit. However, it is more likely that some empirical limits will be established.

In a paper to be published, the author has developed a procedure for setting temperature limits that requires estimating the interfacial stress at the tube-tubesheet junction analytically or experimentally from pullout tests.

The paper suggests that when a joint becomes weaker because the tubesheet material expands with temperature more than the tube, the estimated interfacial stress be used to calculate the room-temperature tube deflection. The operating-temperature thermally caused deflection between the tube and the tubesheet may be calculated by using the tube dimensions, the tube and tubesheet thermal coefficients of expansion, and the operating temperature. The thermally caused deflection is deducted from the room-temperature deflection to give the net operating-temperature deflection. The fraction (net deflection at operating temperature)/(room-temperature deflection) is equal to the fraction (operating-temperature residual interfacial stress)/(room-temperature residual stress). Therefore, it may be used as a joint-temperature efficiency similar to other efficiencies now used in Appendix A for establishing permissible joint loads.

When the tube expands more with temperature than the tubesheet, the room-temperature equilibrium stress at the interface between the tube and the tubesheet is similarly estimated. The sum of room-temperature equilibrium stress and thermally imposed additional stress is compared with the lower of the tube and tubesheet stresses at which first yielding could be anticipated to occur in the tube or tubesheet. The temperature at which the sum of these interfacial stresses is equal to the lower of the tube or tubesheet stress first-yield stress may then be set as the limiting temperature.

It was stated above that it is not always necessary to expand so much that maximum interfacial pressure is developed. For the purpose of sealing crevices or stiffening tubesheets, it is necessary only to maintain tube-hole contact. To stay tubesheets the joint must be strong enough to meet the requirements of Appendix A. Therefore, when the tube thermal coefficient of expansion between operating and assembly temperatures is greater than that of the tubesheet, consider reducing rolling torque or expanding pressure just enough to meet the joint requirements. For joints that carry tubesheet loads to tubes used as stays, shear-load-test a series of specimens with progressively increased expanding torque or pressure until the minimum that will permit meeting Appendix A requirements is determined.

Surface finish. The *TEMA Standards* require tube holes to be free of burrs and to be given a workmanlike finish. The Heat Exchange Institute (HEI) *Standards for Closed Feedwater Heaters* require only that all burrs be removed from tube holes; the HEI *Standard for Power Plant Heat Exchangers* requires the holes to be smooth and burr-free; and the HEI *Standards for Steam Surface Condensers* specifies a hole finish of 500 root mean square (rms) for carbon steel and stainless-steel tubesheet holes and 250 rms for nonferrous tubesheet holes.[22–24]

Production tube-hole finishes range from somewhat smoother than 32 rms to the roughest permissible finish. The range of commercially supplied feedwater heater, heat exchanger, and condenser-tubing surface finishes is usually 60 to 100 rms. Boiler-tubing surface may be as rough as 125 rms.

Tube and hole surface finishes affect strength and tightness differently in roller-expanded and hydroexpanded joints. Usually rough tube holes yield strong rolled joints, and smooth holes yield tight ones. For rolling, rough finishes are acceptable when the tubesheets are hard and the tubes are thick-walled and soft, but for the reverse condition finer finishes are required for tightness.

Early investigators found that for rolled joints a threadlike finish increased joint strength over a smooth finish by as much as 35 percent.[25] On the basis of a limited number of tests of hydroexpanded joints, surface finish does not appear to be a factor in joint strength when the tubes and tubesheets are of different materials. However, when they are the same, improving the surface finish appears to improve the joint strength. (See Ref. 19.)

Annular grooves. Annular grooves are machined into tube holes in an effort to improve the expanded-joint strength and tightness. How the grooves affect the holding power and tightness of the joint depends upon a combination of these factors:

1. The number of grooves
2. The ratio of total groove width to total expanded depth
3. The groove depth
4. The tube diameter-to-thickness ratio
5. The tube and tubesheet yield strengths
6. The groove configuration
7. The degree of expanding pressure applied to the tube

In production, annular-groove dimensions for any configuration may vary substantially from the nominal dimensions and from hole to hole. Consequently, the effect of grooves on strength and tightness may vary from joint to joint.

The reduction of tube–hole-surface contact area caused by installing grooves may be significant in thin tubesheets. For example, two ⅛-in-wide (3.2-mm-wide) grooves in ¾-in-thick (19-mm-thick) tubesheets represent 40 percent of the available contact area based upon a ⅛-in (3.2-mm) setback of rolled region from the secondary tubesheet face. By comparison, the loss of contact area in the 1½- to 2-in (38.1- to 50.8-mm) expanded depth required to develop full joint strength is only 16.7 to 12.5 percent. Therefore, for thin tubesheets consider using only one groove or (for rolled joints) narrower grooves.

Optimum groove width depends upon the tube metal's capability to deform into the groove. In rolling, tube metal extrudes into the groove to form keys that approximate the groove shape. However, when tubes are expanded by uniform pressure, they bulge into the grooves in the arcuate shape shown in Fig. 4.22. Here, to be effective the tube metal

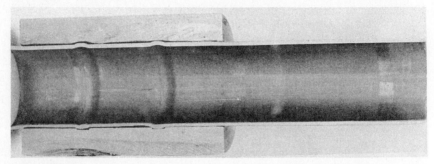

Figure 4.22 Specimen cross-sectioned to show arcuate shape of tube metal in grooves due to hydroexpanding. (*Haskel Incorporated, Burbank, California; courtesy of* Chemical Engineering.)

must bottom out in the groove. Therefore, different requirements apply to groove width and configuration for rolling and for uniform-pressure expanding.

Some of the many groove configurations that have been used with tube rolling are illustrated in Fig. 4.23. Widths vary from $1/16$ to $1/8$ in (1.6 to 3.2 mm). For most geometries and properties, one wide groove and two grooves half as wide, separated by a land, will increase holding power equally. However, two grooves increase tightness by providing more sealing points.

Multiple narrow grooves best enhance strength and tightness in rolled joints made between high-yield-strength, low-elastic-modulus thin-walled tubes. Such tubes extrude more readily into V-shaped and dish-shaped grooves. Wider grooves are more suitable for low-yield-strength, high-elastic-modulus thick-walled tubes. In general, low tube-to-tubesheet yield strength ratios increase groove effectiveness. Groove depth ranges from 0.010 to 0.025 in (0.25 to 0.64 mm). The standard TEMA and HEI configurations consist of two grooves $1/8$ in wide by $1/64$ in deep (3.2 mm wide by 0.4 mm deep).

For uniform-pressure expanding, the recommended groove configuration is rectangular. As the tube deforms into the groove, interference at the groove edges and bottom enhances tightness. Narrow grooves impede tube deformation and bottoming out, but when the grooves are too wide, contact pressure at the corners and bottom is reduced. Suitable groove widths are given for rubber expanding by Eq. (4.4).[26] Values of K varied from 1.5 to 3, with best results in the range from 2 to 2.25.

$$W = \frac{K\sqrt{Rt}}{\sqrt[4]{3(1 - \mu^2)}} \qquad (4.4)$$

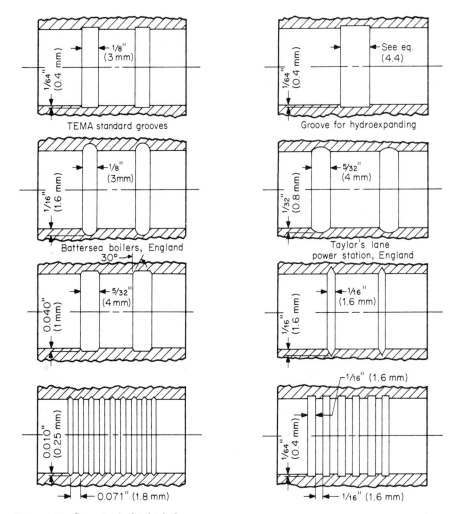

Figure 4.23 Some typical tube-hole grooves.

where W = groove width, in (mm)
  R = mean tube radius, in (mm)
  t = tube wall thickness, in (mm)
  μ = Poisson's constant

In Eq. (4.5), a value of 2.0 has been substituted for K and 0.3 for Poisson's constant. This equation was used to select groove width for hydroexpanding in the experimental evaluation of tube-to-tubesheet joint strengths of Ref. 19.

$$W = 1.56\sqrt{Rt} \qquad\qquad (4.5)$$

Grooves for rolled tubes need only be deep enough to prevent the extruded shear keys from slipping out; deeper grooves require excessive rolling. However, in uniform-pressure expanding the strength increase that grooves provide depends upon the shape of the metal bulged into the groove. Joint strength for rubber-expanded tubes increases approximately linearly with groove depth. The minimum recommended depth is 0.40 mm (about 1/64 in). (See Ref. 19.)

The TEMA and HEI standards specify that the grooves are to be placed in the base metal of clad tubesheets unless the purchaser specifies otherwise. Consider placing one groove in the cladding material when (1) cladding metal is integrally bonded to the base metal, (2) cladding-metal thickness is at least 1/2 in (12.7 mm), and (3) a leak of fluid from one side of the exchanger into the other would cause severe corrosion.

Axial tube extrusion tends to shear the keys formed when tube metal extrudes into rolled tube-joint grooves. For this reason, when tubes are to be rolled regressively into thick tubesheets, place the first groove about 1/2 in (12.7 mm) behind the front tubesheet face and subsequent grooves 1/4 to 1/2 in (6.4 to 12.7 mm) inward.

An early report on tests of the effects of grooves on roller-expanded boiler joints showed that, relative to ungrooved holes, there is a joint strength enhancement of 39 percent for one groove and 53 percent for two grooves. (See Ref. 26.) More recent investigations indicate that the increase in joint strength depends upon the degree of rolling (as measured by percent wall reduction), tube thickness, and tube and tubesheet properties.[27]

In rolling thin-walled, high-strength tubes of materials such as titanium and AL6X,* an investigation showed that one or two TEMA standard grooves increase joint strength very little. However, multiple narrow grooves were reported to increase strength by approximately 50 percent.[28]

Grooving tools. Tools for producing annular grooves consist of a tool holder and a cutting tool. The holder fits into a radial-drill chuck, and the cutting tool into the tool holder. A ball-bearing pilot presses against the tubesheet and guides the cutting tool into the hole. In adjustable tool holders, the groove position is located from the face of the tubesheet by a micrometer screw adjustment and locknut. In holders that are not adjustable, position is fixed by the tool dimensions.

As the drill spindle turns the tool holder, it feeds, forcing the holder against the pilot thrust bearing. Part of the reaction is resolved into force that moves the cutter radially. The recessing tool holder shown in Figs. 4.24 and 4.25 uses a dovetail slide to move the cutting tool.

---

*AL6X is a trademark of Allegheny-Ludlum Corporation, Breckenridge, Pennsylvania.

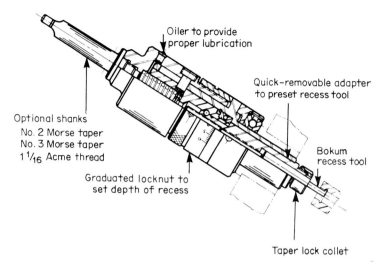

Figure 4.24 Bokumatic recess tool holder. (*Bokum Tool Company, Inc., Madison Heights, Michigan.*)

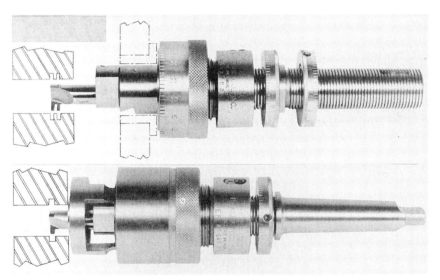

Figure 4.25 Bokumatic grooving tool holder. (*Bokum Tool Company, Inc., Madison Heights, Michigan.*)

After the holder makes contact with the tubesheet face, the tool moves by one-half of the feed distance with each revolution. Another type uses a rack and gear to adjust cutting-tool position and a ball-bearing pilot to center the tool in the hole.

Flaring and beading tube ends

Tube ends may be flared or beaded to enhance joint strength and tightness if pressure or thermal loads tend to push the tubesheet off the tube. They may also be beaded to provide weld joint preparation. Welded beaded joints are strong and tight under tensile and compressive loads. Flaring increases strength because the flared ends must be drawn down to their original dimensions for the tubes to pull out. Beaded ends must be sheared before the tubesheet will pull away from the tubes. Flaring and beading tighten the tube joint by interfering with the outer edge of the tube hole.

Tubes are sometimes flared in order to moderate fluid-flow entrance effects. Figure 4.26 shows an alternative configuration for this purpose. To produce the alternative configuration, expand the tubes flush with the front tubesheet face, then machine a smooth taper or radius from the bore of each tube to a point just short of the middle of the ligament.

Welded and brazed joints

The technology of welding and brazing tubes to tubesheets is highly advanced. Work is continually done to improve processes and techniques by such organizations as the American Welding Society (AWS), headquartered in Miami, Florida, and the New York–based Welding Research Council (WRC), by manufacturers of welding equip-

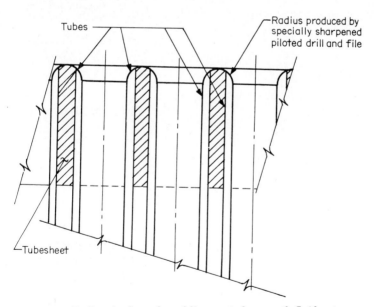

Figure 4.26   Radiused tube ends and ligaments for smooth fluid entry.

ment, and by fabricators. In addition to literature supplied by the AWS and manufacturers, the WRC issues progress, interpretive, and final reports in bulletin form on its work on new processes.[29–31] There is often confusion about what is meant by strength-welding and seal-welding tube-to-tubesheet joints. In *strength welding* the primary purpose is to produce a load-bearing joint; the joint's ability to carry a load depends upon its design. Of course, the joint must also be leaktight. The purpose of *seal welding* is only to seal the joint against leakage. Consequently, seal welding is used as a tightness backup for strength-expanded joints. Despite the fact that seal welding must be done by qualified welders using qualified welding procedures, no credit may be taken for any additional strength that seal welding confers on the tube-to-tubesheet joint.

Use welding, brazing, or welding and brazing in combination to join tubes to tubesheets under these conditions:

1. The joint operating metal temperature is high (welding only).

2. Operation is cyclical.

3. Joints must be very tight.

4. The dimensions and properties of the joint are unsuitable for expanding.

When considering tube-to-tubesheet welding, ask these questions:

1. Can the metals be successfully joined by welding or brazing?

2. What is the most suitable process?

3. Will preheat or postweld heat treatment be required? If so, how can it be accomplished, and how will it affect the exchanger?

4. Has a procedure been established, qualified, and used successfully?

5. How will the tube and tubesheet dimensions and hole layout affect the welding or brazing?

6. Will proximity of the channel barrel or pass partitions to tube holes interfere with producing sound joints?

7. Can the joints produced by the welding or brazing be examined nondestructively? If so, what nondestructive examinations can be used?

These questions cannot be answered independently of each other. Whether or not the metals can be brazed or welded is a question not only of metallurgy but also of the available processes and the tube and tubesheet dimensions and tube layout. For example, titanium tubes cannot be successfully fusion-welded to steel tubesheets but can be explosion-welded with good results. However, explosion welding is not feasible when the tube sheets are thin and the ligaments are narrow.

Exchanger size may affect procedure suitability. For example, the most advantageous position for tube-to-tubesheet welding is horizontal, but few shops can set large exchangers vertically to enable joining to be done in the horizontal position. Hence it may be impractical or too costly to use the most desirable position.

Brazed joints.   In brazing, the tube, hole, and braze metal assembly is heated to a temperature above 800°F (427°C). The nonferrous filler metal melts and flows into the space between the tube and the hole by capillary action. The base metals have higher melting points than the filler metal and therefore do not melt. Both the shellside and tubeside fluids must be compatible with the braze-metal deposit.

The maximum permissible operating temperature for brazed joints depends upon the filler metal as well as upon the base metals. The temperature limit in Section VIII, Division 1, of the ASME code for brazing procedures qualified under the *ASME Code*'s Section IX is 200°F (93°C). However, for some classifications of brazing filler metal, the limit may be raised to 300°F (149°C) if certain additional qualifications are met. Section VIII, Division 1, rules prohibit using brazed joints for lethal service and in unfired steam generators. Section VIII, Division 2, prohibits using brazing for strength-joining tubes to tubesheets.

Brazing requires a suitable flux or atmosphere or a flux-atmosphere combination to exclude atmospheric gases that can oxidize or embrittle the braze metal. Torch or furnace brazing processes may be used. Furnace brazing may be open-flame or closed-furnace. The joint design and brazing technique must ensure the flow of brazed metal into the space between the tube and the hole wall.

It is hard to see if braze metal has fully penetrated from the front tubesheet face into the space between the tube and the hole wall. However, if braze-metal rings are preplaced behind the tubesheet (secondary face), braze metal that has flowed to the front face (primary face) can be visually examined. The efficiencies for such joints listed in Appendix A of Section VIII, Division 1, of the *ASME Code* are higher than for those that cannot be visually examined.

Brazing from the secondary face forward also eliminates the crevice between the tube and the hole. For this reason, it may be done after the tubes have been strength-welded to the primary face. The shellside fluid must be compatible with the braze metal.

Cleanliness of the parts is essential for successful tube-to-tubesheet brazing. Any oil, grease, oxide scale, or foreign matter on the surfaces will cause porosity. Therefore, a cleaning procedure should be included as part of the brazing procedure specification.

Fusion-welded joints.   Most metallurgically bonded joints are made by fusion welding. In this kind of welding, a molten pool forms at the junction of the base metals. The pool consists of the base metals, any added filler, and elements that may be added in the welding flux. Upon cooling, the base metals and components provided in the welding flux form complex solid solutions. A brief summary of fusion-welding processes and their application to tube-to-tubesheet joints follows.

In oxy-fuel-gas welding (OFW), heat of fusion is supplied by burning a gas. In electric-resistance welding (ERW), a voltage gradient is applied to the parts, causing a current to flow against resistance, thereby developing heat of fusion. In electric-induction welding (EIW), current flow is induced in the parts and, flowing against their resistance, develops heat of fusion. In electron-beam welding (EBW), a guided stream of electrons is directed at the parts to generate heat of fusion.

None of these processes is suitable for production-welding tubes to tubesheets. OFW is sometimes used for difficult-to-reach, out-of-position tube joints, and EBW has been used successfully for special applications but not generally.

Metal arc-welding (MAW) processes are the most widely used to join tubes to tubesheets. In these processes, voltage is impressed across a small gap between an electrode and the tube-tubesheet assembly. Current flow as a result of the voltage drop across the gap produces an arc that generates enough heat to melt and fuse the tubesheet, tube end, and filler metal (if added). The current flow across the arc may be direct, with the electrode on the positive or negative side of the line, or it may be alternating. Alternating-current flow may be continuous or pulsed.

As the joint is traversed, the electrode is maintained at an appropriate arc-gap distance to produce a uniform cast-metal weld deposit. The electrode may be consumable or nonconsumable. Consumable electrodes melt into the weld puddle with the parent metals. Nonconsumable electrodes are used only as terminals for the arc. Unintended inclusions of metal from nonconsumable electrodes produce inferior welds. Nonconsumable electrodes may be used for autogenous welding, in which there is no filler metal and only the base metals are fused, and also when filler metal is added to the welding puddle. Filler metal may be fed continuously from spools of wire, at rates controlled to match welding speed, or hand-held wire rod may be fed manually into the arc. For some joints, it is advantageous to preplace filler-metal rings before striking the arc.

Metal-arc welds can be made with unshielded bare wire, but atmospheric gases tend to cause oxidization, embrittlement, and porosity. Therefore, fluxes or shielding gases are used to exclude air from the molten-metal pool. Fluxes may also contribute metal elements to the weld. Three metal-arc welding processes are used for tube-to-tubesheet joining:

1. Shielded-metal arc welding, or SMAW (or stick)

2. Gas-metal arc welding, or GMAW (or MIG, for metal–inert-gas)

3. Gas-tungsten arc welding, or GTAW (or TIG, for tungsten–inert-gas)

The joint configurations shown in Fig. 4.27a through d and k may be made by using any of these processes. The other configurations shown in Fig. 4.27 may be made only by the GTAW process.

Shielded-metal arc welding of tubes to tubesheets is done manually. Gas-tungsten arc welding and gas-metal arc welding may be performed either manually or automatically. In manual welding, weld quality depends upon the welding procedure and the welder's skill in following it. Skilled welders, performing manual welding, may be very successful in compensating for variable welding conditions. These could be current-supply fluctuations, stray magnetic fields in the work area, sloppy fit-up, and variations in metal compositions.

Automatic welding of tubes to tubesheets requires extremely precise control of joint geometry, fit-up, current supply, and ambient conditions. Weld quality and joint repeatability depend upon the system's ability to maintain the experimentally established weld parameters and upon operator training in setting up, operating, and monitoring the automatic system.

In using the shielded-metal arc process, the welder traverses the tube joint with the end of a flux-coated consumable metal electrode that is clamped in the jaws of a welding handle. Ligament widths, tube diameters, and thicknesses must be adequate for successful stick welding. The process is best used with thick-walled large-diameter tubes, in cases where automatic welding heads cannot fit, and for repairs.* It is not suitable as a general production process.

The largest number of welded tube-to-tubesheet joints is made by using the gas-tungsten arc-welding process. The nonconsumable electrode is usually thoriated tungsten. The weld is shielded by a blanket of inert gas (helium, argon, or mixtures). The gas flows at a controlled rate through an annular space between the electrode and the sur-

---

*Any tube-to-tubesheet weld repairs require scrupulous cleaning. However, some foreign matter always remains. SMAW is generally more forgiving of impurities than GTAW. Therefore, it is usually the best process for making such repairs.

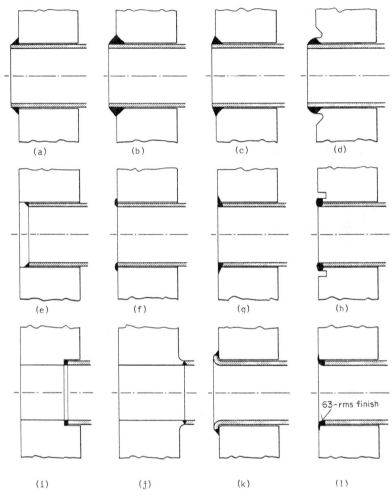

Figure 4.27   Some typical welded tube-to-tubesheet joints. (*Courtesy of* Chemical Engineering.)

rounding nozzle. The back side of the joint may also be blanketed with shielding gas. Great care must be taken not to let the electrode touch the weld puddle because tungsten inclusions embrittle the weld.

GTAW welds may be made autogenously or with filler metal and either manually or automatically. A variety of systems is available for automatically welding tubes to tubesheets by the GTAW process. Typical are the Orbitig* and Arc Machines Inc. systems.

The Orbitig system consists of a gas-tungsten arc-welding machine,

*Orbitig is a trademark of Hobart Bros. Co., Troy, Ohio.

Figure 4.28 Some weld configurations produced by the Hobart Orbitig system. (*Courtesy of Hobart Bros. Co., Troy, Ohio.*)

programmer, automatic tube-to-tubesheet welding head, and motor speed controller. The system automatically controls the flow of prepurge gas, shielding gas, and postpurge gas, wire feed rate, rotation speed, and weld current upslope, downslope, and pulsation. Various accessories are available to control the welding remotely, and record arc voltages, currents, and sequences. These are extremely valuable for establishing welding procedure specifications and controlling their application. Figure 4.28 shows a variety of weld configurations that can be produced by the Orbitig system.

Tubes can be joined to the front or rear tubesheet faces by the GTAW process. If tube-hole projections are forged on the rear face of the tubesheet, the tubes can be butt-welded to the projection.[32,33] When the tubes are welded to the back of the tubesheet, there are no crevices or root-bead notches, as with front-face welds. This eliminates potential sources of corrosion and fatigue failures. The perforations in the tubesheet are the same size as the tube ID. This increases ligament width above the width produced when the holes are drilled large enough to accept tube insertion. The wider ligaments increase tubesheet stiffness, hence decrease required tubesheet thickness. The disadvantage is that it is very difficult to fit the tubes to the forged stubs without offsets.

Kynex Corporation of Rome, New York, provides an on-site automatic tube-to-tubesheet joint-welding service for front- and back-face joints. Figure 4.29 shows its GTAW process gun for welding at or near

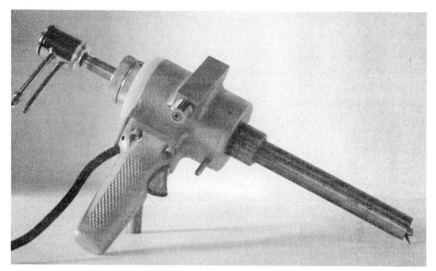

Figure 4.29 Kynex automatic gun for rear-face welding. (*Courtesy of Kynex Corporation, Rome, New York; courtesy of* Chemical Engineering.)

the back side of a tubesheet. Figure 4.30 shows the Kynex automatic welding gun for welding tubes to the front face.

Gas-metal arc welding is quick and inexpensive but may produce tube-joint welds with excessive porosity. It is most suitable for filet-welding large-diameter thick-walled tubes to the front tubesheet face.

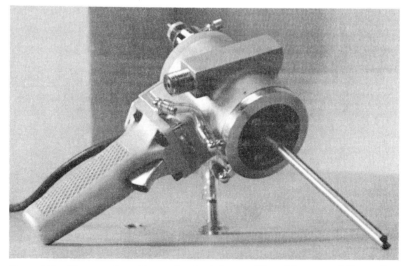

Figure 4.30 Kynex automatic gun for front-face welding. (*Courtesy of Kynex Corporation, Rome, New York; courtesy of* Chemical Engineering.)

The electrode may be solid wire or be a small tube filled with flux that contributes alloying elements to the weld.

Requirements of fusion-welded joints. These are the requirements of fusion-welded tube-to-tubesheet joints:

1. They must be fully fused, resistant to corrosion, and free of porosity, nonmetallic inclusions, and cracks.

2. They must resist hot and cold cracking, cracking resulting from restraint, and porosity from atmospheric gases in the weld puddle.

3. The thermal expansion coefficients of weld metal, tube, and tubesheet must be similar to prevent developing high thermal stress.

4. The heat-affected zone in the surrounding ligaments must be ductile after cooling.

5. The notch toughness of front-face filet welds must be high.

6. The joints must be mechanically reproducible, repairable by simple techniques, and capable of being inspected.

To fulfill these requirements, these conditions must prevail:

1. The weld wire, tube, and tubesheet metals must be compatible over a wide range of dilution.

2. The tube, tubesheet, and filler-metal melting points must be similar to ensure complete fusion.

3. The base-metal grain structure must be uniform.

4. The tube ends and holes must be *completely* free of foreign matter.

5. The environment must be clean and dry.

6. The flux on coated rods must be dry.

7. Shielding gas must be bone-dry.

8. Gases generated by welding must be able to escape the weld puddle.

9. The tube-tubesheet temperature must be kept nearly constant after welding begins.

10. Moisture must be excluded when welding is interrupted.

11. The voltage and current output of the welding source must be kept constant.

12. The welding area must be maintained free of stray magnetic fields.

When the tube-tubesheet pair cannot form tough, crack-free solutions, clad the tubesheet face, prior to drilling, with a metal compatible with the tubes. The cladding metal may be applied by roll or explosive cladding, or it may be deposited by fusion welding. Fusion-weld deposits must also be compatible with the tubesheet metal. For any of the processes, the bond between the cladding metal and the base metal should be examined ultrasonically for substantially the total area to make sure that there are substantially no discontinuities in the bond.

Fusion-weld cladding may be done manually or semiautomatically by GMAW or GTAW. SMAW is rarely used. In Chap. 3, Figs. 3.14 and 3.15 showed semiautomatic GTAW tubesheet cladding in which cladding wire is fed continuously through the shielding-gas nozzle. Figure 4.31 illustrates the more modern plasma cladding being applied to a head.

Cladding may be required even when the chemical compositions of

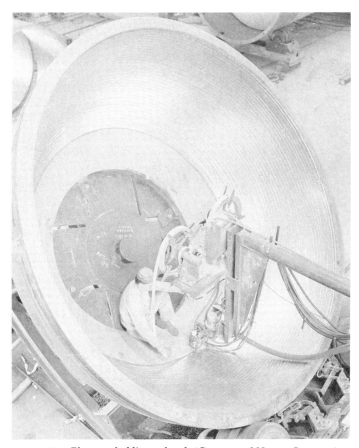

Figure 4.31 Plasma cladding a head. (*Courtesy of Nooter Corporation, St. Louis, Missouri.*)

tube, tubesheet, and weld metal are compatible.[34] The grain structure of tubesheets made from thick steel plates or forgings may vary across the surfaces. If a tube hole pierces the tubesheet where an unsatisfactory local condition exists, it can cause a faulty weld. This may occur at a spot where the local carbon content is too high to make a tough weld.

Consider what happens when carbon steel tubes are welded to forged-steel tubesheets. The tubesheet carbon content will be in the range from 0.17 to 0.35 percent, and the tube carbon content will be in the range from 0.25 to 0.33 percent. This combination will produce a fusion weld with a carbon content of 0.26 to 0.33 percent. Upon cooling the austenitic structure of the weld changes to a very hard, needlelike martensitic one. As a result, the heat-affected zone in the ligaments may become so hard that they fracture at the grain boundaries.

Low-carbon and austenitic stainless steels are unsatisfactory for fusion cladding such tubesheets because (1) at a low cooling rate, low-carbon cladding does not produce a ductile notch-tough heat-affected zone; (2) austenitic stainless-steel cladding requires very careful control of chemistry to inhibit hot cracking; and (3) austenitic stainless-steel cladding has a thermal expansion coefficient more than 25 percent greater than carbon steel. The most successful material is Inconel.* It is the material of choice because (1) its thermal coefficient of expansion is similar to that of carbon steel; (2) it has high tensile strength, ductility, and notch toughness; (3) its corrosion resistance is generally superior to that of carbon steel and the austenitic stainless steels; (4) the heat-affected-zone properties are the same as those of the unaffected regions; (5) there is no underbead cracking; (6) it has good erosion resistance; and (7) its melting point is similar to that of steel.

If the tube and tubesheet are not scrupulously cleaned before welding and maintained clean during welding, there will be weld porosity at best and complete joint failure at worst. Be sure that any weld procedure for joining tubes to tubesheets requires mechanical cleaning of the tube ends, followed by thorough washing with a volatile, chloride-ion-free solvent and filtered-air drying. To assure the quality of the joints, this should be a quality control hold-and-witness point.

Ordinarily, clean untreated atmospheric air is a suitable welding environment, but for some metal pairs the work area must be surrounded by uniform-temperature, controlled-humidity filtered air. For this reason shops that specialize in titanium welding may be completely air-conditioned. Alternatively, welding may be performed in a

---

*Inconel is a trademark of International Nickel Corporation, Huntington, West Virginia.

special room under a slight positive pressure of suitable atmosphere (clean room) or in a housing that surrounds the tubesheet with the appropriate atmosphere.

The consumables—weld rods and shielding gases—must be dry. In evaluating a shop's capability of making sound tube-to-tubesheet welds, make certain that it is standard shop practice to store opened containers of flux-coated rods in moisture-excluding ovens. On the working floor, opened packages of loose rods ought to be held in portable rod warmers. Note also that before a cylinder of shielding gas is connected to the welding apparatus, it should be tested for dryness with a moisture-sensitive paste.

If the gases produced by fusion welding cannot freely escape from the weld puddle, the tube-joint welds may be porous and predisposed to cracking. When joints using the geometries shown in Fig. 4.27 are to be made at the front face of the tubesheet, the tubes must be fixed in place before welding. To do this, they may be tack-welded, or a drift pin may be used to expand the tube ends into line contact with the hole edge. Tack welds must be capable of being fused into the finished welds. Drift-pin setting may split the tube ends.

The ends may also be lightly expanded into the holes. The advantage of preexpanding is that it reduces the weld root gap, making filet welds less subject to root-bead cracking.

Tubes may be preexpanded by rolling or by using a device like the previously described Haskel tube-lock tool. Two disadvantages of prerolling are that (1) it does not allow an escape path for welding-generated gases at the weld root and (2) it may introduce foreign matter to the surfaces to be welded. (If a lubricant is used in rolling, it causes weld porosity; if rolling is done dry, the rolls, cage, and taper mandrel may flake, providing a source of inclusions.) The tube-lock tool does not have these disadvantages.

Benefits of using the tube-lock tool to preexpand are:

1. It introduces no foreign matter.

2. Because it does not make a hydraulically tight connection, it makes it possible to use shielding gas behind the tubesheet and allows welding-generated gases to escape.

3. It does not harden or split the tube ends.

If the tubesheet temperature varies widely during welding, the size of the root opening will vary somewhat from joint to joint because of the different amounts of expansion. As welding heat spreads throughout the tubesheet, the holes deviate from roundness. The amount by which they recover depends upon the change in the radial temperature gradient. As the welds solidify, they shrink. This further distorts the holes near the joint being made. To reduce the amount of distortion, keep the tubesheet at a uniform temperature.

When welding is interrupted, it is advisable to warm the tubesheet before restarting. Restart warming is separate from preheating and postweld heat treating, which serve different purposes. The restart warming helps to dispel condensation moisture. When welding is interrupted for a long time, condensation moisture may settle in the unwelded joints. It can make subsequent welds porous when the moisture vaporizes. Good practice is to put a cloth bag of desiccant in a plastic wrapping around the assembly.

Although it may not be noticeable, line voltage fluctuates. The variations may change current and arc-gap length and cause unseen changes in weld penetration and metal deposits. For best results use a voltage regulator on the supply to the welding machine.

Shops are full of stray magnetic fields (often generated by neatly coiled leads of welding cable). External magnetic fields add to the effect of arc blow (a deflection of welding current in direct-current welding that is caused by variation of magnetic flux in the workpiece). Arc blow may cause skips and uneven tube-joint welds.

The reliability of fusion welds also depends upon the joint design. Major factors to consider are leak path and weld strength. Design practice for front-face welds is to set filet-weld thickness through the throat to some percent of tube wall thickness. The minimum weld throat thickness depends upon the failure mode that is acceptable for the service of the heat exchanger. Tube-to-tubesheet joints may be designed to be as strong as the tube in resisting axial loads, to accept stresses within the restrictions of the *ASME Code*, or to provide a minimum leak path.

The terms *seal weld* and *strength weld* applied to welded tube-to-tubesheet joint tightness and strength are widely used but loosely defined. Many people concerned with such joining hold the opinion that the weld can only be considered to be a strength weld if it is as strong as the tube. This implies that only the configurations shown in Fig. 4.27b, c, d, i, and j are capable of producing strength welds. With enough passes and addition of filler metal, Fig. 4.27g might also be included. An alternative opinion is that strength welds are welds of welded-only tube-to-tubesheet joints that are acceptable by the criteria of Appendix A of Section VIII, Division 1, of the *ASME Code*.

For tightness, the leak path through the weld throat should be at least as long as the tube wall thickness. A requirement for qualifying welding procedures for Section III of the *ASME Code* (the nuclear code) is that specimen welds be metallographically sectioned and examined at 10 × magnification for leak paths equal to at least two-thirds of the tube wall thickness.

The joint design should allow the basic weld configuration to be replicated easily. Furthermore, because there are so many joints in an exchanger that it is likely that some will fail on test or during the life of the exchanger, joint geometry should permit repairing. The joints should be designed so that the finished welds can sustain loads at all conditions including cycling.

For joint designs for high-pressure exchangers or those in nuclear or other hazardous service consider also the following (see Ref. 35):

1. Joint weld stress due to tubesheet flexure
2. Interactions between the tubes and tubesheet resulting from differential thermal expansion
3. Residual welding stress
4. Effects of tube expanding before and after welding

Explosively welded joints.   When the tube and tubesheet metals are not compatible for fusion welding but the tightness and strength of welded joints are desired, consider explosive welding (EXW). The AWS defines explosive welding as "a solid-state welding process wherein coalescence is effected by a high-velocity controlled detonation." (See Ref. 30.)

There are three requirements for explosive welding: (1) the two components must be progressively brought together to produce a collision front that traverses the surfaces to be joined, (2) the velocity of the collision front must not exceed 120 percent of the sonic velocity of the materials, and (3) the pressure created at the interface must be several times the yield strength of the materials to be joined.[35]

When these conditions are met, the component surfaces become molten at the collision front. The molten metal, together with any surface contaminants, is propelled before the collision front in the form of a jet. The jet is ejected from the interface at the tube end. Upon passage of the jet, the cleaned surfaces, which are in contact under high pressure, diffuse into each other to form a metallurgical bond. Any tube projection is severed at the tubesheet face.

The bond interface has the shape of a sinusoidal wave. This prevents complete molten-metal ejection because some is entrapped in the vortices associated with the wave peaks and troughs.

Although the velocity front must not exceed 120 percent of sonic velocity, explosives that produce a higher velocity front are cheap and easy to handle. They may be used by making an angular-joint preparation. Figure 4.32 is a schematic representation of the process. The tube hole, tapered outward toward the front face of the tubesheet, makes an angle with the tube. When the explosion is detonated near

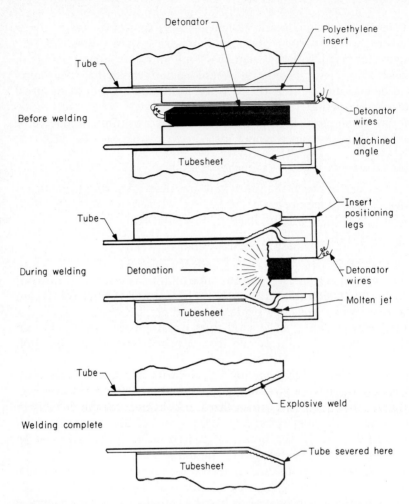

Figure 4.32 Schematic of explosive tube-to-tubesheet welding. (*Adapted from R. C. Hardwick, "Methods for Fabricating and Plugging of Tube-to-Tubesheet Joints by Explosive Welding,"* Welding Journal, *April 1975; courtesy of* Chemical Engineering.)

the junction of the tube and the untapered part of the hole, the blast makes the tube collide with the hole. The distance that the tube must travel to the collision point is progressively greater along the tube because of the taper. This reduces the collision-point velocity below the detonation velocity and makes it possible to use high-velocity-front explosives.

The increasing gap between the tube and the hole limits the surface area that can be welded. However, this is acceptable because enough welded surface can be attained to achieve full weld strength.

The depth of the countersunk taper is usually ½ to ⅝ in (12.7 to 16 mm). The angle used lies between 10 and 20°. High angles produce larger wavelengths than do smaller ones, and this causes less jet-metal entrapment at the interface. Therefore, high angles are used when the combination of molten tube and tubesheet materials produces a brittle intermetallic. However, when the ligament is small, the angle must be reduced in order to machine less metal out of the ligament. A compromise must be made between the geometry and metal requirements.

The tube wall thickness mainly governs the ligament thickness needed to avoid deforming the hole. Because thick tubes accelerate more slowly than thin ones, they need higher charges to reach the collision velocity required for explosive welding. If the tube-wall mass, accelerated to this velocity, distorts the ligament, the collision pressure will be reduced.

This may be partially circumvented by putting tapered plug supports in adjacent unwelded holes. Another expedient is to reduce the tube wall in the region of the joint. Tube wall thicknesses versus ligament widths for unsupported and supported ligaments have been experimentally determined and tabulated. (See Ref. 36.)

Figure 4.33 is a photograph of a cross section of an explosively welded tube-to-tubesheet joint.

Inspecting brazed and welded joints. The configuration of brazed and front-face fusion-welded joints restricts the capability to perform significant nondestructive tests. However, an experienced welding in-

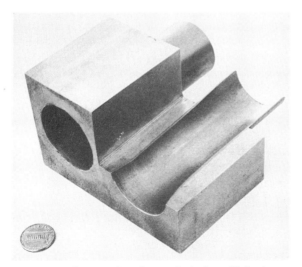

Figure 4.33 Cross section of an explosively welded tube-to-tubesheet joint. (*Courtesy of Explosive Fabricators, Inc., Louisville, Colorado; courtesy of* Chemical Engineering.)

spector, using a strong light and a magnifying lens, can detect most surface flaws. Properly done fluid-penetrant examination can reveal surface porosity and cracks that might not be found visually. Neither visual inspection nor fluid-penetrant examination will disclose the presence of subsurface porosity, inclusion, or cracks. Nevertheless, they are important because (1) surface defects reasonably may be assumed to indicate internal defects and (2) these checks are simple to do.

Tube-to-tubesheet joint weld metal in which surface defects have been found should be removed until sound metal is found. Before attempting a repair, take extreme measures to make sure that the parts are cleaned meticulously. After visual examination with the magnifying lens under bright illumination has disclosed no visible evidence of foreign matter, clean the surfaces with at least three washes of distilled or demineralized water. Follow this with three solvent washes and clean-air drying. Acetone has been used successfully. However, it is highly flammable and exposure to its vapors is undesirable; use it carefully.

Joints made by welding tubes to the rear tubesheet face have been successfully radiographed.[36] Placing the film and source in the nest of tubes is difficult. There is also greater complexity in interpreting the radiographs than there is in isolated butt-welded pipe joints. Filet welds have also been radiographed for defects with some limited success.

Butt-welded tube-tubesheet joints made internally, socket-welded joints, and explosively welded joints can be examined ultrasonically. Interpretation requires preparing models with standard discontinuities for comparison.

Inner surfaces of internal and rear-face welded joints may be examined visually with optical devices.

Combining joining methods

The benefits of preweld expanding and the precautions to take have already been discussed. The heat of welding may relax the equilibrium stress at the tube–hole-wall boundary. When the joints are heat-treated after welding, preweld-expanded tubes will also relax.

For primary joints made by welding at the front tubesheet face, postweld expanding confers these benefits:

1. The crevice between the tube and the hole is closed. For eliminating crevice corrosion, this is preferable to joint configurations that have enlarged holes in the tubesheet behind the part welded to the tubes.

2. The effective perforation diameter is reduced to the tube ID. This

increases the tubesheet stiffness and load-bearing capacity, provided that firm contact is always maintained between the tube and the hole wall.

3. The interference between the tube and the hole reduces discontinuity flexural stress between the tube and the tubesheet.

4. The possibility of weld joint fatigue is minimized.

However, if the tube and the tubesheet have different linear coefficients of thermal expansion and the operating temperature is high, the restraint created by expanding will impose thermal stress on the weld.

It may be difficult to expand after welding because weld metal may overlap the tube end. Deal with this problem by reaming out excess metal at the tube mouth. If weld shrinkage reduces the tube ID at the joint so that it is hard to insert an expander, open the tube end with a drift pin.

In straight-tube exchangers, different joining methods may be used at each end. One alternative is to strength-weld the tubes to one tube sheet and strength-expand them to the other. This is suitable when one end operates at a high temperature and the other end is cool and also for some fluid environments. Another combination is roller expanding at one end and hydroexpanding at the other. With this combination, it may be possible to neutralize axial loads on the tubes due to tube joining.

Joints can be made by combining expanding with gasketing.[37] Figure 4.34 is a photograph of a section through such a joint in an explosively clad tubesheet. To make this joint, the hole was prepared by machining an annular groove into the base metal and another into the alloy cladding. The grooves were somewhat deeper than the TEMA standard depth but not so deep as to substantially decrease ligament thickness. A temperature-resistant silicone rubber gasket was inserted into the grooves. The tube ends were cleaned free of oxide and all foreign matter and rolled into the holes.

Figure 4.34 Expanded and gasketed joint. (*Courtesy of Explosive Fabricators, Inc., Louisville, Colorado; courtesy of* Chemical Engineering.)

The application shown in Fig. 4.34 was for joining high-strength, thin-walled, low-elastic-modulus tubes to low-strength, high-elastic-modulus tubesheets. With this kind of joint, the tubes cannot be assumed to stiffen or support the tubesheet. A modification of this combination is to use O-ring grooves and O rings at one end of a straight-tube unit while fixing the other end (by welding, expanding, or a combination of welding and expanding). Each tube may then float individually to accommodate differential expansion between adjacent tubes.

Failures in tube-to-tubesheet joints

Most failures occur in the region of the rear face of the tubesheet. That is where most tubes are anchored to the tubesheet and where they receive bending and torsional loads. Tubes may also fail in this area if they are subjected to shell-flow-induced vibration.

When tubes are expanded into the holes, there is a transition from the expanded diameter to the original diameter near the back face. Stress in the tube varies from compressive to tensile in and beyond the transition zone, sensitizing the tubes to stress-corrosion cracking behind the tubesheet. This occurs whether the holes are standard or special close-fitting and with all types of expanding.

When fluid enters the tubes, entrance friction may, in addition to creating pressure drop, cause washing away of welds and erosion of tube ends (feathering). In addition, because the fluid regime does not stabilize for a distance of 10 to 20 tube diameters, there may be enhancement of tube-end erosion-corrosion. Expanding may compound this effect because of the reduction of flow area as the stream emerges from the expanded to the unexpanded region.

In thin-walled tubes, an error in expanding technique, in which the tubes are inadvertently expanded beyond the rear tubesheet face, may lead to cracking.

Excessive columnar loads on the tubes created by forward step rolling may contribute to tube breakage in the region of the transition zone.

Inside the tube, failures may result from work hardening and fatigue. Outside, tubes joined only by welding may undergo crevice corrosion.

When austenitic tubes are fusion-welded to tubesheets, there may be precipitation of complex carbides in the heat-affected zone behind the weld. An atmosphere that the austenitic stainless steel ordinarily resists may corrode this zone.

When a tube-tubesheet welding procedure requires preheat or postweld heat treatment, the emplacement of thermocouples to control temperature is critical to avoid distortion and undesired metallurgical changes. Improper placement may be the hidden cause of failures due to the distortion and altered metal structure.

Front-face fusion welds probably fail more from localized stress than from axial loading.[38] This is true because (1) the tubesheets flex under load, intensifying the stress in the ligaments; (2) residual stress due to weld cooling can approach the yield stress of the weld metal, and when added to the operational stress, the residual stress can provide the energy level for crack propagation; and (3) if the tube is not expanded into the tubesheet after welding, there is free relative deformation between tubes and tubesheets due to expansion and contraction.

There is a high probability of undetected flaws in filet-welded joints. Failure may occur because of large gas pockets that are either open to the surface or covered by a thin membrane. This porosity may be caused by lubricants used in prerolling, or the tubes may not have been sufficiently cleansed of drawing lubricants, oxides, or protective coatings. Nearly surgical cleanliness is required to prevent porosity.

Steels that are incompletely deoxidized may cause blowholes. For this reason, it is a good practice to machine the oxide coating off the tube ends and abrasively clean the tube exteriors and hole interiors just before welding. Blowholes may also be caused by inadequate welding technique that permits introducing nonmetallic inclusions or that allows burning through at the tube wall.

Buried porosity, weld shrinkage, fatigue, and corrosion fatigue cause cracks in the weld that propagate into the tube and tubesheet. Weld shrinkage stresses can initiate cracking in fissure- or crack-sensitive materials. All filet-weld designs have exposed roots in which cracks can be caused by improper weld composition, heat-affected-zone hardening, hot cracking in all metal combinations, and aftercooling cracking in carbon steel.

In closed feedwater heaters, filet welds may fail by propagation of a leak path from the root notch at the steam side through the tube to the feedwater side despite the feedwater pressure's being far higher than the steam pressure. The failures are attributable to fatigue or brittle fracture.

Crack failure paths are at the fusion line of weld metal to base-metal junctions and along the weld grain boundaries. The boundary between weld metal and parent metal may be the weakest link in the joint, especially with different tube-tubesheet thermal expansion coefficients. Tube-wall cracks propagate normal to the wall; cracks in fissure-sensitive materials propagate along the weld grain boundaries.

Summary

Pay careful attention to the design and production of tube-to-tubesheet joints because their functions are essential and the consequences of failure are dire.

Make adequate tests of tightness and strength, considering the differences between test conditions and operating conditions.

Be sure that manufacturing procedures and the personnel who use them are qualified.

Relate the kind of joint, manufacturing processes, testing, and nondestructive examinations to the unit's service. Consider the size and shape of an exchanger when selecting a joint design and joining method. Consider that the way in which the joints are made affects the overall structure of the exchanger.

To produce acceptable joints, cleanliness and faithful adherence to qualified procedures are essential.

Pay special attention to the part of the joint where the tube emerges from the rear face of the tubesheet because it is the most likely place for failures to occur.

Bibliography

Further information on expanded joints may be found in the following:

Burgess, N. T.: "Welding of Tubes to Tube Plates," report on select conference held at Hove, England, in October 1962, published by Institute of Welding, London, 1963.

Burndige, K. S., E. J. Glavanek, H. Phillips, and E. J. Lachner: "Innovations in Carbon-Steel Tubed Heater Design, Fabrication and Operation," Pap. 66-WA/Pwr-6, ASME Winter Annual Meeting, 1966.

Fisher, F. F., and G. J. Brown: "Tube Expanding and Related Subjects," Trans. ASME, July 1943, pp. 563–575.

Grimison, E. D., and G. H. Lee: "Experimental Investigations of Tube Expanding," Trans. ASME, July 1953, pp. 497–505.

Impaglizzo, A. M.: "Tube-to-Tubesheet Attachment Welds," ASME Pap. 68-PVP-16, September 1968.

Patriarca, P., G. M. Slaughter, and W. D. Manley: "Heat Exchanger Fabrication," Weld. J., vol. 36, no. 12, December 1957, pp. 1172–1178.

Sebald, J., and L. H. Hawthorne: "Mechanical Effects Resulting from Copper-Base Alloy Tubes to Tubesheets," Power, March 1958.

Slaughter, G. M., Franco Ferreira, and P. Patriarca: "Welding and Brazing of High-Temperature Radiators and Heat Exchangers," Weld. J., January 1968.

Ujiie, A., J. Nagata, and J. Kobayashi: Problems on the Seal-Welding of Heat Exchangers, Kobe Technical Institute, Technical Headquarters, Mitsubishi Heavy Industries, Ltd., September 1968.

References

1. For the analysis of sea water, see H. U. Sverdrup, M. W. Johnson, and R. H. Fleming, The Ocean, Prentice-Hall, New York, 1942.

2. *ASME Boiler and Pressure Vessel Code*, Section V: *Nondestructive Testing*, 1986 ed., American Society of Mechanical Engineers, New York. (New editions are published at 3-year intervals.)
3. S. Yokell, "Calculation of Interference Required to Produce Maximum Strength in Expanded Tube-to-Tubesheet Joints," ASME Pap. 87-JPGC-Pwr-24, presented at Joint Power Generation Conference, Miami, October 1987.
4. *Standards of the Tubular Exchanger Manufacturers Association*, 7th ed., The Tubular Exchanger Manufacturers Association, Tarrytown, N.Y., 1988.
5. J. N. Goodier and G. J. Schoessow, "The Holding Power and Hydraulic Tightness of Expanded Tube Joints: Analysis of the Stress and Deformation," *Trans. ASME*, July 1943.
6. G. Sachs, "Note on the Tightness of Expanded Tube Joints," *J. Appl. Mech.*, December 1947, pp. A-285–286.
7. A. Nadai, "Theory of Expanding Boiler and Condenser Tube Joints through Rolling," *Trans. ASME*, 1943.
8. K. Urigami, M. Sugino, S. Urushibata, T. Kodama, and Y. Fujiwara, "Experimental Residual Stress Analysis of Tube-to-Tubesheet Joints during Expansion," ASME Pap. 82-PVP-61, 1982.
9. A. I. Soler and K. P. Singh, *Mechanical Design of Heat Exchangers and Pressure Vessel Components*, Arcturus Publishers, Cherry Hill, N.J., 1984.
10. A. Nadai, *Plasticity*, McGraw-Hill Book Company, New York, 1931.
11. F. F. Dudley, "Electronic-Control Method for the Precision Expanding of Tubes," *Trans. ASME*, May 1951, pp. 577–584.
12. F. F. Fisher and E. T. Cope, "Automatic Uniform Rolling-In of Small Tubes," *Trans. ASME*, 1974, pp. 53–60.
13. I. Berman and J. W. Schroeder, "Detnaform at Power Plant Installations," Sixth International Conference on High-Energy Rate Fabrication, Essen, Germany, Sept. 12–16, 1977.
14. H. Krips and M. Podhorsky, "Hydraulic Expansion—A New Method for the Anchoring of Tubes," *VGB Kraftwerkstechnik (Federal Republic of Germany)*, vol. 56, no. 7.
15. H. Krips and M. Podhorsky, "Hydraulic Expansion of Tubes," *VGB Kraftwerkstechnik (Federal Republic of Germany)*, no. 1, 1979.
16. S. Yokell, "Hydroexpanding: The Current State of the Art," Pap. 82-JPGC-Pwr-1, presented at Joint Power Generation Conference, Denver, October 1982.
17. S. Roy, "In-Situ Retubing of Steam Generators," *Conf. Proc., Maintenance Welding in Nuclear Power Plants/III*, Knoxville, Tenn., Nov. 6–8, 1985.
18. M. W. Jawad, E. J. Clarkin, and R. E. Schessler, "Evaluation of Tube-to-Tubesheet Junctions," presented at 1986 Pressure Vessels and Piping Conference and Exhibition, Chicago, July 20–24, 1986.
19. K. Uragami, M. Sugino, S. Urushibata, T. Kodama, and Y. Fujiwara, "Experimental Residual Stress Analysis of Tube-to-Tubesheet Joints during Expansion," ASME Pap. P82-PVP-61, 1982.
20. D. A. Scott, G. A. Wolgemuth, and J. A. Aiken, "Hydraulically Expanded Tube-to-Tubesheet Joints," *Trans. ASME*, vol. 186, February 1984, pp. 104–109.
21. A. I. Soler and Xu Hong, "Analysis of Tube-Tubesheet Joint Including Thermal Loading," *J. Press. Ves. Technol.*, 1984.
22. *Standards for Closed Feedwater Heaters*, 4th ed., The Heat Exchange Institute, Cleveland, August 1984.
23. *Standard for Power Plant Heat Exchangers*, 1st ed., The Heat Exchange Institute, Cleveland, 1980; Addendum 1, 1984.
24. *Standards for Steam Surface Condensers*, 8th ed., The Heat Exchange Institute, Cleveland, January 1984.
25. C. A. Maxwell, "Practical Aspects of Making Expanded Joints," *Trans. ASME*, July 1943, pp. 507–514.
26. Yoshitomi et al., U.S. Patent 4,142,581, Mar. 6, 1979.
27. C. J. Gaffoglio and E. M. Thiele, Jr., "Tube to Tubesheet Joint Strengths," ASME Pap. 81-JPGC-Pwr-7, presented at Joint Power Generation Conference, St. Louis, October 1981.

28. K. H. Haslinger and E. D. Hewitt, "Leak Tight, High Strength Joints for Corrosion Resistant Condenser Tubing," ASME Pap. 81-JPGC-Pwr-7, October 1983.
29. *The Welding Handbook*, 5 vols., 7th ed., ed. by W. H. Kearns, The American Welding Society, Miami.
30. *Procedure Handbook of Arc Welding Design & Practice*, 12th ed., The Lincoln Electric Company, Cleveland. (Reprinted annually.)
31. *Welding Journal*, The American Welding Society, Miami. (Published monthly.)
32. E. W. Rowlands, Jr., and J. C. Cooksey, "Internal Welding of Tubes to Tubesheets," *Weld. J.*, July 1960.
33. H. Schwartzbart, "In-Bore Gas-Tungsten Arc Welding of Steam Generator Tube-to-Tubesheet Joints," *Weld. J.*, March 1981.
34. E. B. Norris, P. D. Watson, and R. D. Wylie, "Considerations in Design of Tube-to-Tubesheet Joints in High-Temperature Heat Exchange Equipment," ASME Pap. 68-PVP-11, September 1968.
35. R. C. Hardwick, "Methods for Fabricating and Plugging of Tube-to-Tubesheet Joints by Explosive Welding," *Weld. J.*, April 1975.
36. B. E. Foster and R. W. McClung, "A Study of X-Ray and Isotopic Techniques for Boreside Radiography of Tube-to-Tubesheet Welds," *Mater. Eval.*, vol. 35, no. 7, 1977, p. 43. (Description of a new technique.)
37. R. C. Hardwick, "Tube-to-Tubeplate Welding and Plugging by Explosives," Pap. 40, presented at Symposium on Welding and Fabrication in the Nuclear Industry of the British Nuclear Engineering Society, London, 1979.
38. A. Lohmeir and S. D. Reynolds, Jr., "Carbon-Steel, Feedwater-Heater Tube-to-Tube-Sheet Joints," ASME Pap. 65-WA/PWE-10, August 1965.

5

Tubeside Construction

Introduction

This chapter discusses how the tubeside is built. It examines tubeside pass arrangements, distribution of tubes among the passes, tube pitches, and tube counts. It has guidelines for choosing among fixed-tubesheet, U-tube, and floating-head designs that consider process and maintenance advantages and disadvantages.

The chapter surveys the benefits and drawbacks of the options available for pass arrangements and tube layout patterns. It provides guidance for specifying configurations of channels, bonnets, and return covers that relates construction details to appropriate uses. After addressing pass-partition and nozzle fabrication, it closes with a discussion of the attachments of channels to the bundle and shell.

Tubeside Pass Arrangements

Number of passes

Thermal and mechanical design and manufacturing constraints determine the number of tubeside and shellside passes. Because these considerations are interdependent, shell and tube pass counts are selected in conjunction with each other.

The work of thermal and mechanical heat exchanger designers is also intertwined. They must deal with these factors to determine the number of passes on each side:

1. Service

2. Duty

3. Terminal temperatures

4. Heat transfer paths

5. Quantities flowing

6. Tubeside flow velocity criteria

7. Shellside impingement protection and vibration constraints

6. Available pressure drops

7. Tube distribution requirements

8. Space requirements

9. Pass-to-pass temperature restrictions

10. Venting and draining requirements

The literature on process and mechanical heat-exchanger rating and design is vast*; this chapter covers only manufacturing constraints, tube distribution, and pass-to-pass temperature restrictions.

With some exceptions, tubular exchangers for oil refining and petrochemical production are limited to 8 tubeside passes; those in chemical production seldom exceed 10. The practical upper limit is 16. Exchanger manufacturers base their limits upon workers' abilities to fit the pass partitions into the available space and the bolting and flange design required to yield the gasket pass-partition ribs.

These depend upon:

1. The shell diameter

2. The combination of front- and rear-head types

3. The depth of the heads

4. The inlet- and outlet-nozzle size and arrangement

5. Whether the tubes are expanded or welded into the tubesheets

6. The properties of the gasket material, which must be suitable for the intended use

There must be enough space to fit and weld the pass partitions to (1) the barrels of TEMA Type A and L channels, (2) the barrels and heads of TEMA Type B and M bonnets, (3) the barrels and tubesheets of TEMA Type C and N channels, and (4) each other at their intersections. The shell diameter and the channel or bonnet barrel depth determine whether there is enough room. The choice of front- and rear-head combinations listed in Table 5.1 affects how the pass partitions are sealed to the tubesheets.

---

*Three significant works are D. Q. Kern, *Process Heat Transfer*, McGraw-Hill Book Company, New York, 1950; *Heat Exchanger Design Handbook*, Hemisphere Publishing, New York (five regularly updated volumes); and A. I. Soler and K. P. Singh, *Mechanical Design of Heat Exchangers and Pressure Vessel Components*, Arcturus Publishers, Cherry Hill, N.J., 1984.

TABLE 5.1   28 TEMA Front- and Rear-Head Combinations in
Ascending Order of Cost

1. B–U	2. N–U	3. C–U	4. A–U
5. D–U	6. N–N	7. B–M	8. A–M
9. A–L	10. N–W	11. C–W	12. B–W
13. A–W	14. N–P	15. C–P	16. B–P
17. A–P	18. N–T	19. C–T	20. B–T
21. A–T	22. D–T	23. N–S	24. C–S
25. B–S	26. A–S	27. D–S	28. D–T

Nozzles of the size required for flow which enter axially or tangentially may not fit into the inlet and outlet compartments. As detailed below, nozzle reinforcements may be as much as twice the nozzle IDs. This may make the channel or bonnet barrel depth too long to weld the pass partitions fully to the barrel or integral end closure.

For expanding tubes into tubesheets and for maintenance reexpanding, there must be enough clearance to insert the expanding tool between the peripheral tubes in each compartment and the compartment walls formed by the pass partitions. In addition, when the channel or bonnet is integral with the tubesheet, space for the expanding tool is required between the peripheral tubes and the inside of the channel or bonnet barrel.

The pass partitions must fit between the tubes in adjacent rows. The room that must be allowed depends upon the type of head-to-tubesheet seal and the kind of tube-to-tubesheet joint. For plain- and raised-face gasketed flange-to-tubesheet joints, there need be only sufficient space for the gasket ribs and partitions to fit. (As explained below, pass partitions wider than gasket ribs may be tapered to a width equal to or less than the gasket-rib width.)

If the tubes are to be expanded into the tube holes, allow a minimum of $1/16$ in (approximately 1.6 mm) plus the gasket-rib width. When the tubes are to be joined to the tubesheets by welding, the welds must not overlap the gasket surfaces. The space required for gasket ribs and partition plates depends upon the weld joint design. If the tube end is set below the tubesheet face and filet-welded to the hole, allow the same clearance as for expanded tubes. For all outside filet-welded joints, where the thickness through the weld root is equal to the tube wall thickness, allow a minimum of $1/16$ in (approximately 1.6 mm) more than the gasket-rib width plus 2.8 times the tube wall thickness. For external filet-weld designs with weld leg widths equal to the tube wall thickness, allow a minimum of $1/16$ in (approximately 1.6 mm) more than the gasket-rib width plus 2 times the tube wall thickness.

When pass partitions are welded to tubesheets, it is not acceptable for the welds to overlap the tube-to-tubesheet welds. Therefore, it is necessary to consider the pass-partition-to-tubesheet weld joints. Figure 5.1 illustrates two kinds. The full-penetration flat weld is by far preferable to the filet-weld configuration. Except for special designs, API Standard 660 for refinery exchangers requires welding from both sides or full-penetration welds.[1] For either type, the minimum clearances required are as follows:

1. For expanded and inside filet-welded tube-to-tubesheet connections, twice the pass-partition width

2. For outside filet-welded connections with root widths equal to tube walls, 1/16 in (approximately 1.6 mm) plus twice the pass-partition width plus 2.8 times the tube wall thickness

3. For those with filet-welded joints that have leg widths equal to the tube wall, 1/16 in (approximately 1.6 mm) plus twice the pass-partition plate width plus twice the tube wall thickness

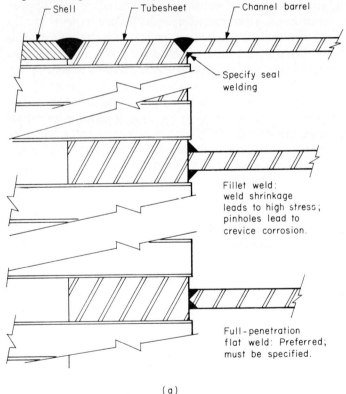

(a)

Figure 5.1   Welds of pass partitions to barrels and tubesheets and of barrels to tubesheets.

During manufacture of TEMA Types C and N, welded tube-to-tubesheet joints may be made before the bonnets or channels and pass partitions are attached. This permits all the welds to be made automatically as described in Chap. 4. However, after the channel barrel and pass partitions have been welded to the tubesheet, repairs to tube-to-tubesheet welds of tubes adjacent to the barrel and the pass partitions can only be made manually.

The initial tightness of a flanged joint that seals the heads and gasketed pass partitions to the tubesheet depends upon gasket properties and flange design. The load applied by bolting up must be adequate to yield the ring of gasket that closes the connection and to make it flow into surface irregularities. To prevent pass-partition bypassing it must also be able to deform similarly the gasket ribs under the pass partitions. The flange and the mating part must be capable of transmitting these forces to the gasket without becoming overstressed. To distribute the bolt load uniformly on the gasket surfaces, the structure must be rigid.

Operating tightness depends upon the gasket's resiliency. The gasket must continue to seal when applied internal pressure tends to separate the mating parts. To maintain a seal, it may also have to accommodate differential expansion between the bolting and the flange-tubesheet assembly. Flange bolting may not be sufficient to yield the gasket ribs, and the structure may not be stiff enough to transmit adequately the bolt load from bolts on the bolt circle to the gasket ribs. Therefore, stud bolts that fit through holes in the channel cover or bonnet head are sometimes installed to contribute additional compression. A gasket surface that seals the penetration must be provided.

Pass layouts

Figures 5.2*a* and *b* schematically illustrate typical tubeside pass layouts for ribbon, quadrant, pie, and mixed flow. Straight-tube units have heads at the inlet end and the outlet or return end. In U-tube exchangers the bend takes the place of the return head. The arrow with a clear circle at its tail indicates flow from the inlet to the outlet of an odd-number pass; the arrow with a solid circle indicates return flow of an even-number pass. As indicated, flow may be ribbon, quadrant, or mixed.

Ribbon-flow layouts. In ribbon flow, the fluid travels through each pass in parallel with a plane through the axial centerline. Flow-through tubes of two-pass exchangers use ribbon flow. The pass partitions for multipass ribbon flow are parallel with each other. The hottest and coldest passes are at opposite segments of the tubesheet, and

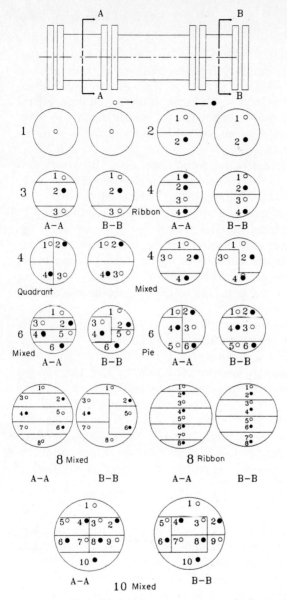

Figure 5.2a Typical tubeside pass arrangements for straight tubes.

the next hottest and next coldest passes border the hottest and coldest passes respectively, and so on. The stress in the tubesheet due to the difference in thermal expansion between the tubesheet material at the inlet and outlet segments is distributed more or less uniformly across the tubesheet from the inlet segment to the outlet segment. Consequently, ribbon flow is advantageous when there is a long tubeside temperature range because there is the least thermal stress. However, it may be difficult or impossible to achieve an acceptable balance of the pass tube counts.

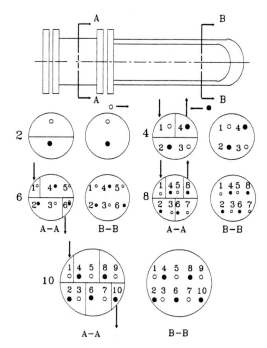

Figure 5.2b Typical tubeside pass arrangement for U tubes.

The centerlines of the tubeside inlet and outlet connections may be set radially, tangentially, or anywhere between. If set axially, they may be located 180° apart. This facilitates designing for fully venting and draining the heads.

Quadrant-flow layouts.   Quadrant flow applies to a four-pass arrangement in which the inlet-end head is constructed with a full-diameter pass partition located on one main centerline and a half-diameter pass partition located on the perpendicular main centerline. In straight-tube exchangers the return head has a full-diameter pass partition in the same plane as the inlet-end half-diameter partition plate. As Fig. 5.2 shows, this arrangement divides the tube field into four quadrants. Inlet and outlet nozzles in the channel or bonnet barrel cannot enter radially, while those that enter axially cannot be set 180° apart from each other. The off-center nozzle arrangement makes it difficult to vent or drain the heads of horizontal units. Figure 5.3 is a view during construction of pass partitions in a modified quadrant arrangement. Here the long partition has been dropped below the centerline to balance the pass counts. Figure 5.4 illustrates the nozzle placement.

Quadrant layouts are the least desirable flow arrangement for tubesheet thermal stress because the hottest and coldest passes are juxtaposed.

Figure 5.3   Bonnet with modified quadrant arrangement of pass partitions. (*Atlas Industrial Manufacturing Company, Clifton, New Jersey.*)

Pie-flow layouts.   Pie layouts are similar to quadrant layouts except that there are more than four passes. The problems with nozzle position and head venting and draining are the same as with quadrant layouts. Pie layouts are not as unfavorable for wide tubeside temperature ranges as quadrant layouts but are less desirable than ribbon or mixed-flow layouts.

Mixed-flow layouts.   Mixed flow, illustrated in Fig. 5.2, makes it possible to use radial inlet and outlet nozzles, separate the inlet and outlet passes nearly as well as in ribbon flow, and achieve a reasonable balance of the pass tube counts. However, the temperature distribution across the tubesheet is not as good from the thermal-stress standpoint as ribbon flow.

The heads can be arranged for complete draining and venting.

Tube Distribution

Except when the inlet pass is dedicated to desuperheating vapor entering the tubes or the outlet pass to subcooling exiting condensate, try to distribute the tubes so that the count in each pass is the total

Figure 5.4 Nozzle placement in barrel of bonnet with modified quadrant arrangement. (*Atlas Industrial Manufacturing Company, Clifton, New Jersey.*)

tube count divided by the number of passes. Geometry seldom permits attaining this ideal, and therefore some deviation must be lived with. The acceptable variance depends upon the thermal design correlations used.

The effect on the thermal design will usually be within the limits of the flow–thermal design correlations if the difference between the largest and the smallest pass tube counts does not exceed 5 percent of the average pass tube count. A less stringent, more frequently used rule of thumb is to allow a deviation of 5 percent from the average of the number of tubes in the passes with the most and fewest tubes. This is essentially a deviation of ±5 percent from the mean. The requirement for shellside impingement protection may make balancing the tube counts in the passes difficult. Frequently it leads to asymmetrical layouts.

Tube Pitches and Counts

The most common drilling pitch patterns are triangular and square. As illustrated in Fig. 5.5, in triangular configurations shell fluid may flow into the apex of the equilateral triangle (triangular pitch) or enter parallel with the base (rotated triangular pitch); square pitch patterns may have shell fluid flowing perpendicularly to the side of the

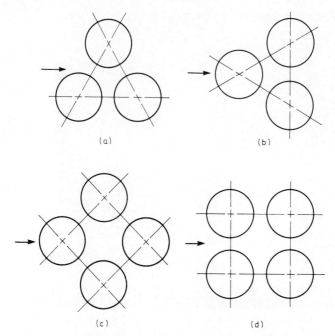

Figure 5.5 Drilling pitch patterns. (*a*) Rotated triangular pitch. (*b*) Triangular pitch. (*c*) Rotated square pitch. (*d*) Square pitch.

square (square pitch) or on the diagonal (rotated square pitch). Tubes in steam surface condensers and in some unusual tubular exchanger designs may be laid out on radial pitch. For these layouts, the pitch distances may be variable. Steam surface condenser tubes have also been arranged on concentric circles with varying pitch distances.

Tubes installed on square pitches are accessible for external cleaning mechanically or hydraulically. The pitch should be great enough to provide a cleaning lane at least ¼ in (6.4 mm) wide. The outsides of tubes arranged on a triangular pitch cannot be cleaned mechanically unless the pitch is great enough to create cleaning lanes approximately ¼ in (6.4 mm) wide. They can be hydraulically cleaned with somewhat narrower cleaning lanes, but the pitch must be spread enough for the high-pressure water to make contact with the fouled surfaces. Spread triangular pitch arrangements are rare. Their use can be justified only for process reasons, never just to achieve cleanability.

Pitch distance is most frequently 1¼ times the tube diameter. This allows just enough ligament for tube joining. It is the minimum permitted by the *TEMA Standards*.[2] The HEI power plant standard follows this practice except for ⅜-in (9.5-mm) tubes, for which the minimum acceptable pitch is ½ in (12.7 mm).[3]

The *TEMA Standards* provide tables of tubesheet ligaments and recommended thickest tube gauges. The tabulated minimum ligament widths are based upon a tolerance not exceeding the sum of twice the drill-drift tolerance plus 0.020 in (0.508 mm) for tubes of less than ⅝-in (15.9-mm) OD and 0.030 in (0.762 mm) for larger-diameter tubes. The drill-drift tolerance is 0.0016 times tubesheet thickness in tube diameters in inches (0.04064 times tubesheet thickness in tube diameters in millimeters). (See Chap. 3 for a discussion of drill drift.)

When the tubes are very small, the ligament becomes so thin that tube rolling may not be successful. However, hydraulic expanding has worked with small-diameter tubes thicker than those recommended in the *TEMA Standards*. Grooving small-diameter tube holes is impractical unless the pitch is increased. For example, if the tube holes for ¼-in-OD (6.35-mm-OD) tubes were to be grooved to the standard TEMA depth of 1/64 in (0.4 mm), 25 percent of the 1/16-in (1.59-mm) minimum ligament width would be removed at the groove locations. The HEI power plant standard recommends increasing the pitch above the listed minima for grooved holes for tubes ½ in (12.7 mm) and smaller.

In selecting the appropriate pitch, designers consider mechanical practicality and available head or pressure drop, then balance first costs and pumping costs.

The limiting circle to which the peripheral tubes may be tangent was defined in Chap. 1 as the outer tube limit (OTL); the limiting circle on which the centers of peripheral tubes may lie was defined as the outer tube center (OTC). Typical OTLs are listed for normal-pipe-size (NPS) pipe shells in Table 5.2. Suggested minimum clearances between OTLs and rolled-plate shell IDs are given in Table 5.3.

The largest number of tubes can fit into a layout with a given OTL when the tubes are arranged on the minimum permissible triangular pitch; the smallest number, when they are on square pitch. Consequently, triangular pitch arrangements are the least expensive per unit of heat transfer surface.

The larger the pitch distance, the fewer the tubes that can be carried in a given pattern. The surface in an exchanger of a specific size and length increases linearly with the number of tubes. Assuming uniform tube distribution, for a specific shellside flow-baffle arrangement and shell size, shell-flow turbulence increases exponentially with the tube count. The shellside heat transfer film coefficient and pressure drop increase accordingly.

Tube counts are established by making geometric layouts that (1)

TABLE 5.2   Typical OTLs for NPS Pipe Sizes, in*

NPS size	Shell OD	Shell ID	Fixed tubesheet and U tube	Outside-packed floating-head device	Floating head with backing device
5	5.625	5.047	4.625	4.1875	4.9375
6	6.625	6.065	5.625	5.1875	4.9375
8	8.625	8.071	7.625	7.1875	6.9375
10	10.75	10.02	9.5625	9.1562	8.9062
12	12.75	12.09	11.6562	10.9688	10.9688
14	14	13.375	12.9375	11.875	12.25
16	16	15.25	14.8125	13.75	14.125
18	18	17.25	16.8125	15.75	16.125
20	20	19.25	18.8125	17.5	18.125
22	22	21.25	10.8125	19.5	20.125
24	24	23	22.5625	21.25	21.625

*OTL = outer tube limit.

TABLE 5.3   Minimum Clearance between Shell ID and OTL for Rolled-Plate Shells*

For rolled-plate shells the OTL is the shell ID less the following minimum clearances.

Fixed tubesheet and U tube		Outside-packed floating head		Floating head with backing device	
in	mm	in	mm	in	mm
0.5	12.7	2.0625	52.4	1.4375	36.5

*OTL = outer tube limit.

disburse the tubes as uniformly as possible throughout the tube field, (2) allow space for pass partitions, (3) drop out tubes to allow for shellside impingement protection, and (4) allow space for suitable tie rods and spacer locations. Manually making layout drawings to find out how many circles of one diameter can fit into a larger-diameter circle, at the same time allowing for various impediments, can be inaccurate, tedious, and time-consuming. To investigate fully for a suitable layout with the maximum number of tubes, single-pass layouts must be made with the apices of pitch triangles or corners of squares set on and also astraddle the main centerlines. Multiple-pass layouts must examine the tube count in each pass with tubes on center and straddling centerlines.

Commercially available computer thermal-mechanical design programs* for optimizing exchanger size, passes, and tube counts es-

---

*For example, the programs of B-Jac Computer Services, Inc., of Midlothian, Virginia.

tablish optimal layouts for each iteration of the optimization path. The programs may be used to generate tapes of the final layouts for use with numerically controlled drilling machines. As with all computer output, judgment must be applied.

Good practice for tubesheet layout drawings is to show the OTL or OTC. It also requires (1) detailing the bolt-hole drilling template when there are bolt holes, (2) indicating the positions of all tube-hole and tie-rod locations, (3) showing the site of impingement protection, and (4) showing where cross-flow baffles or semisupports are cut off. Most computer-generated drawings produced by thermal-mechanical design programs provide this information.

For estimating purposes and for roughing out thermal and mechanical designs, several publications have tables of tube counts or offer mathematical ways to estimate how many small circles can fit into a larger one.[4,5] Some manufacturers publish tube count tables for the configurations that they construct.

Guidelines for Choosing Straight-Tube and U-Tube Designs[6-9]

In the strict order of this book, this chapter would discuss only tubeside considerations for selecting straight-tube or U-tube designs and shellside concerns would appear in the next chapter. However, because the sides are not independent of each other, there is some overlap in addressing the benefits and disadvantages of the various alternatives.

The basic conditions that determine whether to use a straight-tube or a U-tube design and for selecting a straight-tube configuration are that (1) the exchanger must be suitable for the process fluids that are to be transported, (2) it must be able to accommodate the modes of heat transfer and terminal temperature requirements, (3) it must be structurally suitable for the temperatures and pressures, and (4) it must require minimal maintenance. All other things being equal, it is logical to choose designs and configurations that have the lowest first cost.[10-13]

Straight-tube designs

The tubeside of straight-tube units can be arranged for single-pass flow and for even- or odd-number multipass flow. Straight tubes can be cleaned internally mechanically, hydraulically, or chemically or by combinations of these means. Their full length may be inspected internally by borescope and examined by eddy-current and ultrasonic means. Any straight tube with a clean exterior can be removed and replaced.

Manufacturers may purchase and stock standard tube lengths for straight-tube units. Frequently, they can design them with standard diameter, gauges, and lengths inventoried by users' maintenance departments.

A disadvantage, common to all but one of the straight-tube designs, is their inability to operate over large multipass tubeside temperature ranges. A large spread between tubeside inlet and outlet temperatures may produce interpass tube metal temperature differences great enough to create excessive stresses in the tubes, tube-to-tubesheet joints, and tubesheets. A rule of thumb frequently used to avoid such mechanical problems is to limit interpass tube metal temperature differences between adjacent passes to 50°F (approximately 28°C).[14] However, to guard truly against these effects, the loads and restraints must be analyzed.[15] For this purpose, the thermal designer must provide pass-to-pass temperature calculations. For single-pass shell–multipass tubes a relatively simple calculation may be used.[15]

The effects of the differentials depend upon the rigidity of the tubesheet and the tube and tube support geometry. The simplistic analysis that assumes rigid tubesheets can indicate when there is the potential for trouble. For tubesheets to which pass partitions are welded, for example, TEMA Types C and N, the assumption of rigidity (Ref. 15) is reasonably close to actuality. Tubesheets to which pass partitions are not welded should be investigated further, using an analysis that takes account of tubesheet flexibility. The problem can be surmounted by using two shells in series, each with half the number of passes that a single-shell design would have. This reduces the temperature range in each shell. Alternatively, use U-bend units where possible.

The tubeside of horizontal, vertical, and pitched straight-tube units can be completely drained and vented through appropriately located connections. Shellside venting and draining capability depends upon the straight-tube exchanger's configuration.

Fixed tubesheets. Fixed-tubesheet exchangers are the most common straight-tube constructions. The most frequent designs are those where the tubesheet is extended as a bolting flange (see Chap. 3). If the process requires the shellside construction material to be nonferrous, stainless-steel, high-alloy, or other costly material, there is a marked cost advantage of fixed-tubesheet over other straight-tube designs.

When tubeside flow is single-pass or odd-number multipass, fixed-tubesheet exchangers do not require stuffing boxes or seals at the tubeside connections. In contrast, U-tube units must have an even number of passes, and floating-head units with odd numbers of passes must have the tubeside inlet or outlet nozzle sealed by a stuffing box or bellows-type seal where it penetrates the shell cover.

Fixed-tubesheet exchangers are most suitable for use with nonfouling shellside fluids. Except for the seldom-used captive-gasket arrangement, there are no gaskets or packings between the shellside and the atmosphere. Therefore, fixed-tubesheet exchangers are the tightest of all of the configurations against shellside leaks to or from the atmosphere. This is important when (1) the shellside fluid is lethal, noxious, or highly inflammable; (2) a leak of hot shellside fluid could burn passersby or start a fire; and (3) the fluid in the shell must operate under high vacuum.

Access to both tube ends of a fixed-tubesheet exchanger requires only the opening of channel covers or removal of bonnets. Because the shell is integral with the tubesheets, test rings are not required for hydrostatic testing. However, as stated in Chap. 4, leaks through the tube-to-tubesheet joints from the tubeside to the shellside cannot be seen.

Fixed-tubesheet exchangers can readily be built with conventional or integral double tubesheets for services that require such construction.

If the exteriors of the tubes are clean, fixed-tubesheet units may be partially or fully retubed without cutting into the shell. However, more often than not, the shell must be detached from at least one tubesheet to permit full retubing.

There is no access to the shellside for inspection and maintenance. These are limited to what can be seen and done through existing openings or through windows opened by cutting into the shell and closed by welding the cutout into the opening.

The shellside can be cleaned only by chemical means or solvent washing. Chemical cleaning may corrode steel shellside parts of units tubed with high-alloy tubes, thereby drastically increasing baffle-shell and tube-hole clearances. These increases reduce the shellside film coefficient. Furthermore, enlarged tube holes increase the prospect of vibration damage to the tubes. If the tie rods and spacers corrode severely, the baffles and tube supports may shift position enough to destroy an exchanger's usefulness. Accordingly, a necessary precaution in designing for chemical cleaning is to select for the tube supports, baffles, tie rods, and spacers materials that resist corrosion by the cleaning agents or to allow for the corrosion of these parts.

The shell of a fixed-tubesheet exchanger must be fitted with an expansion joint that can accommodate the difference in axial expansion between the shell and the tubes, or the tubes, tubesheets, and tube-to-tubesheet joints must be designed to restrain it. (See Chap. 6 for a discussion of expansion joints.) This problem is intensified for units in cyclical operation.

For a specified tube count and pass arrangement, fixed-tubesheet exchangers require the smallest-diameter shell of all the configurations. Conversely, for a specified shell diameter the number of tubes that can fit into a shell of a given size is the greatest in fixed-tubesheet units. Therefore, they are the least expensive straight-tube configuration.

The dense packing of tubes in the shell may also be advantageous to thermal design and fluid flow because there is less opportunity for shellside fluid bypassing than for other arrangements. As in other designs, seal strips or other means are required to prevent bypassing in shellside pass-partition lanes. Fully packed shells allow no space for inlet and outlet impingement and erosion protection. (Provisions for such shielding are discussed in Chap. 6.) The outer-tube-limit circle (and clearance between peripheral tubes and the shell) is determined by (1) the minimum acceptable edge distance between the outermost baffle holes and baffle edges, (2) the lesser of the channel barrel or shell ID, and (3) the channel-barrel-to-tubesheet attachment.

Fewer straight legs of U tubes than tubes of fixed-tubesheet designs can fit into a given shell diameter because the minimum U-bend radius is approximately five tube diameters. Consequently, small fixed-tubesheet exchangers may be competitively priced with U-tube units despite their having two tubesheets and U-tube units having one. Table 5.4 compares the tube counts of fixed-tubesheet exchangers with the number of U-tube straight-leg lengths that can be contained in shell sizes 5 to 60 (English units) for $3/4$-in-OD (approximately 19-mm-OD) tubes arranged on $15/16$-in (23.8-mm) and 1-in (25.4-mm) triangular pitches.

The shellside of vertical fixed-tubesheet units can be fully vented only by piercing the top tubesheet with a vent connection that passes through the head or by drilling a hole from the underside partway through the tubesheet and a connecting hole from the tubesheet edge. (See Chap. 3 for an illustration of such vents.) When it is important to maintain the underside of the top tubesheet flooded, these openings may be connected to standpipes or a vertical diversion baffle may be attached to the uppermost cross-flow baffle. Complete shellside drainage requires similar arrangements for the bottom tubesheet.

TABLE 5.4   Comparison of Fixed-Tubesheet (FTS) Tube Counts with Numbers of U-Tube Straight Lengths

Shell ID		Tube count per straight tubes or straight legs of U tubes					
		Two-pass			Four-pass		
in	mm	FTS	U tube	Percent	FTS	U tube	Percent
3/4-in OD on 15/16-in Triangular Pitch (19-mm OD on 23.8-mm Triangular Pitch)							
5.047	128	14	6	42.9	12	4	33.3
6.065	154	20	14	70	16	8	50
7.981	203	48	32	66.7	36	24	66.7
10.02	254	76	56	73.7	68	52	76.5
12.00	305	114	92	80.7	100	80	80
13.25	337	140	114	81.4	128	104	86.7
15.25	387	196	166	84.7	176	148	84.1
17.25	438	252	220	87.3	234	204	87.2
19.25	489	326	290	89	302	268	88.7
21.25	540	397	360	90.7	376	340	90.4
23.25	591	480	440	91.7	460	420	91.3
25	635	558	506	90.7	530	488	92.1
27	686	661	614	92.9	632	580	91.8
29	737	773	720	93.1	736	684	92.9
31	787	875	830	94.9	858	804	93.7
33	838	1011	954	94.4	976	916	93.9
35	889	1137	1076	94.6	1098	1040	94.7
37	940	1277	1218	95.4	1242	1184	95.3
39	991	1425	1366	95.9	1386	1324	95.5
42	1067	1669	1600	95.9	1618	1552	95.9
45	1143	1912	1854	97	1878	1800	95.8
48	1219	2189	2122	96.9	2134	2064	96.7
51	1295	2489	2410	96.8	2432	2356	96.9
54	1372	2792	2732	97.9	2752	2664	96.8
60	1524	3477	3398	97.7	3414	3336	97.7
3/4-in OD on 1-in Triangular Pitch (19-mm OD on 25.4-mm Triangular Pitch)							
5.047	128	14	6	42.9	8	4	50
6.065	154	19	10	52.6	16	8	50
7.981	203	38	28	73.7	36	24	66.7
10.02	254	68	56	82.4	60	44	73.3
12.00	305	102	86	85.5	92	72	78.3
13.25	337	124	106	85.5	114	96	84.2
15.25	387	169	148	87.6	160	136	85
17.25	438	228	200	87.7	212	184	86.8
19.25	489	290	254	87.6	272	240	88.2
21.25	540	354	314	88.7	336	300	89.3
23.25	591	420	388	92.4	408	368	92
25	635	489	452	92.4	476	432	90.8
27	686	585	538	92	562	524	93.2
29	737	679	632	93.1	660	612	92.7
31	787	775	732	94.4	756	708	93.6
33	838	891	838	94.1	860	808	93.9

TABLE 5.4 Comparison of Fixed-Tubesheet (FTS) Tube Counts with Numbers of
U-Tube Straight Lengths (*Continued*)

Shell ID		Tube count per straight tubes or straight legs of U tubes					
		Two-pass			Four-pass		
in	mm	FTS	U tube	Percent	FTS	U tube	Percent
¾-in OD on 1-in Triangular Pitch (19-mm OD on 25.4-mm Triangular Pitch)							
35	889	1003	950	94.7	976	916	93.9
37	940	1134	1074	94.7	1090	1040	95.4
39	991	1259	1200	95.3	1222	1164	95.3
42	1067	1461	1406	96.2	1434	1364	95.1
45	1143	1693	1632	96.4	1650	1584	96
48	1219	1941	1879	96.8	1902	1832	96.3
51	1295	2187	2122	97	2134	2076	97.3
54	1372	2465	2396	97.2	2421	2340	96.7
60	1524	3069	2992	97.5	3010	2936	97.5

Floating-head exchangers. Tubesheet constructions for the several types of floating-head tubesheet designs were illustrated in Chap. 3. The advantages of floating-head designs are:

1. They can accommodate differences in axial expansion between the tubes and shell.

2. The bundles are removable.

3. Their shellsides can be cleaned mechanically or hydraulically by removing the bundle or chemically with the bundle in place; mechanical cleaning of bundle exteriors requires the tubes to be arranged with cleaning lanes of at least ¼ in (6.4 mm).

4. Their shells can be inspected, maintained, repaired, and altered without damage to the tubes.

5. Their bundles are replaceable.

6. Shell connections need not be broken to permit removal of a dirty or corroded bundle and replacement with a cleaned or new one.

7. Existing bundles with suitable remaining life may be fitted with new shells to replace ones that have corroded beyond repair.

8. One type can be constructed to permit each pass to float independently, thereby eliminating interpass temperature effects and allowing wide tubeside temperature ranges.

They have these drawbacks:

1. Hydrostatic testing may be much more complicated. In order to see the tube ends at the stationary tubesheet during shellside hydrostatic testing, the design must have a channel that remains in place

with its cover removed, or the stationary tubesheet must be designed to bolt to the stationary-end shell flange. If the front head is a bonnet (TEMA Type B) and the tubesheet OD extends only to the shell gasket OD, it must be held in place by a test fixture. Special test rings and fixtures may be required at the floating-head end.

2. The shellside of head-up vertical floating-head exchangers can be fully vented only through the stationary tubesheet. Either holes must be drilled from the underside to intersect with holes drilled from the periphery, or a vent pipe must be attached to a hole through the top tubesheet.

3. To ensure flooding of the underside of the stationary tubesheet, a standpipe arrangement or vertical baffle similar to those used with fixed-tubesheet exchangers is required.

5. The shellside of head-down vertical units can be fully drained only through the stationary tubesheet.

Double-tubesheet construction at the stationary end of floating-head exchangers presents no problem. The capability to use double tubesheets at the floating end depends upon the type of floating head.

Level control is extremely important when horizontal floating-head units are used as steam generators. If the upper rows of tubes are not submerged, the difference in metal temperature between the wet and dry tubes will cause the bundle to take a banana shape. Some tubes may buckle or be cut by the tube supports.

The following examines some of the uses, benefits, and shortcomings of the various floating-head types.

Internal floating head with backing device: TEMA Type S. Internal-floating-head-with-backing-device construction is used mostly in oil refineries and petrochemical plants for services in which carbon steel shellside materials are acceptable. Its disadvantages are:

1. Stainless-steel or high-alloy shellside materials increase the cost dramatically over fixed-tubesheet and U-tube constructions.

2. The shell cover must be removed to gain access to the floating head.

3. With few exceptions, the floating-tubesheet cover is sealed to the floating tubesheet by a bolted, gasketed joint. A leak in the seal between the return cover and the floating tubesheet permits the higher-pressure fluid to leak into the lower-pressure one; under some circumstances, the lower-pressure fluid can diffuse through the leak into the higher-pressure side. If, instead of a backing device, the floating-head cover is welded to the tubesheet, there is a positive seal, but the weld

joint must be ground flush with the tubesheet OD to permit bundle pulling and access to the tube ends requires cutting off the floating-head cover and subsequently rewelding it to the tubesheet.

4. Because the OD of the backing device must be larger than the shell diameter, the bundle cannot be removed nor can the tube ends at the floating tubesheet be seen without dismantling the shell cover and the return cover. For thermal design reasons the axial clearance between the backing device and the shell-cover flange is kept to the minimum that will permit insertion of a wrench. Therefore disassembly and reassembly are time-consuming and laborious, especially when the exchanger is installed outdoors and the temperature is below freezing.

5. To test the shellside hydrostatically, the shell and floating-head covers must be removed and replaced with a test fixture that seals the floating tubesheet to the shell.

6. It is impractical to use double-tubesheet construction at the floating end.

Pull-through internal floating head: TEMA Type T. Pull-through floating-head exchangers are used in the same industries as TEMA Type S. Their principal advantages are:

1. The bundle can be removed simply by unbolting the stationary-end channel, breaking the gasketed-tubesheet-to-shell-flange connection and pulling it out.

2. The shell cover may be made integral with the shell, thereby eliminating a costly flanged joint with its possibility of leakage. However, the shell cover may be made removable to provide access to the floating head.

3. The space surrounding the bundle is available for distribution of steam or vapors condensing in the shell.

4. The floating end may be constructed with individual tubesheets and closures to allow passes to float independently of each other.

5. The return cover may be welded to the tubesheet without concern for pulling clearance.

The drawbacks of pull-through units are:

1. Units with stainless-steel and other high-alloy shells are as costly as or more costly than those with backing devices.

2. Although the diametral floating-tubesheet-to-shell clearance is on the order of ¼ in (6.4 mm), the distance between the peripheral

tubes and the shell is considerable because of the space required for bolting on the return-cover flange.

3. Even the most elaborate sealing devices permit bundle bypassing.

4. The low velocity of the fluid in the annulus between the bundle and the shell contributes to shellside fouling. Because of this tendency, operating personnel tend to specify greater shell-fouling resistances than for other floating-head types. The consequent excess clean surface may require an initial turndown in the shell-flow rate. The ensuing reduced shell-flow velocity leads to more-rapid-than-anticipated fouling of the outside tube surfaces. The unit must then be shut down for cleaning at frequent intervals.

Maintenance personnel who have to do the cleaning may become insistent that, because the disassembly-reassembly is so frequent, units with backing devices should not be permitted. The problem may then be perpetuated.

5. To test the shellside hydrostatically, the shell and floating-head covers must be removed and replaced with a test fixture that seals the floating tubesheet to the shell.

6. It is impractical to use double-tubesheet construction at the floating end.

Outside-packed floating head: TEMA Type P.   Outer-skirt outside-packed-floating-head construction, which is the recommended TEMA configuration, was sketched in Fig. 3.5e. As an alternative, the skirt may be attached to the inner face of the tubesheet (inner-skirt construction). The advantage of TEMA Type P is that there are no internal gasketed joints that could permit leakage of one fluid into the other: leaks at the seals of the bundle to the shell and the floating-end head to the floating tubesheet are to the atmosphere.

These are some of the drawbacks:

1. Inner-skirt designs with bonnets require test fixtures for hydrostatic testing.

2. The shell connection at the stuffing-box end of inner-skirt designs must be forward of or below the stuffing box. If the shell inlet is at the stationary-tubesheet end, the shell can be fully vented only through the tubesheet and then with difficulty. It can be drained only through the inlet nozzle or the stationary tubesheet. Provision must also be made to avoid a dead spot around the tubes in the region of the skirt.

3. If the packing in the stuffing box is compressed too tightly, it acts as a brake on relative movement between the shell and the bundle.

This may impose excessive loads on the tubes, tubesheets, and tube-to-tubesheet connections. Customarily the joint is permitted to leak in order to avoid such loads and to lubricate the packing.

As a result, some shell fluid must leak to the atmosphere when the shell is under positive pressure, and when it is under vacuum, air must leak into the shell.

4. If the gland follower nuts are not tightened uniformly, the follower cocks and gouges the skirt.

5. The surface on the skirt must be finished to 63 rms for sealing. This requirement adds to the cost and makes it necessary to protect the skirt when pulling or reinstalling the bundle and to make sure it is not gouged or scratched.

6. It may be very hard to reexpand tubes in outer-skirt designs because the cover end of the skirt has a smaller ID than the skirt barrel and because the skirt and any pass partitions welded to the tubesheet restrict access for the expanding tool.

7. The manufacturer must make sure that gland follower and cover bolts of outer-skirt designs clear each other.

8. Double-tubesheet construction at the floating end is practical only for inner-skirt designs.

Externally sealed floating tubesheet: TEMA Type W. Externally sealed floating tubesheets have two opposed stuffing boxes that share a common set of bolts. A lantern ring may be installed between the two sets of packings to provide lubrication and to allow leakage from either side to the atmosphere. Because both sides leak to the atmosphere, there is no point in considering double-tubesheet construction. The main advantage of these tubesheets is that they lend themselves to mass production and standardization and therefore are usually inexpensive. The disadvantages are:

1. Bonnet-type return heads of Type W units must be removed and a test fixture used for shellside hydrostatic testing.

2. Under positive pressure, either side or both sides may leak to the atmosphere; under vacuum, air can leak into either side.

3. It is possible for fluid to leak from one side to the other.

4. The surface on the skirt must be finished to 63 rms for sealing. This makes it necessary to protect the skirt when pulling or reinstalling the bundle and to make sure that it is not gouged or scratched.

U-tube designs

Large U-tube units are invariably less costly than straight-tube equipment. The savings are especially great when the tubeside operates at high pressure. This is the reason that U-tube construction is nearly always used for closed feedwater heaters. All the various types of double-tubesheet arrangements can be used on U-tube bundles.

As with fixed-tubesheet exchangers, access to the tube ends requires only removing the channel cover or bonnet. However, unless the tubesheet is constructed to be integral with the shell (typical feedwater heater construction), shellside hydrostatic testing requires a test ring to fasten the tubesheet to the shell and to resist shellside hydrostatic end load. Although they are not sufficient to resist test pressure, it is good practice to use one of the shoulder-bolt constructions shown in Fig. 5.6 at every fourth bolt location to hold removable U-tube bundles in place. This is especially desirable for head-down arrangements. Shoulder-bolt construction requires the tubesheet to be as large in diameter as the shell flange, which adds to the cost.

Inspection of the bent part of U tubes is difficult and may be impossible for the innermost tube rows. Interior tubes in U-bend equipment may be impossible to extract and replace.

The U bends of the innermost few rows of most U tubes cannot be mechanically cleaned internally. However, internal fouling can usually be removed chemically or hydraulically. As with other removable-bundle configurations, the capability of mechanically or hydraulically cleaning the tube exteriors depends upon the pitch pattern and pitch distance.

U tubes cannot be built with odd numbers of tubeside passes. The arrangement of passes and pass partitions in two-pass U-tube exchanger heads is straightforward. Except for some horizontal reboiler and vaporizer designs, the full-diameter pass partition lies on a main centerline of the head, with the drilling template symmetrical about the centerline. When the drilling template of such an exchanger is symmetrical about a line below the main horizontal centerline, the arrangement is called a D layout because the upper part of the tubesheet is untubed.

When there are more than two passes, as shown in Fig. 5.2, there is one full-diameter pass-partition plate intersected by one or more perpendicular plates of a half diameter or less. When the number of passes exceeds four, the positions of the partial-diameter plates are alternately on one side or the other of the full-diameter plate. Because of

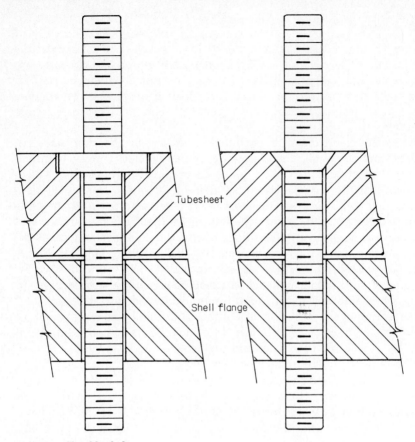

Figure 5.6 Shoulder bolts.

the head geometry, the inlet and outlet nozzles are offset from each other. In 4- and 8-pass heads, they are on the same side of the full-diameter pass partition. In 6- and 10-pass ones, they are on the opposite side.

In Chap. 2, it was noted that the minimum centerline radius on which tubes can be bent depends upon their diameter, thickness, and metal properties. Typically minima are 1½ to 2½ tube diameters. For a bend-centerline distance of four tube diameters (twice the bend-centerline radius), the space between the legs of the innermost tubes is three tube diameters. When the plane of the U bends is perpendicular to the plane of the full-diameter pass partition, this wide gap is undesirable for sensible shellside heat transfer because it permits some shellside fluid to bypass cross-flow baffle systems despite installation of seal strips, dummy tubes, and extra tie rods.

To reduce bypassing and to increase the tube count in a given shell,

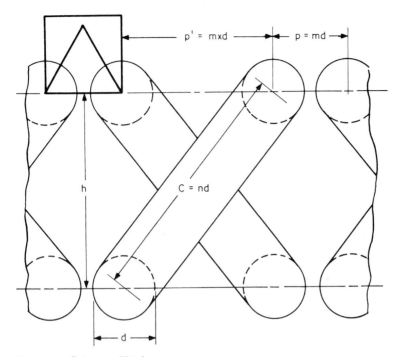

Figure 5.7 Crisscross U tubes.

the tubes in the innermost row may be crisscrossed by rotating the plane of the bends (Fig. 5.7), passing one bend of the crossed pair behind the other. The tube that passes behind must have a longer straight length than the one that it passes.

Following are the geometrical determinants of inner-row U-tube crisscrossing:

C = bend center distance, in (mm)
d = tube diameter, in (mm)
h = distance between drilling lines for inner-tube leg holes, in (mm)
h_m = minimum distance between drilling lines for inner-tube leg holes, in (mm)
m = tube-diameter multiplier for pitch distance ($p = md$)
n = tube-diameter multiplier for centerline distance ($C = nd$)
p = general tube field drilling pitch, in (mm)
p' = lateral crisscross pair drilling pitch distance, in (mm)
w = space required for pass partition, pass-partition groove, or pass-partition gasket, in (mm)
x = pitch multiplier

Referring to Fig. 5.7, it is evident that the distance between the lines on which the legs of the rotated U bends will lie can be found by the pythagorean theorem as shown in Eq. (5.1).

$$h = \sqrt{C^2 - x^2 p^2} \qquad (5.1)$$

Substituting md for p and nd for C, Eq. (5.1) becomes

$$h = d\sqrt{n^2 - m^2 x^2} \qquad (5.2)$$

The minimum distance between the lines on which the legs of the rotated U bends may lie is the greater of the general tube field drilling pitch or the sum of the space required for the pass partition, pass-partition groove, or pass-partition gasket [Eq. (5.3)].

$$h_m = \text{greater of } p \text{ or } w + d \qquad (5.3)$$

The lateral distance between the legs is given by Eq. (5.4).

$$p' = \sqrt{C^2 - h^2} \qquad (5.4)$$

Substituting nd for C and the right side of Eq. (5.2) for h and clearing,

$$p' = mxd \qquad (5.5)$$

When the general tube field drilling pitch is triangular, increase p' to the next larger multiple of p to fit the inner-row drilling into the general pitch pattern. If the tubes are arranged on a square pitch, increments of half a pitch may be used. However, the tube holes of the inner row will not line up neatly with the holes in the general tube field.

Example 5.1   The following example shows how these equations are used.
A bundle is to be designed with 1-in-OD (25.4-mm-OD) U tubes arranged on a 1¼-in (31.75-mm) triangular pitch. The minimum bend-centerline distance is specified to be 4 in (101.6 mm). The gasket-rib width at the stationary tubesheet will be ½ in (12.7 mm), with the space allowed for the gasket ⅝ in (15.9 mm). If the plane of the U tubes is perpendicular to the plane of the pass partition, the space between adjacent legs of the inner row of tubes will be 3 in (76.2 mm). It is desired to reduce this space to the minimum.
The minimum distance between the drilling lines for the legs is the greater of $w + d = 0.625 + 1$ in = 1.625 in (15.9 + 25.4 = 41.3 mm), or 1.25 in (31.75 mm). Therefore, the lines on which the rotated legs will lie will be 1.625 in (41.3 mm) apart [$h = 1.625$ in (41.3 mm)]. From Eq. (5.4), the distance between the pair of legs is found to be 3.66 in (92.96 mm). However, to fit the drilling into the general pitch pattern, this distance is adjusted to 3.75 in (95.25 mm). This requires increasing the bend-line-center distance to 4.09 in (103.8 mm). Actually, it would be adjusted to suit the nearest-size-available bending dies. The result is shown in Fig. 5.8.

In the example, $x = 3.66/1.25$, or 2.93, which was adjusted upward to 3. If x had been reduced to 2, h would have become 3.122 in (79.25

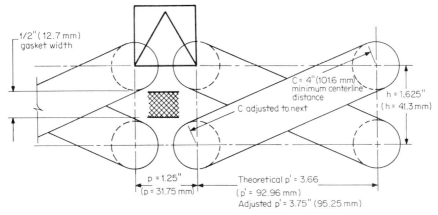

Figure 5.8 Example of use of equations for crisscross tubes.

mm), allowing about 2⅛-in (about 54-mm) clear space between the inner rows of legs.

The bundles of horizontal U-tube exchangers may be arranged with the bends vertical or horizontal. Vertical units may be designed for head-down or head-up installation.

In horizontal units, in which steam is generated or condensed and subcooled in the shell, align the plane of the bends vertically as a precaution against the possibility of inadequate level control. This is especially important when there is a wide tubeside temperature range. If the plane of the bends is horizontal and the upper tubes are allowed to run dry in a steam generator, there may be a substantial metal temperature difference between the submerged and dry tubes. The hotter tubes may seize in the tube support holes, causing tube buckling. But if the plane of the bends is vertical, part of each tube will be submerged, which will reduce the differential growth. In a condenser-subcooler, such as a feedwater heater, the effect of the differential in temperature between the tubes in the subcooling and condensing zones is similar to that of partially dry tubes.

Front and Rear Heads: Channels, Bonnets, and Covers

Following is a guide to the construction of front and rear heads, channels, bonnets, and return covers.

Costs of front- and rear-head configurations

The relative costs listed in Table 5.1 in ascending order for the TEMA front- and rear-head combinations provide a feel for comparing the economics of head configurations. The table assumes the same duty, heat transfer surface, material of construction, and set of design conditions. However, to avoid relying on such generalizations take and evaluate bids for suitable alternatives.

Crossover Area

TEMA Class R standards require multipass channels, bonnets, and return covers to be deep enough to provide a crossover area for flow between successive tube passes equal to at least 1.3 times the flow area through the tubes of one pass; Classes C and B permit the minimum crossover area to be equal to the flow area through the tubes of one pass. The HEI power plant standard specifies that the nominal interpass flow velocity must be no greater than 0.7 times the mean velocity in one tube pass. This is equivalent to a crossover area of $1/0.7 =$ approximately 1.43 times the flow area of the tubes through one pass. Figure 5.9 illustrates how to calculate the crossover area for channels. The calculation is performed in the same way for bonnets and return covers.

Since the nozzles of single-pass TEMA Types S and T exchangers are almost always axial and the *TEMA Standards* require the depth of channels

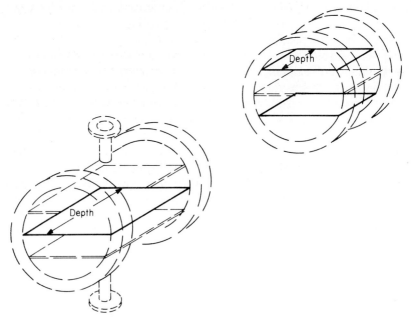

Figure 5.9   Channel, bonnet, and return-cover crossover areas. The inlet and return channel of the A–L configuration are shown in phantom for four-pass ribbon flow of tubeside fluid. The crossover area is the product of the channel depth and the channel width at the location of the pass partition in the opposite channel.

and bonnets with axial nozzles to be at least one-third of the inside diameter of the nozzle, this requirement is also implied for floating-head covers.

Channels with removable covers

TEMA Types A, L, C, N, and D channels have removable covers that allow access for inspecting the tube ends and the part of the tubesheet contained within the channel barrel. Unless the unit is set up for axial flow (rare when the covers are removable), most maintenance can be performed on the exposed parts without disconnecting tubeside piping. The joints of the covers to the channels may be unconfined plain-face or raised-face, fully confined, or confined by rabbeting as described for tubesheet confinements in Chap. 3.

Covers for single-pass channels are designed in accordance with the governing pressure code's rules for flat bolted covers. These rules are based upon limiting the stresses resulting from pressure to acceptable levels; they do not consider the effects of deflection.

When flow is two-pass or multipass, excessive deflection may relieve the compression that the pass partitions apply to the gasket webs. This may occur despite the stresses in the cover being well below the code's allowable stress. Furthermore, although pressure vessel codes require the bolting to be the greater of that required to resist pressure or to yield the ring of gasket between the cover and the channel flange, they make no provision for the bolting required to yield the gasket ribs. As in the *ASME Code*, one is required to apply engineering judgment. For channel covers of multipass units this implies considering the total length of the gasket including the ribs when determining the cross-sectional area of bolting required to yield the gasket.[16]

A combination of deflection and insufficient bolting to compress the gasket webs may lead to pass-to-pass bypassing. A modest trickle hardly affects thermal performance, but such leaks may cause erosion and corrosion of the cover and pass partitions, further increasing the leak rate.[17] The ongoing deterioration may require continuing maintenance or some sort of fix, such as replacing the cover with a thicker one or bracing it against bending.

The *TEMA Standards* mandate the thickness of channel covers at two-pass or multipass ends to be the greater of the *ASME Code*'s required thickness or that computed from a formula based upon generally suitable limits of deflection at the center of the cover caused by pressure and bolting up. These are 0.03 in (0.76 mm) for nominal diameters (nominal diameter/800) through 24 in (609.6 mm) and 0.125 percent of nominal diameter for larger sizes. The *TEMA Standards* provide a formula for calculating the deflection and recommend corrections to be made if the permissible deflection is exceeded.

The HEI *Standard for Power Plant Heat Exchangers* has a nonmandatory similar equation that permits the designer to select the amplitude of the deflection. This standard recommends that the deflection used in the equation be based upon the location of the partitions, the thickness and resilience of the gasket material, the pressure differential across the partitions, and consideration of the consequences of interpass leakage.

When using either the TEMA or the HEI formula, substitute the total bolt load calculated from the actual number of bolts and bolt root area. In the HEI formula, substitute the total bolt cross-sectional area.

Pass-partition covers.   The problem of tightly sealing two-pass channel covers to the pass partition may be obviated by providing a separate cover on the inlet pass. Figure 5.10 schematically illustrates this op-

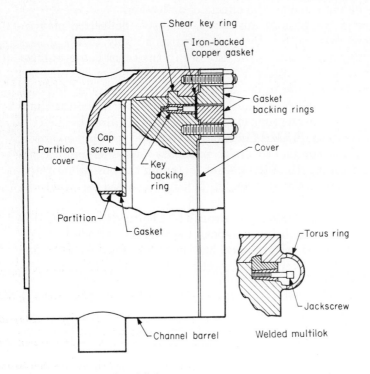

Figure 5.10 High-pressure TEMA Type D channel with pass-partition cover for two-pass flow. (*Reproduced from "Achieving Highly Reliable Feedwater Heaters," by Carl F. Andreone and Robert J. Bell, ASME Pap. 82-JPGC/Pwr-8, by permission of the ASME.*)

tion for a high-pressure TEMA Type D shear-member load-bearing channel design. The sketch shows a Multilok closure in which a shear key ring provides reaction to the pressure thrust and leaktightness is provided by gasketing the channel, shear ring, and cover. The bolts that fasten the gasket backing rings to the cover and channel barrel need only be sufficient to yield the gasket and resist the separating loads applied at the gaskets. The figure's inset portrays a welded Multilok in which a torus ring is welded to the cover and channel to effect the seal. Because it does not use gaskets, the welded Multilok provides a more positive seal, but it must be cut off and rewelded each time that the cover is removed and replaced. Other designs use self-energizing gaskets to prevent leakage past the cover.

Eliminating the cover-to-flange gasket. Figure 5.11 illustrates pass-

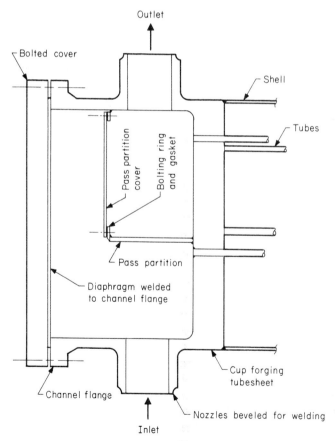

Figure 5.11 Channel with bolted cover and diaphragm seal used with a pass-partition cover for two-pass flow.

partition cover construction for a conventional two-pass TEMA Type N channel that has been modified in order to eliminate any leakage between the channel and the atmosphere. Instead of sandwiching a gasket between the cover and the channel-cover flange, the periphery of a thin diaphragm is welded to the flange. The diaphragm's diameter is approximately that of the OD of the gasket that might otherwise be used. Welding the diaphragm to the channel produces a tighter seal than gasketing. To gain access to the channel, the weld must be removed by grinding, arcing, or burning; to reseal the joint, the diaphragm must be rewelded to the flange. This construction may also be used with single-pass channel designs.

Pass-partition cover bolts are usually welded to a bolting ring as shown. The ring may also be positioned to form a T with the pass partition. Although both sketches show the pass-partition cover sealed to the pass partition and the barrel by a gasket, some are welded in place. To gain access to the tubes, one must make a hole in the cover or cut it completely away.

Most feedwater heaters are constructed with U tubes arranged for two-pass tubeside flow. Except for small low-pressure external condensate coolers, they are almost always built with separate pass-partition covers even when the head is designed as a bonnet welded integrally to the tubesheet.

Channels with removable covers may be bolted to fixed tubesheets or to the shell flanges of removable-bundle exchangers (TEMA Types A and L), or they may be integral with the tubesheet (Types C, N, and D). Those that can be disassembled from the shell provide maximum flexibility for maintenance and repair because they permit complete access to the tubeside face of the tubesheet. However, as previously noted, when a removable-bundle stationary tubesheet is not extended (see Chap. 3, Fig. 3.4f), unbolting the channel flange also disconnects the tubesheet from the shell. To test the shellside, it is necessary to use a test ring designed to match the shell flange.

This is so even when a removable-bundle stationary tubesheet is extended and held to the shell by stud bolts threaded into tapped holes in the tubesheet extension, unless the extension is designed to withstand the bolting up and the hydrostatic end load applied by the shellside test pressure. When shoulder bolts are used to prevent disconnecting the stationary tubesheet and stationary-end shell flange, reinstall the remaining bolts and tighten them and the shoulder bolts to about the same stress levels before applying test pressure. Here, too, use a test ring if the tubesheet extension is not designed to resist the bolt load and hydrostatic end thrust.

When channels are fabricated integrally with the tubesheets (TEMA Types C, N, and D), access to peripheral tubes is limited. As previously noted, the maximum tube count for a given size may be less for integral than for removable construction. Channels integral with the tubesheet have the advantage that, when the bundle is removable, a test ring is not required at the stationary end for shellside testing.

High-pressure heat exchangers have also been built with quick-opening heads. Examples are breechblock closures similar to those used for large artillery and wedge-and-loop closures that simulate breechblocks. Breechblocks have an interrupted flat-crown female thread machined into the barrel end or breech and a mating inter-rupted male thread machined into the OD of the cover or block. In these designs, the covers must be rotated for fastening and opening. When the wedges of wedge-and-loop closures slide between loops on the channel and cover, a spider mechanism is rotated to drive all the wedges into place or pull them out simultaneously. The rotational force is usually furnished by a hydraulic ram.

Although it may not seem possible, such closures have been forced open with pressure in the channel with fatal results. Therefore, make sure that any quick-opening cover is provided with a positive means of relieving *all* pressure before it can be opened. Consider the following:

A forged cover for a 54-in-ID (1371.6-mm-ID) channel constructed in accordance with the *ASME Code*'s rules for flat heads to withstand 1000 lb/in^2 (6895 kPa) and having ⅛-in (3.2-mm) corrosion allowance would be about 7¼ in (about 184.2 mm) thick and would have a mass of about 4700 lb (about 2132 kg). The force that a mere 5 lb/in^2 (34.5 kPa) would apply to the surface would be ap-proximately 11,450 lb (approximately 50,900 N), sufficient to accelerate the cover at 78.44 ft/s^2 (23.9 m/s^2).

At this rate of acceleration, a worker standing 2 ft (0.6 m) in front of the cover would be struck with this force in just 0.16 s.

Removable Bonnets (TEMA Types B and M)

TEMA Type B and M bonnets are generally less costly than remov-able channels because they have but one set of flanges and gaskets while A and L channels have two. The end closure may be a torispherical or elliptically dished and flanged head, or it may be flat. Dished and flanged heads (Fig. 5.12a) may be welded directly to the bolting flange or to an extended barrel. Subject to turnaround space requirements, return bonnet flat heads may be welded directly to the neck of the bolting flange (Fig. 5.12b). Consider flat heads when the bonnet is made of a costly metal. Some advantages are:

1. Depending upon the diameter and the number of passes, the work of fitting and welding the pass partitions to the dished head may be difficult and time-consuming. It is far simpler to lay out and weld the partition plates to flat heads. It is also less complicated to set up

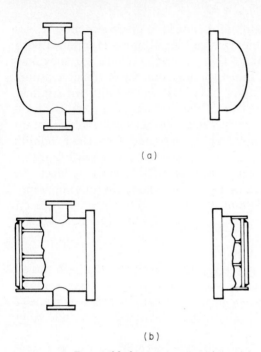

Figure 5.12 Removable-bonnet constructions. (*a*) Dished heads. (*b*) Flat heads.

the bonnet for machining the pass partitions flush with the flange face. Consequently there is a labor saving when the ends are flat.

2. The cover design may take advantage of the support provided by ribs that traverse a full chord if their welds to the plate and barrel are adequate; engineering analysis is required.

3. When it is permissible to use a plate-ring flange for the bonnet flange, the fabricator can usually use the dropout burned out of the plate ring for the flat cover.

With removable-bonnet construction, the whole front face of the tubesheet is exposed during construction, and it can be exposed for maintenance and repair. The disadvantage is that the connections of the nozzles to the piping must be broken to remove the bonnets. Removable bonnets are not usually suitable for the same services as TEMA Type D channels. They may be a better choice than Types C and N if frequent access to the tube ends is not necessary.

Construction with full-access removable covers is always desirable for inspection and maintenance. However, cover-plate thickness increases linearly with diameter and with the square root of pressure. The thickness of the channel-to-cover flange (length of end beyond the shear ring needed to resist blowing the cover out of Type D closures) also increases with these parameters. Therefore, construction at the removable end becomes costly as the diameter and pressure increase. Moreover, since the weight of a disk of a given thickness increases as the square of its diameter, the cover's weight increases as its cube and becomes unwieldy in larger sizes. Special handling devices may be required.

The size limit for this construction depends upon the pressure and diameter. The HEI *Standards for Closed Feedwater Heaters* recommend limiting the diameter of bolted full-access channels to 48 in (1219 mm) for low-pressure heaters.[18] The practical limit is about 54 in (about 1372 mm). However, feedwater heaters with channels as large as 60-in (1524-mm) ID have been built to the TEMA N configuration.

Note that for feedwater heaters it is conventional to define the pressure category in terms of where the heater is located in the system. By this convention low-pressure heaters are those located between the condenser and dearator or after the condensate pump and before the boiler-feedwater pump, and high-pressure heaters are those installed between the feed pump and the boiler. Intermediate-pressure heaters are defined as those used in a supercritical system to boost the temperature of the feedwater between its exit from the dearator and the boiler feed pump.

From the mechanical designer's viewpoint, low, intermediate, and high pressures are arbitrarily selected pressure ranges that do not depend upon a unit's placement. Feedwater heater design pressures less than 1000 lb/in^2 (about 6900 kPa) might be considered to be low. Above 3000 lb/in^2 (about 20,700 kPa) they might be considered high. Intermediate pressures would be considered to lie between these.

Bonnets integral with tubesheets

The bonnets of feedwater heaters not built with full-opening channels are welded to the tubesheet. Therefore, they can be entered only through a manway. As noted in Chap. 1, this is called manway access construction. Manway access heaters must be of pass-partition cover design. However, the pass-partition cover must be built in sections that can be removed and installed through the manway. The minimum clear opening to permit ingress and egress for maintenance should not be less than 16 in (406.4 mm) for round manways and 12 × 16 in (304.8 × 406.4 mm) for elliptical or obround shapes.

Whenever the structure can accept a manway larger than one of these minima, specify it. To understand why, one need only consider the discomfort of a maintenance worker trying to make a welded repair on a peripheral tube-to-tubesheet joint and the risk of being unable to escape quickly. Despite time allowed for a heater to cool down, the bonnet and tubesheet are usually quite warm. The heat of welding adds to the problem. It is difficult to maneuver the welding helmet, hoses, and electrode in the confined space, and even the best exhaust system may not completely eliminate the welding fumes. When a power station does not use bypasses and double-block valves to isolate the heater or does not shut down the whole string, the worker who enters the bonnet is at risk of being scalded in the event of a leak. Larger openings are conducive to higher-quality maintenance work and greater safety.

The bonnet construction options are shown schematically in the nomenclature section of Chap. 1. They are:

1. Hemispherical head welded directly to the tubesheet (see Fig. 1.11)
2. Hemispherical head welded to a short lip forged on the tubeside of the tubesheet (see Fig. 1.12)
3. Hemispherical head welded to a long lip forged on the tubesheet or welded to a barrel that is welded to a short lip forged on the tubesheet (see Fig. 1.13)
4. Elliptically dished and flanged head welded to a barrel that is welded to the tubesheet (see Fig. 1.15)
5. Inverted-hub welding-neck flange with the hub welded to a long lip forged integrally with the tubeside of the tubesheet (see Fig. 1.14)

The manway designs used with integral feedwater heater bonnets are also sketched in Chap. 1. These are:

1. External-bolted-cover manway with sealing diaphragm (see Fig. 1.16)
2. Internal-pressure-sealing-cover manway (Fig. 1.18)
3. External-gasketed, bolted-cover manway (Fig. 1.19)

The construction in which the hemispherical head is welded directly to the tubesheet is unsatisfactory for maintenance because there is not enough room to work on the peripheral tubes. In addition, the feedwater inlet nozzles must be so close to the tubesheet that the tube ends in the feedwater path are likely to erode. For low-pressure units, elliptical-head construction is superior to the directly welded hemisphere and has the additional advantage conferred by radial nozzle entry.

For high-pressure units, the minimum recommended lip length is approximately 4 in (about 100 mm). Heater designers must make sure that the transition from the channel barrel to the flat surface has a generous radius to minimize the stress-raising effects of the shape change.[19] An alternative to a generous corner radius is to make the transition from the barrel to the flat surface by means of a groove (Fig. 5.13).[20] This construction has the advantages of (1) eliminating the corner-notch effect, (2) locating the channel-to-tubesheet weld farther away from the transition radius, and (3) permitting the peripheral tubesheet mass to respond more quickly to temperature changes than the radiused construction.

The high-pressure extended-barrel hemihead and the reverse-flange designs are most satisfactory for piping and maintenance but are expensive. Heater manufacturers will not offer them unless they are specified by the purchasing utility or architect-engineer contractor. However, it is strongly recommended that they be considered, balancing the savings in installation cost, maintenance time, and enhancement of safety over the heater's life against the capital cost.

Of the three manway options, the least expensive to fabricate is the internal-pressure-sealed type. The cover bolts are used only to pull the cover and gasket snugly against the manway frame. Consequently, until enough pressure is built up in the bonnet to create hydrostatic end force on the cover great enough to yield the gasket, this kind of manway is apt to leak. This problem can be overcome by using a soft gasket, but to avoid its being blown out by feedwater pressure it must be retained. Because the cover must be capable of being inserted into the bonnet through the opening, these manways are oval or obround. Therefore, it is costly to mill retaining grooves into the cover or manway frame.

The external-cover gasketed manway is generally a stud pad and cover. The pad metal includes any reinforcement required for the opening in the head. The neck is shorter than in a nozzle-type opening. However, the studs cause some difficulty for workers entering and coming out of the bonnet, and they are usually removed for maintenance. Furthermore, if the tapped holes into which the studs are threaded are not truly perpendicular to the machined surface, it is dif-

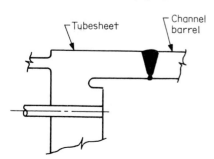

Figure 5.13 Grooved transition from channel barrel to tubesheet.

ficult to remove and reinstall the manway cover without damaging the stud threads. Worn or damaged studs that have been seated for a long period of operation may be very hard to remove and replace. A reinforced flanged nozzle may therefore be a more desirable design despite its having a higher initial cost.

Small scratches on the gasket surface and gasket relaxation may cause manways to leak. Once a leak has started, high-pressure feedwater passing through the opening tends to wire-draw the surface. The only way to repair the damage is to replace eroded material with weld metal and reface the surface with a portable tool. Alternatively, a thin diaphragm may be welded to the surface and the gasket eliminated in a construction similar to that shown in Fig. 5.11. The sealing diaphragm must be removed by grinding or burning and rewelded each time that the manway is opened and closed.

Return covers

With few exceptions return covers are designed to be removable. As Fig. 5.14 shows, this requires an internal gasket between the cover and the tubesheet, which is a possible source of leakage between the shellside and the tubeside. The *ASME Code*'s rules for designing flanges do not apply to the cover flange. However, the code has rules for the configuration shown in the sketch.

If leakage cannot be tolerated, the return cover can be welded to the tubesheet to eliminate the bolted flanged connection. Instead of a dished-only head, the return cover is made from a torospherically or elliptically dished and flanged head, with an OD equal to that of the tubesheet OD. An additional advantage is that if the weld of the head to the tubesheet is ground flush with the tubesheet OD, the bundle can be built with TEMA Type S backing-device design clearances but can be pulled in the same way as with a TEMA Type T pull-through unit. The major disadvantage is that the weld must be removed to provide access to the tube ends. Therefore, the belt-and-suspenders approach must be taken for the tube-to-tubesheet joints. The tubes are usually seal- or strength-welded and expanded into double-grooved tubesheets.

This strategy is most successful for two-pass construction because there are no gasket webs to compress at the floating tubesheet. However, it can be used for multiple-pass construction by welding the floating-end pass partitions to the floating tubesheet and individual flat covers to the pass partitions. Complexity of fabrication makes this option so undesirable that the author has seen it just once in more than 40 years.

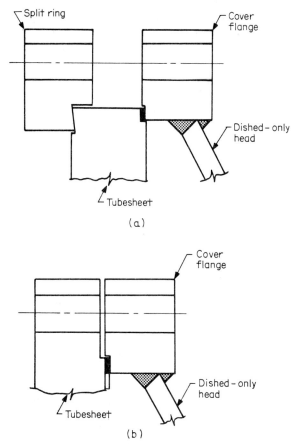

Figure 5.14 Typical return covers at the floating end. (*a*)
TEMA Type S (backing device). (*b*) TEMA Type T (pull-
through).

Pass-Partition Construction

Welding of pass partitions to each other and to pressure parts has
been addressed. The following discusses thickness requirements and
construction details.

Table 5.5 lists the minimum channel and floating-head pass-
partition thicknesses for carbon steel and alloy metals of the *TEMA
Standards* and HEI *Standard for Power Plant Heat Exchangers*. These
thicknesses are not related to the pass partitions' ability to withstand
the difference in pressure in the compartments on either side. The
HEI standard and the current edition of the *TEMA Standards* have
calculation methods to determine the thickness required to avoid *permanent* bending under a substantial difference in pressure. The HEI

TABLE 5.5   Minimum Pass-Partition Thicknesses

Nominal shell inside diameter		TEMA		HEI	
in	mm	in	mm	in	mm
Carbon steel					
4–12	101.6–304.8	0.375	9.5	0.25	6.4
12+–24	304.8–609.6	0.375	9.5	0.375	9.5
24+–25	609.6–635	0.500	12.7	0.375	9.5
25+–39	635–990.6	0.500	12.7	0.500	12.7
39+–59	990.6–1498.6	0.500	12.7	0.625	15.9
59+–60	1498.6–1524	0.500	12.7	0.75	19.0
61–100	1549.4–2540	0.625	15.9	0.75	19.0
Alloy materials					
4–12	101.6–304.8	0.25	6.4	0.25	6.4
12+–24	304.8–609.6	0.25	6.4	0.25	6.4
24+–25	609.6–635	0.375	9.5	0.25	6.4
25+–39	635–990.6	0.375	9.5	0.375	9.5
39+–59	990.6–1498.6	0.375	9.5	0.500	15.9
59+–60	1498.6–1524	0.375	9.5	0.625	15.9
61–100	1549.4–2540	0.500	12.7	0.625	15.9

method is based upon limiting the maximum stress in the plate due to differential pressure to the yield stress. The *TEMA Standards* method limits the maximum stress to 1.5 times the *ASME Code*'s allowable stress at the design temperature.

Following is an alternative for TEMA Type A and L channels that limits the stress in the plate to 90 percent of the yield stress and provides for consideration of elastic deflection. The suggested maximum permissible elastic bending is $\frac{1}{32}$ in (0.8 mm). A similar alternative for Types B, M, C, and N bonnets and channels is based upon limiting the stress in the pass-partition plate to 90 percent of the yield stress.

Figures 5.15, 5.16, and 5.17 are self-explanatory. In these figures:

A = shape factor for deflection calculation
B = shape factor for stress calculation
E = Young's modulus, lb/in^2 (kPa)
L = length of gasketed edge, in (mm)
P = differential pressure, lb/in^2 (kPa)
S_y = partition-plate yield stress, lb/in^2 (kPa)
t_1 = thickness based upon allowable stress, in (mm)
t_2 = thickness based upon allowable deflection, in (mm)
W = welded-edge width, in (mm)
y = allowable deflection, in (mm)

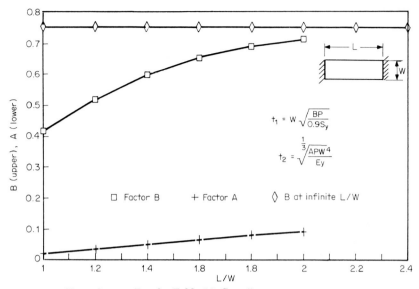

Figure 5.15 Shape factors, Rourke Table 26, Case 5.

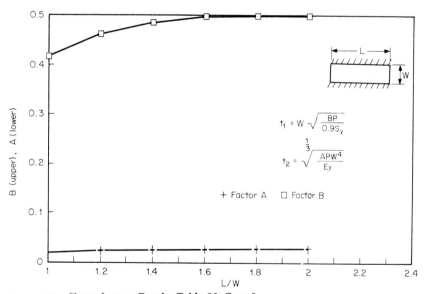

Figure 5.16 Shape factors, Rourke Table 26, Case 6.

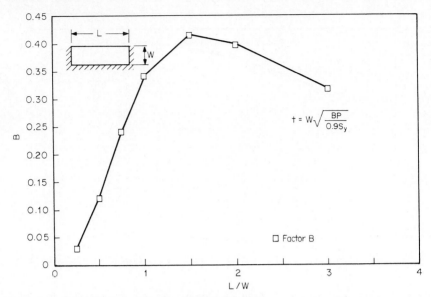

Figure 5.17 Shape factors, Rourke Table 26, Case 9.

The following examples show how to do the calculation:

Example 5.2 How thick should a carbon steel pass partition of a two-pass TEMA Type A channel be to accommodate 100 lb/in^2 (about 690-kPa) differential pressure? The channel ID is 39 in (990.6 mm) ID, and the channel is 19 in (482.6 mm) deep. The yield stress of carbon steel is 24,000 lb/in^2 (165,474 kPa); its elastic modulus is 26 million lb/in^2 (179,263,760 kPa).

solution Using Fig. 5.15, we calculate L/W = 2.05. We estimate shape factor B at 0.715 and shape factor A to be 0.1. Substituting in the equation for t_1, we calculate a thickness of 1.09 in (27.8 mm). Substituting in the equation for t_2 and allowing a maximum of 1/32-in (0.8-mm) deflection, we calculate a required thickness of 1.17 in (29.7 mm). Therefore, the plate should be 1¼ in (32 mm) thick.

Example 5.3 How thick would the pass partition have to be if the channel was a Type C?

solution Using Fig. 5.17 and L/W of 2.05, we find the shape factor B equal to 0.39. The minimum thickness is then 0.81 in (20.5 mm). For gasketed pass-partition construction, the gasket ribs need not be as wide as the plate thickness.

The *TEMA Standards* require the minimum gasket web width to be ¼ in (6.35 mm) for sizes up to 23 in (584.2 mm) nominal and ⅜ in (9.5 mm) for larger sizes. The HEI power plant standard permits the gasket web width to be as narrow as the thickness required for alloy-metal pass-partition plates. (See Table 5.5.) It is also not necessary for the full plate thickness to be carried to the tubesheet when the pass-partition plates are welded on. Figure 5.18 illustrates suggested modifications to thick partition plates.

Figure 5.19 illustrates a pass-partition design used to modify the number of tubeside passes, usually to convert a single-pass unit to two or more passes. The plate is made of a corrosion-resistant material. The fluted shape is produced on a press brake. The maximum thickness of the plate is determined by the ligament space between the tube rows. Since the width of the ligament is ordinarily the pitch distance minus the tube diameter and since the pitch distance is customarily

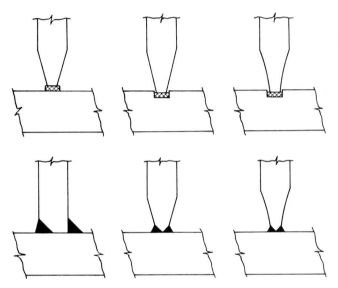

Figure 5.18   Modifications to the tubesheet edge of thick pass partitions.

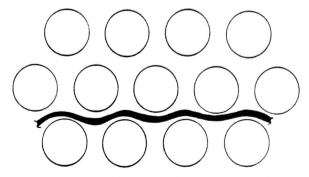

Figure 5.19   Pass-partition design for converting single-pass channels and bonnets to multipass flow.

1.25 tube diameters, the ligament width is ordinarily one-quarter of the tube diameter. Therefore, except for large-diameter tubes or spread-pitch arrangements, the fluted pass partition cannot be as thick as the TEMA and HEI minima, nor can the minimum gasket width requirement be met. The fluting makes the plate more rigid than a flat plate. While this makes it strong enough to resist some differential pressure, it also makes it hard to fit.

Neither the TEMA nor the HEI standards require pass partitions to have an allowance for corrosion. Despite their being welded to a pressure part, the pressure safety codes also do not require corrosion allowance for pass partitions. However, when corrosion or erosion is anticipated, it is prudent to make some provision (additional thickness or alloy metal) for deterioration in service. This is especially desirable when there is a substantial pressure differential between adjacent compartments.

Pass partitions of TEMA Type C, N, and D channels

For most services of TEMA Type C, N, and D channels, it is acceptable to weld the pass partitions directly to the tubesheet and barrel, using the previously recommended full-penetration weld details. This is adequate for relatively thin channel-tubesheet sections in noncyclical service. However, when the combination of high tubeside pressure and channel diameter requires thick sections of the tubesheet and channel and the service is cyclical, the welds of the pass partition to the tubesheet and barrel may crack and the pass-partition plates may buckle. This is so because (1) welded pass partitions restrict the radial growth of the channel wall under pressure and (2) the differential expansion of the structure produced by the thermal gradient across the tubesheet is restrained by the rigidly welded pass-partition plates.

The thermal-gradient problem is most severe in two-pass units such as feedwater heaters. In these heat exchangers, it is not uncommon to bolt the pass partition to a bolting bar welded to the tubesheet face and channel barrel instead of welding the pass partition directly in place. Such construction does not restrict channel wall growth as much as the directly welded type. However, it does not deal with the thermal-gradient problem. Both constructions increase the rigidity of the tubesheet-to-barrel connection. This counters the purpose of the radiused or grooved transition. These designs create a notch that intensifies stress concentrations.

Welded-in circumferential bolting bars for pass-partition covers can cause similar problems. Here, the bar restricts the channel wall locally from radial growth. If the channel nozzles are close to the pass-partition cover support bar, there will be additional stress in the nozzle-to-channel welds.

Therefore, for high-pressure cyclical operation in two-pass channels—for example, for feedwater heaters—the floating pass-partition construction shown in Fig. 5.20 is recommended. In this construction, a relatively thin half-cylinder trough, as long as the pass-partition plate and with a radius just smaller than the inside radius of the channel barrel, is formed with straight ends. The ends are broken on a gradual radius to form flanges that can be butt-welded to the flat pass-

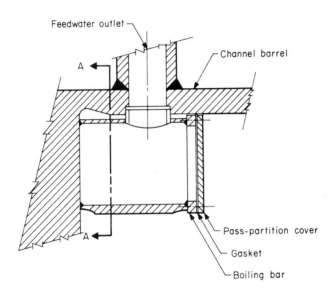

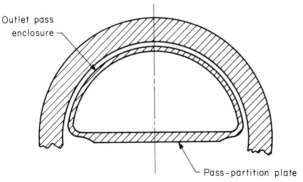

Section A-A

Figure 5.20   Schematic of floating pass-partition construction.

partition plate. The edges of the pass-partition plate are beveled on approximately a 3:1 taper or J-machined to meet the thickness of the flanged ends of the half cylinder. The front and rear edges of the pass partition are also tapered or J-machined. The pass-partition cover bolting bar is welded to the rear of this structure, and the whole assembly is then welded to the front face of the tubesheet so as to enclose the outlet pass.

The feedwater outlet is connected to the outlet pass enclosure by a thin sleeve. It is preferable to join the sleeve to the shell of the flexible enclosure by butt-welding it to a flued-out opening. However, a properly designed full-penetration weld of the sleeve to a circular opening is acceptable.

The flexible enclosure applies little restraint to tubesheet and barrel growth. Furthermore, the clearance between the enclosure and the channel ID permits incoming feedwater to circulate completely around the channel barrel and transition radius, which produces a more uniform channel temperature. This reduces the temperature gradients and the stresses that they cause.

Nozzles

Nozzles may enter channel and bonnet barrels radially (perpendicular to the bundle centerline), tangentially (perpendicular to the bundle centerline but offset as far as physically possible), or anywhere between (Fig. 5.4). In these variations, they may be pitched toward or away from the tubesheet. In manway access hemispherical-head closed feedwater heaters, the nozzles enter at an angle of approximately 30°.

It is generally desirable to keep the barrel depth as small as possible for nozzles that enter the barrel radially, tangentially, or in between. The minimum is determined by the nozzle size, clearances between nozzle and barrel flanges required for wrench access, and any space needed for reinforcing the opening.

Radial nozzles are the least expensive to fabricate. They provide reasonably good distribution of fluid to the tubes. To improve distribution, they may be fabricated with an internal elbow that directs the flow away from the tubes. Most channel and bonnet nozzles of single-pass and ribbon-flow multipass exchangers enter radially. The enlargement or contraction of the fluid channel and the directional change consume fluid energy, resulting in pressure losses.

If the feed stream carries abrasive particles, tangential entry can reduce erosion opposite the entrance by providing a smoother change in direction. A carefully crafted doubler plate (Fig. 5.21) may be installed to extend barrel life. When a bonnet head of a vertical unit is

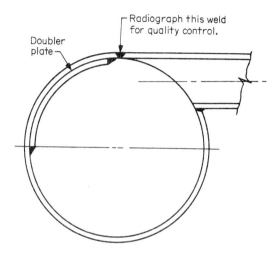

Figure 5.21   Tangential nozzle and channel doubler plate.

hemispherical, torospherical, or elliptically dished, the nozzle may be set tangentially to the crown of the head as shown in Fig. 5.22. An additional advantage of tangential entry is that the more gradual shift of the flow path minimizes frictional energy losses.

Tangential nozzles are the most difficult to fit and weld. Poor fits may be covered with wide welds, dressed by grinding to give the appearance of being smoothly faired to the head or barrel. This procedure may obscure shoddy welds; therefore, the joint should be radiographed.

When tubeside pressure drop must be kept to a minimum, as in vertical thermosiphon reboilers, consider these alternatives:

1. Use the nozzle constructions shown in Fig. 5.21 or Fig. 5.22.

2. Make the bonnets of long-radius elbows of a diameter equal to the shell diameter.

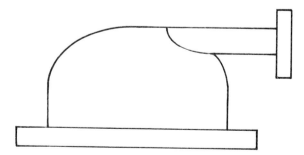

Figure 5.22   Nozzle tangential to the head crown.

3. Make the bonnets and nozzles integral with long-radius mitered reducing elbows (Fig. 5.23).

When possible, avoid nozzles that enter a bonnet axially because they are the most likely to produce tubeside maldistribution. Fluid that enters a bonnet or channel through an axial nozzle may be thought of as a turbulent free jet that entrains the surrounding fluid. The jet angle depends upon the fluid. For water it has been found to be about 14°.[21] Unless the bonnet is deep enough for the incoming fluid fully to diffuse, more fluid will enter the tubes immediately in front of the nozzle than the tubes closer to the periphery of the chamber. Such

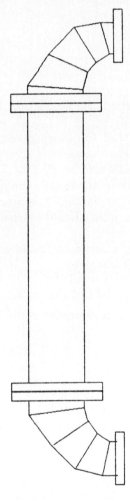

Figure 5.23 Thermosiphon reboiler with tubeside nozzles integral with long-radius five-piece mitered elbow bonnets.

maldistribution may cause inadequate performance and mechanical problems.*

The *TEMA Standards* require a minimum depth at the nozzle centerline of one-third of the inside diameter of the nozzle when an axial nozzle is used in a bonnet or channel (as previously stated, imply a similar depth for TEMA S and T floating-head covers). However, this may be insufficient to prevent maldistribution of the entering stream. Unless the nozzle entrance area is equal to or greater than the total cross-sectional area for fluid flow in the tubes and the distance between the nozzle penetration and the tubesheet is at least 2½ times the barrel diameter, it is advisable (1) to install a diffuser plate or (2) to design the bonnet as a conical reducer with an included angle of 20° or less. The second alternative is costly and usually requires more space than is available. Plates for distributing incoming streams from axial nozzles may be simply perforated disks, solid targets wide enough to disrupt the jet diffusion stream, or circular weir-type distributors.

When feedwater inlet and outlet nozzles enter hemispherical manway access heads at an angle, it may be hard to fit the connections and manway. The degree of difficulty depends upon the nozzle size, head diameter, and manway access construction. In addition, elbows are generally required in the connecting piping. When hemihead construction is used for high-pressure heaters, the walls of the nozzles and connecting piping are relatively thick. Additional reinforcement may be required where the nozzles and manway penetrate the head. A modest deviation from drawing dimensions may cause a major problem for the pipe fitter, who usually has to fit elbows into the connecting piping to construct straight runs. This difficulty can be avoided if the heater manufacturer furnishes "as-built" dimensions before the piping is done. However, the piping usually is in place before the heater is completed.

Nozzle reinforcements and loads

The pressure envelope must be reinforced to counter the weakening created by nozzle openings. The reinforcement consists of metal in the pressure part penetrated, the nozzle walls, and attachment welds beyond that required to resist pressure plus additional metal in reinforcing pads and their attachment welds. Requirements for reinforcement are clearly defined in pressure vessel codes, usually with examples or

---

*For an analysis, see Kanchan Codhury and Sunil Sarangi, "Effects of Flow Maldistribution on Multipassage Heat Exchanger Performance," *Heat Transfer Eng.*, vol. 6, no. 4, 1985.

typical computations.* The *ASME Code* and TEMA and HEI standards permit reinforcement metal to be placed on the outside and inside of channel and bonnet nozzle barrels and heads. The thicknesses of nozzles and the parts they penetrate may also be increased to provide the necessary reinforcement. Increasing the thickness of the nozzle or the part it penetrates to provide the necessary reinforcement creates no additional discontinuities or further stress concentration. The choice of whether to use one or both of these constructions or to weld reinforcements to the pressure envelope is almost always based upon their costs relative to each other. Another consideration is that the space required to install reinforcing pads may require increasing the barrel depth.

For modest amounts of reinforcement, it is usually desirable to increase the nozzle wall thickness because it is economical. When doing so, make sure that the nozzle ID is not reduced so much that inlet or outlet velocity becomes excessive. Long welding necks avoid this problem because the standard-pipe-size ID is maintained.

Unless the user specifies the direction and amplitude of loads that connecting piping applies to nozzles or requires the examination of their capabilities to accept such loads, manufacturers may concern themselves only with the requirements for reinforcement described above. From the manufacturers' viewpoint, heat exchangers should not act as anchor points for piping and should be isolated from external loads. The user may not find this to be practical or desirable.

Although it is possible to analyze stresses of nozzles and the pressure parts they pierce by numerical methods (for example three-dimensional finite-element analysis), it is costly. Most analysis is performed by using a method prepared by the Welding Research Council.[22] The HEI standards for power plant heat exchangers and closed feedwater heaters have simplified versions of this method.

Connections of Channels and Bonnets to the Bundle and Shell

Bolted connections

The stationary tubesheet of removable-bundle exchangers, built with removable bonnets or channels, is sandwiched between a channel and a shell flange. The combinations of diameters, widths, yield strengths,

---

*See, for example, *ASME Code*, Section VIII, Division 1, "Openings and Reinforcements," for details of this division of the *ASME Code*'s requirements; and Appendix L, which has sample calculations.

and resilience of the gaskets between the flanges and tubesheet on each side must be compatible. The flange design must take note of differences in gasket dimensions and properties and flange configurations. Only one set of bolts is available to yield the gaskets during bolting up and to maintain the joints on both sides of the tubesheet tight under pressure. In two-pass and multipass tubeside units, the bolting must be adequate to yield not only the ring of gasket material inside the bolt circle but also the gasket webs that seal the pass compartments from one another.

As with gasketed bolted covers, insufficient gasket compression, deflection of the tubesheet when the tubeside pressure is higher than the pressure in the shell, flange rotation, and noncolinearity of the shellside and tubeside gasket rings may lead to interpass leakage.[23] When a channel is welded to a tubesheet extended as a flange for bolting to the shell, the shell flange is designed as a stand-alone flange. However, the moment applied to the tubesheet by bolting up and shellside pressure must be considered in the tubesheet design.

The large majority of heat exchanger flanges are designed as elastic structures, using an analysis built upon the work of E. O. Waters and J. H. Taylor.[24–26] References 24 and 25 are the basis of the flange design rules of the *ASME Code*'s rules for bolted flanged connections with ring-type gaskets in which the flanges do not make metal-to-metal contact.

The *ASME Code* rules also have requirements for split loose flanges, noncircular shaped flanges with circular bores, flanges subject to external pressure, flanges with nut stops, flanges in which bolt holes are replaced by slots, reverse flanges, and limits on shear stress in laps where the gasket is so located that the lap is subject to shear.

Consider other methods, such as three-dimensional finite-element analysis, for high pressures, large diameters, and odd-shaped flanges with discontinuities. As a guide, note that the limits of the *TEMA Standards* and *ASME Code* are 3000 lb/in^2 (approximately 20,700 kPa).

A nonmandatory appendix to Section VIII, Division 1, of the *ASME Code* (Appendix Y) points the way to designing pairs of flat-faced flanges with metal-to-metal contact. It is based upon the cooperative work of the Pressure Vessel Research Council Subcommittee on Bolted Flanged Connections and the ASME Code Committee's Subgroup on Openings. Several previous works led to publication of the appendix.[27–32] It states that the rules apply to "circular bolted flanged connections where the assemblage is comprised of identical or nonidentical flange pairs, and where the flanges are flat faced and are in uniform metal-to-metal contact across their entire face during assembly before the bolts are tightened or after a small amount of preload is applied to compress a gasket. The rules also apply when a pair of identical flat-faced flanges are separated by a metal spacer. The rules are not intended for cases where the faces are intentionally made nonparallel to each other such that initial contact is at the bore."

The *ASME Code* does not now have rules for designing flanges with full-face soft gaskets, but it does not prohibit their use. An analysis proposed by D. B. Rossheim in 1943, published by Taylor Forge Company as Engineering Department Bulletin 45, has been used successfully. The method is outlined in *Modern Flange Design*, Bulletin 502, Edition VII, G + W Taylor—Bonney Division, Southfield, Michigan. It makes these assumptions: (1) rigidity at the bolt circle before pressurizing, (2) inner flange edge unrestrained, (3) uniform gasket pressure on the annular surfaces on each side of the bolt circle, (4) ring effect and bolt holes causing no significant loss of strength, and (5) countermoment existing between the bolt circle and the flange OD.

The *ASME Code*'s rules will not be repeated in this guide. Some requirements for materials of construction for flanges designed to Section VII, Division 1, Appendix 2 rules are listed below. The list is followed by a review of some basic concepts that apply to the design.

Requirements for flange materials. The material used for flanges must meet the *ASME Code*'s general requirements for materials for pressure-containing parts. Some specific additional requirements are paraphrased here:

1. Flanges made from ferritic steel must be given a normalizing or full-annealing heat treatment when the thickness of the flange section exceeds 3 in (76.2 mm).

2. Material on which welding is to be performed must be proved to be of good weldable quality.

3. Welding must not be performed on steel that has a carbon content greater than 0.35 percent.

4. All welding on flange connections must comply with the division's requirements for postweld heat treatment.

5. Fabricated hubbed flanges may be machined from a hot-rolled or forged billet. The axis of the finished flange must be parallel with the long axis of the original billet. It need not be concentric with the finished flange.

6. Hubbed flanges not machined from a hot-rolled or forged billet may not be machined from plate or bar stock material unless the material has been formed into a ring with the original plate surfaces parallel to the axis of the finished flange. The original plate surface need

not be present in the finished flange. The joints in the ring must be welded butt joints. The thickness to be used to determine postweld heat treatment and radiography requirements is the lesser of the flange thickness or width (outside radius minus inside radius). The back of the flange and the outer surface of the hub must be examined either by the magnetic-particle or the liquid-penetrant method.

7. Bolts, studs, nuts, and washers must meet the division's requirements. The appendix recommends not using bolts and studs smaller than ½ in (12.7 mm). If smaller bolts or studs are used, ferrous bolting material must be alloy steel. Precautions must be taken to avoid overstressing small-diameter bolts.

Basic concepts. Circular flange design involves (1) selecting gasket material suitable for the fluid environment, (2) selecting a desirable confinement, (3) picking the proper gasket type and width for the operating pressure and temperature, (4) choosing an appropriate flange facing, (5) determining the required bolting, and (6) optimizing the hub proportions, flange width, and thickness.

Recommending gasket materials for various environments is beyond the scope of this guide. Most gasket manufacturers will suggest suitable materials. Confinements were discussed in Chap. 3. Note that the gasket type, width, and flange facing are related.

The ASME rules for flanges assume that they are rigid and that the bolt holes do not materially affect flange strength. They provide only for the two load systems shown schematically in Fig. 5.24: gasket seating and hydrostatic end loads. In this figure, W is the flange design bolt load for the operating conditions or gasket seating, as may apply. Calculations must be made for each load system to determine the required bolting and the proportions and thicknesses that will withstand both sets of loads without exceeding permitted radial and tangential stress levels in the flange ring and longitudinal stress in the hub (when present).

When a channel or a bonnet is bolted to a tubesheet, only one set of loads (those imposed on the tubeside) must be investigated. However, when the tubesheet is clamped between a pair of flanges (such as a channel and a shell flange), the tubeside flange, gasket, or both may not be the same as the flange, gasket, or flange and gasket on the shellside. Therefore, the loads must be found for the most severe condition of operating or gasket seating applied simultaneously to both sides. This condition may be (1) gasket seating at atmospheric temperature on one flange together with operating pressure and temperature on the other, (2) gasket seating on each flange at the same time, or (3) operating conditions on each flange at the same time. After the severest-condition loads have been found, calculations to determine

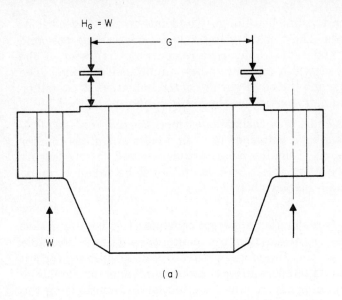

(a)

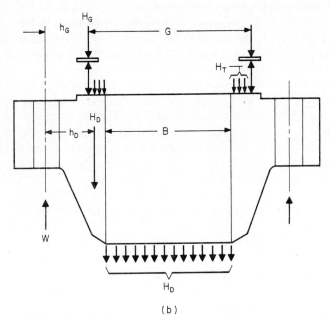

(b)

Figure 5.24   Load systems for ASME flange design. (a) Gasket-seating load system. (b) Internal-pressure load system.

the required bolting, proportions, and thicknesses must be made for each flange.

There are two requisites for the flange bolting which are derived from the load systems: (1) at atmospheric temperature and pressure, the bolting must be able to supply enough initial load ($W = W_{m2}$) to seat the gasket; and (2) at the design pressure and temperature, it must be able to supply force ($W = W_{m1}$) sufficient to resist the hydrostatic end force that tends to part the joint and maintain enough compression on the gasket and joint contact surface to keep the joint tight. At high operating pressures, when W_{m1} is greater than W_{m2}, it determines the amount of bolting required. At low or moderate pressures, the load required to seat the gasket, W_{m2}, will govern.

The total cross-sectional area of the bolts required for seating (A_{m2}) is a function of the gasket material, the effective contact area to be seated, and the allowable bolt stress at atmospheric temperature S_a. For this condition, $A_{m2} = W_{m2}/S_a$. The total cross-sectional area of the bolts required to meet the second condition (A_{m1}) is a function of the gasket material, the effective gasket contact area to be kept tight under pressure, the design pressure, and the allowable bolt stress at the design temperature S_b. For the second condition, $A_{m1} = W_{m1}/S_b$. The minimum cross-sectional bolt area required for the connection A_m is the greater of A_{m1} and A_{m2}.

W_{m1} is substituted for W in the design of the flange when considering operating conditions. W_{m2} is modified to take account of the operating conditions when they govern A_m, as well as the amount of bolting actually provided (A_b). The adjusted load W, for the atmospheric case, is the average of A_m and A_b multiplied by the allowable stress at atmospheric temperature S_a. This provides a margin against abusing the flange by overbolting. However, where additional safety against mishandling is desired or where the flange must be able to withstand the full available bolt load, W may be adjusted to $A_b S_a$.

The load W required to seat the gasket is

$$W_{m2} = \pi b G y \qquad (5.6)$$

Here, in consistent units,

b = effective gasket seating width (This differs from the actual gasket width dimensions.)

G = gasket load diameter

y = gasket yield stress

W_{m2} = bolt load required for seating the gasket, i.e., to make it fill the flange and tubesheet irregularities, thereby effecting a seal

Upon bolting up, the gasket exerts the load H_G over the surface with which it is in contact. As illustrated, at equilibrium the gasket load and bolt load are equal. Note that the effective gasket width actually changes with flange deflection. However, this is not considered because of the assumption of rigidity.

The second load system has the four forces shown on the lower sketch of Fig. 5.24:

1. Hydrostatic end force on the area inside the flange, labeled H_D, shown in Eq. (5.7). This is the product of the internal pressure and projected area of the shell cover or channel. It acts on the flange ring through the hub (in the case of a ring flange, through the channel barrel or shell). If the hub is tapered, its line of action is midhub.

$$H_D = (\pi/4)B^2P \qquad (5.7)$$

where, in consistent units,

B = corroded ID of the flange
P = design pressure

2. Pressure force that acts on the exposed part of the flange face, labeled H_T. This is the difference between the total hydrostatic end force H and the hydrostatic end force on the area inside the flange. The total hydrostatic end force H is the force that would act on the circle of diameter G when pressure P is applied:

$$H = (\pi/4)G^2P \qquad (5.8)$$

H_T is expressed in Eq. (5.9):

$$H_T = H - H_D \qquad (5.9)$$

If the gasket covered the raised face shown in the figure, H_T would be zero, but leakage is assumed to be possible as far as G. H_T is assumed to act on the circle midway between the ID of the flange, labeled B, and the gasket line of action G.

3. The total joint compression load, labeled H_P, given by Eq. (5.10).

$$H_P = 2\pi bGmP \qquad (5.10)$$

where, in consistent units, m = the ratio of residual gasket stress to design pressure required to maintain the joint tight under pressure load. For example, when m is 3, it means that the residual gasket stress at pressure P must be at least $3P$ for the joint to be tight. If the gasket were theoretically perfect, leakage would not start until the fluid pressure just exceeded the gasket pressure. For this condition, the value of $m = 1$.

4. The load W $(=W_{m1})$ supplied by the bolts. It is in equilibrium with the sum of the first three (Fig. 5.25). The equilibrium conditions are expressed by Eq. (5.11).

$$W_{m1} = H + H_p = \frac{\pi}{4} G^2 P + 2\pi GmP \qquad (5.11)$$

Calculations to determine optimal flange thicknesses and proportions are done by cut-and-try methods. For a trial set of flange dimensions, moments are determined for each load system as the products of the various loads and their distances from the bolt circle to their lines of action. Because of the assumption of flange rigidity, the shortening of lever arms due to rotation is neglected in calculating the moments. Longitudinal hub stress, radial flange stress, and tangential flange stress produced by the moments are calculated. (For hubless flanges or where the designer chooses to neglect the strengthening effect of the hub, only the tangential flange stress is determined.) These stresses must not exceed the code's limits.

The stress calculations require computing various factors that involve the assumed thicknesses and shape and the kind of flange. One set of factors concerns the ratio of flange OD to ID. Another is related to the hub proportions. Other factors that depend upon these sets are used in the actual stress calculations. The *ASME Code* has graphs of the dependent factors for flanges joined integrally to the channel barrel or shell (integral-type flanges) and those attached in such a way that the barrel or shell does not contribute to their support (loose-type flanges). It also provides means of

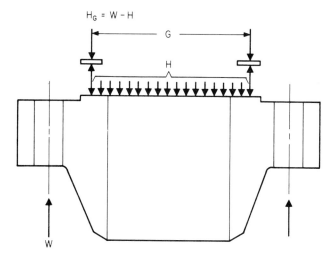

Figure 5.25 Equilibrium between pressure-imposed loads and bolt load.

calculating the factors suitable for computer programming. The moment and stress calculation methods are fully detailed in the *ASME Code* and therefore will not be repeated here.

When a design meets the *ASME Code* rules but has a bolt spacing so wide that it may leak, consider adjusting it by increasing the flange thickness, increasing the number of bolts, or both. A theoretical analysis of bolt spacing indicates proper load distribution when the bolt spacing is $(2d + t)$, where d is the bolt diameter, in inches (millimeters), and t is the flange thickness, also in inches (millimeters).[33]

The maximum recommended spacing B_{max} between bolt centers in the seventh edition of the *TEMA Standards* is $(2d + 6t)/(m + 0.5)$. It is based upon similar considerations but takes into account the ratio m = residual gasket stress to design pressure, required to maintain the joint tight under pressure load. This is the familiar gasket factor m used in *ASME Code* flange calculations.

On the basis of the analysis of Ref. 33 and the *TEMA Standards*, if the bolt spacing exceeds this recommended maximum, one should multiply the total moment calculated for each load system by (B/B_{max}), where B is the actual bolt spacing.

Computerized flange designs.   Computer programs for optimizing heat-exchanger flanges designed in conformity with *ASME Code* rules* require the following input:

1. The type of flange.

2. The design conditions. For a single-sided connection they require only the tubeside conditions. For a tubesheet between a channel flange and a shell flange it is necessary to input both tubeside and shellside conditions.

3. Materials of construction for each flange and for the bolting. If the program does not have in its data bank the *ASME Code*'s tables of allowable stress versus temperature that it can look up or does not have a means for calculating the allowable stresses at atmospheric and design temperatures, these data must also be provided.

4. Type of gasket

5. Gasket confinements.

6. Flange facings.

7. Minimum and maximum permissible gasket widths.

8. The number of tubeside passes.

9. m and y factors. Most programs will default to the values tabu-

---

*For example those of B-Jac Computer Services, Inc., Midlothian, Virginia.

lated in the *ASME Code* for the gasket type and material if these factors are omitted.

The optimization path starts with typical assumed values. The programs iterate to produce the least expensive flange that meets the *ASME Code*'s design requirements and the bolt-spacing adjustment of Ref. 33. To determine flange cost, they calculate the weight of raw material and labor times required to produce the flange. They multiply these by unit costs, updated by regular file maintenance. The computer code is arranged to permit fabrication shops to incorporate their own labor standards and material costs.

Gasket factors, bolting, and bending of mating parts. Some discussion of gasket factors, bolting, and the effects of flange and tubesheet bending follows.

The suggested (nonmandatory) values for gaskets tabulated in the *ASME Code* are based upon a 1941 work of Rossheim and Markl that suggested rules for finding b and presented tables of values of m and y for commonly used gasket materials.[34] Considering that the value of m required to make a tight seal varies inversely with the initial bolt load and that at zero initial pressure m is very high, they developed an empirical formula for y that approximates the m value required to produce a bolt load that would seal the joint at zero internal pressure.

Despite their direct effect on flange design, the *ASME Code*'s values for m and y are not mandatory because they are not founded on an acceptable theory or backed by sufficient experimental investigation. Kent has offered a graphic approach to selecting suitable gaskets based upon these constants.[35] The published values are based upon experience and some experimentation. Because of the many variables that must be examined, testing is time-consuming.[36] However, much has been done to try to establish the interrelationships between gasket dimensions, gasket material properties, leakage, and tightness criteria and to reexamine the method and parameters in current use.[37–45] A proposed procedure that considers leak criteria and tightness, points out that y and m are not independent and suggests establishing "codelike factors" for m and y for various leak rates and contained fluids.[46] These are based upon full gasket width (N as defined in the *ASME Code*), minimum gasket design seating stress, and actual seating stress. As with tube-to-tubesheet joints, required tightness depends upon the service, and much has yet to be done to relate service conditions, leak rates, and the suitable codelike factors.

Most flanges designed by the *ASME Code*'s rules are tight when tested and in use. However, give special consideration to the following:

1. Very-large-diameter flanges
2. High design pressures
3. High design temperatures
4. Severe temperature gradients
5. Differences between bolt material and flange material thermal expansion coefficients
6. Unusual gasket arrangements
7. Services in which there may be short-term temperature or pressure excursions beyond the design conditions

Bolt tightening.   The objectives of bolt tightening are (1) to provide the force required to seal the gasket and maintain tightness during operation, (2) to stress all the bolts equally, and (3) to apply the bolt stresses in such a way that gasket compression and flange stress are not distributed unequally during bolting up. Various strategies are used to achieve these aims with different degrees of success:

1. Tighten the bolts manually in several rounds. Usually four passes in which the feel of the resistance to tightening seems to increase by about 25 percent are adequate. Divide the flange into four quadrants, A, B, C, and D, and number the bolts in each quadrant from 1 to n. For each round of wrenching, bolt up in a sequence that starts with bolt 1 in quadrant A, proceeds to bolt 1 in the opposite quadrant (C), then to bolt 1 in quadrant B, and to bolt 1 in quadrant D. Then in the same sequence of quadrants, for odd numbers of bolts per quadrant alternately tighten bolts numbered $(n + 1)/2$, $(n - 1)/2$, $(n + 3)/2$, $(n - 3)/2$, and so on until bolt-up is complete. For an even number, alternately tighten bolts numbered $(n + 2)/2$, $(n - 2)/2$, $(n + 4)/2$, $(n - 4)/2$, and so on.

The probable bolt stress developed manually with standard wrenches when bolting up is complete is*

$$S = \frac{45,000}{d} \text{ lb/in}^2 \qquad S = \frac{7,880,000 \text{ kPa}}{d} \qquad (5.12)$$

where S = bolt stress, lb/in^2 (kPa), and d = bolt diameter, in (mm).

Therefore, by using hand wrenches it is easy to overstress small-diameter bolts and hard to stress large-diameter bolts enough to achieve tightness. Most shops and maintenance departments use air-driven impact wrenches as a convenience for nut tightening on small studs and as a necessity on large ones.

---

*See Appendix S, Section VIII, page 744, of the 1989 edition of the *ASME Code*.

2. Relate bolt stress to torque by established equations or published tabulated values. Using a torque wrench, tighten the bolts in several rounds, increasing the torque by three or four equal increments. Follow the same tightening sequence as in manual wrenching.

A flaw in these two methods is that inadequate lubrication, foreign matter in the threads, and excessively tight nut-to-stud fits can give false impressions of nut tightness and torque. The only way to determine bolt stress truly (within the limits of the assumptions about material properties) is to measure the bolt elongation. In using an extensiometer or micrometers, this is a time-consuming procedure and would not ordinarily be done. However, inexpensive portable ultrasonic devices* are now available that measure the elongation and read out the bolt stress directly.

3. A more costly method eliminates false readings. Tighten the bolts by means of a hydraulic bolt tensioner, and verify the bolt stresses ultrasonically. These devices require longer stud bolts than those that are tightened by torque wrenches. The ends of groups of four or multiples of four bolts, distributed equally in the four quadrants, are simultaneously gripped by hydraulic rams and stretched within their elastic limits by a predetermined amount. With the studs in this condition, the nuts are run down handtight to the flange, following which the grips are released. The stress in the studs is calculated from the elongation by using Eq. (5.13):

$$S = Ee \qquad (5.13)$$

where, in consistent units, S is the bolt stress, E is Young's modulus, and e is the elongation.

Unless the tensioner can grip all the bolts at the same time, add bolt stress in several increments, using a sequence that will distribute the loads uniformly.

Allowable and actual bolt stresses.   Use the maximum allowable bolt stresses tabulated in the rules to determine the minimum amount of bolting, but be aware that the bolt stress that might actually exist or that might be needed for conditions other than the design pressure may exceed the allowables. Initial tightening prestresses the bolts. The stress it develops in the bolts must be adequate to resist conditions that tend to produce a leaking joint but not so much that it yields the bolt-flange assembly, thereby producing enough relaxation also to result in leakage.

The usual hydrostatic test is 1.5 times the design pressure, multi

---

*For example the Stress-Mike, a product of Strestel Inc., Scotts Valley, California.

plied by the ratio of atmospheric to design temperature allowable stresses. Consequently, the initial bolt stress must be more than that allowed for the design. Otherwise, the bolt strain developed during the hydrostatic test could let the joint separate. The ensuing gasket decompression may be so great that the joint leaks. Proper analysis of how much initial bolt stress is needed during prestress and application of test pressure requires considering changes in bolt elongation, flange deflection, and gasket load. There is a conservative margin between the *ASME Code*'s design stress values for bolting and the bolt yield stresses. Therefore, it is permissible to exceed the design bolt stress, of course guarding against excessive flange distortion and gasket crushing. The margin between the code's yield and allowable stresses is considerably less for flange and tubesheet materials than for bolting. For this reason, where permanently tight bolted joints are desired, always specify using the lower allowable stresses for materials where the code provides two sets of allowable stresses for flange and tubesheet materials.

If bolt stress decreases after initial tightening because of gasket creep or relaxation, restore tightness by retightening the bolts. At high service temperatures, the creep of the gasket (or gaskets, when the tubesheet is held between two flanges) bolts and flange may also allow leakage. This may also be corrected by retightening once or every so often. However, in designing for high temperature, consider the relaxation properties of the materials, especially where creep is the controlling factor in design.

In designing these bolted connections, consider the effects of differential thermal expansion between the flanges and tubesheets on the one hand and the bolts on the other. For the mechanical designer to do so, the thermal designer must provide an estimate of the flange, tubesheet, and bolt metal temperatures at the most severe case of startup, operation, shutdown, or upset.

If the differential is such that the bolts expand more than the mating parts, the gasket may be unloaded, leading to leakage. A common strategy in addition to retightening is to install suitably designed spring washers under the nuts that will maintain constant load on the studs. A successful but less common alternative is to replace the studs with longer ones, installing under the nuts thick washers of a material that has a higher thermal coefficient of expansion than the studs. These fixes may be combined.

More difficult to deal with is the problem when the mating parts expand more than the studs. The increased bolt load can yield the bolts, cause gasket overloading and crushing, and permanently warp the gasket contact surface or surfaces out of true plane.

Flange and tubesheet bending.   The *ASME Code* rules for designing the bolted connections discussed here are concerned only with not exceeding the allowable stresses; they do not consider elastic deflection. However, without exceeding allowable stresses, the parts may bend so much that there is contact at the edges. For this reason, consider using plain faces only for relatively low pressures and with the more easily compressed gaskets.

When the parts bend, the gasket is loaded differently than the design assumes. As may be seen by inspecting gaskets removed from such connections, the outer edge may be crushed and the inner edge hardly deformed. A joint that should have been tight may leak. This may be corrected by replacing the gaskets with ones more easily compressed. Evaluate the flange design to determine if this is acceptable.

Replacing the gaskets with ones that have limit rings may not relieve the problem. However, limit rings may prevent gross crushing under various load conditions. Tightness may be restored by installing a peripheral ring between the edges of the mating parts that is about half the gasket thickness. The flange and bolt stresses should be investigated for the contact condition.

Unbolting.   The tendency in unbolting a flanged joint is to use a nut runner to loosen and remove the bolts one after the other around the bolt circle. However, avoid this procedure because it can plastically deform the mating parts and studs. Consider the following.

When the unit is depressurized, if all the bolts are stressed equally and the joint was tight or nearly tight before shutdown, the gasket reaction and consequent flange bending moments are distributed in the more or less uniform pattern described in Ref. 33. If one bolt is completely removed, and the mating parts are stiff enough to prevent gasket relaxation between the bolts on either side of the empty hole, the stress in the remaining bolts must increase to absorb the gasket reaction. As more bolts are removed, the bolt stress may increase enough to yield the bolts and all the parts may warp in the vicinity of the tight bolts opposite the completely unbolted region.

In some refinery operations, a standard maintenance procedure is to remachine tubesheets and flanges after each disassembly. The probable principal cause of the assumed distortion that the remachining is intended to correct is failure to use a suitable unbolting procedure such as the following:

1. Unbolt in the sequence described under bolting up.

2. Release the bolt load in several passes that unload the bolts inapproximately equal increments.

Integral connections

Except for small units, most closed feedwater heater channels and bonnets are welded to the tubeside of the tubesheet and the shell to its shellside. Because the extraction steam that enters the shell is relatively clean and the foulants it deposits can be removed by chemical cleaning, the savings to be had by eliminating a pair of flanges is deemed to be worthwhile. The shells are carbon steel, which is readily burned by an oxyacetylene torch or carbon-arced. Heater manufacturers indicate the position of a parting or burn line located a short distance behind the tubesheet. To protect the tubes when the shell is severed, they wrap a shield, usually of light-gauge stainless steel, around the bundle in way of the burn line.

Fastening the bundle integrally to the shell limits access to the shellside of the bundle. To maintain the condensing- and subcooling-zone closures and other shellside parts, the shell must be cut loose or windows must be cut into the shell and rewelded.

The tubesheet of fixed-tubesheet exchangers is also connected integrally to the shell by welding. (See Chap. 3 for channel and bonnet connections to the tubesheet.) This suggests that when the only reason for selecting a U-tube bundle unit is to accommodate differential expansion and the shellside fluid is relatively nonfouling (steam, for example), one should consider adopting the construction used for feedwater heaters.

References

1. *Shell-and-Tube Heat Exchangers for General Refinery Services*, API Standard 660, 4th ed., The American Petroleum Institute, Washington, September 1982.
2. *Standards of the Tubular Exchanger Manufacturers Association*, 7th ed., The Tubular Exchanger Manufacturers Association, Tarrytown, New York, 1988, Table RCB-7.42.
3. *Standard for Power Plant Heat Exchangers*, 1st ed., The Heat Exchange Institute, Cleveland, 1980; Addendum 1, 1984.
4. D. Q. Kern, *Process Heat Transfer*, McGraw-Hill Book Company, New York, 1950.
5. P. S. Phadke, "Determining Tube Counts for Shell-and-Tube Exchangers," *Chem. Eng.*, Sept. 3, 1984.
6. R. C. Lord, P. E. M'nton, and R. P. Slusser, "Design of Heat Exchangers," *Chem. Eng.*, Jan. 26, 1970.
7. A. Devore, G. J. Vago, and G. J. Picozzi, "Specifying and Selecting," *Chem. Eng.*, Oct. 6, 1980.
8. F. L. Rubin, "How to Specify Heat Exchangers," *Chem. Eng.*, Apr. 8, 1968.
9. J. P. Fanaritis and J. W. Bevevino, "Designing Shell-and-Tube Heat Exchangers, *Chem. Eng.*, July 5, 1976.
10. J. R. Pudlock, "Comparative Costs of Metallic Corrosion-Resistant Shell-and-Tube Heat Exchangers," *Oil Gas J.*, Sept. 5, 1977.
11. J. R. Pudlock, "The Economics of Shell-and-Tube Heat Exchangers," prepared for Westec Titanium Section, Futura Titanium, Westlake Village, Calif., sponsored by ASM and SME, Mar. 23, 1978.

12. B. J. Noe and G. L. Strickler, "Computerized Cost Estimation of Heat Exchangers," ASME Pap. 83-HT-1983.
13. G. P. Purohit, "Estimating Costs of Shell-and-Tube Heat Exchangers," *Chem. Eng.*, Aug. 22, 1983.
14. N. Afgan and E. U. Schlunder (eds.), *Heat Exchangers: Design and Theory Sourcebook*, Hemisphere Publishing Corp., Washington, 1974.
15. G. K. Pase and S. Yokell, "Interpass Temperature Effects in Multipass Straight Tube Exchangers," *Chem. Eng. Prog.*, July 1983.
16. *ASME Boiler and Pressure Vessel Code*, 1989 ed., American Society of Mechanical Engineers, New York.
17. K. P. Singh, "Method for Quantifying Heat Duty Derating Due to Interpass Leakage in Bolted Flat Cover Heat Exchangers," *Heat Transfer Eng.*, vol. 4, no. 3–4, July–December 1983.
18. *Standard for Closed Feedwater Heaters*, 4th ed., The Heat Exchange Institute, Cleveland, 1984.
19. *Recommended Guidelines for the Operation and Maintenance of Feedwater Heaters*, EPRI CS-3239, Electric Power and Research Institute, September 1983.
20. J. E. Schroeder and S. N. Flesner, *Feedwater Heater Tubesheet System Design Features for Cyclic Operation*.
21. Donald and Singer, *Trans. Inst. Chem. Eng. (London)*, vol. 37, 1959, pp. 255–267.
22. K. R. Whichman, A. G. Hopper, and J. L. Mersmon, *Local Stresses in Spherical and Cylindrical Shells Due to External Loadings*, Welding Research Council Bull. 107, rev. 1, March 1979.
23. K. P. Singh, "Study of Bolted Joint Integrity and Inter-Tube-Pass Leakage in U-Tube Heat Exchangers, Part I: Analysis; Part II: Applications," *J. Eng. Power, Trans. ASME*, 1978.
24. E. O. Waters and J. H. Taylor, "The Strength of Pipe Flanges," *Mech. Eng.*, vol. 49, mid-May 1927, pp. 531–542.
25. E. O. Waters, D. B. Westrom, D. B. Rossheim, and F. S. G. Williams, "Formulas for Stresses in Bolted Flanged Connections," *Trans. ASME*, vol. 59, 1937, pp. 161–169.
26. E. O. Waters, D. B. Rossheim, D. B. Westrom, and F. S. G. Williams, *Development of General Formulas for Bolted Flanges*, Taylor Forge and Pipe Works, Chicago, 1949.
27. R. W. Schneider, "Flat Face Flanges with Metal-to-Metal Contact beyond the Bolt Circle," *J. Eng. Power, Trans. ASME*, ser. A, vol. 90, no. 1, January 1968, pp. 82–88.
28. E. O. Waters and R. W. Schneider, "Axisymmetric, Non-Identical, Flat Face Flanges with Metal-to-Metal Contact beyond the Bolt Circle," *J. Eng. Ind., Trans. ASME*, ser. B, vol. 91, no. 3, August 1969, pp. 615–622.
29. E. O. Waters, *Derivation of Code Formulas for Part B Flanges*, Welding Research Council Bull. 166, October 1971.
30. R. W. Schneider and E. O. Waters, "Some Considerations Regarding the Analysis of Part B Code Flanges—1974," ASME Pap. 75-PVP-48, 1975.
31. R. W. Schneider and E. O. Waters, "The Background of ASME Code Case 1828: A Simplified Method of Analyzing Part B Flanges," *J. Press. Ves. Technol., Trans. ASME*, vol. 100, no. 2, May 1978, pp. 215–219.
32. R. W. Schneider and E. O. Waters, "The Application of ASME Code Case 1828," *J. Press. Ves. Technol., Trans. ASME*, vol. 101, no. 1, February 1979, pp. 87–94.
33. I. Roberts, "Gaskets and Bolted Joints," *J. Appl. Mech., Trans. ASME*, vol. 17, June 1950, pp. 169–179.
34. D. B. Rossheim and A. R. C. Markl, "Gasket-Loading Constants," *Mech. Eng.*, September 1943, pp. 647–648.
35. G. R. Kent, "Selecting Gaskets for Flanged Joints," *Chem. Eng.*, March 1978, pp.125–128.
36. H. D. Raut and G. F. Leon, *Report of Gasket Factor Tests*, Welding Research CouncilBull. 233, December 1977.

37. H. D. Raut, A. Bazergui, and L. Marchand, *Gasket Leakage Behavior Trends*, Welding Research Council Bull. 271, October 1981.
38. J. R. Payne and A. Bazergui, "More Progress in Gasket Testing—the PVRC Program," *Proc. Refining Dept.*, vol. 60, American Petroleum Institute, 1981, pp. 271–290.
39. J. H. Bickford, "That Initial Preload—What Happens to It? *Mech. Eng.*, October 1983, pp. 57–61.
40. A. Bazergui and J. R. Payne, *Progress in Gasket Testing—Milestone Results*, Welding Research Council Bull. 292, February 1984.
41. G. F. Leon and J. R. Payne, "Current Research on the Behavior of Bolted Joints," Pap. 4.3, National Design Engineering Show and ASME Conference, Chicago, March 1984.
42. J. R. Payne, A. Bazergui, and G. F. Leon, "A New Look at Gasket Factors," Pap. Hl, *Proc. Tenth Int. Conf. Fluid Sealing*, Innsbruck, Austria, Apr. 3–5, 1984, pp. 345–363.
43. A. Bazergui, L. Marchand, and J. R. Payne, "Effect of Fluid on Sealing Behaviour of Gaskets," Pap. H2, *Proc. Tenth Int. Conf. Fluid Sealing*, Innsbruck, Austria, Apr. 3–5, 1984, pp. 365–368.
44. "Design Division Problem XIII: Re-evaluation of Gasket Factors Used in Flange Design," *Long-Range Plan for Pressure Vessel Research*, 7th ed., Welding Research Council Bull. 298, September 1984.
45. A. Bazergui, L. Marchand, and H. D. Raut, *Development of a Production Test Procedure for Gaskets*, Welding Research Council Bull. 309, November 1985.
46. J. R. Payne, A. Bazergui, and G. F. Leon, "New Gasket Factors—A Proposed Procedure," *Proc. Press. Ves. Piping Conf.*, vol. 98-2, New Orleans, June 1985.

6

Shellside Construction

Introduction

This chapter deals with shell manufacture, construction of bundles, and assembly of bundles to shells. Shell manufacture covers pipe and rolled-plate shells, shell-fluid distribution belts, vapor belts, and expansion joints, shell connections, impingement protection, and exchanger supports. Bundle construction encompasses shellside pass-partition construction, baffle systems, and tube supports. The section on assembly and attachment to the shell discusses how bundles are put together, inserted into the shell, and fastened.

Differential-pressure design requirements are discussed here despite the necessity for considering the simultaneous tube and shell operating regimes. This is so because the subject naturally follows the preceding chapters. This chapter also has an overview of tube vibration, which is mostly a shell-flow-induced phenomenon. While a detailed treatment is beyond this work's scope, vibration damage to heat exchangers is described and illustrated, the causes and mechanisms of tube vibration are outlined, and the information required for analysis is summarized.

Manufacturing the Shell

Most heat exchanger shells are fabricated from commercially available seamless or welded wrought pipe or from plate rolled into longitudinally welded cylinders. A small number are cast, generally for low-pressure water or steam service. Extruded seamless thick-walled pipe is used for intermediate- to high-pressure service when economical. When shell thickness exceeds commercially available pipe and is beyond the capacities of generally available braking and rolling equipment and extrusion presses, shells are forged.

Pipe shells

Seamless and welded pipe conforming with *ASME Code* specifications is manufactured in cut and random lengths approximately 20 ft (6.1 m) long.[1] Double-random lengths can be had in lengths of approximately 40 ft (12.2 m). Longer double-random length pipes may be obtained by selecting them from a mill run of double-random lengths or on special order.

In the United States, mills produce extruded seamless and automatically formed and welded pressure pipe to the dimensions shown in Table 6.1. Sizes that warehouses usually stock and that mills produce in quantity are shown in boldface. Mills will produce the other sizes and thicknesses on special order. Special-order sizes are costly and difficult to obtain. Therefore, these sizes of shells are usually made from rolled-and-welded plate cylinders or extruded seamless heavy-wall pipe.

Seamless thick-wall pipe is purchased to order. The mill controls the thickness and either the outside or the inside diameter. Variations in thickness and diameter are measured on the uncontrolled surface. Thick-wall pipe for heat exchangers should be ordered to a controlled ID. This will ensure ease of tube bundle insertion and maintenance of design clearances between cross-flow baffles and the shell ID. Table 6.2 lists the available ranges of diameters, wall thicknesses, and lengths of thick-wall seamless extruded pipe for carbon and low-alloy steels and for the austenitic stainless steels that Cameron Iron Works of Houston, Texas, produces. A variety of diameters, thicknesses, and lengths is available between the extremes of the ranges.

Pipe tolerances.   Section II of the *ASME Code* has tolerances for pipe. To account for manufacturing variations in thickness and concentricity, the minimum wall thickness is considered to be 87½ percent of the tabulated nominal wall. Because required thicknesses calculated under *ASME Code* rules are *minimum* thicknesses, designers may use only 87½ percent of the nominal pipe wall in shell thickness calculations.

The *ASME Code* specifications list permissible variations in outside diameter. Typical are tolerances for pipe, NPS 2 and larger, produced to specification SA-53 (identical with ASTM A-53-81-A) and specification SA-106 (identical with ASTM A-106-82) listed in Table 6.3. SA-53

TABLE 6.1 TEMA Shell Sizes and Permissible Pipe Sizes Available in the United States

Sizes in boldface are stock sizes; others require special order.

TEMA size	NPS	OD	Permissible pipe thicknesses; pipe schedule nominal wall thickness, in					
			TEMA classes, carbon steel			TEMA classes, alloys		
			R	B	C	R	B	C
6	6	6.625	....	**40** **0.280**	**40** **0.280**	....	**5S** **0.109**	**5S** **0.109**
			....	**XS/80** **0.432**	**XS/80** **0.432**	....	**10S** **0.134**	**10S** **0.134**
			....	120 0.562	120 0.562	....	**40S** **0.280**	**40S** **0.280**
7	8	8.625	100 0.594	100 0.594	100 0.594	80S 0.500	80S 0.500	80S 0.500
			120 0.719	120 0.719	120 0.719			
			140 0.812	140 0.812	140 0.812			
			XXS 0.875	XXS 0.875	XXS 0.875			
			160 0.906	160 0.906	160 0.906			
8	8	8.625	**30** **0.277**	**30** **0.277**	**30** **0.277**	**5S** **0.109**	**5S** **0.109**	**5S** **0.109**
			60 0.406	60 0.406	60 0.406	**10S** **0.148**	**10S** **0.148**	**10S** **0.148**
			XS/80 **0.500**	**XS/80** **0.500**	**XS/80** **0.500**	**40S** **0.322**	**40S** **0.322**	**40S** **0.322**
9	10	10.625	160 1.125	160 1.125	160 1.125			
			80 **0.594**	**80** **0.594**	**80** **0.5904**	**40S** **0.365**	**40S** **0.365**	**40S** **0.365**
			100 0.719	100 0.719	100 0.719	80S 0.500	80S 0.500	80S 0.500
			120 0.844	120 0.844	120 0.844			
			140/XS 1.000	140/XS 1.000	140/XS 1.000			
10	10	10.625	**30** **0.307**	**30** **0.307**	**30** **0.307**	**5S** **0.134**	**5S** **0.134**	**5S** **0.134**
			40 **0.365**	**40** **0.365**	**40** **0.365**	**10S** **0.165**	**10S** **0.165**	**10S** **0.165**
			60/XS **0.500**	**60/XS** **0.500**	**60/XS** **0.500**	**20S** **0.250**	**20S** **0.250**	**20S** **0.250**

TABLE 6.1   TEMA Shell Sizes and Permissible Pipe Sizes Available in the United States (Continued)

Sizes in boldface are stock sizes; others require special order.

TEMA size	NPS	OD	Permissible pipe thicknesses; pipe schedule nominal wall thickness, in					
			TEMA classes, carbon steel			TEMA classes, alloys		
			R	B	C	R	B	C
10	12	12.75	160 / 1.312	160 / 1.312	160 / 1.312			
11	12	12.75	**80** / **0.688**	**80** / **0.688**	**80** / **0.688**			
			100 / 0.844	100 / 0.844	100 / 0.844			
			120/XX / **1.000**	**120/XX** / **1.000**	**120/XX** / **1.000**			
11	14	14	160 / 1.406	160 / 1.406	160 / 1.406			
			140 / 1.125	140 / 1.125	140 / 1.125			
12	12	12.75	**30** / **0.330**	**30** / **0.330**	**30** / **0.330**	**5S** / **0.156**	**5S** / **0.156**	**5S** / **0.156**
			STD / **0.375**	**STD** / **0.375**	**STD** / **0.375**	**10S** / **0.180**	**10S** / **0.180**	**10S** / **0.180**
			40 / **0.406**	**40** / **0.406**	**40** / **0.406**	**40S** / **0.375**	**40S** / **0.375**	**40S** / **0.375**
			XS / **0.500**	**XS** / **0.500**	**XS** / **0.500**	**80S** / **0.500**	**80S** / **0.500**	**80S** / **0.500**
			60 / 0.562	60 / 0.562	60 / 0.562			
12	14	14	100 / 0.938	100 / 0.938	100 / 0.938			
			120 / 1.096	120 / 1.096	120 / 1.096			
			140 / 1.250	140 / 1.250	140 / 1.250			
13	14	14	....	**20** / **0.312**	**20** / **0.312**	**10S** / 0.188	**5S** / **0.156**	**5S** / **0.156**
			30/STD / **0.375**	**30/STD** / **0.375**	**30/STD** / **0.375**	....	**10S** / **0.188**	**10S** / **0.188**
			40 / 0.438	**40** / 0.438	**40** / 0.438	80S / 0.500	**80S** / **0.500**	**80S** / **0.500**

TABLE 6.1   TEMA Shell Sizes and Permissible Pipe Sizes Available in the United States (*Continued*)

Sizes in boldface are stock sizes; others require special order.

TEMA size	NPS	OD	Permissible pipe thicknesses; pipe schedule nominal wall thickness, in					
			TEMA classes, carbon steel			TEMA classes, alloys		
			R	B	C	R	B	C
13	14	14	**XS** **0.500**	**XS** **0.500**	**XS** **0.500**			
			60 0.594	60 0.594	60 0.594			
			80 **0.750**	**80** **0.750**	**80** **0.750**			
13	16	16	140 1.438	140 1.438	140 1.438			
			160 1.594	160 1.594	160 1.594			
14	16	16	**80** **0.844**	**80** **0.844**	**80** **0.844**			
			100 1.031	100 1.031	100 1.031			
			120 1.219	120 1.219	120 1.219			
14	18	18	160 1.781	160 1.781	160 1.781			
15	16	16	....	**20/STD** **0.312**	**20/STD** **0.125**	**10S** **0.188**	**5S** **0.165**	**5S** **0.165**
			30/STD **0.375**	**30/STD** **0.375**	**30/STD** **0.375**	....	**10S** **0.188**	**10S** **0.188**
			40/XS **0.500**	**40/XS** **0.500**	**40/XS** **0.500**			
			60 0.656	60 0.656	60 0.656			
15	18	18	120 1.375	120 1.375	120 1.375			
			140 1.438	140 1.438	140 1.438			
16	18	18	60 0.750	60 0.750	60 0.750			
			80 0.938	80 0.938	80 0.938			

TABLE 6.1 TEMA Shell Sizes and Permissible Pipe Sizes Available in the United States (Continued)

Sizes in boldface are stock sizes; others require special order.

| | | | Permissible pipe thicknesses; pipe schedule nominal wall thickness, in | | | | | |
| | | | TEMA classes, carbon steel | | | TEMA classes, alloys | | |
TEMA size	NPS	OD	R	B	C	R	B	C
16	18	18	$\dfrac{100}{1.156}$	$\dfrac{100}{1.156}$	$\dfrac{100}{1.156}$			
16	20	20	$\dfrac{140}{1.750}$	$\dfrac{140}{1.750}$	$\dfrac{140}{1.750}$			
16	20	20	$\dfrac{160}{1.969}$	$\dfrac{160}{1.969}$	$\dfrac{160}{1.969}$			
17	18	18	....	$\dfrac{\mathbf{20}}{\mathbf{0.312}}$	$\dfrac{\mathbf{20}}{\mathbf{0.312}}$	....	$\dfrac{\mathbf{5S}}{\mathbf{0.165}}$	$\dfrac{\mathbf{5S}}{\mathbf{0.165}}$
			$\dfrac{\mathbf{STD}}{\mathbf{0.375}}$	$\dfrac{\mathbf{STD}}{\mathbf{0.375}}$	$\dfrac{\mathbf{STD}}{\mathbf{0.375}}$	$\dfrac{\mathbf{10S}}{\mathbf{0.188}}$	$\dfrac{\mathbf{10S}}{\mathbf{0.188}}$	$\dfrac{\mathbf{10S}}{\mathbf{0.188}}$
			$\dfrac{30}{0.438}$	$\dfrac{30}{0.438}$	$\dfrac{30}{0.438}$			
			$\dfrac{\mathbf{XS}}{\mathbf{0.500}}$	$\dfrac{\mathbf{XS}}{\mathbf{0.500}}$	$\dfrac{\mathbf{XS}}{\mathbf{0.500}}$			
17	18	18	$\dfrac{40}{0.562}$	$\dfrac{40}{0.562}$	$\dfrac{40}{0.562}$			
17	20	20	$\dfrac{100}{1.281}$	$\dfrac{100}{1.281}$	$\dfrac{100}{1.281}$			
			$\dfrac{120}{1.500}$	$\dfrac{120}{1.500}$	$\dfrac{120}{1.500}$			
18	20	20	$\dfrac{60}{0.812}$	$\dfrac{60}{0.812}$	$\dfrac{60}{0.812}$			
			$\dfrac{80}{1.031}$	$\dfrac{80}{1.031}$	$\dfrac{80}{1.031}$			
18	22	22	$\dfrac{140}{1.875}$	$\dfrac{140}{1.875}$	$\dfrac{140}{1.875}$			
			$\dfrac{160}{2.125}$	$\dfrac{160}{2.125}$	$\dfrac{160}{2.125}$			
19	20	20	$\dfrac{\mathbf{20/STD}}{\mathbf{0.375}}$	$\dfrac{\mathbf{20/STD}}{\mathbf{0.375}}$	$\dfrac{\mathbf{20/STD}}{\mathbf{0.375}}$			
			$\dfrac{\mathbf{30/XS}}{\mathbf{0.500}}$	$\dfrac{\mathbf{30/XS}}{\mathbf{0.500}}$	$\dfrac{\mathbf{30/XS}}{\mathbf{0.500}}$			
			$\dfrac{40}{0.594}$	$\dfrac{40}{0.594}$	$\dfrac{40}{0.594}$			
19	22	22	$\dfrac{100}{1.375}$	$\dfrac{100}{1.375}$	$\dfrac{100}{1.375}$			

TABLE 6.1   TEMA Shell Sizes and Permissible Pipe Sizes Available in the United States (*Continued*)

Sizes in boldface are stock sizes; others require special order.

| TEMA size | NPS | OD | Permissible pipe thicknesses; pipe schedule nominal wall thickness, in | | | | | |
| | | | TEMA classes, carbon steel | | | TEMA classes, alloys | | |
			R	B	C	R	B	C
19	22	22	$\dfrac{120}{1.625}$	$\dfrac{120}{1.625}$	$\dfrac{120}{1.625}$			
19	24	24	$\dfrac{160}{2.344}$	$\dfrac{160}{2.344}$	$\dfrac{160}{2.344}$			
20	22	22	$\dfrac{60}{0.875}$	$\dfrac{60}{0.875}$	$\dfrac{60}{0.875}$			
			$\dfrac{80}{1.125}$	$\dfrac{80}{1.125}$	$\dfrac{80}{1.125}$			
20	24	24	$\dfrac{120}{1.812}$	$\dfrac{120}{1.812}$	$\dfrac{120}{1.812}$			
			$\dfrac{140}{2.062}$	$\dfrac{140}{2.062}$	$\dfrac{140}{2.062}$			
21	22	22	$\dfrac{20/STD}{0.375}$	$\dfrac{20/STD}{0.375}$	$\dfrac{20/STD}{0.375}$			
			$\dfrac{30/XS}{0.500}$	$\dfrac{30/XS}{0.500}$	$\dfrac{30/XS}{0.500}$			
21	24	24	$\dfrac{100}{1.531}$	$\dfrac{100}{1.531}$	$\dfrac{100}{1.531}$			
22	24	24	$\dfrac{60}{0.969}$	$\dfrac{60}{0.969}$	$\dfrac{60}{0.969}$			
			$\dfrac{80}{1.218}$	$\dfrac{80}{1.218}$	$\dfrac{80}{1.218}$			
23	24	24	$\dfrac{20/STD}{0.375}$	$\dfrac{20/STD}{0.375}$	$\dfrac{20/STD}{0.375}$			
			$\dfrac{XS}{0.500}$	$\dfrac{XS}{0.500}$	$\dfrac{XS}{0.500}$			
			$\dfrac{30}{0.562}$	$\dfrac{30}{0.562}$	$\dfrac{30}{0.562}$			
			$\dfrac{40}{0.688}$	$\dfrac{40}{0.688}$	$\dfrac{40}{0.688}$			
25	26	26	$\dfrac{STD}{0.375}$	$\dfrac{STD}{0.375}$	$\dfrac{STD}{0.375}$			
			$\dfrac{20/XS}{0.500}$	$\dfrac{20/XS}{0.500}$	$\dfrac{20/XS}{0.500}$			

TABLE 6.1   TEMA Shell Sizes and Permissible Pipe Sizes Available in the United States (*Continued*)

Sizes in boldface are stock sizes; others require special order.

TEMA size	NPS	OD	Permissible pipe thicknesses; pipe schedule nominal wall thickness, in					
			TEMA classes, carbon steel			TEMA classes, alloys		
			R	B	C	R	B	C
27	28	28	STD 0.375	STD 0.375	STD 0.375			
			20/XS 0.500	20/XS 0.500	20/XS 0.500			
			30 0.625	30 0.625	30 0.625			
29	30	30	STD 0.375	STD 0.375	STD 0.375			
			20/XS 0.500	20/XS 0.500	20/XS 0.500			
			30 0.625	30 0.625	30 0.625			
31	32	32	STD 0.375	STD 0.375	STD 0.375			
31	32	32	20/XS 0.500	20/XS 0.500	20/XS 0.500			
			30 0.625	30 0.625	30 0.625			
			40 0.688	40 0.688	40 0.688			
33	34	34	STD 0.375	STD 0.375	STD 0.375			
			20/XS 0.500	20/XS 0.500	20/XS 0.500			
			30 0.625	30 0.625	30 0.625			
			40 0.688	40 0.688	40 0.688			

TABLE 6.1   TEMA Shell Sizes and Permissible Pipe Sizes Available in the United States (Continued)

Sizes in boldface are stock sizes; others require special order.

TEMA size	NPS	OD	Permissible pipe thicknesses; pipe schedule nominal wall thickness, in					
			TEMA classes, carbon steel			TEMA classes, alloys		
			R	B	C	R	B	C
35	36	36	STD 0.375	STD 0.375	STD 0.375			
			20/XS 0.500	20/XS 0.500	20/XS 0.500			
			30 0.625	30 0.625	30 0.625			
			40 0.750	40 0.750	40 0.750			
41	42	42	STD 0.375	STD 0.375	STD 0.375			
			XS 0.500	XS 0.500	XS 0.500			

states that the outside diameter shall not vary by more than ±1 percent.

Rolled-plate shells

Rolled-plate shells are made by rolling plate or sheet into open seamed cylinders in plate-bending rolls, press braking, or press braking and rolling. Plate roll capacities are defined in terms of the top roll diameter, which establishes the *smallest*-diameter cylinder that can be rolled; the roll width, which establishes the *longest* cylinder that can be rolled; and thicknesses that can be rolled for various diameter-width and metal property combinations. Depending upon the combination of diameter, thickness, length, and metal properties, rolling may be done cold or hot.

Rolled-plate shells are used under these circumstances:

1. Pipe of the desired size is not available. (The order quantity for special-order pipe may be insufficient for a mill run, or mills may not manufacture pipe from the required material of construction.)

2. Delivery of the required size of commercial pipe is too extended for the construction schedule.

3. It costs less to fabricate the rolled-and-welded cylinder than to buy the pipe.

TABLE 6.2   Range of Sizes of Thick-Wall Extruded Pipe

Bottom end of range			Top end of range		
		English Units			
ID, in ×	Wall, in ×	Length, ft	ID, in ×	Wall, in ×	Length, ft
		Carbon and Low-Alloy Steel			
6.00	1.150	43	41.750	1.750	12
	1.260	43	42.000	1.260	17
	1.385	43		1.385	15
	1.510	43		1.510	14
	1.625	43		1.625	13
		Stainless Steel			
5.650	0.688	43	41.750	1.260	15
	0.793	43	42.00	1.385	14
	0.900	43	51.570	1.260	15
	1.025	43		1.385	13
	1.150	43		1.510	12
				1.510	13
		Metric Units			
ID, mm ×	Wall, mm ×	Length, m	ID, mm ×	Wall, mm ×	Length, m
		Carbon and Low-Alloy Steel			
152	29	13.1	1060	44	3.8
	32	13.1	1067	32	5.1
	35	13.1		35	4.7
	38	13.1		38	4.3
	41	13.1		41	3.9
		Stainless Steel			
146	17	13.1	1060	32	4.6
	20	13.1	1067	35	4.2
	23	13.1		32	4.4
	26	13.1		35	4.1
	29	13.1		38	3.8

Pipe costs depend upon current market conditions. Generally, it is economical to roll and weld austenitic stainless-steel shells larger than standard-weight NPS 12, and nickel, nickel-copper, Hastelloys, and similar materials NPS 10 and larger.

Rolled-plate shell tolerances. The *ASME Code* rules define minimum plate thickness as the ordered thickness less a mill tolerance of 0.01 in (0.25 mm). The designer may use the full plate thickness in *ASME*

TABLE 6.3 Permissible Variations in OD of SA-106 Pipe

	Over		Under	
NPS designator	in	mm	in	mm
Over 8 to 18 inclusive	3/32 (0.093)	2.38	1/32 (0.031)	0.79
Over 18 to 26 inclusive	1/8 (0.125)	3.18	1/32 (0.031)	0.79
Over 26 to 34 inclusive	5/32 (0.156)	3.97	1/32 (0.031)	0.79
Over 34 to 48 inclusive	3/16 (0.187)	4.76	1/32 (0.031)	0.79

Code calculations. The *ASME Code* roundness tolerance for cylinders, expressed as maximum minus minimum OD, is 1 percent of the nominal OD. This is not acceptable for some sizes of heat exchangers built to the *TEMA Standards*.[2] As shown in Table 6.4, at the limit of the *ASME Code*'s roundness tolerances for the shell sizes listed in boldface, when the shell ID minus the cross-flow-baffle OD meets the TEMA maximum diametral clearance, the minimum shell ID will interfere with the baffles. Therefore, the roundness tolerance for most rolled-plate exchanger shells must be less than 1 percent of the diameter.

Effects of forming and welding on plate shells. To facilitate feeding the plate into the bending rolls, the plate is broken 6 in (150 mm) or more back from the leading edge. As a result, there is a flat spot where the plate enters the rolls (Fig. 6.1). In addition, to a degree that depends upon plate width and bending-roll length, shape, and diameter, the leading and trailing edges of the plate curve into an arcuate shape. The surest way to eliminate flat spots and curved edges is to start with a plate longer than the mean circumference of the cylinder into which it is to be formed. The extra length provides an allowance for trimming off the flat and uneven ends. This practice should be required for plates 3/4 in (19 mm) and thicker.

When the plate material is costly or when extra length is not available, fabricators grind or otherwise trim the ends to a fit that provides a uniform root opening for welding the long seam. After completing the welding, they may grind the weld flush and reround the cylinder in the plate-bending roll. Rerolling is desirable even when the flat ends have been trimmed off in order to mitigate the effects of weld shrinkage on roundness. Plate that had to be rolled hot because of the combination of diameter, thickness, and material will have to be rerolled hot.

Grain structure and orientation and physical properties are approximately uniform throughout flat plate. This changes when a plate is rolled. To understand the changes, think of a neutral plane as the

TABLE 6.4   Comparison of ASME Code–Allowed Out-of-Roundness for Formed Plate Cylinders with TEMA Maximum Permissible Diametral Clearances

Nominal OD		Code maximum minus minimum OD		Code undertolerance from mean ID		TEMA maximum diametral baffle-to-shell clearance	
in	mm	in	mm	in	mm	in	mm
6⅝	168.3	0.0663	1.684	0.0332	0.8433	0.100	2.540
8⅝	219.1	0.0863	1.097	0.0432	1.0973	0.100	2.540
10¾	273	0.1075	2.730	0.0538	1.3665	0.100	2.540
12¾	323.8	0.1275	3.238	0.0638	1.6205	0.100	2.540
14	355.6	0.1400	3.556	0.0700	1.778	0.100	2.540
16	406.4	0.1600	4.064	0.0800	2.032	0.125	3.175
18	457.2	0.1800	4.572	0.0900	2.286	0.125	3.175
20	508	0.2000	5.080	0.1000	2.540	0.150	3.810
22	558.8	0.2200	5.588	0.1100	2.754	0.150	3.810
24	609.6	0.2400	6.096	0.1200	3.048	0.150	3.810
25¾	654	0.2575	6.540	0.1238	3.144	0.175	4.445
27¾	704.8	0.2738	6.955	0.1369	3.477	0.175	4.445
29¾	755.6	0.2975	7.556	0.1488	3.780	0.175	4.445
31¾	806.4	0.3175	8.064	0.1588	4.033	0.175	4.445
33¾	857.2	**0.1688**	**4.288**	**0.1688**	**4.288**	0.175	4.445
35¾	908.0	**0.3575**	**9.080**	**0.1788**	**4.452**	0.175	4.445
38	965.2	**0.3800**	**9.652**	**0.1900**	**4.826**	0.175	4.445
40	1016	**0.4000**	**10.160**	**0.2000**	**5.080**	0.175	4.445
42	1066.8	0.4200	10.668	0.2100	5.334	0.225	5.715
44	1117.6	0.4500	11.430	0.2100	5.334	0.225	5.715
46⅛	1171.6	**0.4613**	**11.717**	**0.2306**	**5.857**	0.225	5.715
48⅛	1222.4	**0.4813**	**12.225**	**0.2406**	**6.112**	0.225	5.715
52¼	1327.2	**0.5225**	**13.271**	**0.2612**	**6.634**	0.225	5.715
56¼	1428.8	0.5625	14.288	0.2812	7.142	0.300	7.620
61½	1562.1	0.6150	15.621	0.3075	7.781	0.300	7.620

NOTE: The figures in boldface highlight sizes in which the permissible *ASME Code* undertolerance is greater than the permissible TEMA clearance.

plane that passes halfway through a plate's thickness parallel to its faces. Rolling stretches the fibers outside the neutral plane and compresses those that are inside. This makes the grain structure and orientation vary throughout the thickness. The work of rolling strain-hardens the plate. The intensity of these effects depends upon the plate material and the diameter-to-thickness ratio. Postforming stress relieving restores the plate approximately to its original condition. In common with other codes, the *ASME Code* requires postforming stress relieving, depending on the material, part thickness, extreme fiber elongation, forming temperature, etc.

Plate cylinders too thick to be rolled in bending rolls may be broken in press brakes. In addition to stretching outer fibers and compressing

Flat spot resulting from not trimming rolled plate

└─Shell sinks in where large nozzle enters

Cusp in longitudinal seam resulting from weld shrinkage

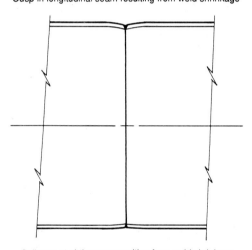

Collapse at girth seam resulting from weld shrinkage

Figure 6.1 Effects of rolling and welding on plate cylinders.

inner ones, the brake leaves marks or indentations on the inner surface. Postforming stress relief requirements apply.

Virtually all heat exchanger seams are fusion-welded. Heat developed in the arc between the electrode and the workpiece melts the edges of the base metals and any filler metal. As the electrode traverses the seam, the trailing molten pool cools, solidifies, and contracts.

Figure 6.1 illustrates how weld metal contraction distorts rolled-plate shells. The long-seam weld produces a cusp that may interfere with installing and removing the tube bundle. Note that the *ASME*

Code's 1 percent out-of-roundness limit includes long-seam weld shrinkage.

Fabricators try to minimize weld shrinkage. They investigate and experiment with welding processes, procedures, and techniques to determine those that will produce the least shrinkage. Generally, they use the lowest arc voltage that will achieve full penetration and at the same time deposit metal that is crack-free and within the pressure safety code's porosity and hardness limits.

It is less costly to use a few heavy weld passes to produce the seam than multiple light passes, but the possibility of distortion increases when heavy beads are laid down. Shops strike a balance between the benefits of minimum welding time and the costs of dealing with distortion due to weld shrinkage.

More than one welding process may be used on a seam. Frequently, the root pass is made by the gas-tungsten arc-welding process and subsequent passes by gas-metal arc, submerged arc, or metal arc welding. When practical, heatsinks are used to minimize distortion. Air-blast and water-spray cooling of the back side of the joint may be employed. If the welding is done from the outside only, a removable ceramic backing strip may be used to ensure full penetration and a smooth, crevice-free inner surface.

Common practice is to brace the shell with temporarily fitted combinations of spiders and internal pipe columns to restrain distortion as the weld metal cools. Nevertheless, there is always some warping, especially in regions of nozzle penetrations. (See Fig. 6.1.) Large-diameter thin-walled shells tend to sink in where large nozzles penetrate despite attempts to maintain roundness by encircling the shell with angle- or bar-ring retainers. Reinforcing rings around such nozzles increase this tendency.

Weld quality and finish. Undercutting and porosity may lead to corrosion in the weld and the adjacent heat-affected zone. Crowns of as-welded seams would interfere with bundle insertion and removal. Therefore, except for kettle-type heat exchangers, the *TEMA Standards* require all weld seams to be flush with the inside surface of the shell. In kettle-type equipment, they require the seams to be flush where the bundle makes contact with the shell. It is a generally unacceptable practice to notch transverse cross-flow baffles to clear the crowns of long-seam welds. Shops may try to grind out excessive distortion at the same time that they grind the seams flush. This is acceptable only if the plate is not thinned below the thickness shown on the manufacturing drawing.

There are limits to what can be achieved by rerolling shells after long-seam welding and grinding. Trying to roll out substantial cusping may crack the weld or the parent metal in the heat-affected zone on either side of the weld. Any stress relieving that may be required after rerolling increases the manufacturing cost. Rerolling does not deal with shrinkage where girth welds join multiple courses. Usually, if the plate-bending rolls are long enough and small enough in diameter to reroll a multiple-course shell, it would not have been necessary to use more than one course.

Longitudinal seams in adjacent courses are customarily offset from each other to minimize discontinuities at the junctions of long and girth seams. Paragraph UW-(9) (d) of Section VIII, Division 1, of the *ASME Code* states, "Except when radiographed 4 in. (101.6 mm) each side of each welded intersection, vessels made up of two or more courses shall have the centers of welded longitudinal joints of adjacent courses staggered or separated by a distance of at least five times the thickness of the thicker plate." Where there are substantial long-seam distortions and flat spots, fitting and welding staggered courses may be difficult. The resulting high spots and out-of-roundness may also cause difficulty in installing and removing bundles.

It is extremely important that multiple courses be fitted so that their longitudinal axes coincide with the longitudinal axis of the finished shell. Otherwise, there will be an angle where the courses are joined. The tubes will bend to follow the angle. This increases the difficulty of inserting and withdrawing removable bundles. In fixed-tubesheet units, it makes it necessary to deform the tube ends in order to insert them into the holes in the second tubesheet to receive the tube ends. If the deformation is severe, it may not be possible to expand the tubes into the holes successfully. Expanded joints that are tight on shop hydrostatic testing may leak early in the life of the unit.

Constrictions that result from weld shrinkage at girth seams may make it hard or impossible to load and withdraw tube bundles. If a bundle cannot be inserted without excessive force and if there is enough excess shell metal, the manufacturer may grind out the constrictions. Otherwise, there is little choice but to trim the cross-flow-baffle diameters to clear the shrunken girth seams. This increases the clearance between the baffles and the shell in the regions on either side of the welds.

The disadvantages of this practice are that (1) when installing bundles in the horizontal position, the baffles tend to catch on the constrictions presented by the shrunken-in girth welds; and (2) unless the shell fluid is very viscous, increasing the clearance between the baffles and main body of the shell permits fluid to bypass the transverse baffles, markedly reducing the shellside film coefficient.

The surest way to produce round, dimensionally accurate shell interiors is to start with excess thickness, stress-relieve after rolling and welding all attachments (nozzles, supports, etc.), and bore to size. This extremely costly alternative is used only for special designs.

Pipe shells versus rolled-plate shells

Commercially produced pipe has these advantages over rolled-and-welded cylinders:

1. Roundness is held more closely in pipe shells than that in rolled-and-welded cylinders. Therefore, there is less chance of fluid bypassing around cross-flow baffles.

2. In welded pipe, internal welding flash is removed flush with the inner wall. This leaves a smooth surface that does not impede inserting and removing bundles.

3. There are no flat spots that may cause fluid bypassing the cross-flow baffles.

4. Seamless pipes have no longitudinal seams. The shells of welded pipe do not cave in at the longitudinal seams, and therefore there is less difficulty in installing bundles.

5. Because long lengths (double random and special long lengths) are available, the shell may be made without girth seams. This reduces weld shrinkage, misalignment, and angularity where courses are joined. There are also fewer possible places for shell nozzles to penetrate seam welds.

6. It is generally less costly to fabricate shells from commercial pipe than from rolled-and-welded plate cylinders.

Distribution belts

The reasons for providing distribution belts in heat exchanger shells are (1) to distribute the shell fluid to the bundle, (2) to reduce the incoming fluid's mass velocity to a level that will neither cause erosion nor induce the tubes to vibrate, and (3) to reduce pressure loss due to turbulence from that created by conventional impingement-plate construction (discussed later on). Instead of fluid entering the bundle only under the nozzle, the incoming stream is directed to several entering locations (Fig. 6.2), or the shell is extended under the inlet nozzle and cut to leave a gap permitting fluid to enter through 360° of the bundle (Fig. 6.3). This design is called shell-gap construction.

Guidelines for distribution-belt sizing. The nomenclature used in the suggested guidelines for sizing distribution belts is as follows:

A_n = nozzle cross-sectional flow area, in^2 (mm^2)
D_s = shell ID, in (mm)
D_n = nozzle ID, in (mm)
G = width of gap in shell-gap construction, in (mm)
L = Axial length of distribution belt, in (mm)
W = space between ID of belt and OD of shell, in (mm)

Referring to Figs. 6.2 and 6.3, an axial length L of 1.5 to 2 times the nozzle ID, D_v, will allow adequate space for nozzle reinforcement and distribution of the incoming fluid.

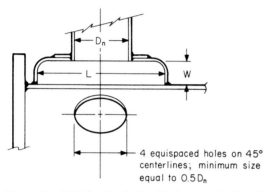

4 equispaced holes on 45° centerlines; minimum size equal to $0.5D_n$

Figure 6.2 Distribution belt with integral shell and four equispaced openings.

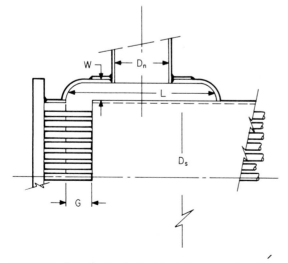

Figure 6.3 Distribution belt with shell-gap construction.

$$L = (1.5 \text{ to } 2)D_n \tag{6.1}$$

The minimum space between the ID of the belt and the OD of the shell should be large enough to provide a flow area parallel with the curvature of the shell at least equal to the nozzle-flow area.

To achieve this,

$$W = A_n/L \tag{6.2}$$

where
$$A_n = \frac{\pi}{4} D_n^{\,2} \tag{6.3}$$

When fluid is led into the shell through openings (Fig. 6.2), the preferred opening shape is circular. If square or rectangular openings are used, the corners should be cut on a radius of no less than three shell thicknesses to prevent the initiation of tears. The edges of the radiused corners should be ground smooth. Good distribution into the bundles will be obtained if:

1. The openings are equispaced.

2. The openings straddle the inlet centerline.

3. There are at least four openings.

4. Each of four circular opening diameters is at least half the inlet-nozzle inside diameter. The cross-sectional area of openings of other shapes are at least one-quarter of the cross-sectional area of the inlet nozzles when four openings are provided.

An alternative to four large-diameter openings is called strainer-plate construction. The shell within the belt is completely or partially perforated with small holes except for an unperforated circle aligned with the inlet nozzle. The diameter of the unperforated circle is at least 1.5 times the inlet-nozzle ID. The pressure loss through the strainer plate is minimized by virtue of the low velocity through the holes that results from the large total cross-sectional flow area. Ratios of strainer plate to nozzle-flow areas in the range of 4 are usually attainable.

In shell-gap construction, the minimum width of the gap in the shell should provide a flow entrance area at least equal to the inlet-nozzle flow area. The minimum gap width is found from Eq. (6.4).

$$G = D_n^{\,2}/4D_s \tag{6.4}$$

Example 6.1 A 37-in (939.8-mm) shell has a 14-in (355.6-mm) vapor inlet. All connections are to be 100 percent reinforced. Size a distribution belt that will meet minimum distribution requirements.

To permit adding external reinforcement economically, the length of the straight part of the vapor belt should be twice the nozzle ID. Assuming a

⅜-in-thick (9.5-mm-thick) nozzle wall, the minimum straight length of the vapor distribution belt is therefore 26½ in (673 mm).

The flow area of the nozzle is 137.9 in² (88,959 mm²). Using Eq. (6.2), the space between the OD of the shell and the ID of the belt is 5.2 in (132.2 mm). This space may be reduced by increasing the length of the distribution belt.

Assuming that four circular vapor openings will be provided, the minimum opening of 6⅝ in (168.3 mm) provides a vapor inlet area of 137.9 in² (88,959 mm²) which is equal to the nozzle inlet flow area.

If shell-gap construction is preferred, Eq. (6.4) gives a minimum gap of 1.19 in (30.13 mm). The practical working dimension would be 1¼ in (about 30 mm).

Vapor domes

Some vapor condensers are built with vapor domes (Fig. 6.4), which are superficially similar to distribution belts. However, they are used to reduce pressure drop by permitting vapor to enter a bundle over most of its length. Vapor traverses the bundle in a manner somewhat similar to pure cross-flow.

Guidelines for vapor-dome sizing. Vapor domes should extend for as much tube length as is practical. Space may be allowed in the regions of the shell not covered by the dome to permit installing non-condensible (inerts) exhausts. Alternatively, a vent connection dip tube may penetrate the vapor belt to pick up inerts in the region of the coldest part of the tubes.

Vapor-belt diameter is set by the condenser operating pressure. The following guidelines are based upon using hydraulic diameters of the shell and bundle to calculate flow velocity:

1. When operating pressure is 0.1 lb/in² (689.5 Pa) or less, limit the product of vapor density and square of vapor velocity to 150 lb/(ft · s²) [223 kg/(m · s²)] in any direction. A more desirable value is 100 lb/(ft · s²) [149 kg/(m · s²)].

2. When operating pressure is between 0.1 and 0.3 lb/in² (689.5 and 2070 Pa), limit the product of vapor density and square of vapor velocity to 225 lb/(ft · s²) [335 kg/(m · s²)].

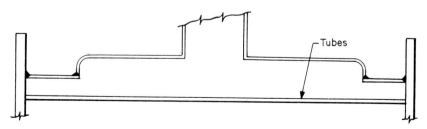

Figure 6.4   Vapor dome in process condenser shell.

3. When operating pressure is between 0.3 and 1 lb/in^2 (2070 and 6895 Pa), limit the product of vapor density and square of vapor velocity to 625 lb/(ft · s^2) [930 kg/(m · s^2)].

End closures for distribution belts and vapor domes.   End closures of the types shown in Figs. 6.2, 6.3, and 6.4 may be designed by using the analysis of Kopp and Sayre and applying the rules of Section VIII, Division 1, of the *ASME Code*'s Appendix CC for flanged-only expansion joints.[3,4] In addition to the flanged-only-head types, end closures constructed as shown in Fig. 6.5 may be used. Although Section VIII, Division 1, of the *ASME Code* does not have rules that apply specifically to distribution-belt and vapor-dome end closures, it is reasonable to adapt the design rules of its Appendix 9 for the end closures of jacketed vessels.

For fixed-tubesheet constructions and for floating-head and U-tube units in which the opening in the shell is less than 50 percent of the shell diameter, it is probably acceptable to design the closure as an Appendix 9, Type 1. For floating-head and U-tube units that have a total opening to the shell of 50 percent or more of the shell diameter, the closure should be designed as a Type 2.

Expansion joints

Expansion joints are used in the shells of fixed-tubesheet units to accommodate differential expansion between the shell and the tubes. The average shell and tube metal temperatures determine whether or not the unit must be fitted with an expansion joint. Figure 6.6 illustrates the effects of the differential between the shell and tube average metal temperatures when an expansion joint is not provided.

In single-pass floating-head TEMA Types S and T units, expansion joints may be used in place of stuffing boxes to seal the outlet nozzle to the shell cover at the penetration. In some straight-tube designs, where the rate of fouling can vary substantially from tube to tube, they are used to seal tubes individually to one tubesheet. Here, the

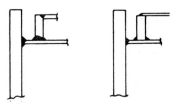

Figure 6.5 Alternative end closures for distribution belts and vapor domes.

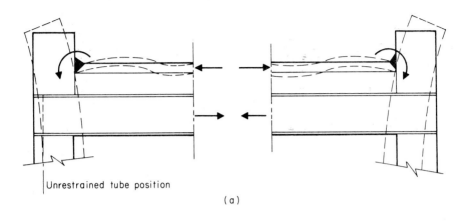

Unrestrained tube position

(a)

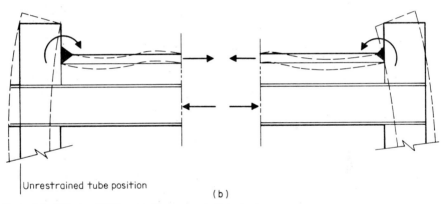

Unrestrained tube position

(b)

Figure 6.6 Effects of differential between shell and tube average metal temperatures on fixed-tubesheet heat exchangers without shell expansion joints. (*a*) Shell hotter than tubes. (*b*) Tubes hotter than shell.

joint accommodates the differential expansion between each tube and the shell and between each tube and every other tube.

At present the *ASME Code* rules for single-layered, flanged-only and flanged-and-flued-head expansion joints (Appendix CC) and thin-walled [bellows thickness $\leq \frac{1}{8}$ in (3.18 mm)] expansion joints (Appendix BB) are not mandatory. After experience is gained in applying the rules of these appendixes, it is likely that they will become mandatory. The reader is referred to the *ASME Code* for specific application of the rules.

The following applies to both appendixes:

1. The rules are limited to applications that involve only axial deflections.

2. The hydrostatic end force caused by pressure and/or the joint spring force must be contained by adequate restraining elements such as the tube bundle, tubesheets, or shell, external bolting, anchors, etc. The average primary membrane stress in the restraining elements must not exceed the maximum allowable stress at the design temperature for the material.

3. Extending or compressing the flexible element or rotating or laterally offsetting connecting parts to make up for a poor fit or misalignment is prohibited unless the effects are accounted for in accordance with the *ASME Code* rules. This very important provision recognizes that stress and cycle-life calculations may be invalidated by predeflecting the joint unless the predeflection has been taken into account. Shop managements should make fitters aware that early failure may result if they stretch or precompress the joint to make up for poor fit.

4. As stated in the *ASME Code*'s Paragraph U-2(g), Section VIII, Division 1, does not contain rules to cover all details of design and construction. The criteria established in the appendixes cover some common expansion-joint types, but they are not intended to limit configurations or details to those illustrated or described in the appendixes. However, designs which differ from the basic concepts of the appendixes must comply with the requirements of U-2(g).

5. The spring rate, force per unit length, may be determined either by calculation or by testing.[5]* (As noted in Chap. 3, when an expansion joint is provided, the tubesheet design and tube-to-tubesheet loads are affected by its stiffness or spring rate.)

6. The design of the expansion joint must conform with the general requirements of the *ASME Code*, Section VIII, Division 1 (Part UG), and the specific requirements of the appendix.

Flanged-and-flued-head and flanged-only expansion joints (Figs. 6.7 and 6.8). The minimum thickness for carbon and low-alloy steels, exclusive of corrosion allowance, is 0.125 in (3.18 mm). For high-alloy and corrosion-resistant metals the minimum thickness is as defined in the *ASME Code*, Section VIII, Division 1, Paragraph UG-16. For most applications this is $\frac{1}{16}$ in (1.6 mm) as specified in Subparagraph (b), "Minimum Thickness of Shells and Heads," an excerpt of which states that "the minimum thickness permitted for shells and heads after forming and regardless of product form and materials, shall be $\frac{1}{16}$ in. exclusive of any corrosion allowance." However, the minimum thick-

---

*The *TEMA Standards* have a calculation method for thick-walled flexible elements that includes the flexibility of the shell in which it is installed.

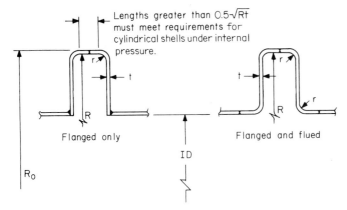

Figure 6.7 Schematic of flanged-only and flanged-and-flued head expansion joints.

Figure 6.8 Fixed-tubesheet heat exchanger with flanged-and-flued-head expansion joint. (*Atlas Industrial Manufacturing Company, Clifton, New Jersey.*)

ness that is practical in producing flanged-only and flanged-and-flued-head expansion joints is about 0.1 in (about 2.5 mm).

The appendix has cycle-life equations for designers' use. The minimum number of cycles for which a joint may be designed is 100. The rules make the designer responsible for establishing the number of stress cycles of pressure and/or deflection anticipated during the life of the exchanger. A frequently used method to estimate the pressure and deflection stresses is the Kopp and Sayre analysis.

Designers who work for heat exchanger manufacturers cannot reasonably be expected to know enough about the proposed operation to estimate the number of stress cycles and reversals. Therefore, users must furnish this information. If they do not, designers may work to the 100-cycle minimum.

Flanged-only-head joints, flanged-and-flued-head joints, and joints made by welding diaphragms to the shell and a thick-walled outer cylinder are much stiffer than bellows-type joints, since the stiffness generally varies with the cube of the thickness. In contrast to bellows expansion joints, for which manufacturers provide spring rates, the mechanical designer must calculate the stiffness.

Section 5 of the current edition of the *TEMA Standards* covers thick-walled expansion joints. The TEMA minimum thicknesses for such joints in the *uncorroded condition* are ⅛ in for nominal diameters 18 in and smaller, ³⁄₁₆ in for nominal diameters from 19 through 30 in, and ¼ in for nominal diameters greater than 30 in (3.2 mm for nominal diameters 45.7 mm and smaller, 4.8 mm for nominal diameters from 482.6 through 762 mm, and 6.4 mm for nominal diameters greater than 762 mm). The standards provide an analysis that uses equivalent geometry similar to the Kopp and Sayre work and formulas derived based upon plate and shell theory. The reader is referred to the *TEMA Standards* for the sequence of calculation and formulas used.

Thin-walled (bellows) expansion joints (Figs. 6.9, 6.10, and 6.11). Heat exchanger users and designers should carefully study and understand the rules of Appendix BB before specifying thin-walled heat ex-

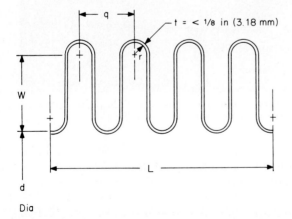

Figure 6.9 Unreinforced bellows expansion joint. $r => 3t$.

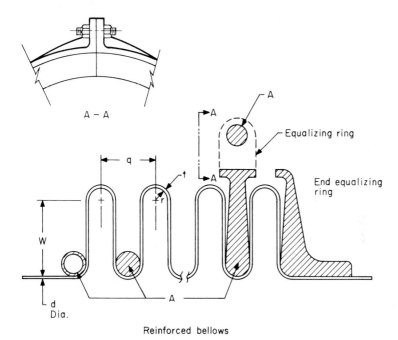

Reinforced bellows

Figure 6.10   Reinforced bellows expansion joint. $r = > 3t$.

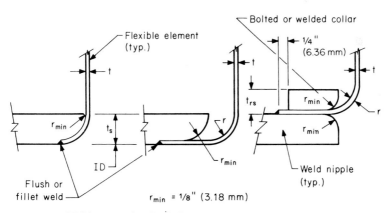

Figure 6.11   Welding nipples for bellows expansion joints. NOTE: t_s = minimum required thickness + corrosion allowance; c = corrosion allowance; t_{rs} = thickness required for pressure.

changer joints. The design rules, which are not easily summarized, are similar to but not identical with those of the *Standards of the Expansion Joint Manufacturers Association (EJMA Standards).*[6] The joint manufacturer will generally provide the mechanical designer with the spring rate.

The *ASME Code*'s required inspections for thin-walled joints cover only materials and workmanship at the expansion-joint manufacturer's plant. *Hydrostatic testing is not required for the joint manufacturer to issue a partial data report.* Therefore, the expansion joint may not be pressure-tested until the heat exchanger manufacturer performs the *ASME Code*'s required hydrostatic test. If the joint leaks at this time, it is virtually impossible to repair it satisfactorily. To replace the joint, either the tubes must be replaced or the unit must be shortened and the tube ends cut, trimmed, and reused in a shorter-length exchanger. Consequently, prudent specifications require thin-walled expansion joints to be hydrostatically tested before installation.

Deciding between thick- and thin-walled expansion joints

These conditions favor using thick-walled joints:

1. The pressure is 300 lb/in^2 (2070 kPa) or less.

2. Deflections per flexible element are moderate—in the range arbitrarily set at $1/8$ to $1/4$ in (about 3 to 6 mm).

3. Application is noncyclical, with few reversals of direction of deflection.*

4. The joint must be capable of being vented and drained.

These conditions favor using thin-walled joints:

1. The shell pressure exceeds 300 lb/in^2 (2070 kPa).

2. Deflections per flexible element are large—arbitrarily, greater than $1/4$ in (about 6 mm).

3. A high cycle life is required.

4. The tendency of the joint material to suffer stress-corrosion cracking in the environment to which it is exposed is minimal.

5. The exchanger is installed vertically, which permits the joint to be self-draining.

6. The expense of a self-draining type, if required in a horizontal exchanger, is acceptable.

Some of the disadvantages of thin-walled joints are:

1. They are extremely sensitive to small imperfections.

---

*See Appendix CC of the *ASME Boiler and Pressure Vessel Code*, 1989 edition.

2. They are easily damaged.

3. They require shielding against catastrophic failure, such as a blowout.

4. Drainable varieties (Fig. 6.12) are expensive.

5. External supports may be required to maintain alignment of the shell sections welded to the expansion joint.

Shell connections

Shell connections consist of inlets, outlets, vents, drains, sumps, vacuum connections, and temperature and pressure taps. Some exchangers are also fitted with special connections such as manholes, handholes, cleanout ports, and sight and light glasses. Except in units pitched off the horizontal or vertical, connections are nearly always perpendicular to the main centerline. The centerlines of flow connections and sumps in pitched units are typically aligned vertically or horizontally. Some special designs have flow nozzles that enter the shell tangentially. The welds of a tangential connection to the shell should be fully radiographed because laying out, fitting, and welding the nozzles to the shell require unusual skill and care.

Nozzle constructions used in heat exchanger shells are like those used in pressure vessels generally. Generally accepted good practices are (1) to require all nozzles 1½ NPS and larger to be flanged; (2) to require nozzles to be made with welding-neck flanges or long weld necks for other than lap-joint connections for shell pressures of 300 lb/in^2 (approximately 2070 kPa) and above and for temperatures of 300°F (approximately 150°C) and higher; and (3) to require the minimum nozzle wall in the fully corroded condition to be as thick as the least of the fully corroded shell, Schedule 40 or ⅜ in (9.5 mm).

Protrusions into the shell are not permissible when bundles are close-fitting. Consequently, the connections are ground flush with the inner surface of the shell. This necessitates all reinforcement either to be integral with the nozzle-neck–shell-wall combination or to be added externally. It is desirable to construct inlet and outlet nozzles

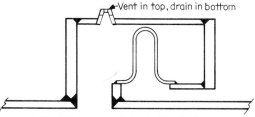

Figure 6.12 Schematic of drainable bellows expansion joint.

with substantially all reinforcement integral in the necks and attachment welds. Doing so permits locating the connections close to the back faces of shell flanges and tubesheets. If reinforcement at these locations is external, using pad diameters as large as the pressure safety code permits requires setting the nozzle centerlines a greater distance away. This increases the span between the tubesheet and the first baffle, which enhances the prospect of tube vibration in this region. Moreover, the low flow velocity in the dead spot between the nozzle and the tubesheet reduces the effectiveness of heat transfer surface and can lead to tube and tubesheet corrosion. If a large distance between the back of the tubesheet and the flow connection is unavoidable, provide a flow-directing baffle (Fig. 6.13).

Figure 6.14 illustrates the limits of reinforcement of Section VIII, Division 1, of the *ASME Code* for a cylindrical nozzle perpendicular to and abutting a cylindrical shell. In the figure D_n is the corroded inside diameter of the nozzle, D_s is the corroded inside diameter of the shell, t_e is the thickness of the external reinforcing pad, t_n is the corroded nominal thickness of the nozzle wall, and t_s is the corroded thickness of the shell. The limits parallel to the shell at a distance on each side of the axis of the opening are equal to the greater of D_n or $D_n/2 + t_s + t_n$. The limit normal to the shell on the outside is the smaller of 2.5 times t_s or 2.5 times $t_n + t_e$, exclusive of weld metal.

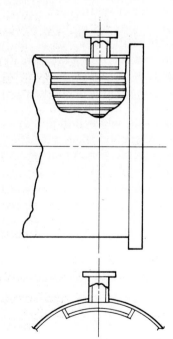

Figure 6.13 Flow-directing baffle in fixed-tubesheet unit.

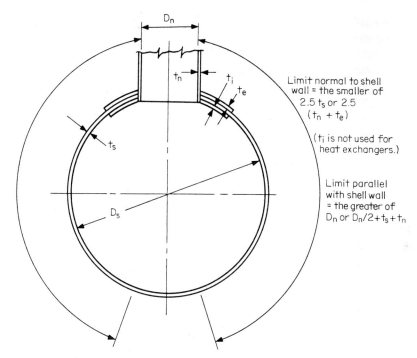

Limit normal to shell
wall = the smaller of
2.5 t_s or 2.5
$(t_n + t_e)$

(t_i is not used for
heat exchangers.)

Limit parallel
with shell wall
= the greater of
D_n or $D_n/2 + t_s + t_n$

Figure 6.14   Limits of reinforcement for heat exchanger nozzles.

This limit can be used to estimate the position of the flow-nozzle centerlines.

Inlets. Piping designers select line average fluid velocities that balance pipeline and pumping costs. Typical are velocities of 8 ft/s (about 2.4 m/s) for water and other liquids and 200 ft/s (about 60 m/s) for atmospheric steam and other vapors. However, velocities are often much higher. If fluids enter the bundle at excessive velocities, erosion and vibration will cause rapid tube deterioration. Tube erosion due to shellside impingement can be minimized by limiting water average velocity to approximately 3 ft/s (about 0.9 m/s) and inlet-steam average velocity to approximately 180 ft/s (about 55 m/s). When the entering fluid is neither corrosive nor erosive, TEMA and HEI standards allow nozzle-flow impact factors of 1500 lb/s² (about 6670 N/s²) for single-phase nonabrasive fluids and 500 lb/s² (about 2225 N/s²) for all other fluids, including liquids at the boiling point and liquids that enter bundles unshielded against fluid impingement. The impact factor is the product of fluid density and the square of fluid velocity in consistent units.

An effective strategy is to reduce line velocity to an acceptable entrance velocity by installing an enlarger in the line to the shell. The small end is the same size as the line; the large end is of a diameter that provides the required lower velocity. The fluid regime must be stabilized before the fluid enters the shell. This can be achieved by setting the length of the larger exit piping from the reducer to approximately 20 times its diameter.

Another way to stabilize the flow is to install a long-radius pipe bend between the reducer and the inlet nozzle. However, such bends may cause excessive swirling and may increase the maximum linear velocity in the inlet stream to well above what would normally be expected on the basis of average velocity. These effects can be moderated by installing a cross-shaped flow straightener in the inlet nozzle.

Frequently, a conical inlet nozzle is used to reduce line average flow velocity to a velocity suitable for the shell inlet. It was previously noted that to avoid maldistribution the included angle must be no larger than about 15° (the approximate profile of a free jet exiting from an open line). This angle produces the least pressure loss at the shell inlet, but fabricating small-included-angle conical sections is impractical. Furthermore, there is seldom enough space to install an exchanger with such an inlet. Therefore, good distribution is usually sacrificed in favor of a mechanically practical included angle.

A disadvantage is that large-angle conical inlets are less effective in reducing the inlet-flow effect on the bundle. The loss of effectiveness has not been quantified by experimental correlations of the variations of linear-velocity profiles at large-end exits with enlarger angles and lengths. Pressure drop through a conical inlet increases rapidly with increasing included angle.[7]

Instead of installing a conical transition or welding reducer, the shell may be fitted with a weld cap and pipe section to provide a larger-diameter shell inlet (Fig. 6.15). Similar considerations apply to the length of the cylindrical section as to conical enlarger lengths.

When the incoming shell fluid is very hot, for example, high-pressure superheated steam, the nozzle may be constructed with a heat shield (Fig. 6.16). This construction leads the hot stream to the bundle before it makes contact with the shell. During startups, the shell in the vicinity of the nozzle can adjust to the high temperature more gradually than if the nozzle were connected directly to the shell.

Impingement protection at inlet connections. When the impact factor exceeds the TEMA or HEI limits and when corrosive, erosive, or two-phase fluids enter the bundle, provide protection against impingement damage. Erosive and corrosive effects attenuate as the fluid crosses

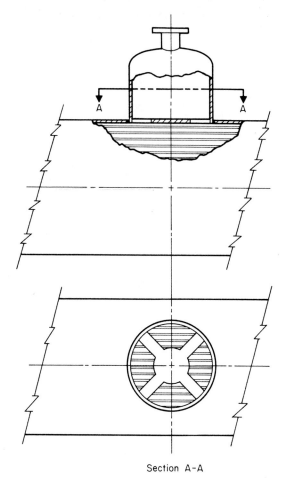

Section A-A

Figure 6.15 Enlarged shell inlet with impingement plate integral with shell.

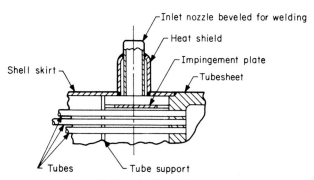

Figure 6.16 Heat shield at feedwater heater inlet nozzle.

the first few rows. Therefore, it would seem to be logical and simple to install thicker tubes in these rows than in the rest of the rows. The wall of the thicker tubes would be selected to fail at the same time as the tubes in the rest of the bundle. However, because there is no way to predict the erosion-corrosion rates that result from fluid entry, other schemes are used.

Perhaps the best scheme for straight-tube bundles is to replace the first three tube rows in the way of the shell inlet with round bars of the same diameter as the tubes. No tubesheet drilling is done at the locations of the tubes in these three rows, but the back face of the stationary tubesheet is tapped to receive the threaded ends of the rods. Plate baffles or supports are drilled to pass the impingement rods. The round bars, which extend from the front or stationary tubesheet through the rearmost baffle or tube support, are threaded on both ends. The far-end baffle or plate is held in position by a double nut, or a single nut is welded to the rods similarly to tie-rod construction. Since the round bars replace tubes in the layout, entering fluid cannot bypass the bundle as it might if tubes were dropped out for plate-type protection.

A nonplate impingement protection consists of snap-on shields about as thick as or slightly thicker than the underlying tube. These are open-sided lengths of tubing that snap onto and fit snugly over the tubes in the first three rows. The open side is about one-third of the shield diameter. Shield length is just shorter than the distance between the tubesheet and the first baffle. Snap-on shields are used primarily as a fix for removable bundles without adequate impingement protection. They have the advantages of only marginally increasing pressure loss over no impingement protection and of being replaceable in removable bundles. Snap-ons are not suitable when crevice corrosion is a concern. Shields have been welded to the tubes to avoid potential crevice corrosion but only rarely.

Angle tube protectors (Fig. 6.17) have also been successfully used. They need not be installed tangentially to the tubes as shown but with clearance to permit fluid flow through the space between the tube and the inside of the angle. This reduces or eliminates the possibility of crevice corrosion. The tube protectors are welded to the tubesheet and the first baffle at the first three rows of tubes before the tubes are loaded into the skeleton.

Most frequently used for impact protection is the impingement plate (impact plate). Although there are many configurations, most often it is a solid, flat circular or rectangular plate placed between the inlet-nozzle opening and the tube bundle. The impingement plate may be fastened to the bundle between the tubesheet and the first baffle. It

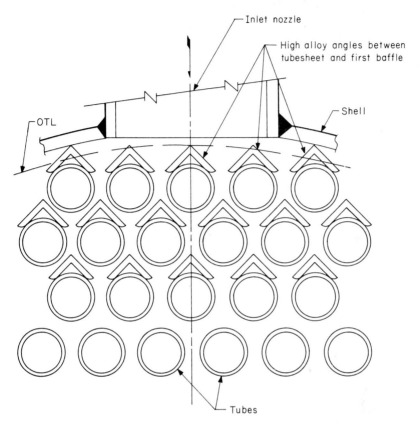

Inlet nozzle

High alloy angles between tubesheet and first baffle

Shell

OTL

Tubes

Figure 6.17 Angle tube protectors against fluid impingement. OTL = outer-tube limit.

may also be wrapped around part of the bundle. Alternatively, it may be fastened to the shell.

If the inlet nozzle enters a conical enlarger or a dome welded to the outside of the shell, the shell under the reducer or dome may be used as the impingement plate. Fluid may enter through peripheral slots as shown in Fig. 6.18, or the shell may be drilled with a pattern of holes that have an open area equal to or greater than the nozzle-flow area. Size impingement plates to a minimum of 1 in (25.4 mm) larger than the projection of a 15° included-angle cone tangent to the inside of the nozzle where it pierces the shell ID (Fig. 6.18).

Impingement plates increase the velocity of the inlet stream to the tubes in the region of their edges. They may be perforated with a pattern of holes to moderate the increase (strainer-plate construction). The manufacturers' standards limit the impact factor to 4000 lb/s^2

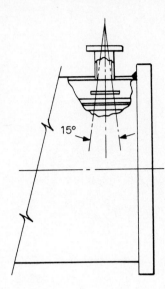

Figure 6.18 Determining minimum diameter of impingement plate. Size of plate 1 in (25.4 mm) larger than projection on face of plate.

(about 17,790 N/s^2) where the fluid enters the shell and bundle. The shell entrance area to use in calculating the impact factor is the sum of the flow area between the tube within the projection of the inlet-nozzle ID and the free-flow area between the bundle and the shell. Plain circular or rectangular impingement plates can be mathematically idealized to provide areas that meet the limits, but it is generally more practical to make bundle layouts.[8]

The requirement for escape areas large enough to accommodate the maximum-impact factor may make it necessary to drop tubes in the way of the impingement plate from the bundle layout. This increases the required shell size and exchanger cost and promotes fluid bypassing. Curving the plate to fit the bundle provides somewhat more escape area.

Vents and drains.   Locate operating vents at the highest possible and drains at the lowest possible points in the shell. In vertical units, unless special precautions are taken, the underside of the top tubesheet may be blanketed with noncondensibles and the top face of the bottom tubesheet may be covered with stagnant fluid. Both conditions reduce the effective heat transfer surface. A more serious problem is the potential for corrosion of the tubes and tubesheets at these locations.

Depending upon the nature of the noncondensibles and the materials of construction of the tubes and tubesheet, a blanket of noncondensibles can cause rapid corrosion. This is especially likely with carbon steel and some nonferrous metals. Stagnant fluid on the inner face of the tubesheet can also corrode the tube and tubesheet. Vertical steam generators with austenitic stainless-steel tubes will generally suffer tube failures unless the water flows across the bottom tubesheet with a velocity of about 3 ft/s (about 1 m/s).

To diminish the potential for corrosion install main or supplementary vents and drains as close as possible to the tubesheets. Because shell flanges of removable-bundle units, channel-to-tubesheet bolting, and tubesheet-to-shell welds get in the way, provide tubesheet vents and drains when feasible. Where they can fit, snorkel pickup drains can be used to remove all but a modest amount of fluid from the bottom tubesheet. Snorkel drains consist of a connection that pierces the shell and that has a leg that extends very close to the inner face of the tubesheet. Pressure in the shell blows the stagnant liquid up the snorkel.

Venting is critical to closed feedwater heater operation. The proportion of noncondensibles in extraction steam increases from the steam inlet region to the vicinity of the outlet from the condensing zone. If this zone is not adequately vented, accumulated noncondensibles cause performance deterioration. The effect on heater life is less obvious. Accumulations of wet noncondensibles that do not significantly affect performance may rapidly corrode the tubes. The corrosion rate depends upon the tube material and boiler-feedwater treatment.

Feedwater heater practice in the United States and Canada is to provide collection channels, perforated central pipes, or other devices for collecting and venting noncondensibles. The collectors lead to an operating vent fitted with an orifice to meter a specific continuous flow. A long-used rule of thumb is to vent ½ percent of the steam flow. Vented noncondensibles must be free to flow to a collection point at the lowest pressure in the system. Vent lines from parallel heater shells that receive steam from identical-pressure stages should not be manifolded. This is so because small differences in fluid friction can create enough pressure differential to block one of the vent streams.

The term *drains* is used to describe shell drain connections in most shell-and-tube heat exchangers but has a different meaning in closed feedwater heater terminology. In feedwater heaters, it means the flow of condensed steam from a heater shell or other source. In this sense it is similar to the process industries' term *drips*. The same word is used for condensed extraction-steam outlet connections. The name *emergency drains* applies to connections used for rapidly dumping an excessive water flow in the feedwater heater shell.

Feedwater heater condensate draining systems must be carefully thought out. Drains led from a heater to the condensing zone of a lower-pressure one flash as they enter. Protection must be provided to prevent water droplets driven by flashing vapor from eroding the shell, tube supports, and tubes. This is best accomplished by means of an austenitic-steel-clad or -lined flash chamber. The flash chamber may be made integral with the shell by extending it beyond the end of the bundle.

Exchanger supports

Welds of supports to shells should be continuous to prevent hidden corrosion from the atmosphere. Plates that bear against shells should have weep holes to permit venting and to indicate when there is a shell leak behind the welded-on plate.

Most horizontal exchangers are supported by two saddles located as near the shell ends as possible, equidistant from the exchanger's center of gravity. Very long exchangers with high length-to-diameter ratios may have an additional support located approximately at the center of gravity. With two saddles, a shift in elevation of one or the other support base hardly causes any load redistribution. Good practice is to have the saddle wrap around 120° or more of the shell.

To accommodate axial shell expansion, it is customary to drill the baseplate at the front or stationary end on the foundation-bolt template and to slot the holes in the other saddles to allow for the anticipated change in shell length. A greased sliding plate may be interspersed between the slotted saddle bases and the supports on which they rest. To prevent the nuts of the foundation bolts from bearing on the movable baseplates so tightly as to foil the purpose of the slots, the slots should be wide and long enough to receive machined sleeves just long enough to protrude through the base. Thick, flat washers, with the ID ⅛ in (approximately 3.2 mm) larger than the foundation bolts and the OD ½ in (12.7 mm) larger in diameter than the slot width, fit over the foundation bolt and bear against the sleeve. The foundation-bolt nuts are tightened against the washer.

Several works on mechanical design of heat exchangers detail the analysis of shell stress, foundation bolting, etc., including the effects of earthquake and wind loads.* Shells may also be fitted with upper saddles for stacked units or to carry the weight of other exchangers set on lower ones. The mechanical design of the shell must provide for the loads they impose. It may be better to avoid possible shell distortion

---

*For example, K. P. Singh and A. I. Soler, *Mechanical Design of Heat Exchangers and Pressure Vessel Components*, Arcturus Publishers, Cherry Hill, N.J., 1984.

by providing a separate structural framework that supports each shell individually. This is not a costly option.

Feedwater heater saddles may be fitted with wheels to allow the heaters to be rolled into place and to accommodate axial expansion and contraction of the shell. The loads imposed by the movements should be considered in the mechanical design.

Horizontal units may also be fitted with two sets of lugs for hanging the unit from rods. Vertical units may be supported by lugs, skirts, legs, or combinations of these supports. The footnoted work has calculation methods for lugs and skirts. Simpler methods are also available.*

Bundle Construction, Assembly, and Attachment to the Shell

A tube bundle (tube nest) consists of a bundle or nest of tubes with the ends attached to a tubesheet or tubesheets. Between the tube ends of most bundles are supports or baffles or a combination of supports and baffles.

Thermal and mechanical design requirements determine bundle construction. Mechanical requirements are that (1) they must have adequate supports to resist the dead load of the tube and the fluid it contains and live loads applied by the shell fluids, (2) they must be able to withstand the effects of temperature differences between the tubes and the shell and between tube passes, and (3) they must be capable of being maintained and cleaned. Thermal requirements are that (1) bundles must provide maximum contact between the shell fluid and the tube outside surface, (2) they must provide maximum mixing of shellside fluids, (3) they must be capable of being vented without excessive accumulation of noncondensibles anywhere in the shell, and (4) they must be capable of being drained.

Fixed-tubesheet bundles are not removable. Both tubesheets are either welded to the shell or fastened to the shell by captive-gasket construction (see Chap. 3). Without cutting into the shell, maintenance cannot be performed beyond chemical cleaning, tube plugging, and sometimes pulling and replacing a few tubes. Since there is no access for mechanical cleaning, the tubes in most fixed-tubesheet bundles are arranged on triangular or rotated triangular pitch. This packs the maximum surface into a shell of a given size. Compared with square

---

*For example, Omar W. Blodgett, *Design of Weldments*, James F. Lincoln Arc Welding Foundation, Cleveland, 1963; 8th printing, August 1976.

pitch, triangular pitch gives better mixing and higher shellside film coefficients. However, the tubes may be arranged on a square pitch to accommodate shellside pressure-drop constraints. Spread pitches may also be used for this purpose or to increase ligament width when required for tube joining. Spread triangular pitches may be used to improve distribution of condensing vapors into the bundle. This practice is often followed in large feedwater heaters.

Some bundles are fitted with heat-transfer-zone control devices. If the heat transfer path in an almost pure shell fluid includes desuperheating and condensing, or condensing and subcooling, or all three, the bundle's surfaces allocated for desuperheating and subcooling may be shrouded or enclosed to separate them from the tubes allocated to condensing. This is the common practice for handling turbine extraction steam used to heat boiler feedwater. It juxtaposes the shell and tube fluids most effectively and permits using support and baffle systems appropriate for each fluid phase.

It is not customary to allot a specific region of the tubes and shroud surface for desuperheating feed to process-vapor condensers. In these condensers, an internal standpipe or an external loop seal ensures flooding the appropriate amount of surface. Some process condenser designs use two-pass shells with uneven tube counts in the shell; the pass with fewer tubes is used to subcool the condensate received from the pass with the larger tube count. This option is similar to partial-pass subcooling-zone feedwater heater construction.

Closed Feedwater Heater Zone Construction

Closed boiler-feedwater heaters heat boiler feedwater or returning condensate with steam bled from the stages of power-generating turbines (bleed or extraction steam). Feedwater or condensate circulates in the tubes and steam in the shell. These specialized heat exchangers substantially improve the cycle efficiency of a power generation facility.[9,10] Often several heaters are arranged in trains or strings of units with the tubesides in series. The shellside of the heater from which feedwater enters the boiler is heated with steam extracted from the highest-pressure turbine stage. The unit that precedes it in the train is heated with steam from the next-lower-pressure stage, and so on. Except for (usually small) external condensate subcoolers, most shell-and-tube feedwater heaters are of U-tube design.

Single-zone heater shells (condensing only in the shells) must meet these requirements:

1. There must be adequate dome space for the bleed steam to enter and disperse into the tube nest without excessive pressure drop.

2. Space must be provided between the bundle and the shell to permit the entering steam to disperse fully around the bundle.

3. The steam inlet nozzle must be positioned so that approximately equal flows of steam will be distributed toward the ends of the shell.

4. The tubes must be protected from the impact of the entering steam.

5. The tubes and shell must be protected against the flashing of drains led to the shell from higher-pressure heaters.

6. A means of venting noncondensibles at startup (startup vents) and during operation (operating vents) must be provided.

7. Tube supports that create the least pressure loss but are adequate to prevent flow-induced vibration are required. Their function includes supporting the U-bend section.

When feedwater heaters receive superheated steam, the shell inlet nozzle enters a shroud around a length of the outlet pass tubes sufficient to transfer all but about 5°F (about 3°C) of the superheat to the feedwater at design-point conditions. The shroud consists of an inverted segment of a cylinder, with a smaller radius than the shell skirt, welded to a flat divider plate. In most heaters, the front end of the half-cylinder and divider-plate assembly is welded to the shellside face of the tubesheet. The other end is open to the condensing zone, and a dam bar is used to seal off the area between the outside of the shroud and the shell skirt (Fig. 6.19).

All heat transfer in the desuperheating zone is sensible. Therefore, a baffle or support system that maximizes the gas-film coefficient on the outside of the tubes and minimizes pressure loss and tube vibration is provided. Most desuperheating zones are fitted with double- or triple-segmental baffles. Nonplate baffles may become state-of-the-art substitutes in newer units.

Feedwater heaters may also be designed to transfer sensible heat from the condensed steam to inlet feedwater. A part of the tubes in the inlet pass, dedicated to subcooling, is enclosed in a subcooling-zone enclosure like the desuperheating-zone shroud except that the saturated-steam end is fitted with a relatively thick end plate. The tube holes in the end plate are close-fitting, but to allow for relative movement between the tubes and the enclosure the tubes are not sealed to the hole walls. The end plate is made thick enough to make sure that condensed steam that might enter the subcooling zone be-

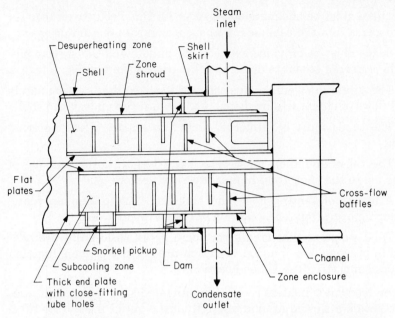

Figure 6.19 Typical construction and attachment of desuperheating and subcooling zones.

tween the tubes and holes does not flash and erode the tubes. Cooled condensate washes the condensate side of the end plate, which acts as a heatsink.

Depending upon the heater manufacturer, all the tubes in the inlet pass of a horizontal subcooling-zone unit may be enclosed for part of their length or some of the tubes in the bottom of the pass may be enclosed for their full straight length. These alternatives are called full-pass, partial-length and full-length, split- or partial-pass subcoolers.

The details of attachment of desuperheating-zone shrouds and subcooling-zone enclosures to the shellside face of the tubesheet can materially affect the life of a heater. The simple welded attachments described above are the least expensive, but they have some disadvantages:

1. In most sizes, there is insufficient room for a welder to make high-quality welds, especially when both zones are present.

2. The dam bars act as stiffeners, rigidly restraining the shell skirt.

3. Inlet steam, which may be very hot, makes contact with the skirt, which can create high thermal stresses in the skirt-to-tubesheet

joint. These stresses are most marked during startups, shutdowns, and load changes. Cyclical operation can cause fatigue failures.

4. In three-zone heaters the divider plates of the desuperheating and subcooling zones are in close proximity. Thermal gradients between the region of the tubesheet exposed to the hot, superheated steam and hot feedwater and the part in contact with much cooler condensate and cold inlet feedwater may be very high.

Basic precautions are (1) requiring the material of construction of the shroud and enclosure to be fine-grain steel; (2) requiring all welds to be full-penetration welds; (3) making sure that the condensing-zone divider plate is designed to accommodate the pressure drop without so much deflection that the welds of the cylindrical-to-flat section crack [pressure drop in the condensing zone should be limited to 7 lb/in^2 (approximately 48 kPa)]; and (4) thoroughly inspecting, insofar as possible, all the welds of the zone assemblies and their attachment to the tubesheet.

A major improvement over the simple design is floating shroud and subcooling zone enclosures (Fig. 6.20). The zone enclosures are attached only to the tubesheet face. As the figure shows, the connection is not direct. Instead, corner-radiused stub bars are welded to the tubesheet and the shroud and subcooling-zone enclosures are welded to the stub bars. The advantages of this scheme are that (1) the short stub lengths make the stub-to-tubesheet joints accessible for producing full-penetration welds that can be nondestructively examined; and (2), when combined with a forged lip and a flexible tubesheet-to-skirt attachment, heat treatment of the assembly of tubesheet, channel, and stubs is facilitated.

The steam inlet to the desuperheating zone and the condensate outlet are connected to the enclosures by flexible sleeves. The stub bars and divider plates are radiused at the transition from the flat to the curved section to minimize stress concentration.

Floating construction permits the shell skirt and its attachment to the tubesheet to move freely under the influence of pressure and temperature changes. Bringing desuperheated steam directly into the shroud through the flexible sleeve isolates the shell skirt from the high-temperature superheated steam.

Plate baffles and tube supports

The tubes are almost always supported between their ends by baffles or tube supports against the loads that the flow of shell fluid applies and the vibration that may be induced. The TEMA and HEI tabulated

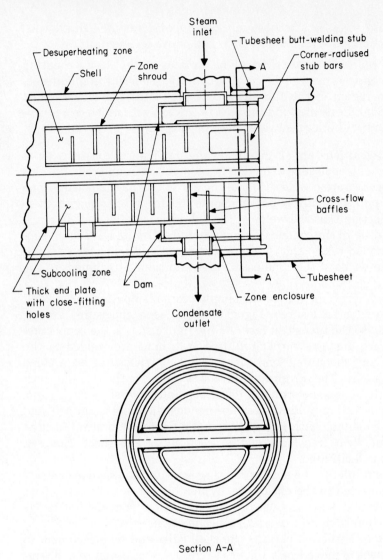

Figure 6.20 Flexible attachment of zone enclosures to tubesheet of feedwater heater.

maximum unsupported straight lengths of tubes are adequate for most anticipated loads. Under pulsating-flow conditions the unsupported tube span should be as short as possible within the limit of available pressure drop. Here, for a permitted pressure loss, if the support span approaches the maxima tabulated in the manufacturers' standards, change the baffle or support design to one that consumes less energy. This will permit using a shorter span. When the installation is pitched or horizontal, baffles and supports also bear the weight of the tubes and the fluid they carry at positions intermediate between the ends joined to the tubesheet or tubesheets.

Some manufacturers of vertical evaporators assume that the large-diameter tubes used in the design are strong and rigid enough to require no intermediate supports. Therefore, they do not follow the TEMA or HEI standards. When these designs are proposed, they should be examined carefully for the possibility of shell-flow-induced vibration damage. Also give consideration to the effects of building and shipping the unit in the horizontal position.

Baffles serve the dual purpose of supporting the tubes and channeling the flow in the shell. Shellside fluid is directed back and forth or up and down across the tubes by *cross-flow* or *transverse* baffles. *Disk-and-doughnut, orifice, egg-crate,* and other nonplate baffles allow flow along the tubes. Plate baffles are made by perforating plates on the tubesheet drilling pattern. Nonplate baffles and supports are made by assembling bars or rods in various arrangements. These may consist of shop-fabricated egg crates or proprietary patented designs such as Phillips Petroleum Company's RodBaffles,* Ecolaire Heat Transfer Corporation's Nests,† or Holtec International's Holtec Non-Segmental Baffles.‡

When baffles are not required to enhance thermal performance but the tubes must be supported, most often perforated-plate supports, similar to cross-flow baffles, are used. Consider nonplate supports when there is concern about pressure drop and shell-flow-induced vibration. They consume less energy and may react less adversely with the tubes when exposed to a vibration-forcing environment.

Plate baffles and supports

Most plate baffles and tube supports are made from metal. However, nonmetallic baffles are used for some environments and services. The *TEMA Standards* set minimum requirements for segmental baffles and supports in each class. The *Standard for Power Plant Heat Exchangers* of the Heat Exchange Institute has similar but somewhat different requirements.[11]

The tabulated thicknesses listed in the TEMA and HEI standards do not include allowance for corrosion or erosion on segmental baffles and tube supports. The standards also do not require manufacturers to allow for corrosion of the baffles, tie rods, and spacers. Therefore,

---

*U.S. Patents 3,708,142, 4,136,736, and 4,127,165.

†U.S. Patent 4,210,202.

‡U.S. Patents 4,579,304 and 4,595,161.

when severe shellside corrosion is expected, use corrosion-erosion-resistant material or add a corrosion allowance to the minimum thicknesses.

The TEMA and HEI permitted maximum spacings are not based upon considerations of vibration. To be reasonably certain that shell-flow-induced vibration will not occur, vibration analysis is required.

Standard construction uses tie rods and spacers to align and position plate baffles and tube supports in the bundle skeleton. The back side of the stationary or front-end tubesheet is tapped to receive long rods threaded at both ends. Pipe or tubing spools are machined to the exact lengths required to space the baffles or supports. The skeleton can be assembled with tie rods and spacers without using special jigs or fixtures to ensure that the baffles or supports are perpendicular to the tubes. If the tube holes in the tubesheets, baffles, and support plates register precisely, there is little chance that the tubes will bind in the baffle or support holes or be cut by the baffle edges.

Tie-rod-and-spacer construction provides a flexible structure that accommodates temperature changes. The flexibility facilitates tube loading and bundle insertion. It is also favorable for damping tube vibration. Because the clearances between the parts permit flushing by the shell fluid, tie-rod-and-spacer design does not ordinarily contribute to crevice corrosion.

Some manufacturers omit the spacers by welding the baffles or supports directly to the tie rods. Some feedwater heater tube support plates are held together by heavy flat bars welded to notches in the support plates. Welding the baffles to the tie rods saves the cost of cutting and machining spacers, but unless the welding completely seals the tie rods to the baffles, it is likely to promote crevice corrosion in some fluid environments. Extreme care is required in aligning baffles or supports perpendicular to the tie rods. Jigs and fixtures may be required. The somewhat inflexible structure may adversely affect exchanger life if misaligned hole edges cut into the tubes. The rigid design is not favorable for exchangers subject to shell-flow-induced vibration damage.

The manufacturers' standards specify the minimum number of tie rods for various shell sizes, but they do not say how many should pierce each baffle or how or where they should be located. Table 6.5 has recommendations for the minimum number of tie rods to pierce each baffle. *This is not a TEMA or HEI requirement.* Tie rods should be located to provide the greatest stability for the skeleton. This may require "ears" on the baffles to permit spreading the tie rods appropriately.

Segmental baffles and support plates. Segmental baffles are plates from which segments of a full circle have been lopped off. Figure 6.21 illustrates three types. The percent cut is defined as follows:

TABLE 6.5   Recommended Minimum Number of Tie Rods to Pierce Each Baffle

TEMA size range		TEMA recommended minimum number	Recommended minimum piercing each baffle
in	mm		
8–15	203–381	4	3
16–27	406–686	6	4
28–33	711–838	6	5
34–48	863–1219	8	6
49–60	1245–1524	10	7 or 8
61–100	1549–2450	12	9

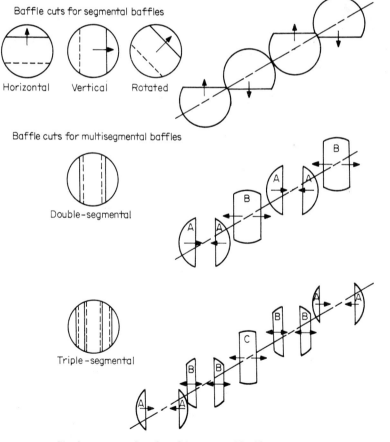

Figure 6.21   Single-segmental and multisegmental baffles.

Percent cut = 100 (segment height cut off)/shell ID

For example, if a length equal to one-quarter of the shell inside diameter is cut off, the baffles are 25 percent cut.

Baffle cuts should be adjusted so that the cut line is either exactly on the centerline of a tube row or, if there is enough space between adjacent tube rows, midway between them. This will prevent edges that cross holes from bending, twisting, and scoring or otherwise damaging the tubes. Saw cuts with burrs removed are preferred, but finely burned edges with slag removed by grinding are usually acceptable.

For thermal performance, it is best to have no clearance between the baffle OD and the shell ID. Therefore, some large exchangers are built with the baffles welded to the shell. This is not practical for smaller sizes. It has the further disadvantages of requiring near-perfect alignment and reduced flexibility of the structure. The diametral clearances tabulated in the manufacturers' standards for baffles not welded to the shell are a compromise between what is thermally ideal and what is mechanically practical.

Small clearances between tubes and holes provide better shellside film coefficients than large ones and are more favorable for controlling vibration. However, they make it difficult to load tubes into the bundle and increase the chance of damaging them. Here again, the clearances that the standards allow are a compromise between the thermally desirable and the mechanically practical. Some special exchangers have the tubes expanded into the baffle holes. Hydro-expanding has been used for this purpose.

The standards allow greater clearances for semisupports than for baffles when the semisupports are not critical to the shellside film coefficient. However, if shell-flow-induced vibration is a possibility, it is prudent to require the smaller clearances.

Single-segmental baffles and supports. When one segment is cut off on a chord as shown in the uppermost sketch of Fig. 6.21 and the baffles alternate, the baffles are called segmental (or single-segment) baffles. Single-segmental tube supports with 45 to 50 percent of the segments removed are called semisupports.

Segmental baffles and semisupports are the simplest to produce and install but have the disadvantages that (1) for a given baffle pitch, they consume the most energy; and (2) unless no tubes are located in the cutoff region, or window (called no tubes in the window, or NTIW), the support span is two baffle pitches for the tubes in the window, or cutoff region. A spacing that uses the full allowable shellside pressure drop may be greater than desirable from the vibration standpoint.

Multisegmental baffles. Because flow patterns around double- and triple-segmental baffles are more axial than with single-segmental baffles, they consume less energy. For a given baffle pitch, double-segmental baffles use up about one-eighth of the pressure drop of single-segmental baffles and triple-segmental ones far less than that.

Double-segmental baffles are arranged along the bundle as ABABAB..., where A baffles are the outer ones and B is the inner one. Triple-segmental baffles are arranged as ABCBABCBABCB..., where A baffles are outermost, B are intermediate, and C is the innermost one.

Full-circle supports. Full-circle supports are desirable for shells that have large clearances between the shell ID and peripheral tubes—for example, bundles in kettle reboilers and closed feedwater heaters. The support span becomes the support pitch, and all tie rods pierce all supports. Feedwater heater bundles may be fitted in the condensing zone with full-circle supports that have large notches cut out for the passage of steam and condensate (Fig. 6.22).

Floating-tubesheet and U-tube-bundle end supports. The support just before the floating tubesheet or U bends may be a full circle from which a hexagonal center piece has been removed (Fig. 6.23). U bends may also be supported by a plate support in the plane of the bend centerline (Fig. 6.24). The pattern of the plate is not significant as long as it supports all the tubes. Alternatives to plate supports at the U bend are bands shown in Fig. 6.25, and bars are shown in Fig. 6.26.

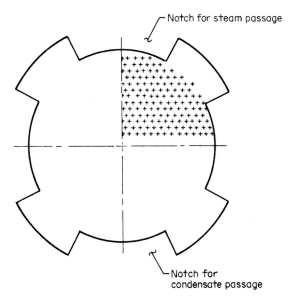

Figure 6.22 Condensing-zone full-circle support for closed feedwater heater.

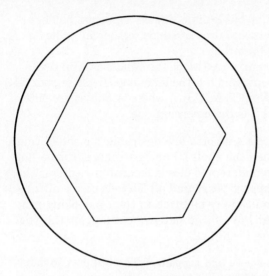

Figure 6.23 Pattern of floating-tubesheet support plate.

Figure 6.24 U-tube plate support in plane of bend centerline. (*Courtesy of Doyle & Roth Manufacturing Co., Inc., New York; courtesy of* Chemical Engineering.)

Figure 6.25 U bends supported by bands. (*Courtesy of ITT Standard, Heat Transfer Division, Buffalo, New York; courtesy of* Chemical Engineering.)

Figure 6.26 U bends supported by bars. (*Atlas Industrial Manufacturing Company, Clifton, New Jersey.*)

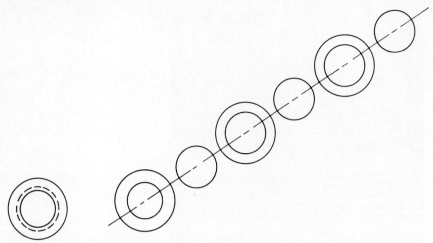

Figure 6.27 Disk-and-doughnut baffles.

Disk-and-doughnut baffles (Fig. 6.27). Disk-and-doughnut baffles consist of full-circle baffles with a large central hole (doughnuts) that alternate with full-circle baffles (disks) just larger enough than the holes in the doughnuts to provide overlap for tie rods and spacers.*†

Orifice baffles. Orifice baffles are full-circle plate baffles in which the baffle holes are enlarged beyond the TEMA standard baffle-hole-to-tube clearance and there are no cuts. All flow is therefore axial along the tubes. This is desirable from a vibration standpoint, but the greater clearance between tubes and holes is undesirable. However, the axial flow eliminates the most important vibration-forcing mechanisms.

Drilling plate baffles. The general subject of drilling was addressed in Chap. 3. Following are some methods and requirements that apply to baffle drilling.

Stack drilling. Oversized-diameter baffle plates are stacked in a tightly packed bundle. The bundle is compressed in a hydraulic press, and stringers of weld bead are run down the stack edges at several locations to maintain stack tightness. The baffle stack may be fas-

---

*For shellside film coefficients and pressure drops, see D. A. Donahue, "Heat Transfer and Pressure Drop in Heat Exchangers," *Ind. Eng. Chem.*, vol. 41, no. 11, November 1949.

†Ratnasamy suggests relative sizes of the hole in the doughnut and the diameter or the disk in "Exchanger Design Using Disc and Donut Baffles," *Hydrocarbon Process.*, April 1987.

tened to a tubesheet or be sandwiched between a pair of tubesheets and the assembly drilled.

The advantages of stack drilling are that (1) the holes in adjacent baffles and tubesheets register with each other and (2) stack drilling is less costly than individual drilling. The disadvantages are that (1) stack thickness is limited by the tendency of the drill to run out and (2) metal turnings may get between the layered baffles and deform them, causing poor hole quality. Numerically controlled drilling is preferred for stacked baffles.

Floating-tubesheet supports should be stack-drilled with the floating tubesheet because the short distance between the support plate and the floating tubesheet makes small displacements of hole positions unacceptable. Misalignment is possible even when numerical controls are used.

Baffle holes must be deburred after drilling because the tool pressure raises a burr as the drill emerges from the underside. Deburring may be done manually with a drill and rosebud tool or semiautomatically or automatically by a variety of wire-brush devices, grinders, etc. Most baffle-hole-deburring equipment is homemade, but commercial machines made for the purpose are available.

Baffle edges must be concentric with the drilling pattern. As-burned deburred edges are acceptable only for tube supports in which machine burning to concentricity with the tube-hole layout can be achieved. Cross-flow baffle ODs should be machined. A 500-rms finish is acceptable.

Nonplate baffles and supports

Various bar, rod, and formed metal baffles and supports may be used to (1) reduce shellside pressure drop, (2) reduce the prospect of vibration, and (3) improve the shellside heat transfer rate. Firms that license patented nonplate systems or manufacture and sell them on the open market usually provide correlations for thermal design.

Egg-crate supports. Variations of egg-crate supports have been used from the earliest days of shell-and-tube manufacture. Each support consists of a grid of slotted bars fitted together like the separations in an egg crate and banded with a bar rolled the easy way. The band is welded to the ends of the bars. To fit the bars together, they must have slots slightly wider than the bar thickness sawed or milled halfway through their width. Milling achieves better quality than sawing but is more expensive. Some egg-crate supports are tack-welded together at the junctions of the crossed bars, but most depend only on friction and the external band to hold them together. Egg-crate supports are spaced apart by longitudinal round bars at intervals appropriate for the flow and support requirements. The spacer bars at the front support are welded to the rear face of the front or stationary tubesheet.

Phillips RodBaffle (Fig. 6.28). The virtues and advantages of this patented system are well documented in the literature. Various manufacturers are licensed to produce and install the Phillips RodBaffle.

Nests. The Nests system (acronym for neoteric endostratiformed tube supports) is available only in the patent assignee's products. Information about its performance is not generally available in the open literature.

Holtec Non-Segmental Baffles. Figure 6.29 illustrates the construction and one of the uses of Holtec Non-Segmental Baffles. They are available to the public through Holtec International Corp., Mount Laurel, New Jersey.

Shellside pass partitions

Multipass shellside construction is an economical way to simulate multiple shells in series in a single shell. The maximum number of shellside passes that users will accept for most services is 2, but some very specialized heat exchangers have been built with as many as 16 shellside passes. Some exchanger users (mainly refineries) will not accept multipass shellside construction. They prefer handling very close approaches and temperature crosses with multiple shells in series.

The principal drawbacks of multiple shellside passes are the possibilities for hydraulic and thermal leakage between the passes and difficulties in construction. Removable bundles for multipass shellside flow are more difficult to assemble properly than ones with single-pass shells.

If more than one pass partition is offered and there are no process or operating objections, the manufacturer's proposed construction should be carefully examined. Figures 6.30 through 6.35 illustrate two-pass shell pass-partition installations.

Uninsulated pass partitions (upper sketch of Fig. 6.30) are most common. Thermal designers must take into account the fact that the thermal leak between the hot and cold shellside passes degrades the mean temperature difference. Alternatively, the pass partition may be designed with double plates that encase a layer of insulation or that have a hollow core filled with air (lower sketch of Fig. 6.30).

Fully welded pass partitions, shown schematically in Fig. 6.31 and in the photograph of Fig. 6.32, are used when the shell is large enough for welding access. When it is too small to allow filet-welding the par-

Figure 6.28 Phillips RodBaffle. (*Courtesy of Phillips Petroleum Co., Bartlesville, Oklahoma.*)

Figure 6.29 Holtec Non-Segmental Baffles installed in the desuperheating zone of a closed feedwater heater. (*Courtesy of Holtec International Corp., Mount Laurel, New Jersey.*)

tition plate to the shell, one of the constructions shown in Figs. 6.33 and 6.34 is used. The designs shown in Fig. 6.33 have a line of slots or holes cut into two sides of the shell centered on the plane of the pass partition. The slots or holes are plug-welded to the pass partition. The shrinkage of the shell that the welding causes makes for reasonable hydraulic tightness between the passes. The alternative channel construction sketched is used with thin sections, usually of high-alloy material.

The advantages of the half-shell, fully welded construction shown in Fig. 6.34 are positive sealing and simplicity of construction. Pressure vessel code rules may not cover this design. Therefore, designers must demonstrate by analysis that it is safe for the pressures and temperatures at which the exchanger will operate.

At high shellside operating temperatures and with long shellside temperature ranges the restraint created by welding the pass-partition plate to the shell may create excessive shell stress. Under cyclical operating conditions, discontinuity and restraint may com-

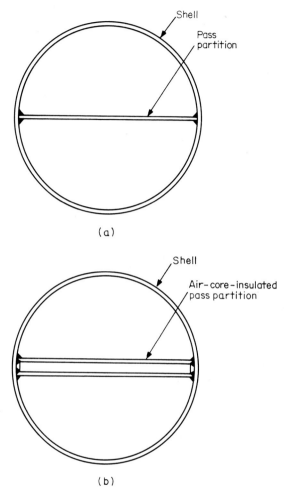

Shell

Pass partition

(a)

Shell

Air-core-insulated pass partition

(b)

Figure 6.30 Uninsulated and insulated two-pass pass partitions. (a) Cross section of two-pass shell construction for large-diameter fixed-tubesheet and U-tube heat exchangers large enough for welding access. (b) Cross section of air-core-insulated pass partition and shell for large-diameter fixed-tubesheet and U-tube heat exchangers with welding access.

bine to cause fatigue failure. If analysis indicates that failure is probable, use multiple shells in series instead of multiple-shell-pass construction.

Removable-bundle shellside pass partitions are constructed as part of the bundle. They are seal-welded to the shellside face of the tubesheet. One of the methods shown in Figs. 6.34 and 6.35 is used to seal them to the shell. The upward curved flexible elements of Fig.

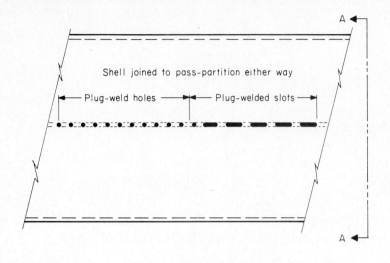

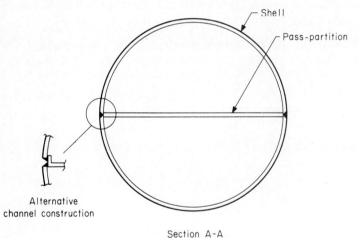

Section A-A

Figure 6.31 Sealing pass partition to shell—shell integrally.

6.34 are in the inlet pass. Therefore, the pressure differential between the inlet and outlet passes assists in sealing. However, the seal depends upon the spring pressure that they exert.

Assembling Bundles and Attaching Bundles to Shells

Most exchangers for the process, refining, and power generation industries are custom-designed for specific services. The nameplates may indicate the customer's name and tag number. Most often one-at-a-time units are built to the TEMA or HEI standards. In the United

Figure 6.32 Pass partition fully welded into shell of fixed tubesheet heat exchanger. (*Atlas Industrial Manufacturing Company, Clifton, New Jersey.*)

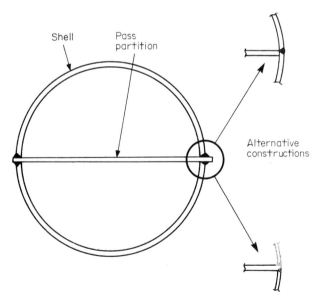

Figure 6.33 Split-shell construction. See ASME Code Interpretation VIII 83-187 (under review). Split-shell construction may be used for small-diameter two-pass fixed-tubesheet and U-tube heat exchangers.

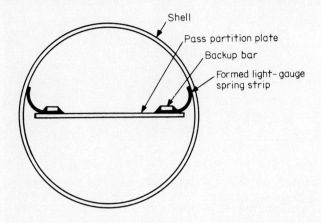

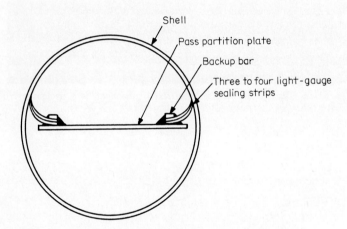

Figure 6.34   Single and multiflex pass-partition sealing strips.

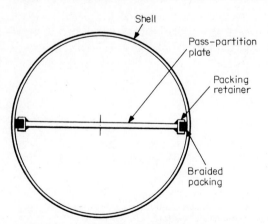

Figure 6.35   Packed pass-partition-to-shell seal.

States and Canada they usually are stamped with a National Board number in addition to the manufacturer's serial number and are registered with the National Board of Pressure Vessel Inspectors. Very often construction conforms to the user's or user's agent's specifications and frequently to another industry standard such as API 660.[12] Design and stress analysis are performed for each exchanger or small group of units identical except for orientation of connections and supports. One, two, or a few more or less identical exchangers may be built as described on one set of drawings.

On the other hand, production lines may use one set of drawings based upon one design analysis to produce many identical or nearly identical units that are purchased from catalogs and have standard nameplate data. These exchangers are used for refrigeration, commercial and industrial air conditioning, components of standard process packages, some small oil coolers, air compressor aftercoolers, and other commercial applications. They are seldom built to conform with TEMA and HEI standards, nearly always meeting only the manufacturer's proprietary standards (which may be more stringent in some areas than the TEMA or HEI standards). There may be an extra charge for code stamping and inspection.

Different procurement and inventory modes, production systems, assembly fixtures, and methods are used for building exchangers one or two at a time and for those manufactured to fill orders from a catalog and price list.

One-at-a-time production

In one-at-a-time production, most manufacturers purchase or produce major components such as tubes, tubesheets, shell and channel flanges, etc., for the specific job. However, they usually keep an inventory of standard items such as ANSI flanges, some pipe sizes, some head sizes, plate and sheet, gasket materials, etc. Manufacturers may also maintain modest inventories of parts that they make to standard drawings. These might be saddles and lugs, ring flanges for various design pressures, and similar components. Depending upon market conditions and past demand, manufacturers may also maintain an inventory of straight lengths of tubing. Inspection personnel make sure that heat numbers and identifying marks are transferred to parts parted out of plate and sheet and the commensurate mill-test reports matched with the bills of materials of the exchangers in which they are used.

Production may be planned by means of a bar chart or with a critical-path program. Because many diverse exchangers are being produced at the same time, machine availability must be considered in the production scheme. In well-organized shops, the amount of movement and handling of the bundle and shell is kept to a minimum. Whenever possible, a part of the assembly floor is assigned to the unit under construction, where it is built. A production flyer accompanies the exchanger during construction. Inspectors indicate their acceptance of the various parts by signing or initialing the flyer.

A burning department manually or machine-burns or plasma-cuts parts to order, generally from drawings issued with a job worksheet. The machine shop or subcontractors prepare machined parts, for example, tubesheets. In most shops, a fitter, working under the direction of a supervisor, is responsible for assembling all the necessary components. This includes requesting the production of sheared, rolled, and formed parts to be ready when needed. The fitter may be skilled in laying out or may call on the services of a layer-out. This is done because, in contrast to production-line work, shells, nozzle penetrations, heads, and bundles are laid out and fitted individually.

Depending upon the shop's management outlook, a fitter may work with the same welders, helpers, testers, etc., from job to job, or the supervisor may assign skilled and unskilled workers from a general pool as the fitter requires them. The fitter is directly responsible for producing the specified level of quality.

Removable bundles and most fixed-tubesheet ones are assembled outside the shell. For this purpose a leveled beam is fitted at one end with vertical members to which the front or stationary tubesheet is clamped (photograph of Fig. 6.36). The tie rods are threaded into the tubesheet. Spacers, baffles, and supports are then slid forward until the skeleton is assembled.

At this point the tubes are loaded and, in U-tube bundles, joined to the tubesheet. In floating-head units the rear or floating tubesheet is clamped in place, parallel with the stationary one, and set so that the tube holes register with those of the baffles and stationary tubesheet. The tubes are guided into the holes and their ends aligned for uniform protrusion or flush with the tubesheets before joining.

In fixed-tubesheet bundles, the tubes remain unjoined until the bundle is stabbed into the shell. Figure 6.37 shows several bundles at this stage of production. Figure 6.38 illustrates how bundles are installed by using slings that will not damage the tubes and that minimize sagging. After the bundle is in the shell, the front tubesheet-to-shell closing seam is made. To diminish tubesheet warping from welding, a ring flange or the mating channel or bonnet may first be bolted tightly to the tubesheet. The rear tubesheet is hung at approximately its position on the shell. The tubes are guided into place and the ends aligned with the tubesheets, and the tubesheet is tack-welded in place. Some manufacturers join the tubes to the tubesheets

Figure 6.36 Setting up a skeleton. (*Atlas Industrial Manufacturing Company, Clifton, New Jersey.*)

at this stage. Others complete the rear tubesheet-to-shell closing seam, then join the tubes.

When the shell is large enough, it is more economical to hang and weld the front tubesheet to the shell. The bundle is then built in the shell, followed by hanging and welding the rear tubesheet and tube joining.

For the most part removable bundles are assembled to shells in much the same way as the fixed-tubesheet bundle previously illustrated. One of the various types of flanged connections is used to complete the joint of the bundle to the shell. However, most modern feedwater heater U-tube bundles are fitted with a shell skirt welded to

Figure 6.37 Tubed skeletons. (*Futura Titanium, Westlake Village, California.*)

Figure 6.38 Using nylon slings to install bundle in shell. (*Courtesy of ITT Standard, Heat Transfer Division, Buffalo, New York.*)

the back face of the tubesheet. Various tubesheet-to-shell skirt joints are made. Most common is a simple bevel and land. However, the stress-concentration problem is the same as on the feedwater side and may be exacerbated by thermal stresses. Heater life may be increased if hubbed construction similar to that recommended in Chap. 5 for the channel-barrel-to-tubesheet connection is used on the shellside.

Production-line assembly

Exchangers built on a production line are assembled from components made to standard parts drawings. Procurement and production are based upon anticipated requirements determined from sales forecasts. As with automobiles, standard models are modified with minor changes based upon order bookings. Production is characterized by computer-generated indented bills of materials, labor standards for parts, and assembly based upon sophisticated time studies and process flowsheets. Parts such as tubesheets, baffles, tie rods and spacers, shells, nozzles, and supports are made in economical quantities with their production often subcontracted.

Storage and handling facilities are required for inventory purchased in anticipation of forecast production requirements. A computerized inventory management system is used to control receipts and disbursements of materials, track heat numbers, and match them with mill-test reports.

The exchanger components move along the production line, where the workforce uses more automatic and semiautomatic operations than could be justified for one-at-a-time production. For example, all the openings in thin-walled shells may be burned or stamped into flat sheets or plates that are subsequently rolled and automatically welded. On the line, each worker repeats a single operation or group of operations on the exchangers that move along the line.

Usually a production controller or production control group reports to a manufacturing engineer or production manager. Quality control and inspection are production functions, with hold points built into the production line. Code inspections may be performed on multiple units at one time.

Bundles for these units are generally put together on a bench fixture with slots for aligning and positioning the tubesheets and baffles along the bundle axis and pins or other devices for aligning the tube holes. The front-end tubesheet with the tie-rod holes and the cross-flow baffles are slotted into place. As the tie rods are run in from the rear end, spacers are dropped into place. The tie rods are threaded into the front tubesheet, and the rearmost baffle is locked in place with double nuts or by welding.

To assemble U-tube bundles, the tubes are loaded and joined to the tubesheet. In floating-head bundles, the rear tubesheet is set into the slot in the fixture. This is followed by tube loading through the rear tubesheet, baffles, and front tubesheet and tube joining. Tubes are loaded manually. Some factories have experimented with tube-loading machines and may have successfully developed more efficient ways. If the tube-to-tubesheet joints are rolled, multispindle rolling equipment is used to speed production.

Some manufacturers build fixed-tubesheet bundles in the same way as floating-bundle ones. They fit the tubesheets with backing rings for positioning the shell. The open-seamed shell cylinder is wrapped around the bundle, pulled together over a longitudinal backing bar or against a consumable backing strip. The assembly is clamped until welding is complete.

More often, before the tubes are joined to the front tubesheet, the bundle is slid into the shell. The rear tubesheet is then aligned, fitted to the shell, and tacked or clamped in place. The tube ends are set to protrude evenly from the outer faces of the tubesheet, and the tubes are joined. The rear tubesheet-to-shell closing seam is welded.

Differential-Pressure Design

Most heat exchangers are designed to accommodate the maximum absolute pressure to which each side may be exposed when it operates independently of the other. In differential-pressure design, the pressure parts exposed to both fluids are designed for the *difference* in operating pressures between the fluids. Differential-pressure design is seldom used when the simultaneous design pressures are less than 1000 lb/in^2 (6895 kPa). The factors to consider for the differential-pressure design option are economics, operating circumstances, and safety. They are discussed in the following paragraphs.

Economic factors are capital cost and the cost of providing additional safety relief required for differential-pressure operation. Differential design of an exchanger reduces the thickness of its tubes and tubesheets below what would be required for conventional design. To make it worthwhile, the capital cost savings must exceed any operating-cost penalty. Capital cost is affected by:

1. The fraction of exchanger cost represented by the tubes and fabricated tubesheets

2. The effect of pressure on tube thicknesses and tube thicknesses on tube cost and the cost of tube-to-tubesheet joining

3. The effect of pressure on tubesheet thickness and of tubesheet thickness on tubesheet material cost

4. The relative costs of drilling, machining, and assembling thinner versus a thicker tubesheet or tubesheets

5. Handling and fitting costs

6. The number of shells required

When the differential-pressure design option is chosen, safety relief protection must be installed beyond that required to relieve pressure that exceeds the MAWP of each side independently. Loss of pressure on either side, in differential-pressure operation, would cause the full pressure on the other side to be applied to the tubes and tubesheets unless some means of relieving a *differential* pressure higher than the design pressure is installed as shown schematically in Fig. 6.39.

These are the operating circumstances that favor differential-pressure design.

1. A common source of supply of the shellside and tubeside fluids

2. Shellside and tubeside operating pressures in the range of 1000 lb/in^2 (6895 kPa) and above, when the pressure in one side is directly controlled by the other

3. High pressure in both sides in which the differential can be measured and controlled

Operating a system designed for differential-pressure operation safely requires thorough training of personnel in the startup procedure and pressurization sequence, the shutdown procedure and depressurization sequence, and procedures for dealing with upsets and

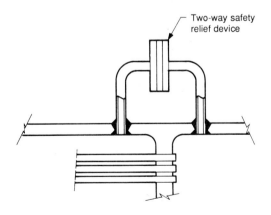

Two-way safety
relief device

Additional safety protection required
for differential-pressure design

Figure 6.39 Schematic arrangement of safety relief device for differential-pressure design.

pressure excursions. Safe operation also requires the ability to relieve high-pressure fluid into the low-pressure side when necessary.

Overview of Tube Vibration

Tube vibration results from a combination of shellside mechanical design and conditions that force the tubes to vibrate. It affects the shellside of the bundle, the tubes, and the tube-to-tubesheet connections. Following is an overview of the kinds of damage that vibration inflicts, mechanisms that force the tubes to vibrate, and information required for analysis. For more detailed treatments see the references at the end of the chapter.

Structural damage and operating problems caused by tube vibration

Vibration damages the structure and may cause operating problems. The kinds of structural damage it breeds, illustrated schematically in Figs. 6.40 and 6.41, and the operating problems it creates are discussed in the following paragraphs.

Interspan-collision tube damage. Tubes collide with each other between the baffles or tube supports when the free vibratory motion is equal to or more than half of the ligament space. For safe operation and long tube life, the acceptable limit of tube motion is 2 percent of the tube diameter. (This is a matter of judgment; motion equal to 5 percent of the tube diameter is permitted in some specifications.)

Wear damage. Wear damage to tubes and baffles occurs when tube motion due to vibration causes extensive rubbing in the baffles or supports at high cyclical rates. When the node of the waveform is between the supports or baffles, it limits the amplitude of the waveform as shown.

Fatigue failure of tubes and tube-to-tubesheet joints. As shown in Fig. 6.40, where the tubes penetrate the tubesheets and at the tube-to-tubesheet connections, vibration produces these effects:

1. The tubes may become cold-worked. The additional strain hardening makes the tubes susceptible to cracking.

2. Locked-in tube-end and tubesheet stress due to tube expanding may be relieved. Loss of the locked-in stresses may weaken the tube-to-tubesheet joints.

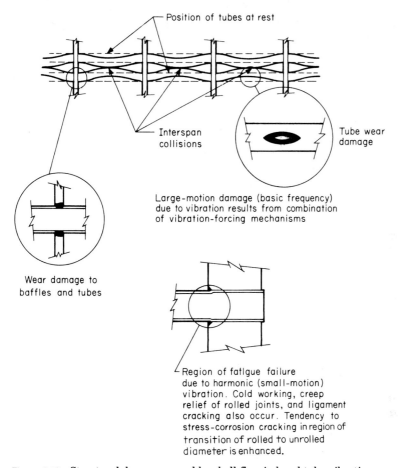

Position of tubes at rest

Interspan collisions

Tube wear damage

Large-motion damage (basic frequency) due to vibration results from combination of vibration-forcing mechanisms

Wear damage to baffles and tubes

Region of fatigue failure due to harmonic (small-motion) vibration. Cold working, creep relief of rolled joints, and ligament cracking also occur. Tendency to stress-corrosion cracking in region of transition of rolled to unrolled diameter is enhanced.

Figure 6.40 Structural damage caused by shell-flow-induced tube vibration.

3. Vibration-caused stresses are superimposed upon pressure and thermal stresses in the tube ends and tube-to-tubesheet joint welds.

Tubesheet ligament cracking. Vibration-induced cyclical dynamic loads overstress and fatigue the ligaments.

Root-bead tearing in tube-to-tubesheet welds. Figure 6.41 shows how vibration-induced tube loads can tear the root bead of a front-face-welded tube-to-tubesheet joint. The tears propagate into the weld, tube, and tubesheet.

Intensified stress corrosion. Vibration-induced dynamic loading stresses are superimposed upon tensile equilibrium stresses. Since

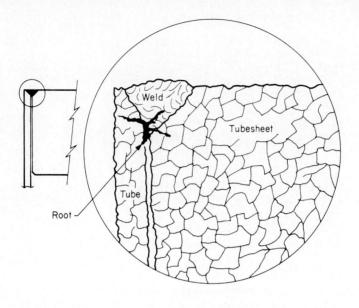

Area of enlargement

Figure 6.41   Root-bead tears propagating into the weld, tubes, and tubesheet.

stress corrosion is related to the intensity of tensile stress, susceptibility to corrosion is increased.

High operating noise.   High operating noise is due to the vibration-forcing mechanism of vortex shedding. Vortex shedding is accompanied by aeolian tones generated when metals vibrate at the fundamental frequency (large-amplitude vibrations).

Increased shellside pressure drop.   The energy required to produce tube vibration is extracted from the shellside fluid. Therefore, the pressure head loss is increased.

Causes of vibration induction

Tubes are induced to vibrate by shell flow, hydraulically coupled induction, and mechanically coupled induction. Shell flow is the most frequent cause of tube vibration.

Shell flow, geometry, and resulting motions.   Following is a brief description of the effects of bundle geometry and shell flow and the motions that result.

Structure.   The tube can be considered to be a continuous beam subjected to steady and fluctuating loads.

Loads.   Steady loads on the beam are due to shell flow in the dominant direction (axial flow). Fluctuating loads on the beam are due to instantaneous shifts in flow direction (cross-flow direction changes).

Motions (Fig. 6.42).   Large tube motions occur at the beam's fundamental frequency. Large tube motion causes the following kinds of damage:

1. Wear of tubes on tubes
2. Wear of tubes on baffles or supports
3. Wear of baffles or supports on tubes
4. Pounding of baffles by tubes
5. Pounding of tubes by baffles

Small motions occur at harmonic frequencies. Small-motion damage is as follows:

1. Tube-to-tubesheet joint fatigue
2. Tube-to-tubesheet weld root-bead tears
3. Ligament cracks

Small motion damage may be catastrophic.

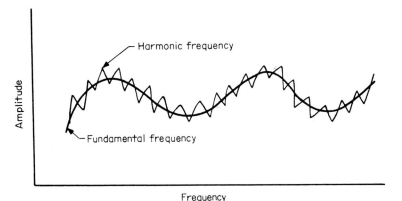

Figure 6.42 Schematic graph of frequency versus amplitude of vibrating tubes.

Shell-flow mechanisms that force tubes to vibrate

These are some of the mechanisms that force tubes to vibrate:

Vortex shedding.   Vortices shed by a velocity curl-back on the wake side of the tube (Fig. 6.43) alternately build up and are shed. The shedding is accompanied by harmonic lift forces *transverse* to the general flow direction. The frequency of tube movement that results varies with (1) the cross-flow velocity, (2) the tube diameter, and (3) the Strouhal number N_S (= frequency × tube outside diameter/velocity). Tube movement frequency is affected by the spanwise correlation.

The magnitude of motions resulting from harmonic lift forces due to vortex shedding varies with (1) the lift frequency, (2) the shellside fluid density, (3) the square of the shellside cross-flow velocity, and (4) the shellside Reynolds number N_{Re} (= tube outside diameter × cross-flow velocity × density/viscosity). Movement magnitude is affected by the spanwise correlation.

The spanwise correlation that affects the *frequency* and *magnitude* is a function of the amplitude response and the synchronizing effect of other excitations.

Turbulent buffeting.   The stream buffets the tubes because of (1) white noise (general background turbulence), (2) diffused vortices from upstream (Fig. 6.44), (3) slit-cavity-slit flow (Fig. 6.45), and (4) axial drag. In axial drag, stream friction along the tubes cyclically compresses the tubes *axially*, then releases them. The factors that affect axial drag are (1) tube flexural rigidity, (2) tube length and diameter, (3) tube static column loading, and (4) transverse span loads applied by other excitations.

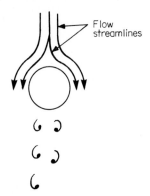

Figure 6.43   Vortex shedding.

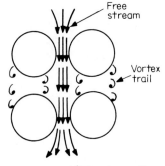

Figure 6.44 Diffused vortices from upstream.

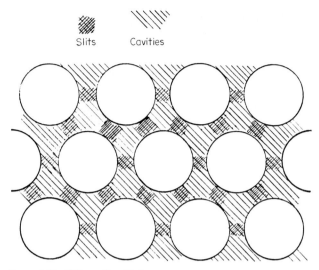

Figure 6.45   Slit-cavity-slit flow.

Fluid-elastic whirling (fluid-elastic swirling).   A row or rows of tubes react to cross-flow with coupled orbital motions shown schematically in Fig. 6.46. Fluid-elastic whirling directly extracts energy from the shell fluid, thereby increasing shellside fluid pressure drop.

Simultaneous lift and drag forces caused by harmonically varying slit widths initiate the motion. After fluid-elastic whirling starts, feedback from the harmonically varying lift and drag continue the vibration. The cross-flow velocity determines the character of the oscillations.

At a velocity defined as the *critical velocity*, the oscillations increase in magnitude without limit. At 55 to 100 percent of the critical veloc-

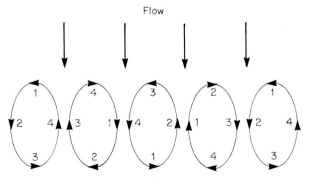

Figure 6.46   Fluid-elastic whirling. Numbers indicate the simultaneous positions of the tubes in a row.

ity, the oscillations are sporadic. The parameters of the critical velocity are (1) system damping, (2) tube unit weight, (3) shell fluid density, (4) tube natural frequency, and (5) tube location in the bundle.

Acoustical coupling

Gas-column standing waves may be propagated along shell stream paths at sonic velocities. The parameters that affect the frequency of acoustical coupled vibration are (1) the flow path length, (2) the standing-wave mode number, (3) the fluid molecular weight, (4) the ratio of fluid specific heat at constant pressure to fluid specific heat at constant volume, C_p/C_v, and (5) the tube natural frequency. Resonance varies directly with tube natural frequency. Acoustical excitations synchronize vortex shedding.

Hydraulically coupled vibration induction

Rhythmic excitations transmitted through the shell fluid cause tube vibrations with effects similar to those of turbulent buffeting. Some causes are (1) pump vibrations, (2) compressor vibrations, (3) rotor slap, (4) pulsed flows, and (5) control-valve hunting.

Mechanically coupled vibration induction

Energy enters through supports and piping in a similar fashion to the energy that causes buildings to vibrate when a heavy truck passes by on the adjacent street.

Amplification and damping

Vibration amplifies the deflection of the tube under static load (its own weight plus the weight of the fluid that it carries). The amount of amplification is called the *gain*. Damping reduces the live deflection.

At a given vibration frequency, the amplitude factor is the ratio of the dynamic-load deflection to the static-load deflection (Fig. 6.47). Theoretical curves of amplification factor versus the ratio (forcing frequency)/(natural frequency) coincide at ratios of forcing to natural frequency below 0.8 and above 1.15 for multispan beams. For ratios between these boundaries it is safe to use the curve for a single-span beam. Damping absorbs energy and sets the amplification factor. It consists of structural and fluid damping. Structural parameters are (1) the number of spans in the tube run, (2) the weight of the tube run, (3) the tube layout pattern, (4) the tube and baffle hardnesses, (5) the ratio of lift to drag forces, and (6) the shell-fluid lubricity.

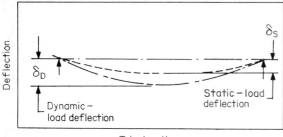

Figure 6.47 Schematic curve of deflection versus tube length under dynamic and static loads. At a given frequency δ_D/δ_S = amplification factor.

The fluid parameters are (1) fluid density, (2) fluid viscosity, and (3) quantity flowing.

Information required for analysis

Fluid parameters.   The analyst must be provided with these fluid parameters listed below at the inlet, the outlet, and intermediate locations of each zone of the unit: (1) temperature, (2) pressure, (3) density, (4) viscosity, and (5) quantity flowing.

Mechanical data.   Mechanical data from construction drawings and design calculations are required for analysis. They consist of complete geometry, including baffle-hole-to-tube clearances and tube axial loadings. Tube axial loadings consist of loads that result from hydrostatic pressure and those that result from restrained differential thermal expansion.

In feedwater heaters, these data are required for the desuperheating zone, the condensing zone, and the subcooling zone. Figure 6.48 shows a set of sample data for a six-leg multitube feed-to-effluent heat exchanger. The parameters are obtained from thermal ratings and pressure-drop calculations.

Sequence of analysis

After all necessary information has been obtained, these calculations are made: (1) tube natural frequencies, (2) coupled system damping, and (3) vibration forces. Lift, drag, and longitudinal forces are calculated for the tubes most susceptible to vibration (usually the peripheral tubes) at sensitive locations. These locations are usually the inlet zone (between the tubesheet and the first baffle or support), the cen-

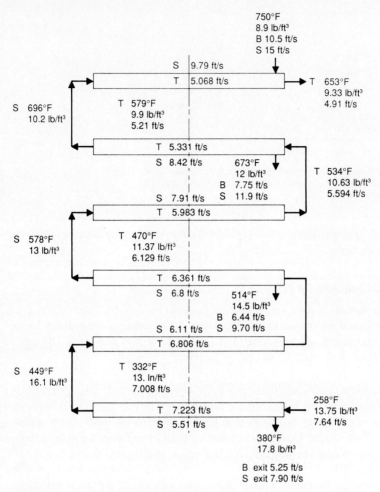

Figure 6.48 Data required for vibration analysis of white-oil feed-effluent exchanger. S = shell; B = bundle; T = tubes.

tral baffle or support span, and through the bundle when static loading varies with the position of the tubes.

The *TEMA Standards* have a section devoted to vibration analysis. However, the subject of tube vibration in heat exchangers is extremely complex, and one cannot blindly apply the standards without adequate study of the subject. Suggested readings on heat exchanger tube vibration are listed below.

Suggested Readings on Vibration

Barrington, E. A.: "Acoustic Vibrations in Tubular Exchanger," *Chem. Eng. Prog.*, vol. 69, July 1973.

Brothman, A.: "Heat Exchanger Vibration Problems," *Practical Aspects of Heat Transfer*, a CEP technical manual based upon the proceedings of the 1976 fall lecture series of the New Jersey and North Jersey sections of the AIChE.

——— and others: AIChE ser. 138, vol. 70, 1974.

——— and ———: "A Vibrations Prediction Method," *Practical Aspects of Heat Transfer*, a CEP technical manual based upon the proceedings of the 1976 fall lecture series of the New Jersey and North Jersey sections of the AIChE.

———, A. Devore, and A. Horowitz: "Heat Exchanger Vibration Analysis," *Practical Aspects of Heat Transfer*, a CEP technical manual based upon the proceedings of the 1976 fall lecture series of the New Jersey and North Jersey sections of the AIChE.

Chen, S. S.: "Instability Mechanisms and Stability Criteria of a Group of Circular Cylinders Subjected to Cross Flow, Part I: Theory," ASME Pap. 81-DET-21.

———: "Instability Mechanisms and Stability Criteria of a Group of Circular Cylinders Subjected to Cross Flow, Part II: Numerical Results and Discussion," ASME Pap. 81-DET-22.

———: *Design Guide for Calculating the Instability Flow Velocity of Tube Arrays in Cross Flow*, Argonne National Laboratory, February 1976.

——— and J. A. Jendrzecjk: *Dynamic Responses of Heat Exchanger Tube Banks*, Tech. Memo ANL-CT-76-25, Argonne National Laboratory, February 1976.

———, G. S. Rosenberg, and M. W. Wambganss: "On Tube-Baffle Impact during Heat Exchanger Tube Vibration," presented at ASME winter annual meeting, New York, December 1970.

Chen, Y. N.: "Flow Induced Vibration and Noise in Tube Bank Heat Exchangers Due to von Kármán Streets," *J. Eng. Ind., Trans. ASME*, ser. B, vol. 90, February 1968.

——— and M. Weber: "Flow Induced Vibration in Tube Bundle Heat Exchangers with Cross and Parallel Flow," presented at ASME winter annual meeting, New York, December 1970.

——— and W. C. Young: "The Orbital Movement and the Damping of Fluidelastic Vibration of Tube Bundles Due to Vortex," presented at ASME winter annual meeting, New York, December 1970.

Chenowith, J. M.: *Flow Induced Tube Vibration in Shell and Tube Heat Exchangers*, ERDA Rept. SAN/1273-1, Heat Transfer Research, February 1977.

——— and R. S. Kistler: *Tube Vibrations in Shell and Tube Heat Exchangers*, Heat Transfer Research Institute Tech. Rept., September 1976.

Connors, J. H., Jr.: "Fluidelastic Vibration of Tube Arrays Excited by Cross and Parallel Flow," *Proc. Flow-Induced Vibration in Heat Exchangers*, New York, December 1970.

Den Hartog, J. P.: *Mechanical Vibrations*, 4th ed., McGraw-Hill Book Company, New York, 1976.

Eiler, J. F., and W. M. Small: "Tube Vibration in a Thermosyphon Reboiler," *Chem. Eng. Prog.*, vol. 69, no. 7, July 1973.

Eisinger, F. L.: "Prevention and Cure of Flow Induced Vibration Problems in Tubular Heat Exchangers," *J. Press. Ves. Technol.*, vol. 192, May 1980, pp. 139–145.

Fits-Hugh, J. S.: "Flow-Induced Vibration and Noise in Tube Bank Heat Exchangers," International Symposium on Vibration Problems in Industry, Keswick, England, Apr. 10–12, 1973.

Kissel, J. H.: "Flow-Induced Vibrations in Heat Exchangers—A Practical Look," *Mach. Des.*, vol. 45, May 3, 1973, pp. 104–107.

Moretti, P. M., and R. L. Lowery: *Heat Exchanger Vibration Characteristics in a "No Flow" Condition*, Oklahoma State University, School of Mechanical and Aerospace Engineering, September 1973.

Nobles, S. D., and J. F. Sebald: "Control of Vibration in Cross-Flow Heat Exchangers," *Chem. Process Eng.*, November 1968, pp. 95–103.

Owen, P. R.: "Buffeting Excitation of Boiler Tube Vibration, *J. Mech. Eng. Sci.*, vol. 7, no. 4, 1965.

Pettigrew, M. J., and D. J. Gorman: *Vibration of Heat Exchanger Components in Liquid and Two-Phase Cross-Flow*, Atomic Energy of Canada, Limited, AECL-6184, May 1978.

Standards of the Tubular Exchanger Manufacturers Association, 6th ed., The Tubular Exchanger Manufacturers Association, Tarrytown, N.Y., 1978, pp. 223–232.

Standards of the Tubular Exchanger Manufacturers Association, 7th ed., The Tubular Exchanger Manufacturers Association, Tarrytown, N.Y., 1988.

Thomsen, W. Y.: *Mechanical Vibrations*, 2d ed., D. Van Nostrand Company, New York, 1953.

Thorngren, J. Y.: "Predict Exchanger Tube Damage," *Hydrocarbon Process.*, April 1970, pp. 129–131.

References

1. *ASME Boiler and Pressure Vessel Code*, Section II: *Material Specifications*, 1986 ed., American Society of Mechanical Engineers, New York.
2. *Standards of the Tubular Exchanger Manufacturers Association*, 7th ed., The Tubular Exchanger Manufacturers Association, Tarrytown, N.Y., 1989.
3. S. Kopp and M. F. Sayre, "Expansion Joints for Heat Exchangers," contributed by the Heat Transfer Division of Alco Products Division of the American Locomotive Co. at the ASME annual meeting, New York, Nov. 27–Dec. 1, 1950; revised May 15, 1952.
4. *ASME Boiler and Pressure Vessel Code*, Section VIII, Division 1: *Unfired Pressure Vessels*, 1986 ed., American Society of Mechanical Engineers, New York.
5. James D. Matheny, "Bellows Spring Rate for Seven Typical Convolution Shapes," *Mach. Des.* (date unknown).
6. *Standards of the Expansion Joint Manufacturers Association*, 4th ed., Expansion Joint Manufacturers Association, Tarrytown, N.Y., 1975.
7. A. T. McDonald and R. W. Fox, "An Experimental Investigation of the Incompressible Flow in Conical Diffusers," *Int. J. Mech. Sci.*, vol. 8, no. 2, 1966, pp. 125–139.
8. K. P. Singh, "How to Locate Impingement Plates in Tubular Heat Exchangers," *Hydrocarbon Process.*, October 1974, pp. 147–149.
9. *Steam: Its Generation and Use*, 37th ed., The Babcock & Wilcox Company, New York, 1965.
10. Joseph J. Singer (ed.), *Combustion Fossil Power Systems*, 3d ed., Combustion Engineering, Inc., Windsor, Conn., 1981.
11. *Standard for Power Plant Heat Exchangers*, 1st ed., The Heat Exchange Institute, Cleveland, 1980; Addendum 1, 1984.
12. *Shell-and-Tube Heat Exchangers for General Refinery Services*, API Standard 660, 4th ed., The American Petroleum Institute, Washington, September 1982.

7

Inspection, Maintenance, and Repair

Introduction

This chapter discusses inspection, maintenance, and repair. The section on inspection is presented primarily as a guide to users, but it can also be useful to designers, constructors, and manufacturers. The American Petroleum Institute's guide for inspecting heat exchangers is a valuable supplement to this work.[1]

Inspection

Careful shop inspection of exchangers during construction may minimize the occurrence of maintenance problems. Regular examinations and inspections are required for progressive maintenance. Fully inspecting exchangers when making alterations and repairs may reveal potential problems that can be dealt with before returning an exchanger to service.

The most effective way to achieve inspection goals consistently is to prepare inspection briefs in clear, concise formats. These documents specify to inspectors and to those doing the work what is to be inspected, how, and when. They set the limits of inspectors' responsibilities and authority. The detail in a brief varies with the quality assurance requirements of the exchanger. Therefore, a particular brief may not require inclusion of all items.

Guide to preparing briefs for inspecting during construction

Assemble and incorporate into the inspection brief the purchase specifications, setting plan, assembly drawing, detail drawings, and manufacturer's bill of materials. Include these items: (1) assembling tools and instruments required for inspection, (2) examining construction materials and their documentation, (3) verifying procedure and personnel qualifications, (4) making certain that quality control practices are as agreed, (5) making physical measurements and examinations of the work, and (6) collecting the documents required to establish a clear path of accountability and to facilitate maintenance.

Tools and instruments

Most equipment, tools, and instruments for inspecting heat exchangers in shops are simple and readily available. Table 7.1 is a partial list of what to use for various inspections and examinations that may be required.

Checklist

Before the initial inspection, prepare a checklist of what to inspect and when. Instruct the inspector to record deviations and their resolutions in an inspector's log. The following are written in the form in which briefs might give explanations and instructions to users' inspectors.

Documentation of construction materials. On the first contact, notify the shop that the documentation of the materials to be used in the heat exchanger must be examined before fabrication commences. These consist both of mill-test reports and certificates of compliance for raw materials (tubesheet material, tubes, flanges, pipe, and plate, etc.) and certifications of parts such as bellows-type expansion joints manufactured by an expansion joint manufacturer and stamped, "U(W) part."

Materials certifications.   The applicable construction code (*ASME Code* in the United States and Canada), standards, and specifications specify the requirements for materials.[2,3] To demonstrate compliance, materials producers make chemical analyses and physical tests on representative samples taken from each production heat or lot. The producer's name or symbol and the heat number must be permanently

TABLE 7.1   Equipment, Tools, and Instruments for Shop Inspection*

What to examine	What to use
Baffle cuts	Scale
Bolt elongation	Micrometer calipers; sonic micrometer
Bolt-hole orientation	Bolts used as pins in holes; level, square, and straightedge
Channel-cover flatness	Straightedge and dial indicator
Flatness of tubesheet extended as a flange	Straightedge and dial indicator
Finish	Tactile comparison samples; optical comparator
Flange flatness	Straightedge and dial indicator
Flange scalloping (distortion between bolt holes)	Feeler gauges when assembled; straightedge and dial indicator before assembly
Ligament distortion	Internal dial caliper; strain gauges
Nozzle and support angularity	Level, straightedge, or square
Pass-partition bending	Scale, straightedge, and dial indicator
Pass-partition location	Scale and straightedge
Tube bowing	High-intensity light
Tube diameter, ovality, and thickness	Hole gauge; internal dial calipers; outside micrometer calipers
Tube-hole diameter	Go–no-go gauge; hole gauge; internal dial calipers
Tubesheet-to-tubesheet parallelity	Steel measuring tape
Tubesheet rotation about longitudinal axis	Level, straightedge, plumb line, and protractor
Tubesheet waviness	Straightedge and dial indicator
Expansion-joint angular deflection	Trammels and scale; level and straightedge
Expansion-joint squirm	Trammels and scale
Weld size	Welding gauge

*Carry a marking crayon to indicate unacceptable use and an inspector's log to record results.

marked on each piece of material made. Analysis and test reports are certified by a person in responsible charge and notarized.

Make sure that the fabricator transfers these heat numbers to materials divided or parted from plate and pipe. Verify that the manufacturer records the original mill-test reports and ties them to the parts listed in the bill of materials. Be aware that the pressure vessel safety code rules pay little or no attention to parts that do not bear pressure but that their chemistry and physical properties are important for the exchanger's use. Code-authorized inspectors are responsible only for determining that the materials and markings of pressure parts and nonpressure parts welded to them conform with code requirements. Furthermore, they may not be interested in specifications listed in the purchase documents and specifications that are more stringent than the code's. Therefore, compare the mill-test reports with the purchase specifications. Discuss any deviations with the engineering department, and note in the inspector's log any that are accepted.

Do not confuse warehouse certifications with mill certificates of compliance. Warehouses frequently offer their own certifications that materials conform with the code specifications. They repeat information listed in the original mill-test reports. Such certifications are usually unacceptable under the prevailing pressure vessel safety code rules. Mill certificates of compliance do not include specific test data but are usually acceptable for such materials as welding consumables.

Parts certifications. Mill-test reports are not required for standard parts produced in quantity, for example, pipe flanges, couplings, and small fittings. However, the part manufacturer's name or trademark, size, rating, and material of construction must be permanently marked on each part.

Manufacturers' partial data reports are not required for such standardized subassemblies as handholes and manways but must be provided for subcontracted subassemblies. These include completely and partially fabricated shells, thin-walled expansion joints, bundles, and channels. In the same category are replacement components for existing equipment. The *ASME Code* rules require the subcontractor or component manufacturer to stamp the assembly or component, which must be inspected and accepted by an authorized inspector (AI). The AI indicates acceptance by signing a manufacturer's partial data report. The report must be backed up by mill-test reports for the materials used in construction.

The heat exchanger manufacturer who incorporates the part in the exchanger is responsible for its final hydrostatic test as part of the completed unit. Therefore, most subcontractors do not hydrostatically test such parts unless required by purchase documents and specifications. The AI who witnesses the final hydrostatic test signs the manufacturer's data report, to which the subcontractor's or part manufacturer's partial data report must be attached. Stamping with the appropriate symbol is then permitted. Verify that the documentation is on hand before subcontracted components or assemblies are incorporated into the exchanger.

Ordinarily, this practice presents no problem. However, bellows expansion joints that fail the hydrostatic test after installation cannot readily be repaired. Therefore, although it is not an *ASME Code* requirement, purchase specifications may require the joint manufacturer to test the joint hydrostatically. When this is so, verify that the AI-signed partial data report includes the hydrostatic-test data.

Procedures and qualified personnel. The manufacturer must use the procedures that are specified in the purchase documents or have been approved by the purchaser's or user's engineers. Code inspectors are obliged to determine that the manufacturer uses qualified written procedures for welding, tube joining, and nondestructive examining and testing the pressure envelope. Procedures acceptable to AIs may be less stringent than the ones in the purchase specification. Therefore, make sure that procedures acceptable to the AI also meet the purchase specification requirements. It is the AI's function to make sure that only workers currently qualified in the accepted procedures do the work and that the procedure specifications are readily available to them.

The AI's responsibility does not extend to such noncode aspects of construction as acid washing, pickling and passivating, sandblasting and coating, cleaning, skidding, crating, and loading. Inspect and observe to make sure that specified and agreed procedures are used for these items. It is especially important to check the sequence in which the work is done. When an exchanger is to be sandblasted, pickled, and passivated, it would defeat the purpose of the acid treatment if the sandblasting followed pickling and passivating.

Adherence to quality control requirements. Most pressure vessel safety codes require manufacturers to follow an approved quality control manual for work done in their shops. The manual may include both noncode and code requirements, but the noncode aspects do not concern AIs. The purchaser's inspector must verify compliance with noncode quality requirements. The most effective way to prepare for checking quality control practices is to review the drawings and specifications with a copy of the manufacturer's quality control manual in hand. Mark off and list purchaser-inspector items.

Physical inspections and examinations. Code inspectors are not obliged to inspect fabrication that does not affect safety or is not covered by the rules of the prevailing code. However, such construction may be critical to an exchanger's installation, operation, and maintenance.

Therefore, confirm that the work conforms with the materials, dimensions, and tolerances shown on the drawings and in the reference standards and specifications. These may be the *TEMA Standards*, the HEI *Standard for Power Plant Heat Exchangers*, the HEI *Standards for Closed Feedwater Heaters*, or API 660.[4-6]

Before the start of fabrication, review with the manufacturer any purchase specifications that demand more than the construction code and referenced standards. At this time establish hold points when fabrication is to be delayed pending inspection. This requires agreeing on the amount of advance notice that the manufacturer will give for inspection readiness and the maximum response time in which the purchaser may make the inspection.

Following is a discussion of items generally to be inspected. State in the brief that specific requirements are as marked in the inspection brief checklist.

Tubesheets. Minor deviations from the exchanger specification sheets in tube count and arrangement are usually insignificant, but the actual tube count, drilling pitch, and pitch orientation and, finally, the approved drawings must match. Do not accept any deviation without consent from the engineering department. If the engineering department approves a variance, require the manufacturer to revise the drawings to show it. Record the change in the inspector's logbook.

Be especially vigilant to make sure that tube-hole drilling does not exceed the oversize tolerance limits of the standards. Tubes that are strength-expanded into oversized holes can be joined to the tubesheet tightly and strongly enough to satisfy the code's requirements. However, the joints may be weaker and leak sooner than those made with holes drilled within the tolerances. Moreover, when the tubes are sensitive to stress-corrosion cracking in either the shellside or the tubeside fluid environment, oversized holes lead to higher stress levels at the transition zone between the expanded and unexpanded parts of the tube. The high stress levels on the inner and outer surfaces directly promote stress-corrosion cracking.

Verify the hole size with a go–no-go gauge like the one shown in Fig. 7.1. Drill drift may also significantly affect tubesheet strength and tube life. This is especially likely in thicker tubesheets. In gen-

Figure 7.1 Go–no-go gauge. (*Photograph courtesy of MGT Inc., Boulder, Colorado.*)

eral, spot-check holes in thin tubesheets for drill drift. However, examine substantially all holes for drill drift when the tubesheet is 3 in (76.2 mm) thick or thicker. Measure drill drift with a dial indicator. Number the tube rows and columns to establish an x–y number for each hole. For example, the number of the tenth tube hole in the second row is 2,10. Mark and record in the inspector's log by hole number the locations of any holes that are oversized or in which drill drift is excessive. Obtain engineering department approval before accepting a tubesheet with oversized holes or excessive drill drift.

Although somewhat undersized holes are beneficial from the standpoint of tube-to-tubesheet joining, they make it hard for the workforce to load tubes into the bundle without damaging the tube and hole surfaces. Lubricating the holes and tubes is not acceptable because the lubricant contaminates the joint. Therefore, require any undersized holes to be reamed to size. If annular grooves have been machined into the holes, reaming undersized holes may reduce the groove depth. The strength that a groove confers on an expanded joint is directly proportional to its depth. Therefore, underdepth grooves must be remachined to the depth specified on the drawing. This is usually 1/64 in (about 0.4 mm).

Examine a representative number of holes to make sure that annular grooving is concentric with the holes and the groove configuration matches the drawing dimensions. If the shop's toolholder has excessive clearance, the grooves may be so eccentric that one side has little or no depth and the other is too deep. Poorly sharpened grooving tools will produce out-of-tolerance hole configurations, whether square, half-round, or V type.

The TEMA and other manufacturers' standards specify a "workmanlike" finish for the inside surface of tubesheet holes. However, they do not define workmanlike. Inspect the holes by using a high-intensity light and a magnifying lens. As a minimum, the surfaces of the holes should be uniform throughout and free of scores, gouges, and spiral, annular, or axial tool marks. If the drawings require a particular finish or thread shape, use plastic or metal comparison specimens to determine by feel if the holes are approximately as specified. Quantitative measurements are not usually necessary. When they are required by purchase documents, the specification will state whether an optical comparator or other measuring device is to be used and the tolerances permitted.

Tube-joint weld preparation must conform with the drawing detail. Deviation may cause inferior welds that either are not as strong as required, are porous, or are subject to inadequate penetration at the root. Visual inspection is ordinarily adequate, but when preparations appear to differ from the drawing, make measurements. Most deviations are unacceptable, but an occasional larger-than-agreed chamfer or J groove is generally harmless. Smaller ones are not permissible and should be remachined when found.

Measure tubesheet flatness across the diameter of the gasket ring for conformity with the specifications. The manufacturer's standards do not have flatness tolerances but do require good workmanship. API 660 tolerances should be shown on the drawings when applicable. If they apply but are not shown on the drawing, refer to the standard and measure accordingly.

On a finished bundle, bowed and dished tubesheets may indicate faulty tube expanding. Inspect fixed tubesheets extended as flanges for deformations due to weld shrinkage. The total deviation from the flat caused by distortion due to welding and bowing due to expanding must not exceed the specified flatness tolerance.

The AI is responsible for seeing that the manufacturer has not skimped on weld size to minimize shrinkage, but he is not concerned with the effects of weld shrinkage on the exchanger's usefulness in service. The shop is not required to machine subsequent to welding and expanding unless the purchase documents so specify. However, the gasket surfaces must be flat enough to compress the gaskets uniformly.

Unless the purchase specifications set limits on out-of-flatness and waviness, it may be necessary to accept pass partitions that have been shaped to fit the contour of the tubesheet. If the out-of-flatness and waviness appear to be unacceptable, request the shop to delay shaping the pass partitions pending approval by the engineering department. If such approval is withheld, it will be the task of the purchasing department to negotiate with the fabricator the cost of machining after tube joining.

Baffles. Examine baffle-hole drilling very carefully. Inspect for cleaning off any metal on the back face upset by the penetration of the drill. None is tolerable. Baffle holes that are undersized are beneficial to flow and reduce the probability of vibration damage during operation. If the tubes can be loaded safely, moderately undersized baffle holes are acceptable. It is very important to note in the inspector's log when undersized holes have been accepted and to insert a memorandum to that effect in the maintenance file. This is so because retubing will be more difficult. Reject baffles in which more than 2 percent of the holes exceed the size limits of the standard. Oversized holes can contribute to vibration damage and reduce the unit's performance.

When the clearance between cross-flow baffles and the shell is greater than the standards allow, the unit will generally underperform. Therefore, the baffles must be finished to fit properly.

The surface finish that the standards specify (250 rms in the *TEMA Standards*) is less relevant to performance than the diameter of the baffle and the ID of the shell. It is the shop's responsibility to finish the baffles in relation to the shell ID so that the bundle can be loaded and at the same time not exceed the maximum clearance limits. Much controversy can be avoided if the finished-shell ID can be inspected and measured before the baffles are machined to size. This sequence and hold point must be worked out in advance of construction with the shop management. It cannot be insisted upon unless the purchase specification requires it.

If the shell is undersized, a bundle assembled with baffles machined to the drawing size will be difficult or impossible to load into the shell. The shop's alternatives are (1) to set the bundle up in a lathe and machine down the baffles to allow the bundle to fit into the shell and (2) to hand-grind the baffles to fit. Most smaller shops are not equipped for turning baffles in an assembled bundle. In either case the edge distance around peripheral tubes may be reduced. Inspect carefully to make sure that the tubes in the way of turning or grinding the baffles are not damaged. Also make sure that hand-ground baffles do not have so much metal removed that the baffle-to-shell clearance exceeds the limits in the standard.

Greater-than-specified baffle segment cutoffs may substantially reduce shellside heat transfer effectiveness. Smaller cuts raise the shellside pressure drop. Therefore, make sure that the cuts match the drawing dimensions. The cuts should be on or close to tube row centerlines, middle of tube lanes, or pass-partition centerlines. The positions should have been accepted on the approval drawings. However, if the approved drawings show different locations of cuts, it is proper to question the shop and engineering department beforehand. An unintentional error may thus be avoided. If it is too late to correct such a situation, it is very important to inspect the baffles at the cuts to make sure that the cut hole edges will not dig into the tubes as they are loaded into the bundle.

Flanged joints. Measure the flatness of flanges after they have been joined to the channel or shell. This may stop a problem in the making. Detect the amount of flange warping by rotating a straightedge on the flange faces to reveal waviness and cupping (Fig. 7.2). If these appear to be excessive by visual inspection, measure the deviations from flatness by mounting a dial indicator on the straightedge and moving it back and forth across the flange. Make these measurements at the quarter, eighth, and sixteenth points.

It is important that all the flange bolts carry approximately the same load. For high-pressure and other services where tightness is

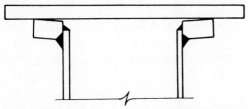

Figure 7.2   Inspecting a flange for cupping due to welding.

critical, verify that bolts tightened with a torque wrench are torqued to the specified values. After all torquing is complete, request the shop to determine the torque that triggers the cutoff on the torque wrench for each bolt.

For high pressures, fluctuating pressure loads, or other reasons, bolt tensioning may have been specified. If this is a purchase requirement, witness the tensioning to make sure that the agreed-upon procedure is followed. Number the bolt positions counterclockwise, beginning with bolt no. 1 at the 0° bolt hole. Measure and record the bolt lengths before and after the joint is made up tight. If an ultrasonic gauge is available, measure and record the stress in each bolt. If any bolts are elongated beyond the elastic limit (permanently stretched), reject the assembly. Insist on the remachining of any warped surfaces and the installation of new bolting.

Channels and bonnets.   Measure the position, main centerline-to-face distance, and angularity of channel and bonnet connections. Use a level, straightedge, and rule to verify that the flange faces are parallel with each other and a straightedge to see if they are warped. Make sure that welding of hinges, lifting lugs, pigtails, or insulation supports to the channel has caused no distortion. Using straightedges and bolts or pins, check for correct bolt-hole orientation.

Pass partitions that do not line up with gasket ribs may make it necessary to use excessive force to seat the gasket. In addition, they may lead to pass-partition bypassing in service. Therefore, make sure that the partitions are located within $\pm \frac{1}{32}$ in (0.8 mm) of the position shown on the drawing. Because welds of pass partitions to the shell and tubesheet can cause lamellar tearing as the welds cool and because improper welding may cause corrosion, it is important to inspect joint preparation and weld production at these locations. When partitions are tapered where they bear on the gasket, see to it that the tapers are uniform and within specified tolerances.

Tubing.   Examine several tubes chosen at random from each heat.

Tap them lightly with an inspection hammer. A high-pitched ring may indicate that they are too hard. Request the shop to test with a portable hardness tester any tubes that sound suspicious. This is especially important for integral low-fin tubes because finning increases hardness, which heat treatment does not always successfully reduce. Reject tubes that exceed the hardness limits in the tubing specification. If more than 2 percent of the tubes inspected exceed the specified limits, make contact with the engineering department for further instructions. If necessary, request the manufacturer to withhold installing the tubes pending receipt of instructions.

Use micrometer calipers to measure the diameter, gauge, and ovality of the random samples. If more than 2 percent are off specification, require all the tubes to be measured before installation and those that exceed the permissible tolerances to be rejected.

Look for scratches, corrosion, and dirt inside and out. Excessively dirty tubes (for example, those on which shop dust has settled on a greasy film) may be made acceptable by cleaning. However, reject corroded, scratched, or mechanically damaged tubes. The tube ends should be deburred completely smooth to the touch, without nicks or splits. The finish and fit of the ferrules on bimetallic tube ends are important. Outer tube metal should have been pared away without damage to the inner tube, leaving no burrs behind. The ferrules should fit snugly.

The ends of tubes to be installed in falling-film evaporators may be notched to provide weirs that control downflow. Make certain that the notches or slots are identical and at the same depth. After the tubes are in place in the exchanger, make a series of straightedge and level measurements to verify that all notch or slot elevations are in the same plane. If, instead of notching the tubes, the ends are fitted with pressed- or welded-on weirs, make similar inspections for the fittings and their installation.

The bottom tube ends of downflow condensers and some knock-back condensers in which condensing takes place inside the tubes may extend below the face of the bottom tubesheet and be cut at an angle. The length that protrudes and the angle at which the tubes are cut affect condenser operation. Therefore, measure the angle and extension for conformity with the drawings.

Measure the center-to-center distance of several tubes in each row of U tubes. Reject tubes that deviate from the bending-schedule dimensions and bending specification. Look for unacceptable excessive flattening of the bends and inner-side crimping. Check heat-treated bends at the discolored region to determine that the specified length has been heat-treated.

Inspect high-fin and other extended-surface tubes for dimensional conformity with specifications. Points of attention are fin heights, spacings, and positions of surface extenders.

After the tubes have been loaded into the bundle but before they are joined to the tubesheets, make sure that their lengths are within the permissible variation. If the drawing or specification requires the tube ends to be flush with one or both tubesheets, reexamine the ends after the joints have been completed.

Shells.   Inspect these items:

1. Shell thickness and inside diameter
2. Shell roundness, flat spots, and weld shrinkage
3. Fit of courses to courses for axial alignment of centerlines
4. Locations, dimensions, and construction of impingement protection
5. Feedwater heater zone separators and shrouds and their joints to the shellside face of the tubesheet
6. Bundle rails or guides
7. Dam or weir overflow heights and underflow clearances
8. Depth of insertion of standpipes and snorkels
9. Collection devices for noncondensibles venting
10. Distribution devices for cascading drains

The clearance between the bundle baffles and the shell must not exceed the referenced manufacturer's standard or that shown on the approved drawings. However, bundles must be able to be inserted and withdrawn without using so much force that the baffles are damaged. Consequently, the shell must be round and free of flat spots, cave-ins at weld seams and nozzles, and internal nozzle and weld projections.

When required by the purchase specification, check for ease of bundle insertion and pulling either by witnessing insertion, removal, and reinsertion of the bundle or a test template. If use of a test template has been specified, witness its passage completely through the shell. The template consists of two rigid disks equal to the *actual* transverse baffle diameter that are mounted 12 in (304.8 mm) apart perpendicularly on a rigid shaft. The requirement for inspecting the insertion of a template should have been specified in the purchase documents. If it was not and it is deemed necessary or advantageous, the purchasing department must negotiate the cost of its preparation and use with the manufacturer. In any event the fabricator should know at the outset that observation of insertion of such a template will be required.

When inspecting the shell, look for the fitter's quarter-point center-punch marks on the natural centerlines of the shell, on all parts assembled to it, and on the tubesheets. (The natural centerlines are the 0–180° and 90–270° centerlines. The quarter points are at 0°, 90°, 180°, and 270°.) Compare the positions of the shell flange or fixed-tubesheet bolt holes relative to the natural centerlines with their locations on the drawings. Measure the angularity of the shell flanges or tubesheets at the quarter and eighth points. It is generally adequate to use a steel tape and a level for these purposes.

Check the positions of connections, supports, vapor belts, expansion joints, and all appurtenances relative to the working points. Measure the shell length at the quarter points and the nozzle and support-base distances to the shell centerline. Check saddle and lug bolt-hole positions against the setting-plan template. Similarly verify dimensions of axial nozzles. Use levels and straightedges to determine nozzle and support angularity.

Misplaced positions of nozzles and supports may not be cause for rejection or require correction even when they exceed the tolerances shown on the drawings and specifications. Check any deviations with the engineering department to determine if they can be accepted. Record condoned variances in the inspector's log and mark up the drawings with the actual dimensions. Request the shop to alter the original drawings to show the as-built dimensions and to provide prints for the record.

Bundles. Baffle locations are important to thermal and mechanical operation. Therefore, measure the spacing from the stationary or front tubesheet to the first baffle, the spacings between baffles, and the distance from the last baffle to the U bend or floating or rear tubesheet. In feedwater heater bundles, verify that the axial positions and elevations of desuperheating-zone shrouds and drains subcooling-zone enclosures conform with the drawing details. The positions of inlets and outlets in the desuperheating and subcooling zones should match the drawing details.

Because dam baffle heights determine how much surface is allocated for subcooling in process condensers, they must be cut in the right place. Impingement-plate dimensions, positions, and attachments affect tube protection. Therefore, the dimensions and quality of the work must also be verified.

Protection of materials and parts. If a manufacturer improperly stores or handles materials and parts, it may lead to early failure of an exchanger. Therefore, during inspection visits observe how the shop stores materials and parts and protects them from damage.

Welding materials especially are affected by dampness. In carbon steel welds, the hydrogen in moisture absorbed by fluxes and coatings

promotes weld cracking. In austenitic stainless steels, damp rod coatings cause weld spatter and porosity. Moist submerged arc fluxes are
subject to the additional disability of not flowing freely. This deprives
the weld puddle of protection from the atmosphere and loss of addi-
tives contained in the flux.

For these reasons, it is important to check the manufacturer's procedures for handling, storing, and rehabilitating welding consumables. Verify that after the seal on a package of coated rod has been
broken, rod issued from the package for immediate use is held in portable warmers. Check to see that rod returned to the toolroom or other
issuing place is stored in ovens at a temperature above 375°F (190°C).
Damp rods and moist fluxes that have been rehabilitated are acceptable if they have been baked at 800°F (425°C) long enough to drive off
the moisture. Fluxes recovered from submerged arc welding should be
mixed with equal portions of fresh flux before they are used.

Preinstallation damage may result if tubes are wet or exposed to
corrosive atmospheres. The damage may vary from slight tarnishing
to deep pitting. Carbon steel tubes transported by ship or stored near
salt water are apt to be pitted. Similarly exposed austenitic stainless-
steel tubes may undergo stress-corrosion cracking because of chloride
ions in the atmosphere and residual stress in the tube surfaces. In cold
climates, stack gases that are generated by burning oil in
salamanders in the plant or that enter a shop from the atmosphere
may be laden with enough sulfur compounds to corrode nickel tubes.
A case has been described in the literature in which zinc chloride used
to preserve the wood of shipping boxes caused corrosion of Inconel 600
tubes after the boxes had been rained on.[7]

Therefore, tubes must be inspected for corrosion before they are
loaded into the bundle. Inspect a representative sample of tubes from
each heat before they are installed in the unit. If tubes in the sample
appear to be corroded, require all the tubes to be laid out for inspection. Do not accept corroded tubes without authorization from the engineering department. Note indications of corrosion in the inspector's
log along with the heat numbers of the affected tubes.

The shop may have bought tubing for the job, taken it from inventory, or combined tubes from stock with ones ordered for the job. This
contributes to efficient production at the lowest cost. However, it
means that the tubes in a unit may be from more than one heat. To
maintain traceability, require the manufacturer to mark up a
tubesheet layout as illustrated in Fig. 7.3 to serve as a map of the location of tubes from different heats. (Note that the manufacturers, dimensions, and heat numbers shown in the figure are for illustrative
purposes only. They do not represent an actual situation.)

How a shop stores tubes may affect their life in the exchanger. They

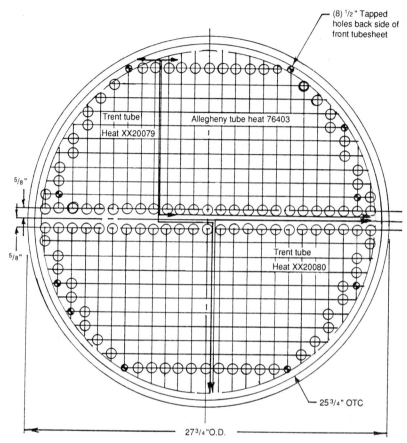

Figure 7.3 Tubesheet layout used as tube-heat map. Drill, ream, and double-groove 430 holes 0.760 in ± 0.002 in on 1-in square pitch. OTC = outer tube center.

are least likely to deteriorate when they are stored in closed boxes or containers. Tubing kept in racks that are isolated from welding and grinding dirt will not corrode if the atmosphere is dry and contact with the metal of the racks does not sensitize them to corrosion. Loose tubes stored in or near fabrication areas are quickly covered inside and out with foreign matter. Frequently, mills coat carbon steel tubes with a rust preventative. Dirt and dust in the shop air that settles on the film form a sludge that is hard to remove. If it is not cleaned off, it will reduce the exchanger's heat transfer capacity. This will not be an inspection problem if the purchase specification requires the tubes to be cleaned prior to installation. All that is required is to verify that the cleaning has been performed as agreed. If the purchase documents do not cover tube cleaning and the tubes appear to be unacceptably dirty, request the shop to withhold installation pending approval by the engineering department.

The way in which the workforce installs tubes affects exchanger life. The tubes will suffer the least damage if they are loaded directly from shipping containers into the bundle. It is acceptable to lay out loose tubes on wooden or noncontaminating metal horses or handling fixtures. Least satisfactory is to pile them on the shop floor, exposed to dirt and in the way of traffic.

When tubes are at their upper oversize tolerance and tubesheet holes are at their lower undersize limit, it is difficult to push the tubes through the holes. Misalignment of baffles and supports increases the difficulty. It is most important to set as a hold point the beginning of tube loading and to witness this operation. Good shop practice is to insert reusable tube guides (sometimes called bullets or torpedoes) into the ends of the tubes being loaded. Despite using the guides, the tubes may be hard to push through the baffle holes. It is not permissible for the shop to lubricate the tube ends or guides unless all lubricant is completely removed from the tube ends and tubesheet holes before the tubes are joined to the tubesheets. In any event, the tube ends should be burnished clean and the tube ends and tube holes solvent-washed with a volatile inert solvent and dried with clean, dry air before the joints are made.

A common shop practice is to tap the tube ends gently with leather- or rubber-headed mallets to drive them into place during loading. If this is done, place a light at one end and sight from the other after the tubes are loaded but before they are joined to the tubesheet. Reject any that have been crimped. The use of steel hammers, sledges, and stakes and excessive force are not permissible because of the potential damage to the tube ends and possibility of crimping. If these are used, request the shop inspector or the individual in authority to correct the situation.

An important hold point is one that requires the inspector's presence when the bundle is loaded into the shell. Whenever possible, witness this operation. Most bundles are inserted into and withdrawn from shells in the horizontal position. During insertion, the bundle drags along a line of contact. If it sags or is cocked as the front end enters, the contact force and consequently the frictional resistance are increased. More force is then required to push the bundle into place. For this reason it is desirable to insert bundles in the vertical position. However, only a few shops have the headroom and are equipped to do the installation vertically. When witnessing bundle insertion, observe how the bundle is supported and aligned with the shell. Excessive force should not be required to slide it in.

Some acceptable ways to support bundles during loading are (1) using a bundle cart that can be positioned to align the bundle and shell, (2) lifting the bundle on pairs of nylon slings suspended from chain hoists, (3) setting the bundle on structural beams or channels lined up with the shell axis and sliding the bundle into the shell, and (4) using homemade or commercially produced bundle installation machines.

In many shops, the force needed to push the bundle into the shell is supplied by parallel pairs of chain pulls (come-alongs) or hydraulic jacks or pistons. Force must be applied in a way that permits alignment to be maintained or easily adjusted. When witnessing this operation, make sure that the attachments and operation of the chain pulls, jacks, or pistons do not cause damage.

Sometimes, a bundle being inserted or pulled hangs up on a flat spot or shrunken-in weld. To jar the bundle loose and bounce it over the obstruction, workers may strike the shell with a sledgehammer. This is acceptable for fixed-tubesheet units from which the bundle will be withdrawn only during retubing. An intervening stake must be used to take the impact and prevent damage to the shell. Hammering the shell of a removable-bundle unit is not tolerable unless the cause of the binding has been investigated and removed. Vibrating the shell to reduce effective friction is not objectionable, nor is lubricating the contact surfaces if the shell side is subsequently cleaned.

On inspection visits, watch how the shop handles bundles. Chain slings used to handle bundles may damage the tubes. Make sure that the shop places wooden blocks that span baffles or tube supports or other protection between the slings and the bundle. Nylon slings are preferable because they neither contaminate nor dent the tubes. Whenever possible, they should bear the weight of the bundle on tube supports or baffles.

A long bundle can be damaged if it is lifted near its center of gravity. Slings should be placed midway between the center of gravity and the bundle ends. It is preferable to keep the slings separated with spreader beams. Very long bundles should be lifted on beams.

Observe how the shop protects machined surfaces and nozzles during handling. It is unsatisfactory to place machined surfaces directly on the shop floor. It is unacceptable for an exchanger to be dragged with nozzles bearing on the floor. Not only will the surfaces be marred, but the nozzles may be bent and distort the shell at their attachments. A packed floating head will not seal against leakage if the manufacturer does not protect the barrel from scratches. Well-run shops store in sealed plastic bags machined parts that are not assembled to the exchanger immediately after being finished. Alternatively, they coat the machined surfaces with corrosion-inhibiting grease or oil and store the parts out of harm's way.

To work efficiently, the shop may weld temporary fitting clamps or lifting lugs to an exchanger during construction. Make sure that (1) the weld deposit is compatible with the exchanger material, (2) the attachments do no harm to the part or parts to which they are welded, and (3) damage caused by removing the temporary fitting is repaired properly.

It is essential to inspect how the heat exchanger manufacturer handles and installs bellows-type expansion joints in fixed-tubesheet exchangers. These joints are very easy to damage and should always be protected from loads for which they were not designed and from dents and weld drags on the flexible element. Protective covers should be removed only for inspection during testing and replaced immediately afterward.

Temporary devices which expansion-joint manufacturers install to maintain precise face-to-face dimensions during shipping, handling, and installation must remain intact until just before the first boil-out or startup. Before the exchanger is shipped, inspect to make sure that the devices are tagged or distinctly marked to alert the startup crew to remove them. During inspection visits make sure that the alignment device has not been removed or tampered with.

Final documentation. The more information collected when a unit is built, the better maintenance workers are equipped to deal with subsequent problems. In the inspection brief instruct the inspector to collect the following documents:

1. The manufacturer's design report when the code requires one

2. The manufacturer's data report

3. A map of the locations of nameplate and serial number and of heat number marks and stamps

4. A tube heat map

5. A record of the locations of any tubes plugged in the shop along with the reasons

6. A table that lists the bill-of-material (BM) numbers and the mill-test report numbers for each BM number

7. Certified original mill-test reports or notarized copies

8. Radiographer's reports (when dual-film technique is specified, the second set of radiographs)

9. Records, charts, and reports of heat treatments

10. Copies of nondestructive examiners' qualifications for all nondestructive examinations performed on the unit

11. Welders' qualifications and stamping symbols of all welders who worked on the exchanger

12. Documentation of noncode materials

Guide to preparing inspection briefs for inspecting used and in-service heat exchangers

The purposes of inspecting a used exchanger are to find out if it can do a job and to estimate whether it will last long enough to justify installing it. Reasons for inspecting in-service heat exchangers are (1) to estimate condition, remaining life, and prospects for life extension; (2) to plan maintenance to be done during scheduled outages; (3) to estimate maintenance times and costs; (4) to evaluate prospects for upgrading by cleaning and retubing with other tube materials or extended-surface tubes; and (5) to decide whether to retube, repair, or replace.

The approach to writing an inspection brief for used and in-service units is the same, but emphasis is on different aspects. Used units are almost always available for inspection. However, most of the time only minimal documentation is available, and there is hardly ever a service and maintenance record. In-service exchangers cannot be completely surveyed without a shutdown, but there is high probability that operating and maintenance records will be available.

Safety considerations. Consult the plant safety engineer for precautionary measures to write into inspection briefs for in-service exchangers. Double-block valving or line blinding may be required before safely opening a unit for inspection. Special flushing, cleaning, and drying are obligatory if the streams are poisonous, irritating, or carcinogenic. Warn the inspector of these requirements in the brief.

Units taken from dismantled plants are stockpiled, sold to used-equipment dealers, or scrapped. (Company stockpiles go by the picturesque name *boneyard*.) As time elapses, records of stockpiled equipment are lost. Dealers usually do not know what flowed through exchangers and to protect themselves offer them for sale as is. Consequently, before requesting an inspector to examine such exchangers, it is important to find out what fluids were circulated. Outline in the brief protective gear and safety measures that the inspector must use if the fluids were:

1. Flammable

2. Explosive

3. Irritating to tissues

4. Noxious

5. Lethal

6. Carcinogenic

7. Threatening to life or health in any other way

Assessing in-service exchangers requires inspections to answer these questions:

1. Is the exchanger safe to operate at current conditions?

2. How much of the metal thickness allowed for corrosion-erosion has been worn away?

3. What maintenance is needed?

4. Are any major repairs in the offing?

Maintenance and process engineering departments must take the inspection report into account in order to answer the following questions:

1. Can the unit be safely operated at proposed new conditions?

2. How long will it have to be out of service for maintenance, repairs, retubing, or rebuilding?

3. Can the unit be safely run while awaiting a replacement bundle or complete exchanger?

4. How close to actual rates were the original estimates of fouling rates used in specifying the heat exchanger?

5. How well is the unit performing its actual service? (This may be far different from the design-point service.)

6. Would a different unit perform better by doing the same work at less pumping cost or recovering more heat?

Inspection of in-service and used exchangers requires more tools, instruments, and equipment than those in Table 7.1. In the inspection brief, list additional items from Table 7.2 that the inspector should carry in a toolbox. Frequently, some of the larger equipment listed in Table 7.3 is required. When this can be foreseen, the brief should alert the inspector. It is important to note that special training and qualifications are needed to use most Table 7.3 equipment and that qualification is also required for personnel who interpret indications that it reveals. Whether nondestructive examinations (NDE) are made with rented equipment and by specialists under contract or with user-owned apparatus and by in-house personnel, the brief should provide a means of coordinating inspection and nondestructive examinations.

Nameplates. The original nameplate is the key to the facts about an exchanger's design and construction. It provides:

TABLE 7.2   Toolbox Inspection Equipment for In-Service and Used Exchangers*

Flashlight

Droplight with extension

10-power magnifying lens

Wire brush

Steel scraper for scraping unmachined surfaces

Brass or copper scraper for scraping machined surfaces

Plastic scraper for scraping machined surfaces that must be copper-free

Pit depth gauge

Hook gauge to measure internal welds and cavities

Inspector's hammer

Lightweight ballpeen hammer

Feeler gauge set

*These items are in addition to the ones listed in Table 7.1.

TABLE 7.3   Supplementary Equipment for Inspecting In-Service and Used Units

Borescope set (preferably with video recorder and CRT screen)

Sandblasting equipment

Hydroblasting equipment

Trepanning equipment; portable hole-drilling equipment and plugging equipment

Fluid-penetrant-examination kit with special lamps as required

Magnetic-particle-testing equipment and iron particles

Ultrasonic-testing equipment

Radiographic equipment or x-ray, shielding, radiation-zone exclusion rope, and warning signs

Eddy-current-testing equipment

1. The manufacturer's name, location, serial number, and year built

2. The manufacturer's registration number if the unit is registered with a central agency such as the National Board of Boiler and Pressure Vessel Inspectors (National Board)

3. Facts about the construction code

4. Shellside and tubeside maximum allowable working pressures and design temperatures

When an original nameplate is stamped Nat'l Bd. No. XXXXX, a signed original of the manufacturer's data report required by the

ASME Code's rules has been filed with the National Board. (XXXXX represents the manufacturer's National Board number for the exchanger on file with the National Board.)

Depending upon the governing construction code, the nameplate may indicate the class of construction or the danger category that governed design and manufacture. These classifications determine which materials were permitted, design requirements, quality assurance and inspection, and even restrictions that limit where and in what service the exchanger may be used. An example is heat exchangers built in conformity with the *ASME Code*'s Section VIII, Division 2.

Repair and alteration nameplates provide a short history of maintenance on the pressure parts. Although these nameplates provide no information about materials of construction, tube count, diameter, gauge and arrangement, type of unit, baffle system, connections, and internals, they do give the maximum allowable pressures and temperatures.

For these reasons, the inspection brief should instruct the inspector to make rubbings of the original and any repair or alteration nameplates.

Documents. Instruct the inspector to collect these documents whenever possible: (1) the manufacturer's data report; (2) supplementary partial data reports; (3) repair and alteration certificates; (4) setting plans, assembly, and detail drawings; and (5) maintenance records. In most codes, the manufacturer's data report lists materials and thicknesses of all pressure parts. It tabulates nozzles and connections by size, rating, and intended use. It also contains the tube count, diameter, gauge, and pitch and describes their attachment to the tubesheet or tubesheets. However, it does not list the pitch orientation or pass arrangements. Attached partial data reports provide valuable information on parts produced by other manufacturers, for example, bellows expansion joints.

Manufacturer's data reports do not describe baffle and tube support systems, numbers of tubeside and shellside passes, pitch orientation, weirs, distributors, allocations of surfaces, and other performance-related information, nor do they describe support details. Detail and assembly drawings provide this information.

Repair and alteration certificates reveal the nature and location of welded repairs and alterations. Under the *National Board Inspection Code* rules, unless the tubes are welded to the tubesheets or the tube material, type, or thickness was changed, these documents do not disclose whether a unit has been retubed.[8] Only maintenance records would provide such retubing information. For this reason, the inspection brief should instruct the inspector to measure the IDs of a representative sample of expanded tube ends and the unexpanded region beyond the tubesheet and calculate the nominal apparent wall reduction. Larger-than-usual wall reductions indicate that the unit was probably retubed.

Maintenance records are invaluable for assessing an exchanger. Having access to the data package supplied by the manufacturer for maintenance permits review of code calculations for upgrading and determining suitability for use in services different from those originally specified. Most often these data will be found within a user's organization for units in service or in a stockpile. They are rarely available from used-equipment dealers.

Inspecting external appearance.   The first inspection step is to examine the exchanger's external appearance. Following are some of the items to include in the external inspection checklist:

1. Excessive corrosion

2. Dents, bent, or twisted nozzles and supports

3. Scored and scratched surfaces

4. Bowed covers

5. Cupped flanges and tubesheets extended as flanges

6. Stretched or bent flange bolts

7. Extruded gaskets in flanged joints

8. Bulged or collapsed parts

9. Stress marks

10. Repairs to welds

11. Patches in the pressure envelope

12. Attachments welded in place in the field

13. Pounded-out holes or slots in supports

14. Spalling of corrosion-resistant metals

15. Numerous pinholes

16. Cracks near welded seams or where there are sharp shape changes

In the brief, instruct the inspector to scrape down to sound metal any areas affected by exterior corrosion. Corroded depth is seldom uniform, and some places may not be corroded. Therefore, the inspector must estimate how deeply the corrosion has penetrated at the worst spots. If the extent of corrosion is obscure, it may be necessary to have the unit sandblasted or hydroblasted to permit making a good estimate.

The positions and characters of dents may indicate hidden internal damage. Distorted connections and supports or collapse of shell cylinders or channel barrels in the region of connections or supports indicate that the unit has been roughly handled or excessively loaded mechanically. Scores and scratches on gasket surfaces indicate that the unit has been dragged. If the floating head of a packed bundle is marred, it is a good indication that the bundle was mishandled or the packing was not properly maintained.

Bowed covers, bent flanges, and stretched or bent bolts point to the tubeside's having been overpressured. Taken together with extruded gaskets, they may also mean that improper bolting-up or unbolting techniques were used. They may also be evidence of extreme efforts to seal the joint. A further clue to sealing problems is stains left by leaking fluids on the bottoms of mating parts. Bulged or collapsed parts (examples are tubesheets concave to the shell and squirmed or blown-out shell expansion joints) are signs of shellside overpressure. These deformations may also be caused by explosions.

Stress marks and creases in metal and cracks in coatings on surfaces normal to projecting parts indicate that deformations were straightened. When these signs are present, examine the unit for work hardening caused by cold straightening. Note that applying heat to some corrosion-resistant metals may destroy their corrosion resistance.

Field repairs to welds are obvious because they are almost always made manually in position. Grinding marks and the start and finish of welding are visible. Very often, repair-weld width, crown height, and appearance are markedly different from the original seam. An isolated weld repair may signify a flaw not detected in the original construction or a spot that was locally sensitive to corrosion. However, when one spot shows signs of having been repeatedly rewelded, it may mean that there is a basic flaw, excessive load concentration, severe localized corrosion, or a combination of these problems. Usually, a trouble spot is covered with an ugly glob of weld metal. A special concern is welds that join fixed tubesheets to shells and welds of nozzle penetrations through the shell in the region of fixed-tubesheet-to-shell joints.

Patches on a shell or channel may mean that a nozzle was relocated or that a damaged or corroded spot was repaired. If a patch was made by fitting a disk formed to the radius of the cylinder into a round hole and butt-welding it, the work was probably done by a shop or repair organization in accordance with the *National Board Inspection Code* requirements. The weld is likely to be fully penetrating with no internal crevice, but only further examination can verify this. Square or rectangular patches filet-welded to the outside surface of the cylinder indicate hastily made field repairs, probably by an unqualified welder and without documentation or testing. Without further inspection, assume that conditions conducive to crevice corrosion exist under the patch. Girth welds in the shell near fixed tubesheets may indicate that an exchanger has been retubed, especially if their appearance is different from other major welds.

Most construction safety codes require the materials of nonpressure parts attached to the pressure envelope and the joining welds to meet code specifications and requirements. Most codes that govern repairs and alterations have similar requirements for attachments made in the field. Undercuts, excessive weld crown heights, and craters in attachment welds indicate either that the work was not done in accordance with such a code or that inspection was inadequate.

Inspecting for shellside fouling. If the external appearance is satisfactory, try to determine how badly the shellside is fouled. This is difficult because fixed-tubesheet bundles cannot be disassembled from their shells and there will hardly ever be a chance to pull a removable bundle from a unit in the boneyard or from one owned by a dealer. Therefore, it may be necessary to use indirect means. Look into the bundle through each nozzle with an articulated inspection mirror and a strong light. Use bent rods to probe as far as possible toward the first baffle at each end. Scrape samples of encrustations or coatings on nozzle walls and accessible tube surfaces to see if they can be readily removed. An analysis of the composition of the samples may indicate whether or not the shellside can be chemically cleaned.

If a suspicion of severe shellside fouling cannot be verified visually, try to determine how freely water flows through the shell just after hydrostatically testing it. Instead of draining the test water, connect the shell to a circulating pump, flowmeter, and drum of water. Install a pressure gauge at the inlet and outlet to measure the pressure loss. The thermal engineering department can calculate the pressure drop for a clean unit. Compare the measured pressure drop with the calculation. If the measured loss is substantially more than the calculated one, the shellside is probably badly fouled.

Inspecting the bundle exterior and shell interior. Whenever possible, pull the bundle and examine the inside of the shell and the outside of the bundle. Arrange to sandblast or hydroblast the shell before examining it for corrosion. Look closely at inlet and outlet connections and their welds to the shell and at the shell surface at the positions of the bundle baffles or supports. Measure the shell thickness at the most badly worn spots. It is preferable to use ultrasound for this purpose, but if an ultrasonic thickness indicator is not available, trepan small plugs out of the shell and make micrometer measurements. The trepanned holes must be plugged after the measurements are complete.

Examine the edges of transverse baffles to see if they have become thin or ragged. Look for rings of erosion-corrosion in the shell at the baffle positions. Examine the holes and tube surfaces where the tubes penetrate the baffles or supports. Enlarged holes and holes with knife-edges indicate corrosion. Beaten-out holes opposite rectangular depressions in the tubes may indicate vibration damage, fretting, and erosion-corrosion. Gradually thinned tube surfaces near baffle penetrations are evidence of corrosion. Rubbed tube surfaces or flat spots between baffles or supports reveal vibration damage.

Check behind the tubesheets for tube and tubesheet corrosion which may have been caused by stagnant fluid or corrosion accelerated by high inlet-pass temperature. Examine the tie rods, spacers, sealing devices, and impingement plates to be sure they are intact.

Inspecting channels, return covers, and shell covers. To examine channels, return covers, and shell covers any residues of the process fluids must be removed. After cleaning, measure the depth of any pits with a pit depth gauge. Examine any suspected cracks or crevices by a fluid-penetrant or magnetic-particle method. These are places to investigate:

1. Welds of pass partitions to channel barrels and tubesheets

2. Parent metal of pass partitions, barrels, and tubesheets adjacent to welds

3. Nozzle weld cover passes

4. Parent metal of nozzles and channels in the region of penetration

5. Gasket surfaces

Inspecting the condition of the tubes and tubesheets. Look at the tube ends in a strong light. If there are etched surfaces, razor-thin or gnarled ends of tubes expanded into the tubesheets, or washing away of tube-to-tubesheet welds accompanied by tube-end thinning, there is unacceptable corrosion. While surveying the tube ends, visually examine the ligaments for deformations and cracks. Verify suspected cracks by fluid-penetrant examination. If the ligaments are damaged, the unit is not a good prospect for further use.

If the unit is a straight-tube one, place a strong light at one end and sight through the other end. This will reveal any large deposits of fouling, gross corrosion (such as snakeskins in nonferrous tubes), and bowed or bent tubes. For a better look at straight tubes and for U tubes, use a magnifying borescope or one fitted with a television camera. Borescoping is the best visual way to assess the condition inside the tubes.

Checking strength and tightness. Hydrostatically test the unit at 1.5 times the nameplate MAWP adjusted for the ratio of allowable stresses at design temperature to those at room temperature. If a leak too small for detection by hydrostatic testing would be hazardous, the inspection brief will outline the bubble test, halogen leak test, or helium leak test to be performed. Be sure that the tubeside is tested without pressure in the shell, the shellside without pressure in the tubes, and both sides at the same time. Try to test removable bundles outside the shell. Test flanges or jury-rigged test rings may be needed for this purpose. The minimum elapsed time without loss of pressure should be 30 min.

Maintenance, Repair, and Alterations

The functions of maintenance are to ensure that there is no deterioration of performance beyond an established limit and to keep the equipment operating safely. Maintenance for safe, leak-free operation may be as simple as regularly inspecting exchangers and tightening the bolts or as complex as field or shop retubing and replacing parts. Repairs may be permanent or temporary and may fully or partially restore capacity. Alterations are closely associated with maintenance and repairs. Their purpose may be to improve performance, to eliminate operating or maintenance problems, or to adapt an exchanger to changed circumstances.

Evaluating the amount, kind, and timing of maintenance, repairs, and alterations requires cost-benefit analysis. Rules of thumb imply such analysis but are generally inefficient. Following the outlook "If it ain't broke, don't fix it" can lead to costly unscheduled outages when an unanticipated failure occurs. While cost-benefit economics is not covered in this work, some items to consider are as follows:

1. Costs associated with the alternatives
2. Costs to the whole system of the outage time required for each alternative
3. Costs of the maintenance procedure, repairs, or alterations
4. Costs of continued operation at reduced capacity, if possible including the resulting cost of reduction of return on capital invested
5. Costs of possible further deterioration of the exchanger if operation is continued in its present state
6. Costs of failing to satisfy the market

7. Costs of purchasing product or power to make up shortfalls

8. Costs of possible increased safety hazards

9. Benefits to be gained by making the repair or alteration, including the benefits of possibly upgrading capacity

10. Benefits of uninterrupted operation

Cost-benefit analysis can be used to optimize decisions if the variation of these factors is known or can be estimated.

Efficient maintenance and repair programs require the following:

1. Keeping records of failure types, occurrence frequencies, and repair and maintenance procedures that have been performed

2. Knowing what physical failure manifestations indicate about failure mechanisms

3. Knowing how the normal operating mode and changes to it affect exchanger maintenance and failure frequency

4. Knowledge of preventative maintenance

5. Knowledge of suitable repair procedures

6. Costs of maintenance procedures

Record keeping

The exchanger manufacturer may furnish a complete book of drawings and design documents and maintenance and repair instructions. This depends upon the kind of unit, its service, and the purchase specifications. Such a maintenance book, carefully updated, can be the heart of a maintenance program.

Computerized records of failure occurrences, repairs, and maintenance are invaluable for scheduling inspections and preventative maintenance. They can also provide a basis for analyzing failures and the effectiveness of the repairs and maintenance. Water treatment logs, shutdown, startup, and operating-temperature charts, and records of repairs and alterations are necessary for a full-maintenance plan.

Tube-plugging records. The appropriate tactic for dealing with tube failures depends upon an exchanger's service. When leaks from one side to the other affect only performance (for example, leaks of feedwater into the steam side of a feedwater heater), it is reasonable to plug tubes as they deteriorate. Here, unless the leaks are massive, changes in level control operation or terminal temperature differences signal the failures. Feedwater heaters are not ordinarily shut down until the next scheduled outage, when the failures can be investigated and the tube ends plugged.

If leaks between the sides cannot be tolerated because of safety hazards, product degradation, or yield losses, the exchanger is shut down for plugging or other action. If the failure is localized and has a readily determined cause that can be corrected and if the unit has enough capacity, it can be plugged and operated for its whole anticipated life. Otherwise, plugging is a temporary measure that allows time for planning to retube, rebundle, or replace the exchanger.

Tabular records of tube plugging are too abstract to reveal tube failure patterns. The most effective way to record tube maintenance information, failures, and plugging is to use a large-scale tubesheet layout as a plug map. Attached to it is an information sheet. Number the tubes. For straight-tube units use the numbering system described for hole drilling. For U-tube units, number the rows in the same way that tube benders and heat exchanger manufacturers do: the innermost row is row 1, the next outer row is row 2, and so on. However, the legs have to be identified. For example, the second tube in the upper leg of the third tube row might be numbered T-3, 2; the corresponding leg in the bottom row would be labeled B-3, 2. Use the prefixes L and R for vertical U-tube legs. Record the following:

1. The date that each plugged tube was plugged

2. The tube number, which indicates where the plugged tube is situated in the tube field

3. The axial location of the failure

4. If possible, the circumferential position of the failure in the tube

5. The character of the failure, if determined by failure analysis

6. The suspected character of the failure when no analysis is done

7. Observations about the condition of tube ends

8. The results of borescope examinations and the tape number of videotaped examinations

9. The results of eddy-current and ultrasonic examinations of the tubes and the report number provided by the nondestructive examiner

If the manufacturer provided a tube-heat map, compare it with the tube-failure map to find out if there is a reason to suspect that the failures are due to a poor-quality heat of tubes.

When operating circumstances permit long-term operation with plugged tubes and the unit's mode and conditions of operation are more or less constant, use the tube-plugging record to establish the trend of the rate of failures. With the graphics programs available for personal computers, the number of tubes plugged and the cumulative total number plugged can be plotted against the months of operation (Fig. 7.4). In base-loaded feedwater heaters and exchangers that operate continuously, after an initial shakedown period the plugging rate is usually constant for a period of years. Then there is a dramatic upturn that indicates the end of the useful life of the tubes. The onset of such an upturn should trigger planning for prompt retubing, rebundling, or replacement.

Records of repairs and alterations. Legal jurisdictions and insurers usually require that records be kept of any alterations or repairs to the pressure envelope. The *National Board Inspection Code* repair and alteration certificates are examples of such records. However, for maintenance purposes and for future replacements and upgrades, it is important to attach copies of such records to prints of drawings that show the repairs or alterations that were made. This should include any increases in design pressures or temperatures and restamping and any derating due to corrosion or erosion. Similarly record changes

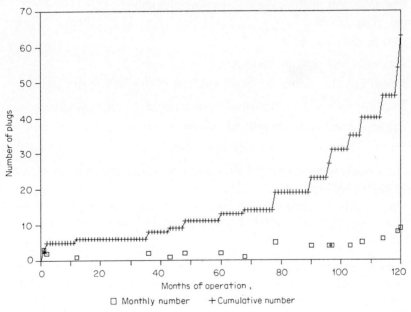

Figure 7.4 Number of plugs versus months of operation. (*Courtesy of* Chemical Engineering.)

to supports and appurtenances not covered by jurisdictional or insurance requirements.

Preventative maintenance

Preventative maintenance should start before an exchanger leaves the manufacturer's factory. Special precautions are required for units that may lie in the field for some time before installation. For such units, after the hydrotest the exchanger should be washed with distilled or demineralized water to which corrosion inhibitor has been added. Then it should be drained as fully as possible and dried with warm, dry air. Where possible, before shipment bags of desiccant should be placed in the channel and shell. Both sides should next be purged with bone-dry nitrogen. After the purging, the unit should be sealed and fitted with pressure gauges with a range of 0 to 15 lb/in^2 (0 to 100 kPa) and padded with nitrogen to a pressure of about 5 lb/in^2 (about 30 kPa).

When even small amounts of moisture in the shell could initiate a dangerous reaction or extremely rapid corrosion, consider the alternatives of (1) pressure testing with bone-dry nitrogen following the code rules prescribed for air testing and (2) liquid testing with an inert material that will not corrode the parts or interfere with the shellside operation.

Replacement bundles should be protected from mechanical damage and the elements. Frequently it is economical to ship bundles in a lightweight sealed steel shell rather than wrapped with waterproof paper and crated or boxed.

It is prudent to preclean and pretreat an exchanger before installation. New exchangers are rarely completely free internally of mill scale, weld spatter, and slag. Despite manufacturers' best efforts to maintain cleanliness, there is almost always foreign matter in the shells, channels, or tubes. It may be as diverse as weld rod stubs, soapstone sticks, marking crayons and chalks, wiping rags, articles of clothing, and remnants of food and food containers.

Steel-tubing manufacturers usually apply oily or greasy coatings to the tubes to protect them from corrosion. Fabricators do not remove the coatings unless the purchase specifications require them to do so. The coatings collect dust, grit from grinding, and other pollutants dispersed in the shop atmosphere. Consequently, the tubes are fouled on both sides before the exchanger is shipped.

Steel pipe may be coated with varnish for corrosion protection. The coating on the inside may adversely affect shellside fluids. When shops recirculate hydrostatic-test water to a storage tank or pit, it may collect substantial amounts of organic and inorganic substances that deposit on surfaces during testing. It is likely that some test medium will remain in each side of a new exchanger after testing. The coatings may concentrate chloride ions, and although the water appears to be acceptable, austenitic stainless-steel tubes may suffer subsequent stress-corrosion cracking.

Stainless steels, copper, brasses, cupronickels, nickel, nickel copper, and other metals resist corrosion by forming protective surface films. Chemically pretreated carbon steel surfaces can form similar barriers to corrosion.

The practical way to promote protective-film formation in carbon-steel-tubed exchangers is to circulate a water solution of appropriate chemicals through the unit. This may be done off-line by means of a mixing drum, pump, and circulating lines. If cooling-tower water circulates through the unit, the corrosion inhibitor may be added to it. The chemistry of the inhibitor should be established with the people responsible for water treatment. More often than not the protective film can be established by a higher concentration of the chemicals used to treat the water. The surfaces must be clean for protective-film formation. Otherwise, the films may have discontinuities, or they may be penetrated by an agent that sensitizes them to corrosion.

An example of a sensitizing agent is iron dust. When it is allowed to remain on the surfaces of austenitic materials in moist atmospheres, rust spots form at the contact areas. This can be avoided by precleaning and pickling and passivating. Pickling and passivating consist of acid cleaning and subsequently treating with a film-forming agent. If substantially all ferroxyl ions and sulfur-bearing material are not removed from nickel surfaces, deep etching may be observed after a short operating period. For this reason, precleaning nickel surfaces must include completely removing any yellow-crayon shipping or fabrication marks.

Coordinate pretreatment for cooling-water service with the general plant water treatment system. The water treatment must address not only inorganic corrosion products and scale deposits but also biological fouling. When cooling-tower water is supplied, the tower water treatment and pretreatment of the exchanger must be compatible. Exchanger pretreatment must also be coordinated with the system used for treating well, river, or brackish water.

It is not adequate just to flush new exchangers with water. Done before putting a new unit into service, this may remove loose surface dirt and rust. However, iron dust (partially dissolved in austenitic stainless-steel surfaces), oils, greases, mill scale, and varnishes remain. If the flushing water is not inhibited, it may sensitize untreated metal surfaces.

Solvent washing can remove oils and greases and most varnishes.

More frequently a detergent is used to preclean. With either, if the surfaces are not immediately passivated, corrosion may set in rapidly.

For carbon-steel-tubed exchangers, the following procedure has been successful in oil refineries.[9] Flush with cooling or service water before precleaning and pretreating. Use either the recirculation or the steam-heating and compressed-air agitation system described below for pretreating.

The recirculation alternative requires a steam-heated solution tank, recirculating pump, interconnecting piping, and vents. In this system, a polyphosphate cleaning solution of 10,000 parts per million (ppm), heated to 130 to 170°F (approximately 55 to 75°C), is made up in the tank and circulated through the exchanger's water side for at least 4 h. The unit is vented throughout this period to relieve any gases that are evolved. The cleaning solution is drained and flushed out of the unit. A chromate zinc passivating solution consisting of 1000 ppm, heated to 130 to 170°F (approximately 55 to 75°C), is circulated at the design water flow rate for at least 2 h.

If the unit is to be put into service immediately, the solution tank and exchanger are flushed. The effluent is added to the cooling-water system. If the exchanger is to be stored, it is sealed with the passivating solution inside.

In treatment by air agitation and steam heating, the exchanger is water-flushed and drained. A slurry of polyphosphate is made in a clean used standard shipping drum and pumped into the unit. With the vent open, it is rapidly filled with service water. Compressed air and steam are used to agitate and heat the solution to the required temperature range. Steam injection maintains the temperature during the cleaning period. The cleaning is followed by water flushing and draining. Liquid chromate-zinc passivation solution is pumped into the exchanger, and it is rapidly filled with service water. Air and steam are used to agitate and heat the inhibitor and water and steam injection to maintain temperature during passivation.

Polyphosphate cleaning will not remove mill scale. Therefore, it is used primarily on exchangers in which the cooling water flows through the tubes which are mill-scale-free. For removing mill scale, a phosphoric acid solution is effective.

The methods described above can be used with other precleaning chemicals and with nonchromate inhibitors. Chromates in effluents are objectionable pollutants in streams and groundwater. They have to be reduced and precipitated. This is what gives rise to the green slimes seen in some settling basins. Bench-scale studies are suggested to establish time and temperature parameters, to evaluate the corrosion control program, and to compare the effectiveness of inhibitors.

Preventative maintenance for intermittent or cyclical operation. Continuous-duty or base-load service is far less harmful to an exchanger than intermittent or cyclical operation. After startup, pressure and thermal loads and the structure's resistance are in equilibrium. If the shellside vents are suitably located and operated properly, there is very little accumulation of noncondensibles. On the other hand, exchangers that cycle or are started up and shut down for peak-load demands go through transient unbalances in loads and stresses in each cycle of operation or startup-shutdown. Shellside venting may not be adequate to purge noncondensibles trapped by baffles and supports and other internal structures.

In designing an exchanger for intermittent service, the number of cycles that it will endure over its life can be reckoned. The frequency of transient thermal differential expansions for the various parts can also be estimated. These approximations are used in selecting expansion joints for fixed-tubesheet exchangers and as a basis for performing any fatigue analysis that may be required.

The primary cause of rapid corrosion of the tubes and tubesheets, zone enclosures, and other shellside parts of units in cycling service is unvented, wet noncondensible gases. This condition is especially prevalent with shellside condensation. Startup and shutdown procedures and the practices followed to maintain a shutdown exchanger markedly affect its life.

The most effective preventative maintenance for this service is to purge the shell with nitrogen at each shutdown. At each startup the vents are open until substantially all the gas is blown out. However, because of all the nooks and crannies in the shell, venting may never be complete. Many feedwater heater strings are fitted with nitrogen purges, but it is not unusual for operators to avoid the purging because of the time it takes to shut down and start up.

An alternative to nitrogen purging the shells of exchangers in condensing-steam or hot-water service is to pad the shellside with low-pressure steam, which remains in the shell during the entire shutdown period. This system works well with U-tube and floating bundles and fixed-tubesheet exchangers that have shell and tube materials with approximately equal thermal expansion coefficients. It is not suitable for a fixed-tubesheet exchanger with stainless-steel tubes and a carbon steel shell unless the unit is fitted with a shell expansion joint that can accommodate the difference in thermal deflection at the steam temperature between the shell and the tubes.

Preventative maintenance on tube ends. Whenever tube ends are exposed, clean and inspect the tubesheet face and tube-to-tubesheet joint. Examine tube-to-tubesheet welds and tubesheet ligaments. Use high-intensity light to spot eroded or washed-away welds. Fluid-penetrant-examine the welds and ligaments for surface porosity and cracks. Carefully observe the condition of the protruding ends of tubes joined by expanding only.

Repair eroded or corroded welds by grinding or filing down to the bottom of any pits or cracks and replacing the lost metal with an appropriate grade of filler metal. The welding process and procedure need not necessarily be the same one used for making the original weld. Shielded-metal arc welding (SMAW), for example, is usually more successful in repairing tube-to-tubesheet joint welds than is gas-tungsten arc welding (GTAW) because it is more forgiving of impurities. However, thoroughly investigate the requirements for pretreating and postweld heat treatment beforehand.

When there are cracked ligaments, investigate the cause. Consider these possibilities: (1) stress-corrosion cracking; (2) thermal shock, which may occur in thin tubesheets but is more likely to be found in those thicker than about 2 in (about 51 mm) when the inlet temperature of one stream is much higher than that of the other; (3) excessive thermal stress in thick two-pass tubesheets when there is a large temperature difference between the inlet and outlet passes; (4) tube vibration; and (5) excessive rolling torque or expanding pressure.

Dress down by grinding any protruding ends of expanded-in tubes that are thinned or ragged. This may prevent the damage from spreading into the joint. However, investigate the cause. Tube-end erosion and corrosion may result from poor inlet-nozzle placement, excessive inlet velocity, inadequate turnaround space in multipass units, and abrasive matter in the tubeside stream.

Cleaning schedules. For the exteriors of exchangers, except where schedules for sanitizing the exteriors of exchangers in food or drug production are set by safety and health requirements, no particular schedule is needed. Ordinarily, it is adequate to clean the exterior during a scheduled outage only as required to prevent deterioration of protective coatings or to maintain a clean and orderly appearance.

The required frequency of internal cleaning depends upon how rapidly an exchanger fouls and the nature of the fouling. In their forward to *Fouling in Heat Exchange Equipment*, Chenowith and Impagliazzo state that fouling is probably the least understood of all the parameters that affect heat transfer.[10] Despite the large amount of analytical and experimental work done after their work, the comment is still valid. Estimates of how long it takes an exchanger to become so badly fouled that it must be cleaned often differ from what is actually experienced.[11]

To visualize how fouling affects performance, it helps to use the concepts of performance index, I_p, and apparent differential fouling resistance, R_{fa}. The performance index [Eq. (7.1)] is the ratio of the overall heat transfer coefficient observed in current service, U_{so}, to the observed overall heat transfer coefficient for identical operating condition for a new or freshly cleaned exchanger, U_{co}.

$$I_p = U_{so}/U_{co} \tag{7.1}$$

The apparent differential fouling resistance is the difference between the reciprocals of the service and clean overall coefficients [Eq. (7.2)].

$$R_{fa} = 1/U_{so} - 1/U_{co} \tag{7.2}$$

Rearranging Eq. (7.2) and substituting in Eq. (7.1) shows the relationship between performance index and apparent differential fouling resistance [Eq. (7.3)]:

$$I_p = 1/(1 + R_{fa}U_{co}) \tag{7.3}$$

These equations are similar to those that relate the cleanliness factor to overall fouling allowance in exchanger design. However, in design the cleanliness factor is the permitted ratio of design to clean overall coefficient.

It is instructive to examine the effects of a given apparent differential fouling resistance on performance for a range of clean observed overall coefficients. Table 7.4 shows the variation for R_{fa} of 0.002 (h · ft^2 · °F)/Btu [0.00035 (m^2 · °C)/W]. This is a value often allowed in designing exchangers subject to moderate fouling. Table 7.4 highlights the fact that there is less leeway to deviate from a cleaning schedule when the clean overall coefficient is high than when it is low.

TABLE 7.4 Comparison of Clean and Service Overall Heat Transfer Coefficients for Fouling Resistance of 0.002 (h · ft^2 · °F)/Btu [(m^2 · °C)/W]

Btu/(h · ft^2 · °F)		W/(m^2 · K)		
U_{co}	U_{so}	U_{co}	U_{so}	$100(U_{co} - U_{so})/U_{co}$
10	9.8	56.8	55.6	2.0
50	45.4	283.9	257.8	9.2
100	83.3	567.8	473	16.7
150	115.4	851.7	655.3	23.1
200	142.9	1135.6	811.4	28.6
250	166.7	1420	946.6	33.3
300	187.5	1703	1065	37.5
350	205.9	1987	1169	41.2
400	222.2	2271	1262	44.4
450	236.8	2555	1344	47.4
500	250	2839	1419	50.0

There is no general agreement about how to set cleaning schedules. Computer monitoring has been successfully used to gather information for fixing schedules for single-phase services at constant flow rates. Extrapolations can be made for variations in rates and stream properties.

For an isolated exchanger, the simplest way to estimate when to shut down and clean is by plotting R_f against time as shown in Fig. 7.5. When the shape of the curve is established, the period until R_f becomes equal to the design fouling allowance determines when to clean. However, this may conflict with system requirements in an actual plant. A critical path for cleaning and maintenance shutdowns must be established for the whole network.

The kind and mode of fouling of the inside and outside tube surfaces may differ. When a unit is new or freshly cleaned, the onset of fouling may not be visible for some time after the start of operation. Fouling on the inside and the outside may also begin at different times. For most industrial cooling waters, the fouling resistance approaches a limit asymptotically with the passage of time and becomes nearly constant. This may be the result of equilibrium between the deposition rate and the rate at which the water shears off accumulated fouling products or of the fact that there is no further deposition. If the constant rate is low enough, it may never be necessary to clean the unit. Therefore, the goal of antifouling water treatment is to achieve asymptotic fouling at a tolerable level.

Cooling water may also foul the tubes nonasymptotically, with the fouling-resistance-versus-time plot straight or curved. Variations in the amplitude of the basic trace of the curve occur with periodic addi-

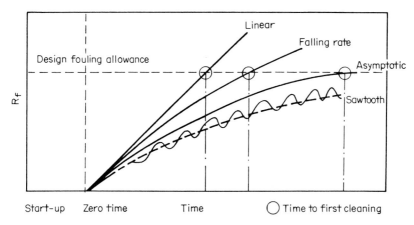

Figure 7.5 Variation of apparent differential fouling with time for industrial cooling waters.

tions to the cooling water of chemicals that reduce fouling. This is called sawtoothed fouling. The several shapes of the fouling-resistance-versus-time curves for industrial cooling waters are shown schematically in Fig. 7.5 labeled linear, falling rate, asymptotic, and sawtooth.

The dashed horizontal line, labeled fouling allowance, illustrates how the interval for cleaning may be set for water-side fouling. Similar curves can be developed for organic-fluid fouling and for different kinds of fouling on each side of an exchanger by means of computer monitoring.

An alternative to plotting R_f against time is to plot the performance index against days from the last cleaning (Fig. 7.6). When I_p declines to the level of the cleanliness factor used in design, it is time to clean the exchanger. For planning, project the day that cleaning will be required by drawing a trend line based upon the output of the monitor as shown in the figure. In the illustration, the exchanger data-sheet service rate has been divided by the clean rate to give a calculated cleanliness factor of 0.550. The trend line of the performance index plotted against days of operation indicates that cleaning should be scheduled after 250 days of operation.

These methods can be applied to a network of exchangers. By comparing clean overall coefficients or design cleanliness factors and monitoring outputs, the cleaning sequence of exchangers can be fitted into a critical path for maintenance.

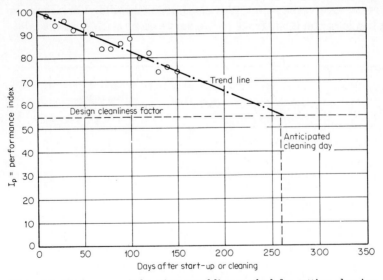

Figure 7.6 Performance-index–time-trend-line method for setting cleaning schedules.

When operating pressure is critical, monitor operating pressure or pressure differential between inlet and outlet instead of temperature differences. The author has successfully plotted the vapor-compression still pressure of a small ship's vapor-compression drinking-water evaporators to predict when they would have to be cleaned.

The thermal designer attempts to minimize fouling by optimizing the exchanger's configuration, flow regime, and tube-wall temperatures. Operators are faced with decisions about when design allowances are used up. Sometimes, the operating period between cleaning shutdowns in water-cooled exchangers can be extended by using antifoulants and chlorinating cooling water to kill microorganisms.

Safety precautions for cleaning. Before opening an exchanger, find out if the fluids that were circulated are flammable, explosive, irritating, noxious, lethal, or carcinogenic or a threat to life and health in other ways. This requires cooperation with the individuals charged with plant safety and health. Users have the primary responsibility for cleaning equipment and rendering it harmless to the personnel who must perform maintenance. However, supervisors of field or shop retubing or repairs are well advised to inform themselves of potential hazards and to have the user certify that it is safe to work on the exchanger before undertaking the job.

Cleaning methods. The common off-line methods of cleaning tubes may be categorized as mechanical, hydraulic, and chemical. Live steam has been used, but it is so dangerous that it is not recommended and will not be discussed. Before settling on a cleaning procedure, consider the following:

1. The kind of fouling in terms of how tenaciously it sticks to surfaces and the most successful and quickest ways to remove it

2. The effects of the process fluids and foulants on the safety and health of people who make contact with them

3. Protection of workers doing the cleaning, nearby workers, and passersby

4. The advantages, disadvantages, and economics of doing the work in place, compared with removing the exchanger or pulling the bundle and cleaning elsewhere

5. How to collect and dispose of the fouling substances, washing fluids, and residues safely and with the least environmental pollution

6. The advantages, disadvantages, and economics of the plant maintenance force's doing the work or of contracting it; if contracted, whether to have the work done on the site or at the contractor's facility

There are many fouling substances that produce a variety of accumulations on tube surfaces by several mechanisms. Although much work on fouling has been reported in the literature, there is no way casually to predict fouling behavior in a given system. Therefore, the problem is how to clean the surface and leave behind as few nuclei for redeposition as possible.

For the purpose of selecting a suitable cleaning method, it is convenient to classify deposits arbitrarily as follows:

1. Hard, tenaciously adhering coatings, exemplified by barnacles, mineral-salt scales, and baked-on varnishes and cokes
2. Soft and loose coatings, such as powdery deposits, sludges, and slimes
3. Gumlike substances

Scales and sludges originate from precipitation. Slimes and barnacles are of biological origin. Collins offered these definitions:[12]

> *Scales* are dense deposits so firmly bonded to their supporting surfaces as to allow virtually no contact between the surrounding fluid and the covered surfaces.
> *Sludges* are amorphous deposits and are seldom bonded to the supporting surfaces.
> *Slimes* are gelatinous deposits resulting from the multiplication of microscopic organisms or the products of their life processes.
> *Barnacles* are nodulelike deposits having semigranular outer shells bonded to the supporting surfaces and enclosing a slurry of putrefying microorganisms.

Although these definitions were for water fouling, they may be extended to fouling of other fluids. Table 7.5 lists off-line cleaning methods recommended for the various kinds of fouling.

Mechanical cleaning. Maintenance workers usually improvise mechanical scrapers for cleaning tube exteriors. The minimum cleaning-lane width between adjacent rows and columns of tubes is reputed to have been established as the smallest space that would accommodate a hacksaw blade used as a scraper. Such flat, flexible strips have the disadvantage of bearing only upon lines of contact. A more effective scraper can be made by drilling a plate just thinner than the ligament width with two rows of holes on the cross-flow baffle drilling pattern. Cut along the tube-row centerlines, and grind the half holes that remain to knife-edges. Weld round bars, of a diameter just less than the ligament width, to the ends as handles that will protrude from either

TABLE 7.5   Foulant Classifications and Suggested Off-Line Cleaning Methods
1 = chemical; 2 = mechanical; 3 = hydraulic.

Type of coating	Suggested method
Hard, tenaciously adhering	1
	1 + 2
	1 + 2 + 3
Examples	Origin
Barnacles	Organic
Mineral-salt scales (deposits so firmly bonded that there is virtually no contact between the surrounding fluid and the covered surface)	Precipitation
Baked-on varnishes and cokes	Organic
Soft and loose	1, 2, or 3
Examples	Origin
Powdery deposits	Miscellaneous
Sludges (amorphous deposits, seldom bonded to the supporting surfaces)	Precipitation
Slimes (gelatinous deposits resulting from the replication of microorganisms or the products of their life processes)	Biological
Gumlike	1 + 3
Examples	Origin
Tars	Refining processes
Caramels, etc.	Degraded organic materials

side of the bundle. To use the scraper, grasp the handles and slide the scraper along the tubes between baffles or supports. This will scrape about half the surface in a pass.

Scrapers of any kind will not remove accumulations in the vicinity of baffles and tube supports. Some buildup may be removed by poking at it with rods.

Small power-driven wire brushes, designed for cleaning inside tubes, may be adapted to fit into cleaning lanes of exchangers that have the tubes arranged on square pitch. The bristles must be flexible enough and the drive shaft small enough to pass through the space between adjacent tubes.

Cleaners for cleaning inside tubes are classified as internal and external types. The external type is also called *drill-type external*. Motors of the internal type enter the tube and traverse its entire length during cleaning. They are coupled to the cleaning head by a holder or coupling. The power they can generate is limited by the size of the housing that can fit into the tube. The motors of the external type remain outside the tube, driving the cleaning head through a flexible drive shaft.

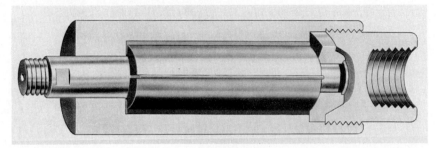

Figure 7.7 Internal-tube-cleaner assembly. (*Photograph courtesy of Elliott Company, Springfield, Ohio.*)

Figure 7.7 shows an internal-tube-cleaner assembly. Commercially available internally driven cleaning heads are made in various configurations (Fig. 7.8). Among these are drill-shaped heads, conically toothed cutters, sectional heads, fixed-diameter brushes, and scrapers. Internal cleaners cannot drive these heads if the tubes are solidly plugged with fouling material or if the deposit substantially reduces the inside diameter.

Use the drill head shown in the upper right of Fig. 7.9 and an internal-type cleaner drive for relatively thick deposits of a soft to medium-hard texture. Use the conical-toothed scraper shown in the bottom left of Fig. 7.9 after drilling with a drill-type cleaner and for thin deposits that are moderately hard to hard.

Use the expanding cutter shown in the upper-left photograph of Fig. 7.9 for light to medium encrustations. Use expanding sectional brushes (Fig. 7.10) to remove dry and scaly fouling that can be knocked off by the vibratory, circular motion imparted by the flexible coupling or universal-joint connector. For similar service in U tubes, use an expanding brush with a flexible shaft. These brushes are available for tube IDs of $\frac{13}{16}$ in (20.6 mm) and larger. For this size, the minimum center-to-center distance that they can accommodate is 10 in (254 mm). Therefore, most U tubes cannot be brush-cleaned successfully since typical center-to-center distances for the smallest bends are five tube ODs.

Expanding brushes are available with bristles of carbon steel, stainless steel, bronze, and nylon. Select the strongest bristles least likely to sensitize the tubes to corrosion. Expanding brushes tend to clog and become ineffective in removing muds and marine growths of algae or seaweed. To clean out these materials, use an expanding scraper. Radial force in expanding brushes and scrapers is applied by centrifugal motion or springs.

In tubes smaller than 1½-in (38.1-mm) OD, a flexible coupling between the drive shaft and the cleaner head is more desirable than a

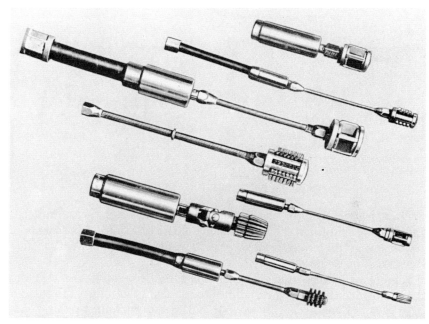

Figure 7.8 Internal-cleaning heads. *(Photograph courtesy of Elliott Company, Springfield, Ohio.)*

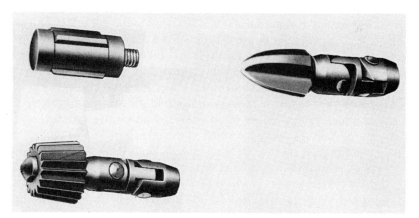

Figure 7.9 Scraper (left), drill head (right), and conically toothed cutter (below left). *(Photograph courtesy of Airetool Division of Dresser Industries, Springfield, Ohio.)*

Figure 7.10 Expanding sectional brush. (*Photograph courtesy of Airetool Division of Dresser Industries, Springfield, Ohio.*)

universal joint. This is so because encrustations are rarely uniform and flexible couplings can absorb some of the torsional impact when a cutter hangs up on a large obstruction. The small motor is thus shielded from damage.

The bigger motors used in larger tubes are better able to accept the shock of suddenly applied resistance to rotation. Therefore, the custom is to use universal joints to couple the drive shaft to the head. Universal-joint couplings can withstand severe service longer than flexible holders. However, they cannot be used to traverse U bends because the coupling must be flexible.

Internal-tube-cleaner motors are driven by compressed air or water. Air-pressure ratings range from 80 to 125 lb/in^2 (approximately 550 to 860 kPa). Water-pressure ratings range from 125 to 250 lb/in^2 (approximately 860 to 1725 kPa). At 90 lb/in^2 (620 kPa) air volume requirements vary from about 10 ft^3/min (about 17 m^3/h) for $\frac{5}{8}$-in-OD (15.9-mm-OD) tubes to 40 ft^3/min (about 70 m^3/h) for 2-in-OD (50.8-mm-OD) tubes. For a given tube size, air motors are more powerful than water ones and stall less often. Water motors are quieter, and their discharge flushes away loosened material. Flushing water pressure is in the range of 50 to 200 lb/in^2 (about 345 to 1380 kPa). Output speeds range from 3800 r/min in direct-drive units, used for cleaning small, lightly scaled tubes, down to 800 r/min for work on heavy deposits in tubes as large as 2-in-OD (50.8-mm-OD). Larger, heavier equipment must be suspended from overhead supports. For this purpose, machine manufacturers supply trolleys fitted with wire-rope block-and-tackle supports.

In the externally driven machines shown in Figs. 7.11, 7.12, and 7.13, a threaded coupling directly connects the drive shaft to the driver output shaft. At the start of cleaning, the drill head is coupled directly to the driver output shaft. As cleaning progresses, lengths of shafting are added between the driver output shaft and the drill head.

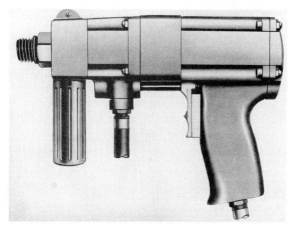

Figure 7.11 Lightweight air-driven tube-cleaning machine with water flushing. (*Photograph courtesy of Airetool Division of Dresser Industries, Springfield, Ohio.*)

Figure 7.12 Heavy-duty air-driven tube-cleaning machine with water flushing. (*Photograph courtesy of Elliott Company, Springfield, Ohio.*)

These extensions are hollow chromium-molybdenum-alloy tubing. Flushing water passes through the hollow shaft and exits at the drill head. In the United States, hollow shaft extensions are made in standard lengths of 6, 10, and 12 ft (1.8, 3.0, and 3.7 m) but can be ordered in nonstandard lengths.

A variety of drill bits is used with externally driven machines. Spade-shaped bits, spade-shaped bits with flutes (Fig. 7.13), and twist drills are suited to scales of various hardnesses. A fluted-star bit is more effective in removing gummy or oily deposits. The bits are made from tool steel and must be sharpened like any other drill bits. To pro-

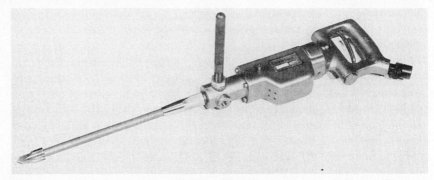

Figure 7.13 Air-driven cleaning machine with tubular extension and spade-shaped bit with flutes. (*Photograph courtesy of Elliott Company, Springfield, Ohio.*)

vide long life and to increase the time between sharpenings, stellite-tipped bits are available. Unless there is previous experience with the substance to be removed, find out the best bit to use and how to sharpen it experimentally.

Figure 7.14 illustrates another kind of cleaner for cleaning inside the tubes: the blow gun. It gives good results with little downtime on straight-tube units fouled with soft, readily removable deposits. Most blow guns are connected to both water and compressed-air hoses. If

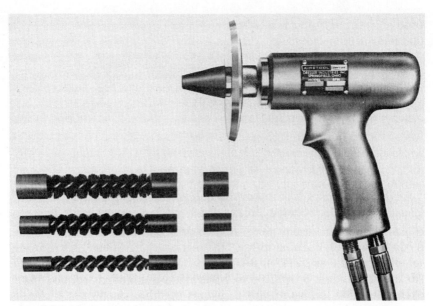

Figure 7.14 Blow gun. (*Photograph courtesy of Airetool Division of Dresser Industries, Springfield, Ohio.*)

necessary, water-main pressure can be boosted with compressed air. A common trigger controls water and air.

To use the blow gun, hang a tarpaulin or wire basket over one end of the unit. Load the tubes at the other end with brushes or plugs. Insert the nose of the gun into the tube, and pull the trigger. This causes a rubber collar in the nose to seal to the tube and releases a jet of water that propels the brush or plug through the tube. A pressure-relief valve in the gun barrel prevents the backfiring that might result from a solidly plugged tube. To use a blow gun successfully, the tube bore must be uniform. Changes to the bore (for example, at baffle locations) cause the plug or brush to hang up.

Hydraulic cleaning.   Hydraulic cleaning (hydrocleaning) consists of directing powerful jets of water at fouled surfaces through special guns, lances, or probes. A variety of nozzles and tips is used to make most effective use of the hydraulic force. The water jets are not abrasive and are not directed at one spot long enough to erode it. The force of the jets exceeds the compressive strength of the deposits, fracturing and dislodging them. Particles that result from removing the outer deposit layers disperse into the jet stream and help to dislodge more particles.

The elements of a hydraulic cleaning system are (1) clean water, (2) high-pressure, high-volume pump and driver, (3) hydraulic hoses, (4) lances or probes, (5) nozzles, and (6) controls. It is common practice to add long-chain-polymeric substances, detergents, and surfactants to the water to try to remove any small amounts of deposits that might otherwise remain as nuclei for subsequent fouling.

The pumps used to pressurize the water may attain output pressures as high as 20,000 lb/in^2 (about 138,000 kPa). However, the usual upper limit for heat exchanger work is 10,000 lb/in^2 (about 69,000 kPa). A wide range of pumps designed or adapted for the service is offered commercially. Most are piston pumps, but when the work can be done adequately with high volumes of water at relatively low pressures, centrifugal pumps may be used.

Typical capacity and pressure ranges for shellside cleaning systems are 150 gal/min at 6000 lb/in^2 (about 9.5 L/s at 41,000 kPa) and 65 to 90 gal/min at 10,000 lb/in^2 (about 4 to 5.7 L/s at 69,000 kPa). For tubeside cleaning, the range is 10 to 30 gal/min at 10,000 lb/in^2 (about 0.6 to 1.9 L/s at 69,000 kPa). The pumps are usually driven by electric motors or diesel engines through gear reducers. However, when very high pressures are required, the driver operates an intensifier that uses oil or water as the low-pressure medium. The required driver power depends upon the service. For the foregoing capacities and ranges, it is approximately 600 hp (approximately 447 kW) for shellside machines and 100 to 200 hp (75 to 150 kW) for tubeside machines.

A high-pressure, flexible hydraulic hose leads water from the pump to a rigid tube with a nozzle at its discharge end. For cleaning the outside of the bundle, one or more probes are used. These consist of short tubes with nozzles at their ends. The probes are directed at the exchanger tubes, at the spaces between tube rows, at the baffle-to-tube junctions, and at the tubesheets.

When accretions are thick, it may also be necessary to insert probes between the tubes. To apply hydraulic force to best advantage, the bundle is rotated to provide all-around access. The probes are hard to control manually. Therefore, workers must be safeguarded with protective clothing and shields. Most external bundle cleaning is done with automatic or semiautomatic equipment. In this apparatus, multiple probes are fed from a manifold. The control console and operators may be housed in a remote booth.

To clean inside tubes, rigid or flexible lances are used. When the lance is rigid, the process is called stiff lancing. The lances are metal tubes about 12 in (about 300 mm) longer than the straight length of the heat exchanger tubes. They are fitted with a cleaning nozzle at one end and connected to a flexible hydraulic hose at the other.

Flexible lances are short metal tubes that have a cleaning nozzle at one end and are connected to a high-pressure, small-diameter flexible tube at the other. The short, rigid tube and nozzle assembly is called a stinger. Cleaning with flexible lances is called flex lancing. Stiff lancing is preferable to flex lancing because the worker can force the lance through the length of the tube. Flex lances are used for on-site cleaning when there is not enough clearance for a rigid lance. The operator must make sure that the nozzle is far enough into the tube not to fly out in reaction to the water jet and must be careful not to remove the stinger from the tube when the lance is in operation. For worker protection, it is advisable to provide safety latches that will prevent the nozzle from backing out until water pressure is released.

To lance inside the tubes manually, one worker positions the nozzle at the tube end and operates a foot control in the high-pressure water circuit. Another person walks with the lance to traverse the tube length. This procedure is called walk lancing.

If the unit is of U-tube construction, a rigid lance is inserted to clean within a short distance of the tube bend line. After the straight leg has been cleaned, a flexible lance is used to traverse the U bend. The force that can be applied to stabbing a rigid lance into a plugged tube is limited by the worker's strength and ability to grasp the lance. The operator is exposed to the hazard that the foulant-laden hydraulic stream will splash back. Another disadvantage is that the rigid lance cannot be used to clean vertical exchangers in place. This is so because the bundle must be in a horizontal position for walk lancing.

Semiautomatic and automatic tube-cleaning machines overcome the disadvantages of walk lancing. Some features of these machines are (1) remote, shielded operation offset from the position of the lances, (2) multiple lances operated from a common manifold, (3) automatic and semiautomatic tube position indexing, (4) hydraulically driven lance insertion and withdrawal, (5) capability of operation in the vertical position with top or bottom insertion, and (6) nozzles that rotate.

When lance insertion is hydraulic, the thrust may exceed 1000 lb (4448 N). Therefore, the machine is anchored to the heat exchanger to contain the reaction. Rotating nozzles may be configured to drill-bit shapes to combine mechanical and hydraulic cleaning. A semiautomatic tubeside cleaning machine with hydraulic lance insertion is shown in Fig. 7.15. Vertical and horizontal indexing is controlled by the two handwheels. The machine is anchored to the bundle tubesheet.

The functions of the nozzle are (1) to direct and meter the water and (2) to convert pressure head to velocity head in order to produce a solid stream of water. Nozzle design depends upon whether the tubes are to be cleaned inside or outside, the degree of fouling, and the system to be used. Some manufacturers use computer programs to investigate how nozzle configuration and orifice parameters affect the application of hydraulic force. However, most designs and arrangements are empirical, based upon field experience. The nozzles are made of stainless steel and may have inserted orifices of tungsten carbide.

Generally, for cleaning tube exteriors and for walk-lance-cleaning plugged tube ends and tube interiors, single forward-directed orifices are used. Multiple orifices are used when there is no plugging inside the tubes. Common positions of orifices in multiorifice nozzles are (1) forward-facing, (2) forward-facing pitched 30° with the vertical, (3) radial, and (4) rear-facing pitched 30° with the vertical. Forward-facing orifices direct water at plugs in the tubes to clear them away. Radial orifices are intended for tube-wall cleaning and breaking up layers of foulant. The orifices arranged for backward-angled flow are intended for cleaning and flushing away foulants.

Hydraulic cleaning can remove very tenacious films, but because the jets do not abrade the surfaces, it cannot remove surface metal oxides or tight corrosion products. To achieve a white metal surface, an abrasive must be added to the water stream. When this is done, the practice is called hydraulic blasting, or hydroblasting. To add the abrasive to the water, an eductor is used. Flow of abrasive into the

Figure 7.15 Semiautomatic hydraulic tube-cleaning machine with hydraulic lance insertion. (*Photographs courtesy of American Powerlance Company, Houston, Texas.*)

hydraulic cleaning water is controlled by a valve that can be rapidly opened or shut.

Hydroblasting is seldom used to clean bundles because their tubes are very thin. However, it is a good way to descale and clean tubesheet faces, shells, channels, channel covers, bonnets, and return covers inside and out. Hydroblasting before an in-service shutdown inspection or before inspecting used exchangers from the boneyard or a dealer's inventory permits thoroughly examining the unit for corrosion and other damage that might be hidden by corrosion products or deposits of foulants.

The manufacturers of hydrocleaning and hydroblasting equipment and contractors who do such work cite the advantages of their process listed in Table 7.6 over chemical and mechanical cleaning methods. As with mechanical and chemical cleaning, the effluent must be disposed of safely without excessively polluting the environment. Various arrangements may be made for collecting and disposing of the dirty water. When the effluent is not volatile, is harmless to health and property, and will not plug sewer lines and when local sewage disposal regulations permit, it is usually dumped to a disposal trench that leads to a common sewer. However, for some services a system is required that injects the water and the waste it carries into the combustion chamber of an incinerator or power boiler.

The reaction to the jet of water that issues from the cleaning nozzle may be very powerful. Therefore, it is necessary to establish proce-

TABLE 7.6   Advantages Claimed for Hydrocleaning by Its Practitioners

1. Less time is required to organize personnel and equipment, prepare the exchanger, and perform the work than for other methods.
2. The cost is less than for off-line chemical cleaning.
3. There is less loss of metal due to corrosive effects of cleaning materials.
4. There is no mechanical damage of the kind that could result from mechanical cleaning.
5. Solidly plugged tubes may be bypassed in chemical cleaning, but hydrocleaned tubes are individually cleaned. With appropriate nozzles, solidly plugged tubes may be entered and cleaned.
6. Burning off of tenaciously adhering organic films may be eliminated by hydraulic cleaning.
7. Disposal of suspended foulants and dilute water solutions is less hazardous than disposal of chemical cleaning solutions that contain foulants.
8. The reaction of foulants with water seldom produces noxious or poisonous gases. The vapors of chemicals used for cleaning and their reaction products with foulants may be noxious or poisonous.
9. It is not always possible to remove foulants chemically.

dures to protect workers who do the work and any people who might be in the vicinity or passing by. These are some of the basic safety measures:

1. Use safety shields and troughs, and rope off the work area with colored ropes that bear warning signs.

2. Arrange equipment designed for automatic or semiautomatic remote operation so that the operator is not positioned in line with a possible back-pressure discharge.

3. Make sure that when manual lancing is to be done, the system has an automatic shutoff that operates whenever the operator's finger or foot is not depressing the trigger.

4. Install safety latches that will prevent nozzles from exiting the tube until pressure is released.

The National Safety Council (NSC) formerly published Data Sheet 633, dealing with high-pressure water-blast cleaning, a *voluntary* practice of generally acceptable safety guidelines for water blasting and hydroblasting. This practice has been discontinued. Therefore, cooperation between operators of water-blasting equipment and owners of exchangers that are to be hydraulically cleaned is required for diligent protection of life, health, and property. Some professional water-blasting organizations provide excellent videocassette safety films and safety training.*

Chemical cleaning.   Chemical cleaning includes solvent washing, detergent washing, inhibited-acid washing, bactericidal treatment, and combinations of these alternatives. It is used (1) to preclean and pretreat new and newly retubed exchangers, (2) to remove fouling deposits and scales during operation, and (3) to try to clean exchangers when no other way will work.

It is usually possible to clean a shutdown unit in place chemically by circulating cleaning agents and subsequently flushing. The exchanger must be valved off from the rest of the system. Badly fouled or scaled exchangers and bundles may have to be removed and immersed in circulating cleaning solution.

How to clean a fouled exchanger chemically depends upon the composition of the deposits. If they can be identified, appropriate chemical solutions can be selected to use on or off stream. Optimum contact times and cleaning-solution temperatures can be determined. In selecting an organization to do chemical cleaning, consider the following:

---

*In 1987 the U.S. Water Jet Technology Association approved and issued *Recommended Practices for the Use of Manually Operated High Pressure Water Jetting Equipment.*

1. Its equipment

2. Its techniques and skills

3. Its experience in removing diverse deposits

4. Whether or not it has laboratories and personnel capable of testing the deposits and recommending optimum treatment

5. Its safety record

The measure of successful on-stream treatment is the change in outlet temperatures that takes place as a result of the cleaning. For selecting appropriate on-stream chemical treatment of exchangers in cooling-water service, Bird and Metz grouped cooling-water foulant deposits into these four main categories:[13]

Group 1   pH-sensitive deposits

Group 2   Biological deposits

Group 3   Thermally sensitive deposits

Group 4   Combinations and unclassified

The pH-sensitive group includes carbonates, phosphates, corrosion products, and similar mineral deposits. (It is assumed that the corrosion products in this group are metal salts.) Biological deposits include the organic slimes and growths defined by Collins.[12] In the thermally sensitive group are silt, organic heat-sensitive materials, and similar suspended matter. The fourth group includes deposits that exhibit the characteristics of two or three groups and organic salts and other substances not easily classified.

To clean tubes in the first group, Bird and Metz recommend acid cleaning in which the system pH is reduced to 3.0 to 4.0 and maintained there for approximately 24 h. Where the presence of iron phosphate and iron oxide deposits, which require even lower pH values, is suspected, they suggest injecting acid locally to reduce pH at the trouble spots without reducing system pH. They suggest sulfuric acid or sulfamic acid, which they consider to be the most effective.

For Group 2 deposits, they suggest using microbiocides, which they classify into three main groups: (1) synthetic amines, (2) chlorophenates, and (3) liberators or chlorine. After testing samples to find out which microbiocidal agent is most effective, cleaning consists of adding shock doses of the selected agent over a 3-day period. Between dosings, samples are taken and analyzed to measure the treatment's effectiveness. During cleaning, the improvement in terminal temperatures and changes in physical characteristics are observed. When time to study the effects of the agents on the deposits is not available, Bird and Metz suggest using a broad-spectrum biocide.

Group 3 substances must also be identified in the laboratory before using the recommended procedure for their removal. To get rid of these deposits, Bird and Metz recommend using organic cleaning and dispersing agents, which consist of modified, condensed tannins. These substances loosen the accumulations and maintain them in suspension until they can be removed by blowing down. A 100-ppm slug is ordinarily effective. However, if there is not enough blowdown or if the amount of thermally sensitive deposits is very large, an additional slug may be required.

If one or more of these on-line chemical cleaning procedures does not restore performance to the clean design rate, consider comprehensive cleaning. Here, the first step is to treat the unit with a broad-spectrum biocide for 24 h. Next is acid treatment with sulfuric or sulfamic acid to reduce the pH to 3.0 to 3.5, where it is maintained for 24 h. During the acid treatment, organic cleaning and dispersing agents are also introduced.

Treatment with inhibitors during acid treatment is discontinued because it is ineffective. Since substantial material is usually removed from the surface, continuous blowdown at a rate high enough to discharge the dispersed substances is required. For this reason, it is necessary to add makeup acid to maintain the low pH. When acid cleaning is complete, blowdown is reduced to the normal rate and the system is brought back to its normal operating pH. Upon the system's reaching neutral pH, shock dosages of inhibitors are added to restore the protective films to the metal surfaces. After the shock dosages of inhibitors have been injected, concentration is maintained at its effective level.

Continuous tubeside cleaning.   Continous tubeside cleaning was first applied to power generation steam surface condensers. This system uses compressible balls, slightly larger than the tube ID, which have about the same density as water. Here, should fouling develop, the plain spongy balls are replaced by abrasive-coated balls until the clean rate is reestablished.

The process has been adapted to water-cooled exchangers, with cooling water in the tubes, using ceramic, glass, or sponge rubber (or other spongy polymer) balls in the cooling water to clear out accretions.[14] More recently it has been used on exchangers cooled with other liquids. For this purpose, the balls must be compatible with the fluid being circulated. In process plants that have many condensers, the system requires a more elaborate trapping and recirculation scheme than for surface condensers. Unless there is a history of success with this kind of continuous on-line cleaning, it is prudent to plan for an eventual shutdown for cleaning.

Figure 7.16 illustrates the kind of buildup that can occur on a

Figure 7.16   Fouled refinery U-tube reboiler bundle. (*Photograph courtesy High Performance Tube Inc., Union, New Jersey.*)

refinery-type U-tube reboiler bundle. Depending upon the character of the accumulation, the outside of the bundle may be cleaned hydraulically, chemically, or hydraulically and chemically or by burning off the organic material in a furnace.

Repair procedures

Making decisions about whether to repair or replace an exchanger or bundle and the procedures to use require analyzing the associated costs and benefits. Table 7.7 lists some of the factors to be balanced.

Safety.   Whenever maintenance, repairs, or alterations are to be done, take the necessary precautions to protect life, health, and property recommended for inspecting used and in-service units. In addition, take all usual and customary safety measures for working in the plant. These include (1) instructing supervisors to limit, document, and control access to the work area; (2) roping off the work area; (3) providing protective clothing and adequate ventilation; (4) using low-

TABLE 7.7   Benefit and Cost Factors for Maintenance Procedures

Benefits	Costs
Anticipated life extension achieved by repairs	Cost of repairs; cost of downtime required for repairs, including the cost of replacement product or power for resale
Longer life of a new unit	Cost of a new unit
Upgrading system possible with a new unit	Cost of downtime required for removing old and installing new unit, including cost of buying replacement product or power for resale
Benefit of repairing in place	Cost of repairing in place
Benefit of repairing with plant maintenance force	Cost of repairing with plant maintenance force
Benefit of having the work done by a qualified repair organization	Cost of having the work done by a qualified repair organization
Benefit of maintenance shop repair	Cost of removal, transporting to and from shop and reinstallation
Benefit of having the work done in a heat exchanger repair shop	Cost of having the work done by a heat exchanger repair shop

voltage lighting, explosionproof, where necessary; (5) providing and requiring the use of safety harnesses and watchers for workers who enter closed spaces; (6) providing fire watches; (6) line-blinding or double-block-valving lines to the unit; (7) training personnel in the safe use of tools and equipment; and (8) establishing and enforcing firm rules for safe performance of the work. An important rule is never to permit anyone to enter an enclosed space unless another person is assigned to monitor constantly the condition of the individual who is confined.

Following is a guide to some frequently required repair procedures.

Locating leaking tubes and tube-leak positions.   It is not always possible to find by simple inspection which tubes or tube-to-tubesheet connections are leaking. Furthermore, even when pH records and conductivity cell measurements or other evidence indicates that there is a leak, the location may be difficult to spot. Which tubes are leaking may be found in these ways: (1) hydrostatically testing the shell with the tube ends exposed, (2) bubble-testing the tube ends with air in the shell, and (3) halogen or helium leak testing by using probes as described in Chap. 4.

Since these methods all apply pressure to the shell and the leaks must be observed at the tubesheet faces, it is possible for friction-fit plugs placed in tube ends without adequate venting of the tubes behind the tubesheet to blow out and injure the observer. Therefore, safety measures must be taken to prevent an injury from a loosened tube plug's blowing out. Simplest is the use of a clear, high-impact-strength plastic shield. It is also safe to use a mirror to observe the tube ends, but it is far less convenient.

To hydrotest to reveal tube leaks, drain the tubeside and blow down the tubes and tubesheet faces with compressed air so that there is substantially no water in the tubes or on the faces of the tubesheets. Fill the shell with water (or inert fluid, if water is unacceptable) and pressurize it to 1.5 times the nameplate MAWP. Allow at least one-half hour for leaks to become apparent. Examine the tube ends with a strong light to see which ones are wet. If a leak is not manifest, hammer the shell to dislodge any matter that may be sealing a tube leak. Another reason for hammer testing is that external pressure may seal longitudinal cracks in tubes; the hydraulic shock applied by hammering the shell may open the cracks enough to allow the test medium to leak into the tube.

If the leak cannot be found by hydrostatic testing, drain and dry the unit and fill the shell with air at a pressure equal to the lower of the MAWP stamped on the nameplate or 50 lb/in^2 (345 kPa). Allow a minimum of 15 min of soaking time, and brush on bubble former. Observe for the characteristic formation and collapse of bubbles that indicates a leak.

If neither of these efforts discloses which tubes are leaking, bleed the pressure down to about 30 lb/in^2 (about 207 kPa). Add 10 percent by volume of tracer gas to the pressurized air, and allow a soaking time of about one-half hour. Insert the probe into the tube ends for about 1 in (about 25 mm). Also sniff the tube-to-tubesheet joints. Confirm that leaks are present by pressure-testing tubes that are suspected of leaking but have not tested positively by any of the above tests (Fig. 7.17).

Using the previously described tube-numbering systems and record format, mark the tubes that are found to be leaking. To assess the possible cause of the leak, it is important to ascertain the axial position of the failure and, if possible, to locate it radially. This can be done in several ways. Eddy-current testing will expose transverse flaws better than axial ones. Ultrasonic scanning, when feasible, will reveal axial flaws. Borescoping (Figs. 7.18 and 7.19) gives a visual view of what the failure looks like and its position.

A frequently used system to locate penetrations axially is to pressurize the shell with air and to push a close-fitting plug that seals to the tube ID along the length of the tube. The rush of air out of the tube end indicates when the plug passes the break in the tube. This method

Figure 7.17 Pressure-testing individual tubes. (*Photograph courtesy of Yuba Heat Transfer Corp., Tulsa, Oklahoma; courtesy of* Chemical Engineering.)

Figure 7.18 Borescoping a tube. (*Photograph courtesy of Yuba Heat Transfer Corp., Tulsa, Oklahoma; courtesy of* Chemical Engineering.)

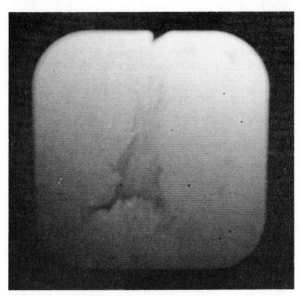

Figure 7.19 Borescope photograph of a flaw in a tube. (*Photograph courtesy of MGT Inc., Boulder, Colorado; courtesy of Chemical Engineering.*)

Figure 7.20 Axial tube-leak position finder. (*Photograph courtesy of MGT Inc., Boulder, Colorado.*)

finds the first penetration aft of the tubesheet. It cannot be used to find other leaks farther along the tube.

The author has devised an axial leak position finder shown in Fig. 7.20 that is simpler to use and can locate all the tube breaks. It consists of a round bar, about 2 in (about 50 mm) long, drilled with a blind hole for most of its depth. The open end of the blind hole is tapped with a standard pipe thread. Two O-ring grooves are machined into the exterior about 1 in (about 25 mm) apart, and between them a ⅛-in (3.2-mm) hole is drilled to intersect with the axial blind hole. The round bar and O rings, with which it is fitted, are sized to make a snug seal with the tube ID. To use the leak position finder, lengths of threaded pipe are screwed into the tapped end. The O rings are lubricated, and the leak position finder is inserted into the tube end. Pressurized air is led into the other end, and the device is moved into the tube. A sudden loss of pressure indicates the precise point of the leak nearest the tubesheet. If there are a series of leaks separated by unpenetrated regions, their positions can be found by continuing the axial motion. After locating the axial sites of the leaks, the most effective way to determine their locations on the circumference is by borescope examination.

The causes of some tube failures become obvious from their locations. If there is a series of leaks where the tubes penetrate the baffles or supports, the cause is most likely vibration or crevice corrosion combined with fretting. If there is a group of tube failures in the tubes in the way of the shell inlet located within about 1 or 2 in (about 25 to 50 mm) of the impingement-plate periphery, the cause is probably inadequate impingement protection. Failures directly in line with and scattered along the tube in the vicinity of the inlet generally indicate excessive vibration. A complete failure analysis may require pulling and examining the failed tubes, when possible, or pulling removable bundles and cleaning and examining the bundle and shell. The time required is seldom available.

Locating tube-to-tubesheet joint leaks.   Use hydrostatic testing, bubble testing, and tracer-gas sniffer testing to find out which tube-to-tubesheet joints are leaking. If the tube ends are welded to the front face of the tubesheet, regular fluid-penetrant examinations may disclose cracks and hidden porous spots in the welds that have opened during operation. An additional benefit of such regular examinations is the disclosure of ligament cracks that may not be found by visual inspections. Before performing a fluid-penetrant examination, be sure to detergent-wash the tubesheet face and follow with at least three clear-water rinses and a solvent drying wash.

Joints that are suspected of leaking may also be tested with a proprietary type of tool for hydrostatically testing individual tube-to-tubesheet joints.*

---

*A tool called the Hydrotest Tool for this purpose is produced by Haskel Incorporated of Burbank, California. It is distributed by Torque and Tension Equipment Inc., Santa Clara, California.

Reexpanding tubes. When an expanded joint leaks, the higher-pressure fluid that oozed between the hole wall and the tube may act as a lubricant that reduces the effective coefficient of friction. Fluid in the joint is also an impediment to successful reexpanding. Any deposits of scale or gummy materials inside the tube ends will also impede tube reexpanding. Therefore, the first requirement for reexpanding is to rid the mating surfaces and tube interior of foreign matter.

A second requirement is to reseal the tube to the hole wall without distorting the surrounding ligaments. If there is substantial distortion, adjacent tube-to-tubesheet joints are likely to be loosened. This can cause what shop workers call "a dog chasing its tail," or progressive loosening of joints adjacent to or near those that are reexpanded. It can also cause ligament work hardening, fatigue, and cracking, leading to scrapping the unit.

A third requirement is to limit the amount of tube-end thinning caused by the expanding process. For most tube walls and materials, the practical upper limit of permissible wall reduction is about 12 percent. Very thin high-strength tubes generally undergo less wall reduction when the joints are made than thicker and weaker tubes. Therefore, the tolerable wall reduction during reexpansion is also less.

Following are some recommendations for field rerolling and field hydraulic reexpanding.

1. Always detergent-wash and solvent-clean the surfaces. Use at least three washes with a detergent effective on the material to be removed. Follow detergent washing with clean-water rinses until all detergent has been removed. After this wash at least 3 times with a solvent in which any possible remaining foreign matter is soluble. The solvent should be chemically inert in order to avoid causing subsequent tube and tubesheet corrosion. After the last solvent wash, dry with clean, warm dry air.
2. Burnish the tube-end interior smooth.
3. Measure the expanded and unexpanded parts of the tube ID. From the tube measurements and tubesheet drilling details, estimate the apparent existing percent wall reduction. Here, it is necessary to use nominal dimensions of the tubes and holes rather than the measured ones used for establishing rolling procedures for new construction. (See Chap. 4.)
4. To reroll use a four- or five-pin rolling tool if available. Set the rolling torque experimentally to increase the nominal and maximum wall reduction of the original rolling procedure specifications by about 10 to 20 percent. This means that if the original nominal percent wall reduction was 5 percent, the final reexpanded nominal reduction will be about 5.5 to 6 percent. If the original maximum for

tubes that were harder to seal was 10 percent, the maximum for reexpanding will be 11 to 12 percent.

    a. If leakage was general, investigate and eliminate the cause. Reroll all the tubes, following the original procedure specification except for wall reduction.

    b. For isolated leaks, fabricate removable, tightly fitting ligament support plugs and insert them in the tube ends surrounding the leaking joint (Fig. 7.21).

5. To reexpand hydraulically:

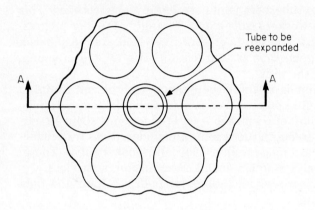

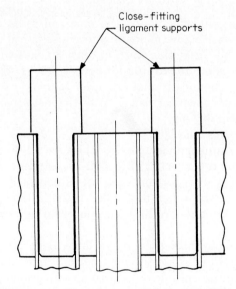

Figure 7.21 Supporting ligaments when reexpanding a single tube.

a. Examine the tube and tubesheet mill-test reports for yield stresses.

b. Select a hydraulic mandrel appropriate for the measured tube IDs.

c. Use the expanding pressure calculated from Fig. 7.21. If the expanding pressure from Fig. 7.21 is more than 115 percent of the tubesheet yield stress, either support the ligaments as shown in Fig. 7.21 or use two expanding mandrels, one about half the tubesheet thickness and the other the full depth. Insert the shorter mandrel so that it is centered halfway between the tubesheet faces, and expand at full pressure. Then insert the longer mandrel and expand at approximately 80 percent of full pressure. This procedure will ensure tightness, especially in grooved holes, and will ensure that the tube remains in intimate contact with the hole.

d. Hybrid reexpanding may be the most satisfactory way to reseal tubes. In this process expand the tubes hydraulically at 80 percent of the pressure indicated in Fig. 7.21. Reroll, setting the torque control to limit torque output to about half that required for making the original joints.

Repairing tube-to-tubesheet joint welds. The procedure for repairing tube-to-tubesheet joint welds depends upon the kind, extent, and cause of the damage. Fatigue cracks that result from vibration cannot be successfully repaired unless the whole weld is trepanned out and the cracks in the tube and tubesheet are chased to their end and filed, chipped, or ground to sound metal to prevent further propagation of the cracks. When it is not possible to reach the end of a crack, chase it as far as possible. Where no further metal removal is possible, drill a small round hole centered on the crack. That will establish the root position of the reweld.

Clean the surfaces to be welded thoroughly, following the procedure described for reexpanding tubes into tubesheets. Repair the welds by using a welding procedure appropriate for the materials and work position. As previously stated, manual SMAW is usually the most successful process for repair welding. However, if gas-tungsten arc welding (GTAW) is to be used, add filler metal because autogenous welds are apt to be porous in units that have been in service. When feasible, use inert-gas backing behind the tubesheet. Upon completion of repair welding, fluid-penetrant-examine all the repaired welds before hydrotesting. Depending upon the required degree of integrity, bubble-test the repaired welds or test with a tracer gas and sniffer.

Seal-welding expanded tube-to-tubesheet joints. When reexpanding tube ends does not cure leaks in expanded joints, the life of an exchanger may be extended by seal-welding the tubes to the tubesheet. Gases generated by the welding process produced when the heat of welding vaporizes volatile foreign matter cannot escape through the expanded section. Therefore, they escape through the weld puddle, which causes weld deposit porosity. This limits the effectiveness of seal welding after a unit has been in operation. However, if the process fluids are volatile and leave no residue on the surfaces or if the residues will not cause weld porosity or cracking, the repair may be successful.

To be effective, postoperation seal welding must be preceded by very thorough cleaning. If the seal welding is to be at the tubesheet face, good results may be obtained by using SMAW with the smallest-diameter rod available. GTAW with filler metal may also be successful. This depends upon the tube protrusion, tube wall, and tube and tubesheet metals.

In-bore autogenous GTAW has been adapted to repairing expanded tube-to-tubesheet joints in surface condensers.[15] Autogenous welding is a relatively low-temperature process that minimizes thermal distortion. The weld is usually made at the neutral line of the tubesheet (assumed to be halfway through its thickness) to control the thermal distortion. However, further in-bore weld repairs may be made on either side of the neutral line.

To implement the process, specimen expanded joints are exposed to an environment that simulates actual operating conditions. They are allowed to dry to establish a residue base similar to the one that will be encountered in the condenser. The specimens are welded and extensively examined before entering production repair welding.

The developers of the equipment and procedure for in-bore repair welding have successfully made repairs in tubes with bores of ⅜ to 1¼ in (9.5 to 31.75 mm) and a maximum wall thickness of 0.16 in (4 mm). There should be no problem welding larger-diameter tubes, but autogenously welding thicker-walled ones may not be successful. There is no specific lower wall-thickness limit. However, the tube's diameter-to-thickness ratio affects the stability and profile of the weld.

Repairing damaged ligaments. Eroded and corroded ligaments may be repaired to extend an exchanger's life. If the ligaments have cracked from fatigue or excessive stress, welded repairs should probably be viewed as temporary measures pending bundle or exchanger replacement. At least one firm offers a service in which a large part of the tubesheet is gouged out and puddled with weld. They have had suffi-cient success to offer time-limited guarantees on the work.

A general guide to ligament repairs follows.

1. Thoroughly wash the surfaces with detergent, fresh water, and volatile solvent until all visible foreign matter is removed.

2. Fluid-penetrant-examine the ligaments for cracks and porosity.

3. Grind out all porosity. Chip out file cracks to their initiation points if possible. Drill a small hole into the initiation point. If it can-not be reached, drill a small hole into the farthest point reached.

4. Thoroughly rewash the surfaces with detergent, fresh water, and volatile solvent.

5. Dry with filtered, warm air.

6. Weld the eroded, corroded regions or cracks by using a procedure appropriate for the metal. When possible, use the SMAW process. If the metals are unsuitable for SMAW, use GTAW with filler metal.

7. Examine with fluid penetrant.

8. Remove flaws and repeat cleaning, rewelding, and examination until no further flaws are apparent.

9. Hydrostatically test at 1.5 times the nameplate MAWP of the higher-pressure side. If the unit is derated, hydrostatically test at 1.5 times the derated pressure.

Plugging tube leaks.   Tube plugging is the most common procedure for restoring exchangers to operation when a tube or tube-to-tubesheet joint leak occurs. Plugging has the following effects: (1) it reduces the effective surface in direct proportion to the number of tubes plugged; (2) it increases the tubeside flow velocity by the ratio of the number of tubes in the original count to the number that remain unplugged; (3) it increases pressure drop through the tubes as the square of the ratio of increased tube velocity to original tube velocity, therefore, as the square of the ratio of original tube count to the count of unplugged tubes; and (4) it increases the overall coefficient of heat transfer by increasing the tubeside heat transfer film coefficient.

The increase in the overall heat transfer coefficient may be substan-tial if the original tubeside resistance to heat transfer was high rela-tive to the shellside, tube metal, and fouling resistances. However, the increase in overall heat coefficient transfer does not make up for the loss of heat transfer surface.

To examine the thermal effects, it is necessary to rerate the ex-changer, using the full tube count to determine the shellside film coefficient and the count of tubes that remain unplugged for the tubeside coefficient. Given the availability of computer programs for thermal design, the effects of plugging, based upon design-point conditions, can be estimated before putting a new unit on line. The results can be plotted to determine when plugging will no longer be acceptable for the operation. If actual operating conditions deviate substantially from design-point ones, it is relatively simple to substitute actual operating data in the computer program and to generate performance plots for duty-related output temperatures and pressure drops versus the count of tubes that remain unplugged.

Used together with a plugging record and plot illustrated in Fig. 7.4, such information makes obsolete rules of thumb that suggest replacing a bundle or unit when some arbitrary percentage of the tubes has been plugged.

Such rules of thumb are common for feedwater heaters. They are inconsistent; some utilities replace bundles or heaters when as few as 7½ percent of the tubes have been plugged, while at the other extreme an occasional utility will continue reduced-rate operation with as many as 35 percent of tubes plugged.

Some common types of plugs are illustrated in Figs. 7.22, 7.23, and 7.24. These plugs depend upon friction to hold them firmly in place and to maintain intimate contact to create a hydraulic seal. Tubeside pressure higher than that in the shell contributes to keeping the plugs seated. Higher shellside pressure tends to blow the plugs out. The surface available for friction increases linearly with the plug diameter, but the pressure surface increases as the square of the diameter. Therefore, plugs tend to become tighter with increasing tube ID when the higher pressure is in the tubes and looser when it is in the shell.

Tube-end plugs can be divided into those that work by creating hydraulically tight friction fits between the plug and the tube and between the tube and the tubesheet hole and ones that are welded to the tube and tubesheet. It is important to realize that friction-fit plugs can be knocked loose accidentally or intentionally. If substantial pressure has been built up in the enclosed tube space behind the plug, it can be ejected with great force when it is loosened. Therefore, before installing a friction-fit plug, perforate or cut the tube ends behind the inner face of the tubesheet. If the tube is cut all the way through, install an internal support to prevent the loose end of the tube from flopping around and damaging surrounding tubes. The support may consist of a tube-length rod just smaller than the tube ID, welded to one end of the tube, or a loose-fitting piece of tubing long enough to bridge the perforation or cut and expanded or welded into the tube end forward of the inside tubesheet face, or simply a rod welded to the inner end of the tube plug.

Another important preliminary step in installing friction-fit plugs is to descale and burnish the inside of the tube ends whenever possible.

Most frequently used are plain one-piece tapered plugs (sketch *a* of Fig. 7.22). These plugs are 2½ to 3 in (about 65 to 75 mm) long with a taper angle of about 5½°. Taper plugs are inexpensive, are readily available commercially or from the maintenance shop, and can be used to provide a backup for welding when friction plugging does not suffice. They have these disadvantages: (1) improper installation can damage the surrounding tubesheet ligaments and spring nearby expanded tube ends loose; (2) they create a crevice behind the contact surface between the plug and tube, which can lead to crevice corrosion; and (3) the tensile stresses they generate in the tubesheet may sensitize it to stress-corrosion cracking.

When taper plugs are driven into the tube ends, the initial line of contact between the plug and the tube quickly becomes a surface as the force of the blows deforms the tube. The deformation creates an interference fit at the ring of plug-tube contact surface and a similar interference fit between the parallel ring of the outer tube–tube-hole-

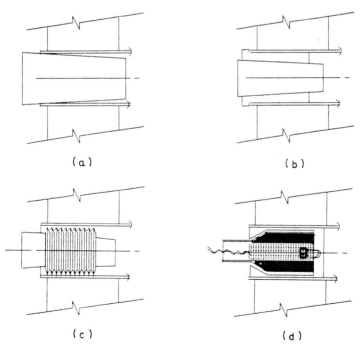

(a)   (b)

(c)   (d)

Figure 7.22 Some friction-fit tube plugs. (*a*) Plain one-piece tapered plug. (*b*) Plain two-piece tapered plug. (*c*) Serrated two-piece tapered plug. (*d*) Explosive plug before detonation.

wall contact area. The tightness of the plug depends upon the interfacial-fit pressure between the tube and plug, the coefficient of friction, and the area of the ring of contact between plug and tube. The tightness of the seal between the tube and the hole is similarly determined.

To install one-piece tapered plugs use only enough force to contain the leak. As a safety measure fit ligament supports (Fig. 7.21) into the tubes surrounding the tube to be plugged before driving.

Two-piece tapered plugs (sketches b and c of Fig. 7.22) depend upon three friction fits for tightness: between the pin (inner tapered plug) and the ring (outer piece), the ring and the tube ID, and the tube OD and the tube hole. However, the contact surface areas between the pin and the ring and between the ring and the tube are much greater than with plain tapered plugs. This means that considerably less interfacial-fit pressure is required to make a seal. The advantage of two-piece plugs is that there is little prospect of excessively deforming ligaments or starting adjacent tubes loose from their connections to the tubesheet. Major disadvantages are (1) the additional requirement to seal the pin-ring interface and (2) the need for some initial clearance between the tube ID and the pin to permit plug insertion. The latter requires substantial deformation of the ring to produce the required interfacial pressure between the ring and the tube.

When it is not possible to clean and burnish before plugging, use the serrated type (Fig. 7.22, sketch c). The teeth produced by serrating the outside of the ring are intended to bite through any scale or other foreign matter in the tube end. The high contact forces under the crowns of the serrations cause them to dig into the tube and also force the tube into tight contact with the hole, thereby increasing tube-to-hole tightness.

It is a good practice to grind the tube end flush with the tubesheet before plugging with a two-piece plug. This is so because the shoulder of the ring which bears against a protruding tube end can knock the tube loose from its seat as the pin is driven home.

Sketch d of Fig. 7.22 illustrates an explosive friction-fit plug. Friction-fit explosive plugs may be plain, as sketched, or serrated. They are used principally with thick tubesheets to seal as much of the tubesheet depth as is desired. The explosive charge is detonated under controlled conditions that do not produce a weld. The process is similar to kinetic expanding used for tube-to-tubesheet joints and for expanding tube inserts. With sufficient charge and appropriate tube and tubesheet dimensions, explosive plugs may also be metallurgically bonded to a tube or tubesheet.[16] A great advantage of explosive plugs is that they can be placed in tube ends that are inaccessible or difficult to see, for example, in peripheral tubes of feedwater heaters. Their

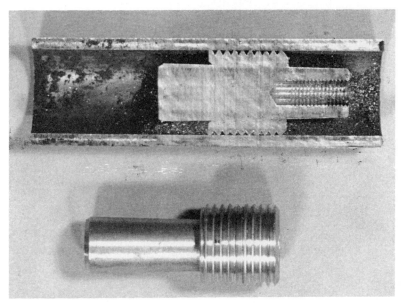

Figure 7.23 Two-piece serrated breakaway plug (Pop-a-Plug). (*Photograph courtesy of Expando Seal Tools, Inc., Montgomeryville, Pennsylvania; courtesy of Chemical Engineering.*)

disadvantages are that the work cannot be done by the user's maintenance force and that it is necessary to take precautions against fire or explosion. The patented process is licensed worldwide to installers.

A variation of the two-piece plug is the breakaway two-piece plug, or Pop-a-Plug,* shown in the photograph of Fig. 7.23. Its advantages are that (1) thick tubesheets can be plugged with two plugs to encapsulate the tube end and the hole (a breakaway plug is used at the back face and a conventional plug at the front) and (2) tubes can be plugged with a breakaway plug at an inaccessible rear tubesheet from the front end of the exchanger. The encapsulation of the tube ends in thick tubesheets excludes further entry of shellside or tubeside fluids, thereby reducing the chance of corrosion.

The capability of plugging a rear tubesheet from the front of an exchanger makes it possible to plug a floating tubesheet without removing the shell cover or the return cover. The sequence for installing a breakaway plug is shown schematically in Fig. 7.24.

Figure 7.25 is a sketch of a thimble-type plug. These plugs may be roller-expanded into the tube end but mostly are hydroexpanded into the tube ends. Their major advantages are that (1) they practically eliminate the prospect of ligament distortion, (2) installing them does

---

*Trademark of Expando Seal Tools, Inc., Montgomeryville, Pennsylvania.

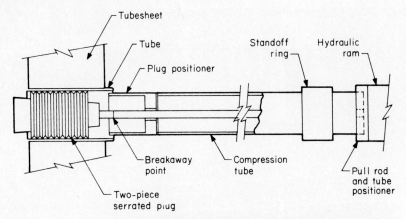

Figure 7.24 Schematic of breakaway plug installation. Sequence of installation: 1. Clean the tubes thoroughly. 2. Measure tube ID with a micrometer to set plug gauge range. 3. Plug gauge to determine plug OD to use. 4. Measure actual tube length. 5. Set standoff ring to fix plug position. 6. Set plug position and compression tube. 7. Retract hydraulic ram until rod breaks away.

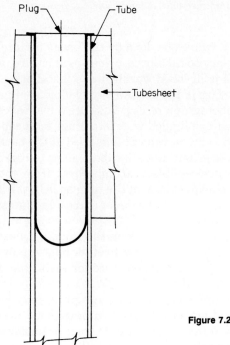

Figure 7.25 Thimble-type plug.

not start adjacent tubes loose, (3) they can be as long as the thickness of the tubesheet, and (4) they can be used as welded plugs. The disadvantage of thimble plugs is that their thin section may not be suitable for a corrosive environment.

For high-pressure services, weld the plugs to the tube end and tubesheet. Cut the tube back from the front face of the tubesheet about ¼ to ½ in (about 6 to 13.5 mm). Thoroughly clean the surfaces, and set the plug into the tube at the cut-back location. Weld the plug and tube to the hole wall, using at least two passes of filler metal. The sealing weld need be only a multipass filet weld. However, the whole end may be covered with weld flush with the tubesheet face.

If a thimble plug is to be welded into place, omit the flange. Hydroexpand the plug snugly to the tube beyond the weld.

In addition to thimble plugs and explosively welded plugs, a variety of homemade plugs is used for welding. The simplest consists of a short length of round bar, pressed into the tube flush with the cut-back tube end. While the sealing weld need be only a multipass filet weld, the whole end may be covered with weld flush with the tubesheet face. When there is concern that corrosion will occur in the unplugged length of tube in the tubesheet, the length can be increased to protrude beyond the back face. The inserted end of the plug is machined to a taper or rounded to facilitate its installation. The fit of the plug to the tube is made as tight as can be installed by hammer blows.

Insurance plugging.   Insurance plugging is plugging tubes that immediately surround a tube that has failed when tubeside pressure is high enough to cause leaking fluid to impinge on adjacent tubes. Erosion consequent to the impingement may have thinned the walls of the surrounding tubes almost to the point of failure. Therefore, they are plugged to prevent their failing at an inconvenient time. The practice is used with closed feedwater heaters because their tubes are relatively thin-walled and the feedwater pressures in the tubes are high relative to the extraction-steam pressures.

Because of the reduction in exchanger capacity there is an understandable reluctance to plug tubes that have not failed. Various kinds of examinations and pressure tests may therefore be performed to avoid insurance plugging. It is difficult to tell accurately whether or not there is substantial loss of metal in the tubes being considered for insurance plugging, but experiments have shown fairly consistent thickness loss measurements by using eddy-current examinations. If a large enough surface has been thinned, pressure-testing a suspect tube may cause it to fail. However, small rounded partial penetrations will not.

An alternative to insurance plugging is to sleeve or line the adjacent tubes in the vicinity of the failure in the plugged tube.

Installing ferrules, sleeves, and liners.   Ferrules, sleeves, and liners are used to prevent tube-end erosion and to extend the useful life of the tubes. They consist of thin tubes approximately 0.01 to 0.02 in (approximately 0.25 to 0.5 mm) thick that are fitted to the inside of the tube with an interference fit. Although their walls are quite thin, there is a significant reduction in cross-sectional area from that of the tube ID. For example, if the tube has a 0.625-in OD and is 0.049 in thick (15.9-mm OD and 1.24 mm thick), installing a sleeve 0.01 in (0.25 mm) thick reduces the flow area by 7.3 percent. Because it takes between 10 and 20 tube diameters for the fluid regime to stabilize after the fluid enters the tubes, installing ferrules or sleeves in the tube may create some detrimental downstream erosion inside the tubes. Successful installation of ferrules, sleeves, and liners requires the inside of the tube to be clean and free of scales or other accumulations. Therefore, the tube should be cleaned before attempting installation.

When there is evidence that entrance turbulence is eroding the tubesheet and tube ends, consider installing ferrules. These devices are thin metal or plastic tubes approximately 0.01 to 0.02 in (approximately 0.25 to 0.5 mm) thick and flanged at one end. The unflanged end fits snugly into the tube end and is then rolled or hydroexpanded into intimate contact with the tube ID. The inserted end may also be welded to the tube ID. The flange diameter should be approximately equal to the tube OD plus one-third of the ligament width. The other end should be tapered to a thin edge. The length of most ferrules is equal to the thickness of the tubesheet plus about ½ in (about 13 mm).

In some exchangers (for example, feedwater heaters and steam generators) tubes fail in the region between the tubesheet and first tube support while the rest of the tube remains in good condition. Adjacent tubes may be considered for insurance plugging as a result of the impingement of high-pressure tubeside fluid. If the cause of the failure can be identified and corrected, it may be economical to extend the life of the tubes by sleeving to bridge the failure and sleeving the adjacent tubes instead of plugging them. As with ferrules, the sleeves should be flanged over to protect the tube ends.

Straight tubes may also be lined to extend their life. In this process, a thin inner tube of the same length as the tube to be lined is inserted. A metal sizing ball is forced through the liner by hydraulic pressure. The ball is just large enough in diameter to expand the liner into a tight interference fit with the tube ID but not so large as to deform the outer tube. The process has been used successfully to restore previously plugged tubes to service.

Safe ending.   Safe ending consists of butt-welding short lengths of high-temperature-resistant-alloy tubing to the tube ends. Its purpose is to deal with tubeside inlet temperatures beyond the capability of the main body of the tubes to withstand. It can also be used when the tubes and tubesheet are not compatible for fusion welding. For this purpose, the safe end must be compatible for fusion welding with the tubes and the tubesheets.

Heat shielding. Tubesheets and tube ends that show evidence of deterioration caused by hot gases may have their lives extended by installing a heat shield. The shield consists of a perforated disk of high-temperature-resistant material about ¼ in (6.4 mm) thick and with as large a diameter as can be fastened to the tubesheet. The heat shield hole layout is identical with the tubesheet drilling template. The holes are drilled to the tube ID. Installation holes are drilled in the shield to fit over studs fastened to the tubesheet. Snugly fitting dowels are set into the holes, and the tubesheet face is covered with a layer of ceramic heat-resisting cement. The shield is installed over the dowels and bolted to the support studs, creating a sandwich of tubesheet, ceramic cement, and heat shield cover. When the ceramic cement has set, the dowels are removed.

An alternative is to drill the heat shield to receive thin-walled stub tubes that will fit snugly into the heat exchanger tubes. The stub tubes are welded to the front face of the heat shield and extend a short distance behind the inner face of the tubesheet after installation. After the heat shield is in place, the stub tubes are fastened to the heat exchanger tubes by welding at the stub ends, hydroexpanding, or both. With this alternative, the shellside fluid cools the tubesheet and heat exchanger tubes enough to mitigate the problem.

Repairing and replacing expansion joints. It is not generally feasible to repair thin-walled expansion joints that have failed because of fatigue or have squirmed. Thin-walled joints with perforations and weld skips have been repaired by welding. However, one must be cognizant of the possibility of weld metal deposits creating stress raisers that may quickly lead to subsequent failures. Repairs to thick-walled joints are usually made to seal off corroded-through regions or cracks. Consider such repairs as a stopgap pending replacement.

Before proceeding with a repair or replacement, try to find out why the expansion joint failed and whether the failure caused damage to other parts of the unit. Possible reasons for failure are fatigue, stress-corrosion cracking, general corrosion, erosion, excessive pressure, deflections greater than design, unanticipated angular deflections, and unanticipated rotational loads on the expansion joint.

Fatigue appears as cracks in thin-walled element roots and crowns and in the knuckles of flanged-only and flanged-and-flued-head joints.

The life of an expansion joint will generally be shortened if it is subjected to greater axial, angular, or rotational deflection than was assumed in design. Fatigue failures from excessive axial deflection appear as cracks in element crowns. Those due to excessive angular deflection appear as cracks in the compressed and stretched regions.

Stress-corrosion cracking occurs in austenitic materials in the crowns on the bottom of horizontal units that are not drainable. General corrosion of thin-walled elements appears as pits and etched surfaces. Erosion is indicated by holes that penetrate the wall. Under excessive pressure, thin-walled single-corrugation joints and thick-walled joints bulge at the sides. Multicorrugation thin-walled bellows fail under excessive pressure by squirming.

In planning a replacement when a joint has failed, consider the following:

1. Install a higher-cycle-life joint.

2. Make the joint in the replacement from a material less sensitive to stress corrosion-cracking.

3. Provide an internal sleeve in the replacement joint to protect against erosion.

4. Select and design the joint for the correct axial deflection.

5. Eliminate the cause of angular or torsional deflection, or install a joint that can accept these deflections.

6. If the cause of angular deflection cannot be eliminated, install shell alignment guides to restrain it.

7. Remove any impediments to free shell movements.

8. Provide a more effective shell pressure-relief device.

9. Replace the joint with one designed to withstand the higher pressure that caused the original failure. Note that the higher the design pressure, the less flexible the elements that can withstand it.

Thick-walled joints may be replaced in sections. Weld three or four temporary bridges to the shell before cutting out the failed joint. The bridges must be able to maintain alignment of the shell sections on either side of the gap left by removing the joint. All the welds of the replacement sections should be transverse. Because the welding is done from one side only, it is desirable to use inert-gas backup and consumable backing for the weld joints between adjacent sections. Where possible, radiograph or ultrasonically examine the welds.

The simplest way to repair an exchanger in which a thin-walled joint has failed is (1) to cut out the failed joint, (2) to extract the tubes, (3) to recondition the tubesheet holes, (4) to install a replacement joint between the two halves of the shell, and (5) to replace the tubes with new ones. This is essentially full retubing.

Figures 7.26 and 7.27 show two other options. The procedure for the first is as follows:

1. At the end where the tie rods are not fastened to the tubesheet (the rear tubesheet), if a large enough band saw is available, saw-cut the shell behind the tubesheet as close as possible to the tubesheet's rear face. Before cutting, center-punch lines along the shell at the quarter points (this is for future realignment). Cut out a band of shell behind the saw cut approximately 6 in (about 150 mm) long.

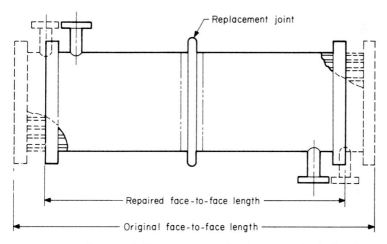

Figure 7.26   Replacing a shell expansion joint by shortening the shell and re-using the tubes. (*Courtesy of* Chemical Engineering.)

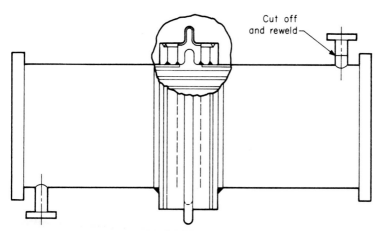

Figure 7.27   Installing a larger expansion joint over a failed joint. (*Courtesy of* Chemical Engineering.)

2. If a band saw is not available, cut out a 6-in (150-mm) band of shell behind the tubesheet with one edge of the cutout as close as possible to the tubesheet's rear face. Cut the tubes with an abrasive wheel as close to the tubesheet as possible.

3. Pull the unit apart.

4. Drill out the tube stubs from the rear tubesheet, or pull them out with a stub puller. Recondition the holes.

5. Thin the tube ends in the front tubesheet, and drive the tubes. Recondition the tubesheet holes.

6. Cut the failed joint out of the shell and replace it with the new joint. Be sure to center-punch the shell parts on the quarter points to restore alignment.

7. Join the rear tubesheet to the shell.

8. Measure tubesheet-to-tubesheet faces, and abrasive-cut the tubes to fit the measured length. Be sure to deburr the tubes after cutting.

9. Install the tubes in the shortened unit.

10. Hydrostatically test.

The constraints of this procedure are that (1) it requires considerable labor; (2) the surface is reduced; (3) connecting piping must be relocated, as must the exchanger support structure; and (4) either the tubesheet-to-baffle spacing is reduced or the spacers must be trimmed to adjust the baffle pitch. The procedure is worthwhile only when the tubes are uncorroded, undamaged, and expensive or hard to get.

The constraint of the second procedure is that the larger-diameter expansion joint may make the tubesheet inadequate to withstand the original design pressure. This will require downrating.

This is the second procedure:

1. Weld closures in section to the shell on either side of the failed joint. The closure OD must be about the same as that of the tubesheet (or in C and N units, the same as the channel flange OD).

2. Cut off any nozzles or appurtenances that protrude beyond the tubesheet or channel flange.

3. Slide the new, larger-diameter joint over the tubesheet, and weld it to the closures. Although the expansion-joint welding stubs are shown single-butt-welded to the closures, a simpler design may be used in which the stubs are filet-welded to smaller-diameter closures. The design of the closures is similar to the design of closures for a jacketed cylinder.

4. Reweld the cutoff nozzles and appurtenances to the shell.

5. Hydrostatically test.

Retubing.[17] *Retubing* is a blanket term for a repair that requires removing and replacing tubes. It covers replacing individual tubes, replacing a substantial number but not all the tubes (partial retubing), and replacing all the tubes (complete retubing). In complete retubing, the whole tube nest may be rebuilt, using only the original tubesheet or tubesheets. The equipment and methods used vary with the extent of the repairs. Following is a guide.

A most important safety consideration before commencing any kind of retubing is to remove any plugs in the tube ends before pulling the tubes or cutting into them. This applies whether the plugs have been welded shut or held in place by friction. Although it may not be obvious, despite tubes having been perforated to allow ventilation before plugging, the vent holes may plug. Volatile materials, which may be flammable, explosive, or otherwise hazardous, may be trapped between solid regions of foulants or behind the plugs in the tube ends. The pulling, cutting, or burning operation may release trapped material in a jet that strikes the worker.

Instruct workers who remove plugs not to stand directly in front of the plugged tubes but to take a position to one side. This will avoid their being struck by any plug propelled by pressure in the tube or burned or scalded by any material emitted when the plug is removed. Provide shielding to prevent injury to passersby from plugs ejected from the tube end.

Unless there was an isolated flaw in its manufacture, if one tube has failed, it is likely that others will soon fail. However, unless the cause is investigated, it cannot be determined whether the failures will be localized in one region or will be general throughout the tube field. Examples of localized failures are (1) tubes that erode through in front of an inlet nozzle not protected adequately against impingement, with no failures in tubes farther into the bundle; and (2) failure of most of the tubes in one pass of a multipass unit. In the first example, the failed tubes protect tubes deeper in the bundle. In the second, failure may stem from a variation of the corrosion rate with temperature or from fluid maldistribution. Therefore, when the first tube fails, it is desirable to find out how and why it failed.

If the failure is localized, self-limiting, and due to a correctable cause, the choices of action are as follows: (1) plug the failed tubes without eliminating the cause; and (2) correct the deficiency and replace the tubes that have failed and those that have probably been damaged. In considering the appropriate action, take note that there is less potential for damaging tubesheets if individual tubes are replaced than if they are plugged. If hydraulic tube extraction equipment is available, it takes a maintenance crew about one-half hour more to pull and replace a tube than to plug it. Repair-shop replacement of single tubes is so uneconomical that it is not feasible.

Removing tubes.   To remove straight tubes, the tubesheets must be accessible. Floating-head bundles may first have to be extracted from their shells. U-tube bundles must be removed from their shells. It is not always possible to remove single U tubes because there is hardly any access to tubes in the inner rows.

If the tubes are welded to the tubesheet, the welds must first be trepanned out. After the tube has been removed, the holes must be prepared for welding the replacement tubes to the tubesheet.

Either U tubes must be driven, or the tubes must be cut behind the tubesheet, pulled out of the bundle from the U-bend end, and the stubs removed from the tubesheet. Straight tubes may be driven or extracted. Extracting is preferable because (1) driving may buckle the tubes, making them virtually impossible to remove; (2) because of the Poisson effect, driving increases and pulling decreases tube diameter; and (3) pulling attachments grip the tube, but driving force is applied to the tube end, where misalignment or tool slippage can damage the tubesheet. Either way, the tube holes must be dressed after tubes have been removed to enable a replacement tube to be joined successfully to the tubesheet.

When tube exteriors are heavily encrusted with scale or hard foulants, tube driving or extraction may damage the baffles. This is so because cross-flow baffles and semisupports are perforated plates with very little strength in the direction of the tube axis. In removing straight tubes, work outward uniformly from the tubes nearest the center. Here is why.

The baffles are simply supported against axial loads near their edges by the tie rods and spacers. Consequently, bending loads applied near the baffle center apply the greatest bending moments. When the first tubes are pulled, the surrounding tubes may partially support the baffle if they have been cemented to it by scale or crud. To the degree that such support is provided, the pulling load is resisted mostly by shear in the baffle ligaments that surround the tube being pulled. However, as tubes are removed, there is less and less support. Therefore, the entire untubed region tends to bend.

On the other hand, if tubes are sequentially removed from the periphery inward, progressively greater bending moments will be applied and support from adjacent tubes will progressively decline. The extreme is reached when the last tube at the very center is pulled with all the other baffle holes empty.

To drive a tube, reduce the tube ends with a commercially available tube-wall reducing tool or a specially sharpened drill bit until they are thin and provide a shoulder for a driving tool. Insert a close-fitting rod into the tube to prevent its buckling in the bundle. (It is almost impossible to drive a tube that has buckled.) Use a spade-shaped tube-end collapsing tool to pry the tube end free of the far-end tube hole. Drive the tube with a tube drift manually or with an air hammer. After the far end emerges, attach a pulling device and pull the tube out.

Commercial hydraulically operated tube and stub pullers are described below. When they are not available, jury-rig a puller from a portable hand drill. Do this by attaching a means of exerting pulling force to the drill. In place of the drill bit, insert a stud extractor (easy-out) that can be jammed into the tube end. Spin the tube while exerting pulling force. Such homemade pullers are less likely to cause damage to the baffles than commercial ones because it is seldom possible to apply as much force with them as with commercial devices and, by spinning the tube during pulling, to screw it through the crud. This shears the binding material rotationally and axially instead of just axially.

Following is some information on some well-known commercial tube and stub pullers.

The Elliott spear-type puller is a device designed for pulling whole tubes ½ to 2½ in (12.7 to 63.5 mm) in diameter. It has a 30-ton (about 265-kN) double-acting ram with a 6-in (152.4-mm) travel. The system consists of a reservoir, hose, pump and selector valve, spear, spear-to-ram adapter, and adapter-to-ram horseshoe lock. The spear is a rod threaded on one end to mate with the tapped end of the adapter. Its other end is tapered and fitted with self-tapping threads. The adapter is a rod tapped at one end to receive the connecting end of the spear. Its other end is milled to a square drive for a hand or impact wrench. It is machined in front of the drive end to receive the horseshoe-lock collar.

The pulling sequence is as follows: (1) Thread the spear into the adapter; (2) turn the spear into the tube with the hand or impact wrench; (3) fit the ram cylinder over the adapter until it butts up to the tubesheet at the ligaments; (4) lock the adapter to the back end of the ram cylinder with the horseshoe lock; (5) apply pump pressure to pull the tube; (6) drive the other end with a knockout tool, or use a second ram to tear the tube apart; and (7) after a full ram stroke, reverse the valve and retract the ram, following this with alternate strokes and reversals to provide impact if desired.

The Hydro-Pull* HTP 500 (Fig. 7.28) is designed to pull tubes from ½ in through 1¼ in (12.7 mm through 31.8 mm) continuously through

Figure 7.28 Hydro-Pull HTP 500 tube and stub puller. (*Photographs courtesy of Torque and Tension Equipment Inc., Santa Clara, California; courtesy of* Chemical Engineering.)

the gun. Larger tubes [up to 3 in (76.2 mm)] may be pulled through a collar to the gun entrance. The length pulled depends upon the collar length. The drive is an air-operated hydraulic pump. From front to rear in the figure are the collar, gun, and jaw-retaining ring. The pulling mandrel is shown above the gun. The main hydraulic piston has a capacity of 30 tons (about 265 kN) and a 3½-in (89-mm) stroke for tube pulling. A second, rear hydraulic piston operates the jaws.

To pull tubes or stubs with the Hydro-Pull 500, (1) screw the threaded end of the mandrel into the tube with a hand or impact wrench, (2) assemble the gun with the collar and jaws, (3) slip the gun over the mandrel until the collar butts to the ligament area around the tube, and (4) pull the trigger. On pulling the trigger, the jaws clamp the mandrel's protruding drive end. The main piston strokes to push the collar against the tubesheet and pull the tube out. For tubes 1¼ in (31.8 mm) and smaller, the tube travels through the gun as stroking continues. When mandrel travel is exhausted, the jaws clamp the tube and pulling is continued.

The Elliott collet-type puller system (Figs. 7.29 and 7.30) is most suitable for tubes in relatively thin tubesheets. It consists of a hydraulic pump and extractor that use a split, toothed collet and drawbar, shown in Fig. 7.30 before and after insertion. The extractor has a nosepiece that bears against the tubesheet, a threaded bushing, and a thrust cap. The machine's range is ½ through 1½ in (12.7 through 38.1 mm). Its pulling capacity is 22 tons (200 kN). Its stroke is 6 in (150 mm).

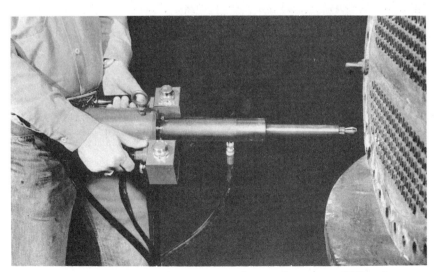

Figure 7.29 Elliott collet-type tube extractor. (*Photograph courtesy of Elliott Company, Springfield, Ohio.*)

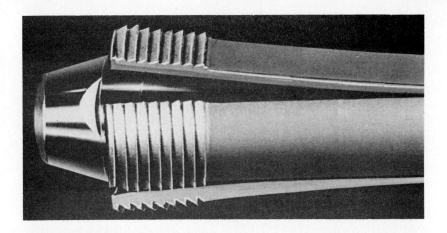

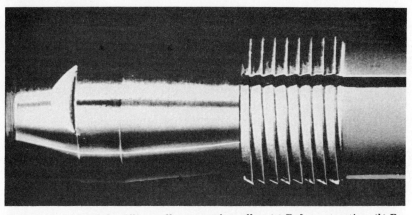

Figure 7.30 Jaws of the Elliott collet-type tube puller. (*a*) Before retraction. (*b*) Retracted. (*Photographs courtesy of Elliott Company, Springfield, Ohio; courtesy of* Chemical Engineering.)

The drawbar and collet are inserted into the tube end. Depressing the pull button signals the hydraulic piston to retract the pull bar. The expanded collet's teeth bite into the tube, pulling it along with the pull bar for the stroke length. The collet is freed by pressing the retract button.

Internal tube cutting. When the tubes to be removed are relatively soft and do not quickly surface-harden, it may be effective to use internal tube cutters to cut the tubes behind the tubesheets. The tube stubs that remain must be removed and the holes dressed before replacement tubes are installed. The stubs may be removed with one of the tube pullers described above; they may be removed by thinning the ends and collapsing, driving, or pulling them; or if all the tubes have been cut and the tubesheet separated from the shell, the stubs can be drilled out followed by finish reaming.

Most tube cutters consist of hollow shanks with extendable cutting tips that pass through slots in the cutting end of the shank. The shank passes through a thrust collar that bears against the tubesheet ligament. When it is inserted into the tube, the position of the cutting tips is set by the thrust collar's location on the shank. The cutting tips of air-operated or electrically operated internal tube cutters are extended or retracted by a hand-operated mandrel built into the drive body. Push-type cutters are not integral with the driver but are chucked into a hand drill. Extension of their cutting tips depends upon how hard the operator pushes against the resistance of the tubesheet. Other kinds also are commercially available.

Internal tube cutters may be used to cut both ends of tubes in removable bundles. Tubes in a fixed tubesheet should be cut at one end only and the tubes and stubs pulled. Internal tube cutting is especially valuable for cutting tubes between adjacent double tubesheets and behind the inner tubesheets of double-tubesheet exchangers when partially retubing. In the procedure specification for this work, include a requirement for maintaining adjacent tubesheets parallel by emplacing peripheral machined spacers between the tubesheets in the vicinity of the tubes to be replaced.

External tube cutting.   The fastest way to remove tubes for complete retubing is by external cutting with a band saw. This is an especially good way to cut off the outer tubesheets of double-tubesheet exchangers. In describing the procedure for replacing expansion joints it was suggested that the saw cut be made at the far end, where the tie rods are not fastened to the tubesheet. This also applies to external tube cutting for floating-head bundles. However, with U-tube bundles, there is no choice but to cut the tubes and tie rods behind the tubesheets. Therefore, the tie rods must either be repaired or be replaced.

Partial retubing.   Partial retubing is suitable mostly for straight-tube units, but it may be done on the outer rows of U-tube bundles. In considering whether or not to partially retube an exchanger, it is necessary to determine the causes and locations of failures. Consider partial retubing under the following circumstances:

1. All failures are confined to a discrete part of the tube field.

2. Failure is the result of corrosion in an inlet or outlet pass when the corrosion attack rate varies with temperature.

3. Failure has resulted from fluid maldistribution, and the maldistribution is correctable.

4. There is reasonable life expectancy for the rest of the bundle.

Full retubing. Full retubing lends itself to cost-benefit analysis. Compare the cost of a new bundle or exchanger with the retubing cost. Consider:

1. The availability of a spare bundle or exchanger

2. The time required for procuring a new bundle

3. The costs of downtime for retubing

4. The possible benefits of retubing with higher-grade or thermally more efficient tubes

Other alternatives to evaluate are the benefits of field and shop retubing.

Before deciding to fully retube a removable-bundle unit, pull the bundle and inspect the inside of the shell and evaluate the condition of the bundle. Appraise the estimated life remaining in the shell and the condition of the baffles, tie rods, spacers, and other bundle parts. Usually it is not possible to examine the internals of fixed-tubesheet exchangers. Be prepared for the additional expense and delay required to replace baffles, tie rods and spacers, and other bundle parts that may be found to be severely corroded or eroded upon disassembly.

Extracting and replacing removable bundles. Bundles of exchangers used in power generation are seldom if ever removed for cleaning. Feedwater piping is usually welded directly to feedwater heater channels. Therefore, except for heaters installed in condenser necks, the shells are removed when it is necessary to examine feedwater heater bundles. Either feedwater heaters are retubed in situ, or the whole unit is removed and shipped to the shop. The action taken depends upon the current economics of power generation. However, in other industries removable bundles are often extracted for cleaning and repairs and then reinstalled. This is a common practice in oil-refining and petrochemical production. Following is a guide to extracting and reinstalling bundles.

The impediments to removing and installing bundles are shell out-of-roundness, leading to interference between cross-flow baffles or tube supports, and severe shellside fouling. Bundle flexibility may impede removing and installing horizontal units. However, in vertical exchangers bundle flexibility is desirable. In these the effects of inter-ference and fouling can be dealt with by supplying sufficient pulling force to overcome the frictional resistance they create. Bundle flexibil-ity in horizontal units must be handled differently.

As pulling force is applied to extract a horizontally installed bundle, drag on the bottom or on rails (where installed) tilts the baffles as much as clearances in the tie rod and tube holes permit. Therefore, the baffles tend to wedge in the shell. As the bundle emerges, it sags be-tween the grasping point and the shell flange. This contributes to wedging the remainder of the bundle in the shell.

In installing a horizontally slung bundle, imprecision in locating the center of gravity, combined with sag, makes the bundle enter at a slight angle with the shell. Once it has entered, the baffles tilt and tend to wedge as in extraction. Therefore, new construction, mainte-nance, and retubing require the ability to push bundles into and pull them out of horizontal shells without damage. This requires the capa-bility of aligning the parts and providing force uniformly to overcome the frictional resistance between the bundle and the shell.

Conventionally, cranes and slings are used with come-alongs as pre-viously described. Jacks are arranged to support the outside bottom edge of the tubesheet, take up misalignment, and adjust for flexibility. However, it is difficult to balance the forces applied by several come-alongs. Banging and vibrating the shell to jar the bundle loose when it hangs up have already been discussed.

Machines like the Hydro-Extractor, shown in Figs. 7.31 and 7.32, and the Bundle-Wagon* overcome the problems of imbalance and mis-alignment while applying force uniformly at the appropriate loca-tions. The Hydro-Extractor uses the fine control and great force avail-able from hydraulic cylinders. A complete description is available in the literature.[18] The Bundle-Wagon uses an air-mechanical system for the same purpose.[19] Fast turnarounds can be achieved with these com-mercially available hydraulic and mechanical machines.

Adding impingement protection to an existing bundle. At the design stage, manufacturers investigate impingement protection require-ments. Under appropriate conditions, an exchanger may be built with-out such protection. In either case, the most fully tubed layout is gen-erally used because of its economic, thermal, and mechanical advantages. If the actual shell fluid properties and flow rates deviate from design, tubes in front of the inlet may erode. Here are some ways to deal with this situation.

---

*Trademarks, respectively, of Hydro-Extractors Inc., Beaumont, Texas, and M&H Manufacturing Co., Vidor, Texas.

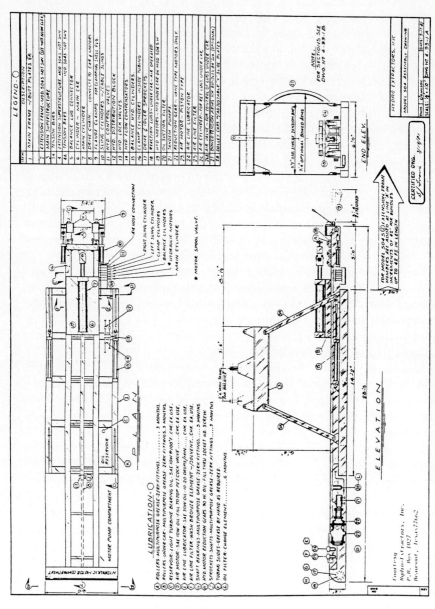

Figure 7.31 Assembly of model 504 Hydro-Extractor. (Hydro-Extractors Inc., Beaumont, Texas.)

442

Figure 7.32   Model 504 Hydro-Extractor. (*Photograph courtesy of Hydro-Extractors Inc., Beaumont, Texas.*)

Enlarging the inlet nozzle.   The simplest procedure is to cut out the inlet nozzle and install a new nozzle large enough to accommodate the flow conditions or to install a new larger reducing nozzle with built-in impingement protection described in Chap. 6. Set the larger-nozzle ID tangent to the hole left by removing the original nozzle at the point nearest the shell flange or tubesheet. Before making this alteration, check the position of the baffle nearest the tubesheet and the baffle spacings to make sure that the inlet flow will not bypass bundle crosses. Carry the new-inlet-size pipe at least 10 nozzle diameters before reducing it to the line size, or install the reducer on the far end of a long-radius elbow that feeds the connection.

Alternatives to the reducing nozzle are a blister with an adequately sized impingement plate and escape area. In place of an impingement plate, a strainer plate may be welded into the space in the shell from which the original inlet nozzle was removed. (See Chap. 6 for strainer-plate construction.)

Installing a distribution belt.   A more expensive alternative is to install a distribution belt described in Chap. 6. If the belt and openings into the shell are properly sized and located, the inlet-nozzle size need not be changed.

References

1. *Guide for Inspection of Refinery Equipment*, chap. VII, "Heat Exchangers, Condensers, and Cooler Boxes," 2d ed., The American Petroleum Institute, Washington, 1967; reaffirmed, 1973.
2. *ASME Boiler and Pressure Vessel Code*, 1989 ed., American Society of Mechanical Engineers, New York. (New editions are published at 3-year intervals.)
3. *Standards of the Tubular Exchanger Manufacturers Association*, 7th ed., The Tubular Exchanger Manufacturers Association, Tarrytown, N.Y., 1989.
4. *Standard for Power Plant Heat Exchangers*, 1st ed., The Heat Exchange Institute, Cleveland, 1980; Addendum 1, 1984.
5. *Standards for Closed Feedwater Heaters*, 4th ed., The Heat Exchange Institute, Cleveland, August 1984.
6. *Heat Exchangers for General Refinery Service*, API Standard 660, 1st ed., The American Petroleum Institute, Washington, 1976.
7. J. L. Kratz, "Shell-and-Tube Heat Exchanger Failures in Feedwater Heaters, Condensers and Other Heat Exchangers," ASME Pap. 81-JPGC-Pwr-1, presented at ASME-AIEE Joint Power Generation Conference, St. Louis, October 1981.
8. *National Board Inspection Code*, American National Standard ANSI/NB-23, editions revised as required, The National Board of Boiler and Pressure Vessel Inspectors, Columbus, Ohio.
9. R. M. Pastoris, "Pretreating Mild-Steel Water-Cooled Heat Exchangers," *Chem. Eng.*, Nov. 16, 1981.
10. "Fouling in Heat Exchange Equipment," ed. by James Chenowith and M. A. Impagliazzo, presented at Twentieth ASME-AIChE Heat Transfer Conference, Aug. 2–5, 1981, ASME HTD, vol. 17, American Society of Mechanical Engineers, New York.
11. J. L. Haluska, S. H. Leach, and W. L. Van Nostrand, *Economic Penalties Associated with the Fouling of Refinery Heat Transfer Equipment*, Troy, N.Y., 1981.
12. L. F. Collins, "Fouling in Water Circuits and Evaporators," *Trans. ASME*, October 1949, p. 871.
13. P. G. Bird and B. A. Metz, "Onstream Exchanger Cleaning Works," *Hydrocarbon Process.*, January 1968, p. 133.
14. A. F. Stegelman and R. Renfftlen, "On Line Mechanical Cleaning of Heat Exchangers," *Hydrocarbon Process.*, January 1983.
15. H. N. Franklin, D. R. Roper, and D. R. Thomas, "Internal Bore Welding Method Repairs Condenser Leaks," *Weld. J.*, December 1986.
16. "Explosive Welding Does Bang-Up Job in Heater Repair, *Weld. J.*, February 1980.
17. R. Clapper, "Your Guide to the Repair and Retubing of Tubular Heat Exchangers," *Power Eng.*, ca. 1963. (Facts of publication from *Power Engineering*, Barrington, Ill.)
18. S. Yokell, "Hydraulic Methods in Construction and Repair of Shell and Tube Heat Exchangers," *Proc. Second Symp. Shell-and-Tube Heat Exchangers*, Houston, Sept. 14–16, 1981; American Society for Metals, Metals Park, Ohio.
19. J. Singletary, "Bundle-Wagon Eases Maintenance for Mobil Chemical Co.," *Oil Gas J.*, Jan. 8, 1979.

Guide to Codes and Standards*

Introduction

This chapter is a guide to pressure vessel codes and mechanical standards that apply to heat exchangers. The pressure vessel codes address only safety requirements for pressure-containing equipment. Compliance with the mechanical standards for both pressure-bearing and nonpressure parts determines a unit's quality, usefulness, and performance. Because safety, performance, and mechanical requirements are interactive, most mechanical standards specify that construction must conform to the governing pressure vessel code.

Most pressure vessel codes contain provisions that apply to tubular heat exchangers, but there is no pressure vessel code exclusively for them. This guide discusses these pressure vessel codes: (1) the *ASME Boiler and Pressure Vessel Code*, hereafter simply called the *ASME Code*; (2) the *National Board Inspection Code*, which will be called either the *National Board Code* or NBIC; and (3) the *American Petroleum Institute (API) Standard 510 Inspection Code*, which will be referred to as either API 510 or the *API Inspection Code*.[1-3]

The guide covers these mechanical standards for tubular exchangers: (1) the *Standards of the Tubular Exchanger Manufacturers Association*, hereafter the *TEMA Standards*; (2) the *Heat Exchange Institute Standard for Power Plant Heat Exchangers*, hereafter called the *HEI Power Plant Standards*; (3) the *Heat Exchange Institute Standards for Closed Feedwater Heaters*, from now on called the *Closed Feedwater Heater Standards*; and (4) API Standard 660, *Shell-and-Tube Heat Exchangers for General Refinery Services*, subsequently called API 660.[4-7]

---

*This chapter is an expansion of the author's "Understanding Pressure Vessel Codes," *Chem. Eng.*, May 12, 1986.

Pressure vessel codes

The *ASME Code* applies directly only to the design and construction of new units. However, its rules are followed in the National Board and API codes, which cover repairing and altering *ASME Code*–stamped vessels. At present there is no internationally accepted pressure vessel code, nor are there federally accepted and enforced codes in the United States and Canada. Various pressure vessel codes are enforced within national and state or commonwealth boundaries. Problems may occur when a heat exchanger is designed in one country, fabricated in another, and installed in a third. The situation in the states and provinces in North America is a parallel one.

In the United States and Canada, the National Board of Boiler and Pressure Vessel Inspectors (hereafter simply called the National Board) facilitates acceptability of pressure vessels between political jurisdictions. There is no international organization that performs this function between countries. Therefore, when exchangers are to be shipped across national borders, it is necessary to determine the national requirements that will prevail.

Information on many codes and standards used outside the United States and Canada may be obtained from the catalogs of standards maintained by the American National Standards Institute (ANSI) in New York and from the Standards Information Center of the National Institute of Standards (NIST) in Washington. English translations of the codes and standards of many countries are available from Technical Help to Exporters, Hemel Hempstead, England. Table 8.1 lists some of the codes, code bodies, and publishers of the codes in Europe and Japan.

National pressure vessel codes are too numerous to examine in detail or to compare with each other in this work. Each is voluminous and represents a major engineering effort. However, the *ASME Code*, *National Board Inspection Code*, and the *API Inspection Code* discussed here are typical. M. Morris has summarized and compared various mechanical design codes for heat exchangers and provided an index to the pressure vessel codes that apply to heat exchangers of the United States, the United Kingdom, and the Federal Republic of Germany.[8]

Governing authorities establish or adopt safety codes and standards for boilers and pressure vessels. Rule makers consider the interests of the general public, manufacturers, insurers, architect-engineer firms, and other concerned groups. An engineering society's codes may be given the force of law by incorporation into the codes of government agencies.

Separate codes are usually issued for fired and unfired equipment,

TABLE 8.1   Codes outside the United States and Canada

Country	Code and body or issuer
German Federal Republic	*A. D. Merkblatt* Carl Heymans Verlag KG Gereonstrasse 19-32 D-5000 5 Köln Federal Republic of Germany
Italy	ANCC Casa Ditrice Luigi Di Pirola vi Comelico P.O. Box 3680 Milano, Italy 24688
Japan	*The Pressure Vessel Code (Dai Isshu Atsuryoku Youki Kousou Kikahu)* The Ministry of Labor The Japan Boiler Association 5-35-4, Shiba Minato-Ku Tokyo, Japan
	JIS B 8243-1977 *Construction of Pressure Vessels* Japan Standards Association 4-1-24 Akasaku Minato-Ku Tokyo, Japan
	High Pressure Gas Control Law Ministry of International Trade and Industry Pressure Gas Engineering 32-Nishikubotomoe-Cho Minato-Ku Tokyo, Japan
The Netherlands	*Regels voor Toesellen onder Druck* Ministry of Social Affairs Dienst voor het Stoomwesen Government Printing Office Christoffel, Plantjnstraat The Hague, The Netherlands
Sweden	Tryckkarskomissionnen IVA P.O. Box 5073, S-102-42 Stockholm, Sweden
United Kingdom	BS 5500 British Standards Institution 2 Park Street London, WIA 2Bs, England
U.S.S.R.	Gost Standards

TABLE 8.1   Codes outside the United States and Canada (*Continued*)

Country	Code and body or issuer

In the United States information on most foreign countries' codes may be obtained from the catalog of standards of the particular country. Catalogs may be purchased from:

The American National Standards Institute (ANSI)
1430 Broadway, New York, N.Y. 10018
(212) 354-3379

Those interested in keeping abreast of current proposed regulations of foreign countries should register with:

Standards Information Center
National Institute of Standards
Technology Building, Room B166
Washington, D.C. 20234
(301) 921-2092

Obtain information and translations into English from:

Technical Help to Exporters
Maylands Avenue
Hemel Hempstead
Herts HPQ 4SQ, England

---

or a blanket code may have separate rules for each equipment type. In unfired pressure vessels, pressure may be applied or be generated incidental to the process. An example of applying pressure is using steam in the shell to vaporize fluid entering the tubes of a thermosiphon reboiler. An instance of generating pressure incidental to a process is the development of pressure in the tubeside as the process fluid heated by steam in the shell boils.

How pressure is generated determines whether to apply rules for fired or for unfired pressure vessels. Most codes require heat exchangers that develop pressure as a direct result of combustion gas to be designed and built to the rules for boilers and fired pressure vessels. However, if combustion gas passing through a pressurized exchanger does not cause a pressure rise, the exchanger may be considered an unfired pressure vessel.

When heat is supplied by combustion gas, exchangers that generate steam are usually classified as boilers or fired steam generators. Combustion gas may be generated directly by burning fuel or be produced incidentally as in the waste-heat boiler shown in Fig. 8.1. Here, a hot process-stream gas enters the tubes of an aftercooler-steam generator. Feedwater, introduced to the shell for the process-gas cooling, is maintained at a liquid level, and the generated steam is used to heat jacketed reactors.

Safety or convenience may require steam generation without a conventional steam boiler—for example, heat supplied by a hot-oil system or a fired-hydrocarbon-vapor boiler. Tubular exchangers used as

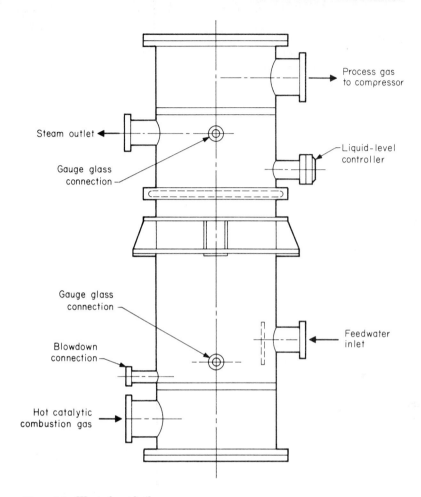

Figure 8.1   Waste-heat boiler.

unfired steam generators can be designed as unfired steam generators or as boilers, subject to the restrictions of the code rules.

Most pressure vessel codes provide for dealing with dangerous substances or hazardous operations. In the Netherlands, code rules provide for danger categories.[9] The *ASME Code*'s unfired pressure vessel rules have special requirements for equipment to be used in lethal service. There is also a separate body of rules in the *ASME Code* for nuclear service equipment.

Guide to the *ASME Code*

The *ASME Code* has rules for the construction of boilers, pressure vessels, and nuclear components for fixed and marine installations. ANSI has adopted the ASME rules as an American national standard. The rules deal only with safe design and construction. These rules refer to many documents. Here, we paraphrase, outline, and may inadvertently alter the *ASME Code*'s intents and meanings. Be cautioned that only the *ASME Code, ASME Code* Addenda and Interpretations, and *ASME Code* cases are authentic. Following are some questions and answers about the *ASME Code*.

Questions and answers about the *ASME Code*

How is an exchanger that has been built to the ASME Code *identified?* Such items have an official *ASME Code* symbol stamp. "ASME," "ASME Standard," or one of the code symbols may not be marked on any item not constructed in accordance with all applicable *ASME Code* requirements. Exchangers may not be described on ASME data report forms or similar forms referring to ASME that imply that all *ASME Code* requirements have been met when they have not. Forms for items that do not fully comply should not refer to ASME or should clearly identify all exceptions to ASME requirements.

Does an ASME Code *stamp mean that an exchanger has been approved by ASME?* ASME does not approve, certify, rate, or endorse any item, construction, or activity. An *ASME Code* symbol on a nameplate means only that the exchanger was made to *ASME Code* requirements.

What knowledge is needed to apply the ASME Code? A basic understanding of the physical principles that apply to pressure vessel design and construction. Despite its many formulas, charts, and illustrations, the *ASME Code* is not like a cookbook. Specific problems require engineering analysis; formulas and closed-form solutions to design problems are not provided for all permissible designs and constructions. Construction not covered by specific rules must be shown to be at least as safe as that covered.

ASME Code rules define users, manufacturers, and authorized inspectors (henceforth called authorized inspectors, inspectors, or AIs) of *ASME Code*–stamped equipment and assign them specific responsibilities. Some of these responsibilities are discussed later on. Application of specific rules to heat exchangers and analysis and design not specified in the rules are not covered in this book. Several works have been devoted to this cause.[8,10]

Who makes the rules? The ASME Boiler and Pressure Vessel Code Committee organizes the rules. Its purpose is to formulate construction codes and associated recommended rules covering care and operation and in-service inspection of boilers, pressure vessels, and nuclear components and to recommend their adoption by the appropriate board on behalf of the ASME.

The committee and its subdivisions represents boiler and pressure vessel manufacturers, materials manufacturers, users, regulatory agencies, insurance and inspection agencies, engineering educators, and consulting engineers. It seeks the public's cooperation and guidance through conference committees.

How are the rules and revisions established and revised? Committee members propose the rules. They may support them by their technical work, be it their own or work from the literature, offered by interested members of the public, or provided by technical committees of private associations.

Some concerns in establishing rules are materials, design, fabrication, inspection during fabrication, users' needs, manufacturers' needs, inspectors' needs, protection of life and property, and margin for deterioration in service. The committee does not analyze data or prepare design information for parts that cannot be stamped or are not subject to the *ASME Code* rules.

The public is invited to suggest changes, additions, or deletions to the *ASME Code* rules and to provide technical information to the committee. Technical meetings are open to the public. Visitors may view documents under consideration, provide technical information, and participate in the discussions. However, they may not vote on matters before the committee.

The ASME Board on Pressure Technology Codes and Standards (Pressure Technology Board), acting for ASME and ANSI, must approve rules for nonnuclear service boilers and pressure vessels before they are published for general use. The Board on Nuclear Codes and Standards (Nuclear Board), acting for ASME and ANSI, must approve rules for nuclear service equipment.

These are voluntary nongovernmental organizations. Although representatives of various governmental agencies in the United States and Canada may serve on the committee as volunteers, the *ASME Code* rules are not produced by federal, state, or provincial governments.

In the United States and Canada, states, commonwealths, and provinces or local political jurisdictions may adopt the rules as a whole or in sections by reference, or they may repeat them in their entirety in their laws and regulations. Enforcement is not a federal function in either country. Political bodies outside of the United States and Canada may adopt the rules and provide for their enforcement.

The committee makes revisions to correct errors, clarify rules in light of interpretations, and provide for new materials and construction methods. It follows ASME–ANSI consensus procedures, in which nonnuclear items are approved by the Pressure Technology Board and nuclear items by the Nuclear Board. Figure 8.2 illustrates the ASME-ANSI consensus procedure for nonnuclear items. The procedures provide for consideration of public comment. Revisions to the rules are published in regularly issued addenda.

The revised rules may be followed at the date of publication. Except for work that has already been contracted, rules become mandatory within 6 months of their issue date (except for a section of the code that establishes a different basis).

What about correspondence and inquiries? The *ASME Code* secretary receives and responds to all correspondence about the *ASME*

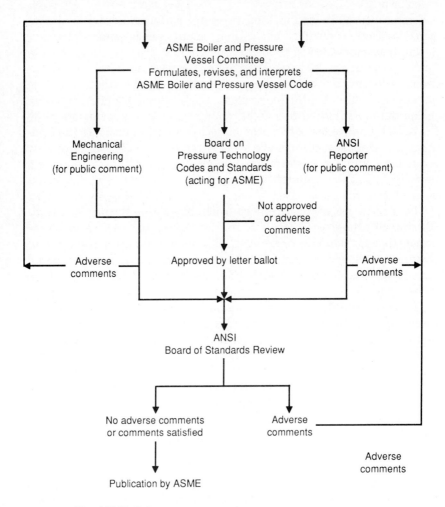

Figure 8.2 The *ASME Code* consensus procedure.

Code. Write to: Secretary, Boiler and Pressure Vessel Code Committee, the American Society of Mechanical Engineers, 345 East Forty-seventh Street, New York, New York 10017. The secretary has the discretion to reply to nontechnical inquiries that do not require interpretations of the *ASME Code* rules.

Limit technical inquiries to requests for interpretations of existing rules or consideration of revisions to the present rules on the basis of new data or technology. The inquiry must cover a single rule or closely related rules.

State whether you are asking for an interpretation of existing rules or consideration of a revision to present ones. Furnish pertinent background material and sketches that will help the committee to understand your inquiry. Omit superfluous and nontechnical material. Refer to the applicable section, division, edition, paragraphs and subparagraphs, figures, and tables.

Describe what you think the rules require. If you believe there should be a revision, include its proposed wording.

How is an interpretation requested? Send a legible handwritten or typewritten request to the secretary. When possible, phrase it so that your questions can be answered yes or no or yes or no with provisos. Refer to a specific section, division, etc. Do not ask for approval or endorsement of a proprietary or specific design. The committee does not approve or endorse them. Do not ask which method to use in design or construction: the *ASME Code* rules do not limit your selection of methods. Do not question the rationale or basis for the *ASME Code* rules; if you think that these are incorrect or inadequate, you may offer technical advice and participate in meetings concerning the rules.

Figure 8.3 is a copy of an inquiry submitted to the secretary; Fig. 8.4 is a copy of the reply. Note how the inquiry has been restated. The question and reply appeared in the published interpretations as Interpretation VIII-82-57.

What are code cases? If a reply to an interpretation request is of widespread importance, the response may be in the form of a code case. The purposes of code cases are (1) to make sure that an interpretation is broadly distributed; (2) to facilitate reference by manufacturers and users and acceptance by regulatory authorities; (3) to clarify specific *ASME Code* requirements, without changing their meaning, unless conditions change or new developments warrant such a change; and (4) to provide rules for materials or constructions not covered by existing *ASME Code* rules when the need is urgent.

Code cases are numbered sequentially. As Fig. 8.5 shows, they use the same question-and-reply format as interpretations. Code cases expire 3 years from the issue date and are automatically annulled unless they are reaffirmed or extended. (The case shown in Fig. 8.5 has since

MGT Inc.
Suite 5 E, The Livery
209 Cooper Avenue
Upper Montclair, NJ 07006   201-744-3633

                                             December 3, 1981

                                             Re: J-104-CH-12

Mr. G. Eisenberg, Secretary
Boiler and Pressure Vessel Code Committee
American Society of Mechanical Engineers
United Engineering Center
345 East 47 Street
New York, NY 10017

Subject: Section VIII - Division 1, UG-99, External Pressure Testing

Gentlemen:

Paragraph UG-99(b) of Section VIII, Division 1 of the Code states
the requirements for hydrostatic pressure testing vessels designed
for _interal_ pressure.

        1.   What are the requirements for hydrostatic pressure
testing of pressure vessels designed for external pressure, such
as a containment vessel subjected to a high pressure external
atmosphere?

        2.   What rules apply to external hydrostatic pressure
testing of the inner shells of jacketed vessels and the tubes of
shell and tube heat exchangers tested under the provisions of
UG-99(b) and UG-99(c)?

                        Sincerely yours,

                        MGT Inc.
                  By: Stanley Yokell, P.E.,
                        President

Figure 8.3 An inquiry for an interpretation of the *ASME Code* rules.

been annulled.) However, if you have contracted for an exchanger before the expiration date, the code case remains in effect.

A code case that is officially available for use is published as a supplement to the code case book. It is also published in the ASME's *Mechanical Engineering* for public comment.

A rule is hard to live with. How does someone get a hearing? Submit
a written petition to the secretary. Whenever possible, the Main Committee will have the proper subcommittee or special committee hold
the hearing. However, you or the hearing committee's chair may request the Main Committee to hear you. The hearing committee's chair

The American Society of Mechanical Engineers

United Engineering Center • 345 E. 47th St., New York, N.Y. 10017 • 212-644-7722 • TWX-710-581-5267

June 3, 1982

RCETR

JUN 7, 1982

STANLEY YOKELL, P.E.

Mr. Stanley Yokell
MGT Inc.
Suite 5E, the LIVERY
209 Cooper Avenue
Upper Montclair, NJ 07043

SUBJECT: External Pressure Testing, UG-99 Section VIII,
                 Division 1

ITEM: BC-81-718

REFERENCE: Your letter dated December 3, 1981

Dear Mr. Yokell:

Our understanding of the questions in your inquiry, and our replies, are as follows:

Question (1): What are the requirements of Section VIII, Division 1 for pressure testing of single chamber pressure vessels designed for external pressure above 15 psi? The requirements of UG-99(b) and (f) do not appear to apply.

Reply (1): Section VIII, Division 1 does not contain specific rules for pressure testing of a pressure vessel as described in the inquiry. The requirements of U-2(g) would apply.

Question (2): For combination units, what rules apply to external pressure testing of the inner shells of jacketed vessels and the tubes of shell and tube heat exchangers tested under the provisions of UG-99(b) and UG-99(c)?

Reply (2): Except as covered in UG-99(f), there are no specific rules for "external pressure testing". However, tests in accordance with UG-99(e) are required. In the test of such vessels, the tubes or inner shell is subjected to an external pressure established by the internal design pressure and temperature. In some cases, particularly where the temperature correction ratio of UG-99(b) is relatively high, damage to the tubes or inner shell might result. Manufacturers should consider this condition in design to guard against the possibility of such damage.

                                        cont.

Figure 8.4   Reply to an inquiry about the *ASME Code* rules.

Mr. Stanley Yokell
BC-81-718
cont.

-2-

You should consider if the vessel of Question 1 is under the scope of PVHO-1, Pressure Vessels for Human Occupancy.

Very truly yours,

Alan Roby
Assistant Secretary, Boiler
and Pressure Vessel Committee
(212) 705-7808

/cmm

ECEI
JUN 7, 1982
STANLEY YOKELL, P.E.

Figure 8.4 (*Continued.*)

CASES OF ASME BOILER AND PRESSURE VESSEL CODE

Meeting of March 12, 1982
Approved by Council, May 25, 1982

This Case shall expire on June 30, 1983
unless previously annulled or reaffirmed

CASE

1749

Case 1749
Machining of Hubs of Tubesheets or Flat
Heads from Rolled Plate
Section VIII, Divisions 1 and 2

Inquiry: Paragraphs UW-13(f) in Division 1 of
Section VIII and Ad-413.1 in Division 2, prohibit
machining hubs of tubesheets or flat heads from
rolled plate for butt welding them to shells,
heads, or other pressure parts as shown in Fig.
UW-13.3 and AD-701.1, respectively.

For vessels manufactured under Section VIII,
Divisons 1 and 2, may such hubs be machined
from rolled plate if the plate is manufactured by
any process which will provide material having
adequate properties in the direction of the thickness and provided that appropriate tests are
made to demonstrate that the propeties specified for the plate are met in a direction parallel to
the axis of the vessel (through the thickness of
the plate)?

Reply: It is the opinion of the Committee that,
for vessels manufactured under Section VIII,
Divisions 1 and 2, hubs of tubesheets and flat
heads may be machined from rolled plate when
the plate is manufactured by a process that
produces plate having through thickness properties which are at least equal to those specified in
the material specification. Such plate can be but
is not limited to that produced by methods such
as electroslag (ESR) and vacuum arc remelt
(VAR). The plate must be tested and examined
in accordance with the requirements of the material specification and the additional requirements specified in the following paragraphs.

Test specimens, in addition to those required
by the material specifications, shall be taken in a
direction parallel to the axis of the hub and as
close to the hub as practical, as shown in Figs.
UW-13.3 in Division 1 and AD-701.1 in Division
2. At least two tensile test specimens shall be
taken from the plate in the proximity of the hub
with one specimen taken from the center third of
the plate width as rolled, and the second speci

men taken at 90° around the circumference from
the other specimen. Both specimens shall meet
the tensile and yield requirements of the SA
material specification. All the dimensional requirements of Figs. UW-13.3 and AD-701.1 shall
apply.

Subsize test specimens conforming to the
requirements of Fig. 5 of SA-370 may be used if
necessary, in which case the value of "elongation in 2 inches," required by the material specification, shall apply to the gage length specified in
Fig. 5.

The reduction-of-area shall not be less than
30%. (For those materials for which the material
specification requires a reduction-of-area value
greater than 30%, the higher value must be
met.)

Before and after machining, the part, regardless of thickness, shall be ultrasonically examined in accordance with the requirements of AM-
203 of Section VIII, Division 2, except that the
acceptance standard for straight beam examination shall be modified as follows:

(1) No areas showing indications accompanied by loss of back reflection larger than 60% of
the reference back reflection.

(2) No indications larger than 40% of the
reference back reflection when accompanied by
a 40% loss of back reflection.

Before welding the hub of the tubesheet or flat
head to the adjacent shell, the hub shall be
examined by magnetic particle or liquid penetrant methods in accordance with Appendix VI or
VIII of Section VIII, Division 1, and Article 9-1 or
9-2 of Appendix IX of Section VIII, Division 2.

After welding, the weld and the area of the hub
for at least 1/2 in. from the edge of the weld shall
be 100% radiographed in accordance with Par.
UW-51 of Section VIII, Division 1, or Article 1-5 of
Section VIII, Division 2. As an alternate, the weld
and hub area adjacent to the weld may be
ultrasonically examined in accordance with Appendix U of Section VIII, Division 1, or Article 9-3
of Section VIII, Division 2.

Figure 8.5   A code case of the *ASME Boiler and Pressure Vessel Code.*

schedules hearings. No decisions are taken at hearings; action is taken at a later date.

What if I don't like the hearing results? You can appeal committee proposals and actions which remain objectionable to you by writing to the secretary, who will direct your appeal to the subcommittee that originated the action. You may attend the subcommittee meeting, present your objections, and provide supporting data.

The subcommittee may refer an appeal that it cannot resolve to the Main Committee. If the Main Committee cannot reach a mutually acceptable solution, you may further appeal to the Pressure Technology Board or the Nuclear Board, whichever is appropriate.

To make such a further appeal, file written notice of your intent to appeal with the secretary within 10 working days of the date that the Main Committee mails the report of its action on your appeal. Within 20 working days of mailing your letter of intent, submit a written official appeal to the board.

Include the following: (1) a statement of the item in question, (2) the standards-developing committee's action and your statement of why it should be modified, and (3) your suggested modification. Within 7 days after the board hears your appeal and acts, the board's secretary will notify you, the committee, and others concerned of the board's decision.

Which rules apply to shell-and-tube heat exchangers? Table 8.2 lists the current sections of the *ASME Code* rules that apply to shell-and-tube heat exchangers. Because the rules undergo changes, new rules are added and the organization of the *ASME Code* changes from time to time, it is necessary to examine the current edition.

Construction rules for heat exchangers classified as fired heaters, steam generators, or boilers are in Section I. Construction rules for unfired heat exchangers are in Sections III and VIII. The sections cover boilers, pressure vessels, and heat exchangers of metal.

Section II contains specifications for materials permitted by the rules of the construction sections. Section V contains requirements and methods for nondestructive examinations and tests that the construction sections require. Section IX contains requirements for qualifying welding procedures, welders, and welding-machine operators. The construction rules apply these sections by reference. Construction rules may impose additional requirements and restrictions or permit exemptions beyond those of Sections II, V, and IX.

At present work is under way to consolidate the rules in Section VIII, Division 1, that apply to tubular heat exchangers in a part or

TABLE 8.2   Organization of the *ASME Boiler and Pressure Vessel Code*

   I.   Power Boilers
  II.   Material Specifications†
        Part A: Ferrous
        Part B: Nonferrous
        Part C: Welding rods, electrodes, and filler metals
 III.   Subsection NCA: General Requirements for Division 1 and Division 2‡
 III.   Division 1
        Subsection NB: Class 1 Components
        Subsection NC: Class 2 Components
        Subsection ND: Class 3 Components
        Subsection NE: Class MC Components
        Subsection NF: Components Supports
        Subsection NG: Core Support Structures
        Appendixes
  IV.   Heating Boilers
   V.   Nondestructive Examination
  VI.   Recommended Rules for Care and Operation of Heating Boilers
 VII.   Recommended Rules for Care of Power Boilers
VIII.   Pressure Vessels
        Division 1
        Division 2: Alternative Rules
  IX.   Welding and Brazing Qualifications
   X.   Fiberglass-Reinforced Plastic Pressure Vessels
  XI.   Rules for In-Service Inspection of Nuclear Power Plant Components
Addenda
Interpretations
Code Cases

*Sections in boldface apply to shell-and-tube heat exchangers and closed feedwater heaters.
†Material specifications are similar to or identical to ASTM and AWS specifications.
‡This is the nuclear code.

appendix. Until such work is complete and published, be guided by the following paragraphs.

Section II: Materials specifications

The construction rules specify which materials may be used, their acceptable forms, and conditions for use. The construction sections provide tables of allowable stress or stress intensity and metal properties versus temperature, charts for external-pressure calculations, fatigue curves, and similar information.

Each construction section imposes limits, restrictions, and requirements on the use of the listed materials. Some materials in Section II may not be permissible under the rules of a construction section. All construction sections require that the composition and physical properties of materials be certified, identified, and tracked prior to and during fabrication and that records be kept. Section III, in addition, requires materials suppliers to be qualified.

Most Section II specifications are identical with or similar to specifications of the ASTM or the American Welding Society (AWS). Joint logos and parenthetical notes to specification headings, as shown in Figs. 8.6 and 8.7, indicate when the specifications are identical. Material that is produced solely to ASTM, AWS, or any other specification may not be used. Mill-test reports of materials must indicate that they conform with the ASME specification number.

Section V: Nondestructive Examinations and Tests

Sections I, III, and VIII tell when nondestructive examinations and tests must be performed to detect surface and internal discontinuities in welds, fabricated parts, and components. Section V specifies nondestructive examination and test methods. However, the construction section that calls for the examinations or tests contains the acceptance standards. The manufacturer must establish suitable procedures and qualify the examining personnel to perform examinations and tests in Section V. The referencing construction section specifies requirements for qualifying personnel.

Section IX: Welding and Brazing Qualifications

Construction rules call for welding and brazing to be done according to qualified procedures. These rules also require welders, welding operators, brazers, and brazing operators who work on a pressure-containing part of a pressure vessel to be qualified to use these procedures. Section IX specifies what the procedures must include and how procedures, brazers, and brazing operators are to be qualified and provides typical forms for recording the qualifications.

SPECIFICATION FOR SEAMLESS COLD-DRAWN LOW-CARBON STEEL HEAT-EXCHANGER
AND CONDENSER TUBES

                SA-179

(Identical with ASME Specification A 179-75)

Figure 8.6 Specification heading for ASME–ASTM joint specification.

SPECIFICATION FOR CARBON STEEL
COVERED ARC WELDING ELECTRODES

    SFA-5.1

(Identical with AWS Specification A5.1-78)

Figure 8.7 Specification heading for ASME–AWS joint specification.

Construction sections may impose additional welding and brazing requirements or may permit exemptions to Section IX. Procedure or performance qualifications that meet Section IX requirements may not be acceptable unless they meet the additional requirements specified in the construction section.

Section I: Power Boilers

Section I contains rules for the design and construction of power boilers. These apply to fired tubular heaters and to shell-and-tube heat exchangers when combustion gases flow into one side and generate steam or other vapor in the other side. When steam or other vapors are produced in unfired steam boilers, either Section I or Section VIII, Division 1, may be applied. Section VIII, Division 1, rules for unfired steam generators have special requirements for welding, heat treatment, and radiographic examination.

Section III: The Nuclear Code; Power Plant Components

Section III rules do not apply to heat exchangers outside the reactor system. Because shell-and-tube heat exchangers are seldom used as components of a nuclear power reactor system that contains reactor fluids, very few exchangers must be built to Section III. The section does not apply to evaporators for concentrating radioactive waste (radwaste evaporators) or to feedwater heaters in the secondary loop. These units are usually built to the rules of Section VIII, Division 1.

The owner of a nuclear power system is responsible for preparing a design specification. Its purposes and requirements are (1) to describe functions and set boundaries of the equipment; (2) to set design requirements including overpressure requirements; (3) to describe environmental conditions including radiation; (4) to set materials including impact-test requirements; (5) to refer to other appropriate documents which specify the operating requirements of the component when the component must always be capable of operating; (6) to choose the effective *ASME Code* edition, addenda, and code cases to be used in construction; and (7) to set a code classification of the unit.

The design specification becomes a principal document governing design and construction. Its information must be made available to the authorized nuclear inspector (ANI). Copies must be filed at the location of the installation and made available to enforcement authorities.

Owners classify components by their importance and risk to the system and consequences of a failure. Classifications of heat exchangers depend upon their location and situation in the nuclear reactor system and whether they must function during an accident or may be isolated from the system by valves.

Subsection NB construction rules apply to Class 1 components; they are the most stringent. Subsection NC construction rules apply to Class 2 components; they are less demanding. Subsection ND construction rules for Class 3 components are the least severe. The rules of a more demanding section may be employed for a lower-classification component. Manufacturers must have certificates of authorization to apply *ASME Code* symbols N1, N2, or N3, corresponding with Class 1, Class 2, and Class 3.

The responsibilities of manufacturers who hold N certificates are detailed in Subsection NCA. Among them are (1) achieving structural integrity; (2) providing a design report; (3) qualifying material manufacturers, material suppliers, and suppliers of subcontracted services; (4) establishing, maintaining, documenting, and filing a quality assurance program; and (5) preparing manufacturers' data reports.

These are the requirements for the design report: (1) it must include stress analysis of parts and appurtenances; (2) it must reconcile design drawing changes with the design report; (3) it must be certified by a qualified, registered professional engineer (PE); (4) the design report and its documentation must be made available for the ANI's review; and (5) it must be provided to the owner for review, certification of review, and filing at the installation site.

Section VIII: Pressure Vessels

For nonnuclear services, tubular exchangers are built to Section VIII, Division 1 or Division 2. Most are built to Division 1, which applies approximate methods of calculation. Units built to these rules and inspected by an AI are stamped with the *ASME Code* U symbol. Exchangers outside the scope of Section VIII may be stamped with the *ASME Code* symbol if they are constructed in accordance with all the rules of the governing division.

Under Division 1 rules, exchangers meeting certain conditions may be exempted from inspection by an authorized inspector. These units are stamped UM. However, if in spite of the exemption they are inspected by an AI, they may be stamped with the U symbol. With some exceptions, exchangers built to Division 1 may also be built to the alternative rules of Division 2 and stamped U-2.

The rules of Division 2 provide an alternative to the minimum construction requirements of exchangers which fall within the scope of Division 1. The alternative rules are based upon more precise calculation methods and are more restrictive. They do not permit use of some materials allowed by Division 1, prohibit some common design details, and specify in detail which fabrication procedures may be used.

Engineering and manufacturing to Division 2 is more costly than to Division 1. However, where the stress intensity value is controlled by ultimate or yield strength, Division 2 permits you to use higher design stress intensity values in the range of temperatures covered. Consider using Division 2 rules for the following conditions:

1. Service is severe enough to indicate the need for intensive analysis.

2. Fatigue may affect the safety and useful life of the exchanger.

3. Shape changes may cause high discontinuity stresses, for example, in the joint of an eccentric cone to a reboiler shell.

4. Pressure exceeds 3000 lb/in^2 (20,670 kPa).

5. The product of pressure times shell diameter exceeds 60,000 lb/in (1.216 N/M).

6. The ratio of shell diameter to thickness is less than 16, or shell thickness calculated under Division 1 rules exceeds 3 in (76.2 mm).

7. The costs of the necessary engineering analysis and more rigorous construction requirements are justified by the savings anticipated in materials and labor.

Table 8.3 compares the applicability of the two divisions.

Responsibilities of users, manufacturers, and authorized inspectors listed in Section VIII

The following summarizes Section VIII's allocation of responsibilities among users, manufacturers, and inspectors. For details, the reader is referred to the current edition of the code.

User's responsibilities: Division 1.   Under Division 1 rules, the user is responsible for establishing a heat exchanger's design requirements. The user may designate an agent to fulfill this responsibility. A des-

TABLE 8.3   Comparison of Coverage of Section VIII of Divisions 1 and 2 of the
ASME Code **as They Apply to Heat Exchangers**

Division 1	Division 2
Included in the Scope*	
Exchangers for containment of internal or external pressure resulting from external or internal sources or combinations.	Exchangers for containment of internal or external pressure resulting from external or internal sources or combinations.
	Except where specifically prohibited, types which may be constructed in accordance with the rules of Division 1.
	Exchangers installed at fixed (stationary) locations for specific services and maintained by the user responsible.
	Units permanently installed in oceangoing vessels (Specific conditions must be met.)
Pressure limit of 3000 lb/in² (20,670 kPa). Pressure may exceed this limit if all Division 1 rules are met.	No specific pressure limit. Very high pressures are permitted if all Division 2 rules are met. "Very high" not defined.
Exchangers subject to direct firing from the combustion of fuel (solid, liquid, or gaseous) which are not within the scope of Sections I, III, or IV.	Exchangers subject to direct firing from the combustion of fuel (solid, liquid, or gaseous) which are not within the scope of Sections I, III, or IV.
Where the exchanger is to connect to external piping—the welding-end connection for the first welded circumferential joint to external piping, the first threaded joint for screwed connections, the face of the first flange for bolted flanged connections, and the first sealing surface for proprietary connections.	Where the exchanger is to connect to external piping—the welding-end connection for the first welded circumferential joint to external piping, the first threaded joint for screwed connections, the face of the first flange for bolted flanged connections, and the first sealing surface for proprietary connections.
Welds of pressure to nonpressure parts whether internal or external.	Welds of pressure to nonpressure parts whether internal or external.
Pressure-retaining covers such as channel covers and shell covers.	Pressure-retaining covers such as channel covers and shell covers.
Provision for pressure-relief devices.	Provision for pressure-relief devices.
Unfired steam boilers as defined in Section 1.	
Evaporators and heat exchangers.	Evaporators and heat exchangers.

TABLE 8.3   Comparison of Coverage of Section VIII of Divisions 1 and 2 of the *ASME Code* as They Apply to Heat Exchangers (*Continued*)

Division 1	Division 2
Excluded from Scope	
	Unfired steam boilers as defined in Section 1.
Exchangers within the scope of other sections.	Exchangers within the scope of other sections.
Fired process tubular heaters.	Fired process tubular heaters.
Exchangers having internal or external operating pressure not exceeding 15 lb/in² (103 kPa) with no limitation on size.	Exchangers having internal or external operating pressure not exceeding 15 lb/in² (103 kPa) with no limitation on size.
Exchangers with an inside shell diameter not exceeding 6 in (152.3 mm) without length or pressure limitation.	Exchangers with an inside shell diameter not exceeding 6 in (152.3 mm) without length or pressure limitation.

*This list does not contain all items included in the scope of these divisions.

ignated agent may be a design agency engaged specifically for the purpose, the manufacturer of a system for a specific service which includes the heat exchanger, or an organization which offers heat exchangers for sale or lease for specific services. In the following discussions the term *user* will be employed for the user or the user's designated agent.

The user must describe the conditions of normal operation, startup, shutdown, and upset in sufficient detail for the manufacturer to design and build a safe unit. A user who purchases heat exchangers to meet performance requirements may specify fluid flows, fluid properties, inlet and outlet temperatures and pressures, and mechanical configuration. In response, the manufacturer offers a guaranteed thermal and mechanical design. The manufacturer will calculate metal temperatures in the clean and fouled conditions to establish metal design temperatures. The user must advise the manufacturer of startup, shutdown, and any upset conditions.

Users may also arbitrarily establish design pressures and temperatures for exchangers that they buy to meet performance requirements. When they do so, they must advise the manufacturer of the most severe conditions to enable the mechanical design to be performed.

Alternatively, the user may perform the thermal design and provide a manufacturer with an exchanger specification sheet that shows only the mechanical arrangement. When users follow this practice, they must establish design metal temperatures and pressures for the shell, tubes, tubesheets, and other pressure-containing parts. To do so, they must consider coincident metal operating temperatures and the effects of heat flow in the parts.

Because exchangers foul, users have to provide the metal temperatures to the manufacturer for the most severe of clean and fouled conditions at startup, shutdown, and normal operating and upset conditions. It is not adequate for users to provide just the inlet and outlet fluid temperatures for the various conditions if they perform the thermal design.

Division 1 rules make the user responsible for specifying corrosion allowance beyond that required by the rules. Users must state whether the service is lethal. They must also specify heat treatment beyond that required in the rules and identify the need for piping, valves, instruments, and fittings in unfired steam boilers.

User's responsibilities: Division 2.   For construction to Division 2, the user or an agent acting on the user's behalf is responsible for providing a user's design specification. (In the discussion of Division 2, wherever *user* appears, it means user or agent.) A PE must certify that the user's design specification describes the operating conditions in enough detail to constitute an adequate basis for selecting materials and designing, fabricating, and inspecting the exchanger as required to meet the rules of the division. This responsibility is analogous to the user's responsibility for establishing design requirements contained in Division 1 rules. The user's design specification must also describe how the exchanger is to be supported.

Division 2 users are responsible for specifying whether or not a fatigue analysis is to be made for an exchanger in cyclic service. Division 2 provides rules for evaluating service conditions to establish the need. If the operating conditions listed in the user's design specification indicate that fatigue analysis is needed under the service evaluation rules, the analysis is mandatory.

If a user specifies fatigue analysis, sufficiently detailed information must be provided to permit the analysis to be done. If the design specification states that fatigue analysis is not required, it must also state that the intended operation of the unit satisfies the requirements of the service evaluation rules for no fatigue analysis.

Users are also responsible for specifying corrosion-erosion allowances and to determine if the service is lethal. Consider a service to be lethal if a very small amount of the fluid in either side of the exchanger, whether mixed or unmixed with air, is dangerous to life when inhaled. If the service is determined to be lethal, the design specification must contain a statement to that effect. The rules provide special requirements for equipment to be used in lethal service.

Manufacturers' responsibilities: Divisions 1 and 2.   Manufacturers are responsible for structural integrity. After the user has specified the conditions of operation, the manufacturer is responsible for designing and manufacturing a heat exchanger that will safely operate under the specified conditions. A partial list of specific manufacturer's responsibilities and a discussion of some of these items follow.

A manufacturer must:

1. Have an appropriate certificate of authorization from the ASME Boiler and Pressure Vessel Committee before beginning to build an exchanger that is to be code-stamped. Among other requirements this obligates the manufacturer to have a contract for inspection with an authorized inspection agency (often called AIA). It must remain in effect during the time that the manufacturer has custody of the *ASME Code* symbol and authorization to apply it.

AIAs may be units of state or local governments, insurance companies, or independent organizations devoted to inspection and authorized by the ASME. They provide the services of authorized inspectors under contracts with the manufacturers whose work must be inspected.

2. Make available to the inspector the drawings and design calculations or the manufacturer's design report.

3. Obtain and make available to the inspector mill-test reports or material certifications for all materials used in the pressure parts or welded to them.

4. Obtain partial data reports when required by the division rules and attach them to the manufacturer's data report.

5. Provide access for the AI to areas of the shop and suppliers' facilities concerned with supply or fabrication of materials.

6. Keep the inspector informed about the progress of the work and provide enough advance notification for required inspections to be made in the proper sequence.

7. Examine all materials before fabrication to make sure that they are as thick as required by the design calculations or design specification.

8. Document required impact tests.

9. Obtain the AI's concurrence before making any repairs required by the rules.

10. Examine head and shell sections to confirm that they have been properly formed within permissible tolerances.

11. Qualify welding procedures before they are used in fabrication.

12. Qualify all welders and welding operators before they engage in production work.

13. Examine all parts before joining to make sure that they have been fitted properly for welding and that the surfaces have been cleaned and alignment tolerances maintained.

14. Examine parts as fabrication progresses to make sure that materials are identified, that there are no surface defects, and that the dimensions conform with the drawings.

15. Provide to the inspector records of all heat treatments.

16. Provide to the inspector records of all nondestructive examinations and tests, including radiographic films.

17. Subject the exchanger to the required hydrostatic or pneumatic testing, and have the required inspection performed by the AI during the testing.

18. Stamp the exchanger or nameplate with the required stamping.

19. Prepare the required manufacturer's data report and have it certified by the inspector.

20. Provide for retention of radiographs, ultrasonic-test reports, manufacturer's data reports, and other reports required by the division rules.

Division 1 requires the manufacturer to perform design calculations for the parts of the exchanger subject to pressure. It *does not* contain rules to cover all details of design and construction. Where it does not give complete details, the manufacturer is responsible for providing design and construction details as safe as those that the rules provide. Such details are subject to the AI's acceptance. When the strength of any part cannot be computed with a satisfactory assurance of safety, Division 1 provides procedures for establishing its maximum allowable working pressure (MAWP).

Division 2 obliges the manufacturer or a design agent responsible to the manufacturer to make calculations. They must demonstrate that the design shown on the drawings conforms with Division 2 rules and meets the requirements of the user's design specification. The manufacturer must prepare a manufacturer's design report which includes the drawings and calculations showing compliance with Division 2 rules. If an analysis for cyclic operation has been made, it must be included in the manufacturer's design report.

A PE experienced in pressure vessel design must certify that the manufacturer's design report complies with the rules of Division 2. The manufacturer must furnish a copy of the manufacturer's design report to the user. The user's design specification and the manufacturer's design report must be kept on file at the manufacturer's plant for at least 5 years.

The manufacturer who completes a heat exchanger to be stamped under the *ASME Code* rules is responsible for complying with all applicable requirements of the division to which it is built. The manufacturer must also assure that all work done by others on the heat exchanger or its parts is shown by proper certification to comply. This means that a manufacturer who buys an expansion joint or subcontracts construction of channels or bonnets has the responsibility for those parts upon performing the final assembly and stamping the exchanger with the *ASME Code* symbol. The suppliers of such parts must have certificates of authorization to apply the *ASME Code* symbol. They must have the parts inspected by an authorized inspector, stamp them as required by the *ASME Code*, and certify on the appropriate form that construction has accorded with the code rules.

Manufacturers who subcontract forming, heat treating, and nondestructive examinations must ensure that the work done by others meets all the applicable requirements of the division. After code compliance is ensured and the inspector accepts the subcontractor's work, the part supplied to the manufacturer may be stamped. Subcontractors who complete units and perform the hydrostatic test stamp the completed exchanger. Special requirements apply to welding performed by welders who are not directly employed by the manufacturer.

Both divisions require manufacturers to have quality control (QC) systems that cover all aspects of *ASME Code* construction. The QC systems must include materials, design, fabrication, examination by the manufacturer, and inspection by the AI. These requirements must be incorporated in written checklists or manuals which explain what documents and procedures the manufacturer will use to produce a unit to the code rules.

The manufacturer is responsible for quality control and for performing any required detailed examinations and tests at appropriate construction stages. The manufacturer must make all information affecting the mechanical design of the exchangers specified by the user and the manufacturer's design calculation or the design report available to the AI.

Manufacturers may use any combination of the fabrication methods that the rules permit. The service limitations are those that apply to the fabrication method with the division's most restrictive requirements. Similarly, combinations of all classes of materials that a division permits are allowed. Adequate consideration must be given to requirements of Section IX for welding dissimilar metals.

The design must accommodate differential thermal expansion or account for restraint, especially at points of stress concentration. Metallurgical changes, which may take place at high temperature, must also be accounted for. Stamping and manufacturer's data reports must also comply with the applicable division's rules.

Inspectors' duties.   Inspection during construction is a major requirement of the *ASME Code* rules. Only inspectors authorized by the ASME may perform the inspections. Throughout the *ASME Code*, the terms *authorized inspector, authorized code inspector, authorized nuclear inspector*, and *inspector* apply only to individuals authorized by the ASME to inspect boilers and pressure vessels.

In the discussion of manufacturers' responsibilities, it was stated that inspectors are employed by independent authorized inspection agencies. However, under Section VIII rules, AIs may also be employed by a company that manufactures pressure vessels exclusively for its own use and not for resale. When so employed, they are called user-inspectors.

Each construction section specifies the inspector's authority and responsibilities. Inspectors examine but do not verify design calculations, reports, and manufacturing drawings before construction begins. They schedule with the manufacturer points at which work is to be stopped pending inspection and approval. These are called *hold points*. The manufacturer lists the hold points on a document that travels through the shop with the exchanger. This document is called a *traveler*. As the shop meets the inspection requirements, the inspector signifies completion of the inspection and acceptance of the work by dating and initialing the traveler alongside the listed hold points.

Inspectors have the following duties:

1. Making sure that the manufacturer has a valid certificate of authorization and is working to the quality control system embodied in the manufacturer's quality control manual.

2. Making all inspections required by the *ASME Code* and any other inspections that the inspector deems necessary to be satisfied that all code requirements have been met.

3. For Division 1 construction, verifying that the applicable design calculations and drawings are available; for Division 2, making sure that the user's design specification, the manufacturer's design report, the design drawings, and related documents are available.

4. Determining that the materials used in construction comply with the requirements of the division.

5. Checking to see that all welding procedures used in construction have been qualified, that all welders and welding operators using the procedures have been qualified, and that copies of the qualified welding procedures are available to the welders.

6. Making sure that all required heat treatments, including partial heat treatments, have been performed and are documented.

7. Making sure that any imperfections in material that the manufacturer has repaired by welding have been acceptably repaired and reexamined.

8. Seeing to it that the manufacturer has performed all the required nondestructive examinations and that the results are acceptable and documented.

9. Visually inspecting to confirm that identifying material numbers marked or stamped on raw materials have been properly transferred to cut or burned-out parts.

10. Performing internal and external inspections and witnessing hydrostatic or pneumatic tests.

11. Verifying that the required stamping has been applied and that the nameplate has been permanently attached.

12. Signing the certificate of inspection on the manufacturer's data report when the exchanger is complete and complies with all the requirements of the applicable division.

Inspection and examination

The *ASME Code* rules make a distinction between *inspection* and *examination*. They make a similar distinction between *authorized inspectors* and *examiners*. However, in some standards referred to or directly incorporated in the code rules, *inspection* and *inspector* describe what the *ASME Code* calls *examination* and *examiner*. The standards to which the *ASME Code* rules refer or those which they incorporate may not make the *ASME Code*'s distinctions between examination and inspection and between examinations and examiners and inspectors. To avoid confusion, it is important to understand that the terms *inspection, testing,* and *examination* in these standards do not involve the work of the *ASME Code* authorized inspector but rather that of the manufacturer's examination personnel.

How inspectors are qualified.   To become qualified, an inspector must pass a written examination under the rules of any state of the United States or province of Canada that has adopted the *ASME Code*. To become an authorized nuclear inspector, an inspector must also meet the applicable qualification requirements of ANSI.

The nuclear code requires the authorized inspection agency to maintain a staff of authorized nuclear inspector supervisors. These people are often called ANISs. Working together, the authorized nuclear inspector and the authorized nuclear inspector supervisor must be competent in evaluating all the examination and test methods that apply to the units to be inspected.

When a province or state qualifies an inspector and issues a commission, the inspector's authorization to inspect is limited to work produced within the provincial or state boundaries. Other provinces or states may not recognize the commission or accept the validity of the qualifications. Furthermore, they may not permit the use of *ASME Code*-stamped pressure vessels inspected by an inspector commissioned in another province or state.

As previously noted, the governments of Canada and the United States do not prepare or enforce national boiler and pressure vessel safety laws. There is no supervening national law or international treaty that requires all jurisdictions to recognize inspectors' commissions issued by any province or state. However, most political jurisdictions will accept *ASME Code*-stamped boilers, pressure vessels, and heat exchangers inspected by an inspector who holds a commission from the National Board of Boiler and Pressure Vessel Inspectors. In the rest of this chapter we will call this organization the National Board or abbreviate it Nat'l Bd. For acceptance, National Board stamping is required in addition to *ASME Code* stamping.

Manufacturers' data reports, documentation, and registration for Section VIII

The code requires manufacturers to fill out manufacturer's data report form U-1 for each completed and pressure-tested unit built to Section VIII, Division 1, and stamped with the U symbol. They must fill out corresponding form A-1 for equipment built to Division 2 and stamped U-2.

Parts of exchangers or pressure vessels fabricated by one manufacturer for another and subject to pressure are stamped "PART." Part manufacturers are required to fill out form U-2 for Division 1 work and form A-2 for work in Division 2. For an *ASME Code*-stamped replacement bundle, the manufacturer provides a partial data report on one of these forms. If the part is subject to pressure on only one side (for example, a replacement channel), alternative forms U-2A and A-2A for single-chamber vessels may be used.

On data reports for Division 1 units, the manufacturer's authorized representative signs a certificate of shop compliance and the inspector signs a certificate of shop inspection, which are both included on the form. For Division 2 units, the manufacturer also certifies the design. The Division 2 certification must state where the user's design specification and manufacturer's design report are filed and the names, states, or provinces of registration and registration numbers of the registered professional engineers who certified them.

Unfired pressure vessels stamped UM must meet all other *ASME Code* requirements but are *not* inspected by an authorized inspector. The manufacturer provides form U-3, the certificate of compliance, signed only by the manufacturer.

When Division 1 heat exchangers are built for services to which special requirements apply, manufacturer's data reports must list the service and applicable paragraphs of the special requirements. This proviso pertains to units in lethal service and low-temperature service and to unfired steam boilers and direct-fired units.

Data reports for parts.   When parts are made by one manufacturer for inclusion in another manufacturer's heat exchanger, the parts manufacturer must forward partial data reports in duplicate to the completing manufacturer. On the basis of acceptance of the part manufacturer's inspector and acceptability of the completed exchanger, the completing manufacturer's inspector approves and witnesses the application of the *ASME Code* symbol to the unit.

The completing manufacturer must attach the partial data report to the manufacturer's data report. For replacement parts of an existing unit, the parts manufacturer furnishes the partial data report directly to the user.

Data reports for completed units.   Manufacturer's data reports for completed units are furnished to the user. Upon request, they are also furnished to the inspector. Most jurisdictions which have boiler and pressure vessel laws require the user to file a signed original with the jurisdiction's designated authority. Insurance carriers responsible for in-service use and inspection usually require a signed original too.

Manufacturers' records

For Division 1 exchangers, the manufacturer must either keep a copy of form U-1 on file for 5 years or register the exchanger and file the

U-1 with the National Board. For exchangers built to Division 2, the A-1 must either be kept on file for the longer of 10 years or the life of the unit, or the exchanger may be registered and the A-1 filed with the National Board. If registry and filing are not with the National Board, the manufacturer must also file a copy of the A-1 with the jurisdiction in which the exchanger is to be installed if the jurisdiction's laws so require.

Manufacturers of parts of exchangers or complete exchangers stamped U-2 are required to keep the whole file for at least 5 years after completion. The file must contain (1) all material certifications; (2) partial data reports; (3) records of examinations, tests, and heat treatments; and (4) manufacturing procedures, specifications, and drawings used, including all data on repaired materials, components, and assemblies. The records must be fully identified by pertinent material or item identification numbers. They must include all data on repaired material, components, and assemblies.

During the 5-year period of record maintenance, the records must be made available to the inspector upon 24-h prior notice. After that the manufacturer may either keep the files or offer them to the user. If the user refuses the offered files, the manufacturer may destroy them.

National Board registry. As said before, jurisdictions may not permit using boilers, pressure vessels, and heat exchangers built outside their boundaries unless these meet local laws and regulations. They may require the manufacturer to obtain authorization and symbols from the jurisdiction and further require that the units be inspected by an inspector who holds a commission from the jurisdiction. The problems that these requirements can cause may be surmounted by having *ASME Code*–stamped exchangers also stamped "Nat'l Bd" and registered with the National Board.

National Board registry works this way. Manufacturers who are authorized to stamp vessels with an *ASME Code* symbol may apply to the National Board for approval to stamp the vessels with the National Board stamp in addition to the stamp of the *ASME Code*. The Board of Directors of the National Board issues the manufacturer a facsimile of the approved stamping. The manufacturer may then stamp *ASME Code* vessels which have been inspected by a National Board–commissioned inspector "Nat'l Bd."

Under National Board rules, any boiler or unfired pressure vessel built after July 1, 1922, stamped with an ASME symbol and a National Board stamp, may be used within the jurisdiction of any National Board member. This does not supersede the laws and regulations of local jurisdictions. However, most states, provinces, counties, and cities which have pressure vessel laws accept or require National Board stamping for units built outside their boundaries.

In addition to the manufacturer's serial number, a separate National Board number must be stamped on the vessel and shown on the manufacturer's data report. Each manufacturer starts with National Board number 1 for its first vessel stamped "National Board." All subsequent National Board–stamped vessels must have consecutive serial numbers.

Nameplates and stamping

Most stamping is applied to permanently attached, corrosion-resistant nameplates. However, the data may be on the shell under some conditions permitted in a division. Figure 8.8 shows the form of stamping for exchangers stamped with the U, U-2, and UM symbols. The illustrations for U and U-2 stamping also show the National Board stamping.

Stamping must include information about construction, heat treatment, radiographic or ultrasonic examination, impact testing, special-service category, and any other information required by various paragraphs of the divisions. By examining the nameplate markings before making repairs or alterations, the work can be planned so as to maintain the unit's integrity.

The relationships among the *ASME Code*, the laws and regulations

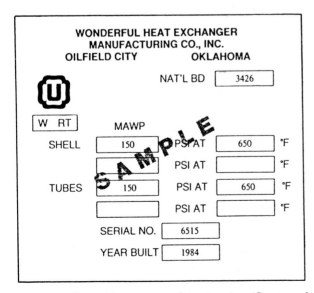

Figure 8.8   Heat exchanger nameplate stamping. (*Courtesy of Chemical Engineering.*)

of jurisdictions, and the National Board are often misunderstood. A discussion of this organization and the Uniform Boiler and Pressure Vessel Laws Society follows.

National Board of Boiler and Pressure Vessel Inspectors

The National Board of Boiler and Pressure Vessel Inspectors is a nongovernmental organization made up of the chief inspectors of cities in the United States with populations of 1 million or more and the states and commonwealths of the United States and provinces of Canada. Its purpose is to promote safety in design, construction, repair, and use of boilers and pressure vessels. In furthering this aim, it tries to concert actions by all interested parties and the public.

The National Board maintains liaison with manufacturers, authorized inspectors, authorized inspection agencies, users, the ASME Boiler Code Committee and its various subcommittees, and other organizations interested in the safe construction and use of boilers and pressure vessels. An example of such an organization is the Uniform Boiler and Pressure Vessel Laws Society. Each year, the ASME Boiler Code Committee and the National Board participate in a joint conference.

The National Board promotes the use of one code (the *ASME Code*) and one standard of stamping for boilers and pressure vessels in the cities and states of the United States and the provinces of Canada. It fosters uniform boiler and pressure vessel laws and regulations in all United States and Canadian jurisdictions.

To assure acceptance and interchangeability of boilers and pressure vessels among jurisdictions, the National Board maintains uniformity in construction, installations, inspection, and repairs. To encourage uniform administration and enforcement of the code, it seeks consistent and complete use of all of the *ASME Code* rules and uniform boiler and pressure vessel laws and regulations in all political jurisdictions of the United States and Canada.

To avoid jurisdictions' not accepting the qualifications of each other's inspectors, the National Board promotes one qualifications standard. To implement this goal, it provides training courses and prepares and grades uniform examinations to qualify inspectors. National Board members administer the examinations in their jurisdictions and forward them to the National Board for grading. Individuals who are not residents of the United States or Canada may apply directly to the National Board for examination.

An inspector who passes the examination is issued a certificate of competency by the jurisdiction that administered the test. Any inspector who holds a certificate of competency from a National Board member may apply to the National Board and be issued a commission. To inspect in a jurisdiction other than the one that issued the certificate of competency, an inspector must obtain a reciprocal certificate.

Inspectors who hold National Board commissions may use their commission numbers only on *ASME Code* vessels stamped with the National Board stamping. They may be further examined to determine their qualifications for specialized or supervisory activities. When inspectors pass such additional examinations, the National Board's executive director endorses their commission renewal cards as evidence of the additional qualification. The National Board supports AIs by providing a central source of information about the application of the *ASME Code*.

The National Board gathers and makes available useful information and statistics about boilers and pressure vessels. At present, no subset of information exclusively on tubular exchangers is provided. The National Board includes what it learns about the circumstances, causes, and results of failures. It assists jurisdictional authorities and the ASME in assuring the competency of manufacturers who hold ASME symbols and the National Board facsimile.

When a jurisdiction cannot or will not evaluate or audit the quality control programs of manufacturers within its authority, the National Board does so. It assesses the manufacturers' facilities, their technical competence and engineering backup, quality control system and manual, and performance of the quality control system as a whole.

The National Board's major publications are the *National Board Bulletin*, the quarterly official publication of the National Board; the *National Board Inspection Code*, discussed below; and the *Manufacturers and National Board Repair Certificate Holders Directory*. Other publications include the *National Board Information Booklet, National Board Authorization to Repair ASME and National Board Stamped Boilers and Pressure Vessels*, manufacturer's data report forms, and National Board repair-alteration forms.

The National Board issues authorizations and repair stamps to qualified organizations for making repairs to *ASME Code*–stamped vessels. The repair symbol that it issues for unfired pressure vessels is the R symbol. Under *National Board Inspection Code* rules, repairs may be made to *ASME Code*–stamped unfired pressure vessels, which include heat exchangers, only by holders of a U, U-2, or R symbol.

The National Board investigates reports of *ASME Code* violations when they are brought to its attention. If you believe that an exchanger violates the *ASME Code* rules, here are suggested guidelines: (1) Do not put a new exchanger into operation if you think it is unsafe; (2) if you believe you have uncovered a violation in an operating unit, reduce the operating pressure below 1-atm gauge, providing it is safe to operate under positive pressure; and (3) notify the National Board. Provide the manufacturer's name, the exchanger's National Board and serial numbers, and the year when the exchanger was built. Describe the nature of the violation and the *ASME Code* paragraphs that have not been complied with.

If your allegations are proved, the National Board will take appropriate disciplinary action to the authorized inspector who inspected the unit. It will also recommend to the ASME that it discipline the manufacturer. These actions are in addition to any legal actions, which are not within this work's competence to discuss.

Despite the National Board's efforts, boiler and pressure vessel laws and regulations in various jurisdictions diverge. This situation led to the organization of the Uniform Boiler and Pressure Vessel Laws Society, called in the following for simplicity the society.

Uniform Boiler and Pressure Vessel Laws Society

In its literature, the society describes itself as "a nonpolitical, noncommercial, nonprofit, technical body supported by their voluntary contributions of its members who are individuals, firms and organizations engaged in the manufacture, sale, use, insurance or inspection of material or apparatus related to the boiler and pressure vessel industry." The society recommends the *ASME Code* as the standard for new construction and the *National Board Inspection Code* as the standard for inspection and repair.

It cooperates with the ASME Boiler and Pressure Vessel Committee, the National Board, and other organizations. It works closely with officials charged with enforcement of boiler and pressure vessel inspection, laws, rules, and regulations. The society publishes and maintains an updated synopsis of jurisdictions' requirements. If you are concerned with installations and repairs or alterations of units in different locations, a subscription to the society's publication *Synopsis of Boiler and Pressure Vessel Laws, Rules and Regulations by States, Cities, Counties and Provinces (United States and Canada)* is invaluable.[11]

Obtaining authorization to apply code symbols

Although of some general interest, this part of this chapter is addressed primarily to manufacturers.

The *ASME Code* symbol stamp is used to indicate that items

stamped conform with the requirements of the most recent edition of the *ASME Code* section to which the stamp applies. Only the ASME Boiler and Pressure Vessel Committee's accreditation department furnishes ASME certificates of authorization and *ASME Code* symbol stamps. Unfired pressure vessel stamps are issued for a maximum of 3 years. UM certificates of authorization and UM stamps are issued only to holders of valid certificates of authorization to stamp with the U stamp.

A condition for obtaining a certificate of authorization and *ASME Code* symbol stamp for power boilers is that Sections I, II, V, and IX of the *ASME Code* and Addenda and ANSI Standard B31.1 for power piping be on hand. For U and UM, Sections II, V, VII, Division 1, and IX must be in the manufacturer's library. For U-2, manufacturers must have the sections required for Division 1 plus Section VIII, Division 2. For N, Sections II, III, V, and IX are needed.

The rules in Divisions I, III, and VIII provide detailed requirements for quality control manuals. These may be referred to from time to time as QCMs.

To obtain a stamp, it is necessary to submit a notarized application, hold a valid certificate of authorization, and have an inspection agreement in effect with an authorized inspection agency. Request application forms for ASME boiler and pressure vessel accreditation from the code secretary. The ASME will reply with a package of information and procedures for obtaining ASME boiler and pressure vessel certificates of authorization and code symbol stamps and application forms. The package will include the current accreditation procedure for the conduct of boiler and pressure vessel quality control system reviews. It will also contain a list of AIAs.

When the ASME receives the completed application, accompanying documents, and fee, it will make contact with the manufacturer's AIA. It will ask the authorized inspection agency to verify that there is an agreement for third-party inspection. When the AIA provides the verification, the ASME will notify the jurisdictional authority that it and a representative from the AIA (called a review team) may together conduct a shop review of the applicant's facilities.

The ASME will send the jurisdictional authority a qualification review report form to be used in conducting the review. If there is no jurisdictional authority or if the jurisdictional authority does not wish to participate or has delegated the conduct of the review to the National Board, the review will be conducted by a representative from the National Board and one from the AIA. If the jurisdictional agency is also the authorized inspection agency, the review will be conducted by a review team consisting of an ASME designee and a representative of the AIA.

The shop review includes an on-site evaluation of the quality control system. It consists of a review of the written description and a demonstration of how the program is implemented.

On their initial shop visit, review team members meet with responsible shop personnel, to whom they describe their affiliations. They emphasize that the ASME administers the accreditation activity to enhance public health and safety.

Review team members ask about products and operations and answer questions about how the review is conducted. They request a facilities tour to get a general idea of the layout and flow of work. They scrutinize the manufacturer's application to make sure that it correctly provides all necessary information. The team verifies that the applied-for certificates of authorization and *ASME Code* symbol stamps are appropriate to the products being manufactured. It makes clear that its purpose and responsibility are to perform the review, document its findings, and make recommendations to the ASME Subcommittee on Boiler and Pressure Vessel Accreditation.

The sequence of the review team's actions is as follows: (1) Review the QCM; (2) review the manual with the manufacturer; (3) review how the manufacturer implements the QCM; (4) advise the manufacturer of any deficiencies and provide an opportunity to make immediate revisions, verify that the revisions have been made, and accept them; (5) report its findings and proposed recommendations to the manufacturer and resolve all questions on its findings before leaving; and (6) report its findings and recommendations to the ASME, using the qualification review report.

The review team may use the *National Board Inspector's Guide* as a checklist to assist it in evaluating the quality control manual. However, under no circumstances may the team use it or any other document to increase or decrease the quality control program requirements established by the applicable ASME codes and interpretations.

Each team member must sign the qualification review report to indicate concurrence with its contents and recommendations. The team leader identifies the information that will be included as a summary report to accompany the qualification review report form.

The decision to accredit is not up to the review team but only to the committee. Manufacturers who cannot reach agreement with the review team on its findings have the right to make contact with the ASME accreditation staff. After the ASME has evaluated the review team's report, it will either advise the manufacturer that the certificate and stamp are issued or state the additional requirements that must be met before the application can be further considered. The manufacturer must pay directly any fees that the jurisdictional authority, National Board, and authorized inspection agency charge for the qualification review.

Enforcement of *ASME Code* rules

The laws and regulations of jurisdictions that adopt one or more sections of the *ASME Code* usually provide for registration and enforcement. When a jurisdiction has no law or regulation, the public must rely on the common law. Most insurance carriers require pressure vessels, which include heat exchangers, to be *ASME Code*–stamped. However, basic enforcement lies with the authorized inspection agencies and authorized inspectors.

Alterations and Repairs: Guide to the National Board and API 510 Inspection Codes

ASME Code stamping and certification apply only to new construction. However, the *ASME Code*'s technical information is a sound basis for making repairs and alterations that maintain a unit's integrity. By applying its new-construction requirements for design, materials, welding, and examination to repairs and alterations, confidence in the unit can be maintained throughout its life. This is the basis of the provisions of the *National Board Inspection Code*, hereafter called the NBIC, and the *API 510 Pressure Vessel Inspection Code*, subsequently called the *API Code*.

Both codes have rules and procedures for making repairs and alterations and for inspecting, testing, and documenting repaired and altered pressure vessels, including exchangers. Although the NBIC does not always give specific rules for welded repairs and alterations, its intention is that, subject to approval of the inspector, all repairs and alterations conform insofar as possible to the *ASME Code* section and edition most applicable to the best performance of the work. The *API Code* requires adherence to the *principles* of the *ASME Code*.

Both codes have similar provisions for alterations and repairs. The NBIC stipulates that where any of its provisions present a direct or implied conflict with any lawful regulation in any governmental jurisdiction, the lawful regulation governs and is to be complied with. It recognizes the special nature of the *API Code* (which applies to oil refinery pressure vessels) by stating that the NBIC is intended to cover installations other than those that the *API Code* covers unless a jurisdiction rules otherwise.

According to the Uniform Boiler and Pressure Vessel Laws Society's synopsis, most jurisdictions accept, adopt, or incorporate the NBIC. Therefore, the following discussion is centered on it. Differences between repair and alterations requirements of the two codes will be highlighted.

Repairs

A *repair* is the work necessary to restore an exchanger to a safe and satisfactory operating condition, providing there is no deviation from the original design. Under API 510, if restorative changes result in a change of design temperature or pressure, the unit must be rerated. API 510 repairs also include adding or replacing pressure or nonpressure parts that do not change the pressure rating of the exchanger. These are typical repairs:

- Weld repairing or replacing pressure parts or attachments that have failed in a weld or base metal such as tube-to-tubesheet joints.

- Replacing tubesheets in accordance with the original design.

- Replacing pressure-retaining parts identical with those existing on the original unit and described on the manufacturer's data report. These are examples: (1) rewelding a circumferential or longitudinal seam in a shell or channel; (2) replacing nozzles of a size for which reinforcement is not a consideration.

- Installing new nozzles when reinforcement is not a consideration.

- Installing a flush patch.

- Replacing a cylindrical course.

- Welding wasted or distorted flange faces.

- Replacing slip-on flanges with weld-neck flanges, or vice versa.

Alterations

An *alteration* is any change from the heat exchanger's description on the original manufacturer's data report when the change affects its pressure-containing capability.

Examples of alterations are as follows:

- Adding new nozzles or openings except for those classified as repairs.

- Changing dimensions or contours.

- Replacing a pressure-retaining part with a material of a nominal strength or composition different from that used in the original design. This means that if you retube with tubes of a nominal composition or thickness different from that originally used, you have altered the exchanger.

NBIC alterations include nonphysical changes. Examples of nonphysical changes are changes in the internal or external MAWP and changes to the design temperature of the shellside or tubeside. When the minimum design temperature is reduced to the point that the *ASME Code* would require additional impact testing, it is considered to be an alteration. Under this definition, rerating an exchanger to increase its MAWP or to decrease its minimum allowable working temperature is an alteration. The API 510 definition, on the other hand, does not consider rerating to be an alteration. In the latter code, it is also permissible to derate a unit to provide for corrosion.

Both codes require repairs or alterations to be acceptable to the responsible authorized inspection agency and to be inspected by an authorized inspector. In the NBIC, the AI must hold a National Board commission, but not in API 510.

The inspector must be employed by one of the following: (1) a jurisdictional AIA, (2) the AIA of the organization making the repair or alteration, (3) the AIA that insures the exchanger, and (4) an owner-user inspection agency responsible for in-service inspection of the exchanger.

Repair and alteration organizations

A *repair organization* may be either the holder of a valid ASME certificate of authorization for use of the appropriate *ASME Code* symbol stamp or an organization authorized by the legal jurisdiction. In the API 510 rules, *repair organization* also means an owner or user that repairs its own equipment in accordance with API 510 or a contractor whose qualifications are acceptable to the owner or users and who makes repairs in accordance with API 510.

An *alteration organization* is the same as a repair organization, but the alterations it makes must be within the scope of its authorization.

Repairs in accordance with the NBIC may also be made by organizations that hold certificates authorizing the use of R stamps for Section VIII exchangers and NR stamps for Section III units. Following are general requirements for making repairs and alterations.

Authorization

The NBIC permits no repairs or alterations to be initiated without the authorization of the authorized inspector. The AI must be satisfied that the welding procedures and welders are qualified and that the repair or alteration methods are acceptable. Subject to the jurisdiction's administrative procedures, the AI may give prior approval for limited repairs. The repair and alteration procedures and methods must be acceptable to the AI and calculations made available. If the authorized inspector considers it to be necessary, the exchanger may be inspected before authorization.

Acceptance

Subject to jurisdictional requirements, the repairs or alterations must be acceptable to the authorized inspection agency responsible for the unit.

Welding

The organization making repairs or alterations must maintain records of results obtained in qualifying welding procedures and welders' performance. It must certify the records and make them available to the AI before beginning the work.

Welding procedure specifications (WPSs) must be on hand for all welding done. WPSs must meet the requirements of Section IX and be qualified as required by the applicable section of the *ASME Code*. Welding data and test results must be recorded in procedure qualification records (PQRs). Welders and welding operators must qualify in accordance with Section IX for each welding process they use in doing the work.

In most jurisdictions, welders and welding operators are qualified only by the organization that employs them. They must be requalified each time that they change employment. The term *certified welder* for *ASME Code* work is meaningless except when the welder is employed by an organization holding an *ASME Code* symbol or a National Board repair symbol. When jurisdictions license welders, the license applies only to work within the jurisdiction.*

Heat treatment

The NBIC suggests minimum temperatures for preheating before welding. Preheating must be specified on the WPS. If you intend to preheat and preheating is not specified on the WPS, you must qualify a new procedure. The welders and welding operators must be retested

---

*The American Welding Society (AWS) has initiated programs called Welder Certification (QCW) and Accreditation of Test Facilities (QCTF) which, when approved by the necessary AWS Committees and accepted by the ASME Code Committee, has the capability of transferring welding qualifications from job to job. (See *Welding Journal*, July 1989.)

and qualified in the new procedure. Details of postweld heat treatment must comply with *ASME Code* requirements. However, when full compliance is inadvisable or impractical (for example, tube-to-tubesheet joint repair welding in a C-type channel), any other method acceptable to the AI or special welding methods may be used.

Nondestructive examination

The requirements and acceptance criteria that applied to the original construction under the ASME rules apply to repairs and alterations. When these are not possible or practical, alternative methods acceptable to the AI may be used.

Materials requirements

Materials to be used in making repairs or alterations must conform with the requirements of the *ASME Code* section that applied to the original construction or meet one of the specifications listed in Section II of the *ASME Code*. ASTM specifications not listed in Section II are not acceptable. Carbon steel with more than 0.35 percent carbon content may not be welded under the NBIC rules.

Weld joint design

Butt joints must penetrate completely and be fused fully for the entire weld length. As-welded finish is acceptable if it does not prevent performing required nondestructive examinations.

Replacement pressure parts

Replacement parts on which no welding is done are considered to be materials. This applies whether they are formed by forging, bending, or other methods. Such parts must be identified by heat numbers matched to the part number on the bill of materials. The supplier must supply a certificate of compliance, certified as required under the *ASME Code* rules.

Preassembled welded pressure parts that are not required to be shop-inspected under the *ASME Code* rules must be identified by drawings or bills of materials. The supplier or manufacturer must certify that the materials, design, and fabrication comply with the applicable section of the *ASME Code*.

A replacement pressure part (for example, a replacement bundle) may require shop inspection by an AI under the *ASME Code* rules. In this case, it must be fabricated by a manufacturer having an ASME certificate of authorization and appropriate *ASME Code* symbol stamp. The part must be stamped with the applicable *ASME Code* symbol and the word "PART." The part manufacturer must furnish a completed manufacturer's partial data report and maintain the same kind of files and documents required for completed units. When the part is added to the exchanger, the partial data report must be attached to National Board form R-1, *Report of Welded Repair or Alterations*.

Pressure tests

Pressure tests must be conducted at 1½ times the MAWP stamped on the original nameplate unless the unit has been rerated. The test temperature must be between 70 and 120°F (21 and 49°C). Relief devices must be blocked out during testing. Under certain conditions, you may wish to specify a higher test pressure. When you do, it is necessary to make calculations to demonstrate that stresses imposed by pressure testing will not damage or permanently deform the unit.

The inspector may require a pressure test after the completion of repairs. This applies to (1) identical replacement bundles installed by welding (as into feedwater heater shells at their skirts), (2) retubing with tubes of specifications identical to the original ones, and (3) welded repairs such as tube-to-tubesheet joint rewelds.

Pressure testing is required upon completion of alterations. The following must be pressure-tested: (1) units that have been rerated; (2) exchangers retubed with tubes of a gauge, material, or grade different from that originally installed; and (3) replacement bundles when there is any change to the design of the pressure parts from the manufacturer's original design.

Documentation

Dual-purpose form R-1 (Fig. 8.9) is used to document alterations and repairs done in accordance with the NBIC. When form R-1 is used to document repairs, it is a report of welded repair; used to document alterations, it is a report of alteration. Under National Board rules for documenting repairs, the repair organization must prepare the R-1 and submit it to the inspector for acceptance. It must attach the form to any manufacturer's data reports and certifications for replacement parts used in the repair.

The rules require the repairer to send a set of R-1s and attachments to the owner-user and, as required by its administrative procedures, to the local jurisdiction. A set must also be made available to the authorized inspection agency responsible for in-service inspection of the unit. These requirements may be waived for minor or routine repairs. However, the owner-user is required to keep a record of the repairs.

When a unit is to be rerated with no physical change to the ex-

FORM R-1, REPORT OF WELDED   ☐REPAIR OR   ☐ALTERATION
as required by the provisions of the National Board Inspection Code

1. Work performed by _____
(name of repair or alteration organization)   (P.O. no., job no. etc.)

_____
(address)

2. Owner _____
(name)

_____
(address)

3. Location of installation _____
(name)

_____
(address)

4. Unit identification _____ Name of original manufacturer _____
(boiler, pressure vessel)

5. Identifying nos.: _____
(mfr's serial no.) (original National Board no.) (jurisdiction no.) (other) (year built)

6. Description of work: _____
(use back, separate sheet, or sketch if necessary)

_____
_____
_____
_____

_____ Pressure test, if applied _____ psi

7. **Remarks:** Attached are Manufacturers' Partial Data Reports properly identified and signed by Authorized Inspectors for the following items of report: _____

_____
_____
_____
_____

(name of part, item number, mfr's name, and identifying stamp)

CERTIFICATE OF COMPLIANCE

The undersigned certifies that the statements made in this report are correct and that all design, material, construction, and workmanship of this _____ conform to the National Board Inspection Code.
(repair or alteration)

Certificate of Authorization no. _____ to use the _____ symbol expires _____ , 19 ___ .

Date _____ 19 ___ _____ Signed _____
(repair or alteration organization)   (authorized representative)

CERTIFICATE OF INSPECTION

The undersigned, holding a valid Commission issued by The National Board of Boiler and Pressure Vessel Inspectors and certificate of competency issued by the state or province of _____ and employed by _____ of _____ has inspected the work described in this data report on _____ , 19 ___ and state that to the best of my knowledge and belief this work has been done in accordance with the National Board Inspection Code.

By signing this certificate, neither the undersigned nor my employer makes any warranty, expressed or implied, concerning the work described in this report. Furthermore, neither the undersigned nor my employer shall be liable in any manner for any personal injury, property damage or loss of any kind arising from or connected with this inspection, except such liability as may be provided in a policy of insurance which the undersigned's insurance company may issue upon said object and then only in accordance with the terms of said policy.

Date _____ , 19 ___ Signed _____ Commissions _____
(Authorized Inspector)   (National Board (incl. endorsements), state, prov. and no.)

This form may be obtained from the National Board of Boiler and Pressure Vessel Inspectors, 1055 Crupper Ave., Columbus, OH 43229   NB-66 Rev. 4

Figure 8.9 National Board dual-purpose form R-1 for repairs and alterations.

changer, the original manufacturer must prepare the R-1. The R-1 must be accepted by the manufacturer's authorized inspection agency. However, if an R-1 cannot be obtained from the original manufacturer, it may be prepared by a registered PE and verified by the authorized inspection agency responsible for the in-service inspection of the unit.

When a physical change has been made with or without rerating, the R-1 report of alteration must be prepared by the holder of the ASME certificate of authorization who made the alteration and be verified by the holder's authorized inspection agency. This applies in the case of a heat exchanger bundle returned to the original manufacturer for a tube replacement with tubes of an alloy or grade different from that originally supplied.

Copies of the original manufacturer's data report and any manufacturer's partial data reports for pressure parts used in the alteration must be attached to and made part of the R-1. Legible copies of the R-1 report of alteration must be distributed to the authorized inspection agency responsible for in-service inspection of the exchanger, to the owner-user, and, when the unit has been registered there, to the National Board.

To rerate an exchanger to the *API 510 Code*, either obtain calculations from the manufacturer or have an owner-user's engineer experienced in pressure vessel design, fabrication, or inspection justify the rating. The rerating must be established in accordance with the requirements of the edition of the *ASME Code* to which it was built or to a later edition if all essential details comply with the later edition.

The *API 510 Code* does not use a report of welded repairs. It has an example form for alterations or rerating of pressure vessels, reproduced here as Fig. 8.10. Current inspection records must verify that the unit is satisfactory for the proposed service and that the corrosion allowance provided is adequate.

The vessel must be pressure tested at 1½ times the new MAWP. In lieu of testing, maintenance of integrity may be demonstrated by special nondestructive evaluation inspection techniques. The rerating must be acceptable to the AI. It is completed when the AI oversees the attachment of an additional nameplate or additional stamping that has the information listed below for the *API Code*.

Nameplates and stampings

The additional nameplate or stamping for a rerated exchanger must contain the information shown on Fig. 8.11. Under the NBIC rules, if a heat exchanger is altered, an alteration plate of the form shown in Fig. 8.12 must be attached. For repairs made in compliance with the NBIC, a stamp or nameplate, as shown in Fig. 8.13, must be applied

FORM DATE _____

OWNER OR USER _____

FORM NO. _____

VESSEL NAME _____

1. Original vessel identification _____

2. Original vessel location _____

3. Manufacturer _____   Serial no. _____

4. Design temperature _____   Year built _____

5. Test pressure _____   Position _____

6. Material _____

7. Shell thickness _____   Head thickness _____

8. Proposed vessel identification (new location) _____

9. Proposed new vessel location _____

10. Work on vessel classified as: ☐ Alteration   ☐ Rerating

11. Manufacturer performing work _____

12. Order number _____   Date _____

13. Design temperature _____

14. Maximum allowable working pressure _____

15. Test pressure _____   Position _____

16. Type of inspection(s) performed:

    ☐ Radiographic Test   ☐ Ultrasonic Test

    ☐ Magnetic Particle   ☐ Penetrant Test

    ☐ Visual

17. List work performed by manufacturer (attach drawings, calculations, and other pertinent data):

18. See attachments for additional data ☐.

STATEMENT OF COMPLIANCE

We certify that the statements made in this report are correct and that all material, construction, and workmanship on this ☐ alteration, ☐ rerating conform to the requirements of the Pressure Vessel Inspection Code API 510, _____ Edition, _____ (year).

_____

(alteration or rerating organization)

Signed _____

(authorized representative)

Date _____

STATEMENT OF INSPECTION

I, the undersigned, and inspector employed by _____ _____ , having inspected the work described above, state that to the best of my knowledge, this work has been satisfactorily completed in accordance with the Pressure Vessel Inspection Code, API510, _____ Edition, _____ (year).

Signed _____

Date _____

Figure 8.10   API 510 form for alterations and repairs.

Figure 8.11   Form of stamping or nameplate for rerated heat exchangers.

Figure 8.12   Form of stamping or nameplate of a heat exchanger altered under the National Board code rules.

Figure 8.13   Stamping on nameplate for exchangers repaired by welding.

adjacent to the original manufacturer's stamping or nameplate. A single nameplate may be used for more than one repair if the repairs are carried out by the same repair organization. The repair organization must stamp the date of each repair on the nameplate. The date must correspond with the date of the R-1.

Guide to the *TEMA Standards*

The *Standards of the Tubular Exchanger Manufacturers Association (TEMA Standards)* are applied worldwide to tubular exchanger design and construction. Most specifications incorporate all or part of the *TEMA Standards* by reference. You can be reasonably sure that exchangers built to the *TEMA Standards* will meet your process requirements and will be reliable.

However, the *TEMA Standards* have been established by *manufacturers* to set *minimum* requirements for acceptable construction within the industry. Therefore, they may not be acceptable as the sole basis for specifying design requirements of a specific unit.

Table 8.4 shows the range of the *TEMA Standards*. Table 8.5 lists the sections into which the *TEMA Standards* are organized. Each section is identified by an uppercase-letter symbol which precedes the paragraph numbers of the section and identifies the subject matter.

Section 5 has mechanical standards that apply to three classes of heat exchangers R, C, and B, based upon their intended service. Paragraphs in Section 5 marked with an asterisk have additional information in Section 10, the recommended-good-practices (RPG) section. The corresponding paragraph in the RPG section has the identical paragraph number but is prefixed with RPG.

The mechanical standards of Class R are the most rigorous. They are intended for tubular exchangers used in petroleum and related industries but are often applied for other severe services. Those of Class C are meant for the generally moderate requirements of commercial and general process requirements. Class B mechanical standards apply to heat exchangers in chemical process service. They have been

TABLE 8.4   Range of *TEMA Mechanical Standards*

Parameter	Limit
Inside diameter	60 in (1524 mm)
Nominal diameter × pressure	60,000 lb/in (10,500 N/mm)
Pressure	3000 lb/in^2 (20,670 kPa)
Shell wall	2 in (51 mm)
Stud diameters (approximate)	3 in (76 mm)
Code conformity	ASME Section VIII, Division 1
Pressure source	Indirect (unfired units only)

TABLE 8.5   **Organization of *TEMA Mechanical Standards***

Section	Symbol	Paragraph	Description
1	N		Nomenclature
		1	Size and type-recommended practice
		2	Nomenclature of heat exchanger components
2	F		Fabrication tolerances
		1	External dimensions, nozzles, and supports locations
		2	Recommended fabrication tolerances
		3	Tubesheets, partitions, covers, and flanges
3	G		General fabrication and performance information
		1	Shop operation
		2	Inspection
		3	Nameplates
		4	Drawings and *ASME Code* data reports
		5	Guarantees
		6	Preparation of heat exchangers for shipment
		7	General construction features of TEMA standard heat exchangers
4	E		Installation, operation, and maintenance
		1	Performance of heat exchangers
		2	Installation of heat exchangers
		3	Operation of heat exchangers
		4	Maintenance of heat exchangers
5	RCB		Mechanical standards TEMA class RCB heat exchangers
		1	Scope and general requirements
		2	Tubes
		3	Shells and shell covers
		4	Baffles and support plates
		5	Floating-end construction
		6	Gaskets
		7	Tubesheets
		8	Flexible shell elements
		9	Channels, covers, and bonnets
		10	Nozzles
		11	End flanges and bolting

TABLE 8.5   Organization of *TEMA Mechanical Standards* (Continued)

Section	Symbol	Paragraph	Description
6	V		Flow-induced vibration
		1	Scope and general
		2	Vibration damage patterns
		3	Failure regions
		4	Dimensionless numbers
		5	Natural frequency
		6	Axial tube stress
		7	Effective tube mass
		8	Damping
		9	Shellside velocity distribution
		10	Estimate of critical-flow velocity
		11	Acoustic vibration
		12	Design considerations
		13	Selected references
7	T		Thermal relations
		1	Scope and basic relations
		2	Fouling
		3	Fluid temperature relations
		4	Mean metal temperatures of shell and tubes
8	P		Physical properties of fluids
		1	Fluid density
		2	Specific heat
		3	Heat content of petroleum fractions
		4	Thermal conductivity
		5	Viscosity
		6	Critical properties
		7	Properties of gases and vapor mixtures
		8	Selected references
9	D		General information
10	RGP		Recommended good practice
		G-7	General construction features of TEMA standard heat exchangers
		RCB-1	Scope and general requirements
		RCB-2	Plugging tubes in tube bundles
		RCB-3	Shells and shell covers
		RCB-4	Baffles and support plates
		RCB-6	Gaskets
		RCB-7	Tubesheets
		RCB-9	Channels, covers, and bonnets
		RCB-10	Nozzles
		RCB-11	End flanges and bolting
		T-2	Fouling

adopted by the American National Standards Institute as ANSI 78.1. The following applies to the three classes except that where requirements differ among the classes the differences will be shown.

Section 3 (symbol G) sets forth the manufacturers' administrative and commercial requirements, guarantees, and limits of liability.* It provides a heat exchanger specification sheet for listing the performance and construction details and mechanical standards upon which the manufacturer's guarantee is based. Section 3 also lists fabrication requirements that apply generally. Following are some typical Section 3 fabrication requirements.

The manufacturer must provide all heat exchangers with supports designed to avoid undue stress or deflection in the supports or shell. It must fit horizontal units with at least two saddles with round holes for anchor bolts in one and with slots or elongated holes in the other to allow for shell expansion and contraction or provide other supports that will accommodate shell expansion. The supports of vertical units must extend from the shell far enough to bear on a structure large enough to clear the end flanges.

Manufacturers must supply lifting lugs, rings, or tapped holes for eyebolts for channels, bonnets, or covers that weigh more than 60 lb (27 kg).

Purchasers must specify in their inquiries design requirements for wind and seismic forces.

Section 4 (symbol E) puts the burden on the user for correct installation, proper operation, and preventative maintenance. It lists some causes of performance failures. Here are found general installation requirements for dismantling clearance: foundations, foundation bolts, and exchanger leveling; dirt removal; fittings; and piping. There is also a brief discussion of the consequences of improper operating procedures and suggestions for starting up, shutting down, and end flange tightening. In addition, Section 4 provides some commonsense suggestions for heat exchanger maintenance.

By following the appropriate class of the mechanical standards, the fabrication tolerances, the installation, operation, and maintenance recommendations, and the recommended good practices, a level of quality commensurate with the service requirements can confidently be established.

The following highlights some of the mechanical standards. The language is paraphrased. For specific applications, refer to the origi-

---

*Paragraph G-5 of the *TEMA Standards* states," Unless otherwise agreed upon by the manufacturer and purchaser, the following paragraphs in this section will be applicable." It should be carefully studied by specifiers and purchasers of exchangers built to the *TEMA Standards* and any differences or exceptions resolved *before* a purchase order is issued.

TABLE 8.6   Comparison of Corrosion Allowances for Carbon Steel and Cast Iron for TEMA Classes R, B, and C

Class	R	C	B
Corrosion allowance, in	⅛	1⁄16	1⁄16

TABLE 8.7   Comparison of Recommended Tube Pitches for TEMA Classes R, B, and C

Class	R	B	C
Minimum center distance		1.25 × tube OD, all classes	
Exceptions	None	None	For expanded-only joints and tubes ⅝ in (15.9 mm) or less, may be reduced to 1.2 × tube OD
Minimum cleaning lanes for mechanical cleaning specified by purchaser			
Shell diameter 12 in (304.8 mm) or less			
in	¼	3⁄16	
mm	6.35	4.76	
Shell diameter greater than 12 in (304.8 mm)			
in	¼	¼	
mm	6.35	6.35	

nal standards. Tables 8.6 through 8.13 compare some of the requirements of the three classes.

ASME Code requirement

All three classes require construction to comply with Section VIII, Division 1, of the *ASME Code*. Unless specified otherwise at the time of purchase, the manufacturer must stamp each unit built to the *TEMA Standards* with the *ASME Code* symbol. If there is a state or local code at the site of installation, the manufacturer is responsible for conforming with its special requirements. However, the buyer must specify the plant location where the exchanger will be installed.

Metal temperature limitations for pressure parts are those prescribed by the *ASME Code*.

Corrosion allowance

The *TEMA Standards* require the manufacturer to provide a minimum corrosion allowance for the wetted surfaces of all carbon steel pressure parts except tubes and for all cast-iron parts. These are ⅛ in (3.2 mm) for Class R and 1⁄16 in (1.6 mm) for Classes C and B. No cor-

TABLE 8.8   Comparison of Shell Thicknesses for TEMA Classes R, B, and C—Carbon Steel

Nominal shell-cover thickness is the same as minimum shell thickness.

Nominal shell diameter	Minimum permissible thickness; pipe schedule or thickness					
	Pipe			Plate		
	R	B	C	R	B	C
English Units: Pipe Sizes, NPS; Plate Thicknesses, in						
6	Sch. 40	Sch. 40	Sch. 40			
8–12	Sch. 30	Sch. 30	Sch. 30			
13–23	$3/8$	Sch. 20	Sch. 20	$3/8$	$5/16$	$5/16$
24–29	$3/8$	Sch. 20	Sch. 20	$3/8$	$5/16$	$5/16$
30–39	...	...	...	$7/16$	$3/8$	$3/8$
40–60	...	...	...	$1/2$	$7/16$	$7/16$
Metric Units: Pipe Sizes and Thicknesses Approximate; All Thicknesses, mm						
152.4	7.1	7.1	7.1			
203.2	7.04	7.04	7.04			
254	7.8	7.8	7.8			
304.8	8.38	8.38	8.38			
330–431	9.52	7.92	7.92	9.52	7.94	7.94
457.2–584.2	9.52	9.52	9.52	9.52	7.94	7.94
609.6–736.6	9.52	12.7	12.7	9.52	7.94	7.94
762–990.6	...	...	...	11.11	9.54	9.54
1016–1524	...	...	...	12.7	11.11	11.11

rosion allowance is required for alloy parts. A user-specified corrosion allowance may be employed if conditions of service make a different allowance more suitable.

The standards do not require floating-head backing devices to have a corrosion allowance. This applies to split rings and internal bolting. The material of internal floating-head backing devices must be equivalent in corrosion resistance to the material of the shell interior. No allowance for corrosion is required on pass-partition plates unless the purchaser specifies it.

Corrosion allowance in tubing.   The *TEMA Mechanical Standards* exclude tubes from the minimum corrosion allowance requirements. This does not mean that an allowance is not required for tube deterioration in service. However, the standards recognize that tubes may be replaced.

When tube corrosion or erosion is anticipated, consider the effect of the higher-pressure stream's leaking into the lower-pressure one. In some exchangers (feedwater heaters, for example) such leaks present little or no danger. When a small amount of high-pressure feedwater leaks into the lower-pressure steam side, it affects heater operation

TABLE 8.9   Comparison of Shell Thicknesses for TEMA Classes R, B, and C—Alloys

Nominal diameter	Minimum permissible thickness, pipe or plate		
	R	B	C
English Units, in			
6	$\frac{1}{8}$*	$\frac{1}{8}$*	$\frac{1}{8}$*
8–12	$\frac{1}{8}$*	$\frac{1}{8}$*	$\frac{1}{8}$*
13–23	$\frac{3}{16}$	$\frac{1}{8}$	$\frac{1}{8}$
24–29	$\frac{3}{16}$	$\frac{3}{16}$	$\frac{3}{16}$
30–39	$\frac{1}{4}$	$\frac{1}{4}$	$\frac{1}{4}$
40–60	$\frac{5}{16}$	$\frac{1}{4}$	$\frac{1}{4}$
Metric Units, mm			
152.4	3.18†	3.18†	3.18†
203.2–304.8	3.18†	3.18†	3.18†
330.2–584.2	4.76	3.18	3.18
609.6–736.6	4.76	4.76	4.76
762–990.6	6.35	6.35	6.35
1016–1524	7.94	6.35	6.35

*Sch. 5S is permissible for 6-in and 8-in shell diameters.
†Approximately 2.8-mm-wall pipe is permissible for 152.4-mm and 203.2-mm diameters.

and maintenance, but there is no immediate safety hazard. Therefore, unless the leakage rate is too large, it is a common practice in power plants to operate until a heater can be shut down and the leaking tubes plugged. The station continues operating plugged units until so many tubes are plugged or plugging is so frequent that operation is uneconomical.

However, in other services leaks through the tubes may cause product deterioration or present a safety hazard. An example is a tube leak in the cooler of a system that uses a heat transfer oil with a high vapor pressure for heating and cooling process vessels. Such systems consist of two loops: one loop circulates heat transfer oil through a direct-fired heater, while the other loop circulates heat transfer oil through a storage tank and a water-cooled shell-and-tube cooler.

When oil from the hot-oil loop is used for initiating and sustaining reactions in the user vessels, the cold loop is isolated by valves. When oil from the cold-oil loop is used to slow reactions and cool the products, the hot-oil loop is valved off. However, if cooling water leaks through the tubes of the cooler into the oil in the cooling loop, it may eventually be carried to the heater from the user vessels. Vaporized water in the oil being heated in the fired heater may steam-distill oil vapor over to the hot-oil expansion tank. A flashback from the fired heater may ignite or explode the vapor. Oil-cooler tubes of carbon steel inevitably corrode through because of impurities in the oil and

TABLE 8.10   Comparison of Transverse-Baffle or Support Thicknesses for TEMA Classes R, B, and C

Nominal shell ID	Plate thickness for distance between adjacent segmental supports or for half the distance between full supports								
	R	B	C	R	B	C	R	B	C

	English Units, in								
	12 and under			Over 12 to 24			Over 24 to 36		
6–14	⅛	¹⁄₁₆	¹⁄₁₆	⅛	⅛	⅛	³⁄₁₆	³⁄₁₆	³⁄₁₆
15–28	³⁄₁₆	⅛	⅛	³⁄₁₆	³⁄₁₆	³⁄₁₆	¼	¼	¼
29–38	¼	³⁄₁₆	³⁄₁₆	¼	¼	¼	⁵⁄₁₆	⁵⁄₁₆	⁵⁄₁₆
39–60	¼	¼	¼	¼	¼	¼	⅜	⅜	⅜
	Over 36 to 48			Over 48 to 60			Over 60		
6–14	¼	¼	¼	⅜	⅜	⅜	⅜	⅜	⅜
15–28	⅜	⅜	⅜	⅜	⅜	⅜	½	½	½
29–38	⅜	⅜	⅜	½	½	½	⅝	⅝	⅝
39–60	½	½	½	⅝	⅝	⅝	⅝	⅝	⅝

	Metric Units, mm								
	304.8 and under			Over 304.8 to 609.6			Over 609.6 to 914.4		
152.4–355.6	3.18	3.18	1.59	3.18	3.18	3.18	4.76	4.76	4.76
351–711.2	4.76	4.76	4.76	4.76	4.76	4.76	6.35	6.35	6.35
736.6–965.2	6.35	4.76	4.76	6.35	6.35	6.35	7.94	7.94	7.94
990.6–1524	6.35	6.35	6.35	6.35	6.35	6.35	9.52	9.52	9.52
	Over 914.4 to 1219.2			Over 1219.2 to 1524			Over 1524		
152.4–355.6	6.35	6.35	6.35	9.52	9.52	9.52	9.52	9.52	9.52
351–711.2	9.52	9.52	9.52	9.52	9.52	9.52	12.7	12.7	12.7
990.6–1524	9.52	9.52	9.52	12.7	12.7	12.7	15.9	15.9	15.9
39–60	12.7	12.7	12.7	15.9	15.9	15.9	15.9	15.9	15.9

TABLE 8.11   Comparison of Tie-Rod Requirements for TEMA Classes R, B, and C

Nominal shell diameter	Class R tie rod		Class B tie rod		Class C tie rod	
	Diameter	Number	Diameter	Number	Diameter	Number
	English Units, Diameters in Inches					
6–15	⅜	4	¼	4	¼	4
16–27	⅜	6	⅜	6	⅜	6
28–33	½	6	½	6	½	6
34–48	½	8	½	6	½	8
49–60	½	10	½	10	½	10
	Metric Units, Diameters in Millimeters					
152.6–381	9.52	4	6.35	4	6.35	4
406.4–685.8	9.52	6	9.52	6	9.52	6
711.2–838.2	12.7	6	12.7	6	12.7	6
963.6–1219.2	12.7	8	12.7	6	12.7	8
1244.6–1524	12.7	10	12.7	10	12.7	10

TABLE 8.12   Comparison of Gaskets: Confinement and Gasket Surface Flatness for TEMA Classes R, B, and C

Parameter	TEMA R	TEMA B	TEMA C
Confinement	Required	Optional	Optional
Flatness tolerance of peripheral gasket contact surfaces	± ¹⁄₃₂ in (0.79 mm) from any reference plane; maximum deviation not to occur in less than 20° of arc	Flat enough for hydraulic tightness	Flat enough for hydraulic tightness
Metal or metal-jacketed required	All joints in contact with hydrocarbons and all joints for pressure over 300 lb/in² (2068 kPa); all internal floating-head joints	All joints for pressure over 300 lb/in² (2068 kPa)	All joints for pressure over 300 lb/in² (2068 kPa)

TABLE 8.13   Minimum Tubesheet Thickness for Expanded Joints for TEMA Classes R, B, and C

Tube OD	Minimum tubesheet thickness in expanded region		
	Class R	Class B	Class C
	The greater of ¾ in including corrosion allowance or the thickness listed below minus corrosion allowance		The thickness listed minus corrosion allowance
English Units			
1 in and less	Tube OD	¾ of Tube OD	¾ of tube OD
1¼ in	Tube OD	⅞ in	⅞ in
1½ in	Tube OD	1 in	1 in
2 in	Tube OD	1¼ in	1¼ in
Metric Units			
25 mm and less	Tube OD	¾ of tube OD	¾ of tube OD
32 mm	Tube OD	22.2 mm	22.2 mm
38 mm	Tube OD	25.4 mm	25.4 mm
51 mm	Tube OD	31.8 mm	31.8 mm

water-side corrosion. Therefore, the prudent designer will always make sure that the oil pressure in the cooler is higher than that of the cooling water. This precaution will ensure that when a leak eventually occurs, the heat transfer oil will leak harmlessly into the cooling water and show up in the effluent.

To provide a margin for tube deterioration, either specify an allowance for tube corrosion or a tube gauge greater than the thickness required to resist pressure. The amount to allow depends upon the anticipated service corrosion rate. The anticipated rate may be based upon records of corrosion rates for similar services or upon accelerated corrosion tests. For example, if the anticipated corrosion rate is 0.0125 in per year (0.32 mm per year) and the heat exchanger specification sheet corrosion allowance (which excludes the tubes) is 0.125 in (3.2 mm), it will take 10 years before the metal allowed for corrosion in the pressure parts excluding the tubing will be consumed. The useful life of ¾- or 1-in-OD × 0.083-in-thick (19- or 25.4-mm-OD × 2.1-mm-thick) tubes would be about 5 years for most services before retubing would be required. This allows 0.018 in (0.46 mm) for resisting pressure and 0.065 in (1.66 mm) for wastage.

To calculate the anticipated tube life for a given service, deduct the thickness required to resist pressure from the total tube thickness, and divide the remaining thickness by the anticipated corrosion rate. When the thickness required to withstand pressure is very small, it may be necessary to increase the tube wall arbitrarily to facilitate assembling the tubes into the exchanger.

The reader's attention is called to Paragraph UCS-25 of Section VIII, Division 1, of the *ASME Code*, which reads in part: "Vessels with a required minimum thickness of less than ¼ in. that are to be used in compressed air service, steam service, or water service shall be provided with a corrosion allowance on the metal surface in contact with such substance of not less than one-sixth of the calculated plate thickness except that the sum of the calculated thickness and corrosion allowance need not exceed ¼ in." Although this paragraph refers to plate and does not apply to tubes, it is prudent to follow its requirements for carbon steel tubes.

Service limitations

The *TEMA Mechanical Standards* place service limitations on cast-iron pressure parts and packed joints. They prohibit using cast iron for pressures greater than 150 lb/in² (1034 kPa). Classes R and B further limit cast-iron pressure parts to water service. However, Class C permits cast iron for any service that is not lethal. None of the classes permits using packed joints when the fluids with which they are in contact are lethal or flammable.

Nozzle construction

Except by agreement between the purchaser and the manufacturer, radial nozzles are standard. Nozzles must conform with *ASME Code* requirements. Vent and drain connections must not protrude beyond the inside contour of the shell, channel, or bonnet. Shell nozzles may not protrude past the inside contour of the shell if they can interfere with inserting or removing the bundle. However, channel nozzles may protrude into the channel.

Flange dimensions and facings must comply with ANSI B16.5, with bolt holes straddling the natural centerlines. The mechanical standards for Classes R and B state that *ASME Code* procedures must be used to design nozzle flanges outside the scope of ANSI B16.5. A pipe tap connection for TEMA R must be 6000 lb/in^2 (or the metric equivalent) or greater and be fitted with a round-head bar-stock plug conforming with ANSI B16.11 of the same material. When there is a potential for galling, the plug may be of a different material but not cast iron. For TEMA B and C, the couplings must be 3000 lb/in^2 (or the metric equivalent). Those of TEMA B must be fitted with plugs of the same material, with the same exceptions that apply to TEMA R.

TEMA Standards heat exchangers are not intended to serve as anchor points for piping. Unless they are informed otherwise, manufacturers assume that there are only negligible loadings on nozzles due to piping and that no other loadings will be imposed. They will not perform calculations to determine the maximum loads or moments that the nozzles can withstand. If they are provided with the magnitudes and directions of piping loads and moments, manufacturers will design the nozzles with the required structural strength. They will add to their prices the cost of the required analysis and any modifications to the nozzle construction made necessary by the additional loads and moments. The RGP section has literature references helpful in analyzing effects of nozzle loads.

Protecting bundle components against entering and exiting fluids

The three classes of *TEMA Standards* have identical limitations intended to prevent or curtail erosion of tube bundles at the entrance and exit areas. They require impingement plates in the way of fluid inlets for any of these conditions: (1) when fluid impact values expressed as mass/(distance $\cdot$ time^2) exceed 1500 lb/(ft $\cdot$ s^2) [2230 kg/(m $\cdot$ s^2)] for noncorrosive, nonabrasive single-phase fluids; (2) when fluid impact values exceed 500 lb/(ft $\cdot$ s^2)[745 kg/(m $\cdot$ s^2)] for all other liquids, including liquids at their boiling points; and (3) for all other gases and vapors, including saturated vapors and liquid-vapor mixtures.

The maximum fluid impact value permitted for fluids entering and leaving bundles is 4000 lb/(ft $\cdot$ s) [5950 kg/(m $\cdot$ s)]. The standards define the flow areas into and out of the bundle with and without impingement plates. They caution the designer to consider tube-end erosion when an axial inlet nozzle must be used and whenever the product of the square of tubeside average linear-flow velocity and density exceeds 6000 lb/(ft $\cdot$ s) [8925 kg/(m $\cdot$ s)]. However, they provide no specific nozzle-sizing criteria.

The RPG section of the current edition of the *TEMA Standards* has six figures that illustrate how to calculate shell entrance or exit areas with and without impingement plates.

Vents, drains, pressure gauge, and thermometer taps

The three classes of mechanical standards require manufacturers to provide vents in the high points and drains in the low points of shellside and tubeside. The vents must be at least ¾ in (19 mm) in diameter but, at the manufacturer's option, may be larger.

TEMA R and B require all flanged connections 2 in (50.4 mm) and larger to be fitted with a ½-in-IPS (12.7-mm metric equivalent) pressure tap and those 4 in and larger to be fitted with a 1-in-IPS (25.4-mm metric equivalent) thermometer connection. However, these connections may be omitted in one of the two mating connections between the stacked units. Pressure and temperature connections for TEMA C units are as specified by the purchaser.

Safety relief devices

Manufacturers do not furnish safety relief devices except by agreement with purchasers. The *ASME Code* specifies requirements for safety relief to maintain pressure within safe limits related to the MAWP on each side of the exchanger. The user or system designer must calculate the capacity and size of the required safety relief devices. The purchaser must specify the number, size, and location of connections for the safety relief devices.

End flange bolting

Bolting must conform with *ASME Code* requirements and consist of through-bolted studs. The studs must be threaded full-length, with a removable nut on each end. When the nut is fully engaged, each end of the stud must project approximately ⅛ in (3.2 mm). Note that this allowance is not sufficient for bolt tensioning because there is not enough length for engaging the tensioner.

Bolt spacing must be even and straddle the natural centerlines. The natural centerlines of horizontal units are defined as the vertical and horizontal centerlines. The bolt count must be a multiple of 4, except for special cases.

An important distinction between the three TEMA classes is the minimum bolt size permitted for end flanges. For R it is ¾ in (19 mm), for B it is ⅝ in (15.9 mm), and for C it is ½ in (12.7 mm). Thread series are American national coarse below 1 in and eight-pitch thread series for 1 in and larger.

Guide to the Heat Exchange Institute Standards

The Heat Exchange Institute (HEI), located in Cleveland, Ohio, publishes standards for tubular exchangers used in power generation. Therefore, these apply to units that handle boiler feedwater and steam generated for the production of electric power. Among these standards are (1) *Standard for Power Plant Heat Exchangers* (HEI PPS) and the *Standards for Closed Feedwater Heaters* (HEI CFHS). The following highlights these standards; for specific applications, refer to the originals.

HEI Standard for Power Plant Heat Exchangers

The HEI PPS is used for auxiliary power plant tubular exchangers. It is applied primarily in the United States and Canada. Although it is not meant to be used for feedwater heaters and steam surface condensers, its data are consistent with the data of those standards. It suggests using the *ASME Power Test Code* for measuring temperature, pressure, and flow when evaluating the performance capability of exchangers.

This standard has a heat exchanger specification sheet similar to the TEMA one. In addition, it lists the minimum data that purchasers must provide to the manufacturer. These data include minimum overload and abnormal conditions and other information necessary for the manufacturer to perform a comprehensive fatigue and operability analysis.

The HEI PPS requires the purchaser to describe the following:

1. The mode of operation
2. The maximum allowable pressure losses for abnormal operating conditions
3. Thermal and hydraulic transients
4. Thermal conditions for intended chemical cleaning

The standard states that if this information is not provided, the manufacturer will design for steady-state operation at the specified design point.

In comparison with the HEI PPS, the *TEMA Standards* are less specific. They require a purchaser only to provide the manufacturer with all information needed for a clear understanding of performance requirements, including any special requirements. In response, the manufacturer guarantees performance based upon operation at the specified design conditions.

The HEI PPS briefly discusses operating modes that can cause deviations from the design point. It lists some of the possible results of overload or abnormal operation. It suggests that design specifications describe any operations that can lead to deviant modes, pointing out that such deviations may accelerate wastage and failure. However, it has no guidelines for determining the relationship of time at overload or abnormal conditions versus acceleration of wastage and failure.

The HEI PPS parallels the *TEMA Standards* in many ways, but there are enough differences so that one cannot be substituted for the other. This standard is organized into 7 sections and 11 appendixes. Numbering of sections and their subparagraphs follows the multiple-decimal system. The sections are:

1.0   Scope and purpose
2.0   Definitions
3.0   Heat exchanger performance
4.0   Materials of construction

5.0   Mechanical design standards

6.0   Heat exchanger protection

7.0   Site installation, inspection, maintenance, and cleaning

Appendixes are numbered A through K as follows: A and B contain thermal design information; C has an approximate procedure for calculating nozzle external forces and moments in cylindrical vessels; D, E, H, and K provide mechanical and mathematical information; G has dimensional tolerances for nozzles and supports; and J has sketches of typical arrangements of shells and channels, details of the HEI system for describing them, and nomenclature of their parts.

Flow criteria and nozzle sizing. The HEI PPS lists maximum recommended average linear velocities for flow in the tubes of water of boiler-feed quality. Table 8.14 lists the HEI criteria for establishing inlet- and outlet-nozzle sizes for shellside and tubeside connections for subcooled liquids, liquids near their saturation point, and gases or dry vapors.

ASME Code construction. Heat exchangers built to this standard must be *ASME Code*–stamped. In contrast to the *TEMA Standards*, which require construction to meet the requirements of Section VIII, Division 1, the HEI PPS includes units conforming with Section VIII, Division 1, Section VIII, Division 2, and Section III, Division 1, Class 1, 2, or 3.

TABLE 8.14   HEI Criteria for Establishing Minimum Nozzle Sizes for Shellside and Tubeside Inlet and Outlet Connections

	Maximum value of (mass velocity)^2/density			
	Tubeside nozzles		Shellside nozzles	
	Inlet	Outlet	Inlet	Outlet
English Units				
Liquids, subcooled	6200	6200	4000	4000
Liquids, near saturation	1000	250	1000	250
Gases and dry vapors	2000	2000	2000	2000
Metric Units				
Liquids, subcooled	9230	9230	5950	5950
Liquids, near saturation	1490	370	1490	370
Gases and dry vapors	2975	2975	2975	2975

Corrosion allowance. Unlike the *TEMA Standards*, the *Standard for Power Plant Heat Exchangers* does not specify a minimum corrosion allowance (except for the corrosion allowance required by *ASME Code* construction). Instead, it requires the purchaser to specify corrosion allowances. It points out that useful tube life is affected by service conditions and differently by long- and short-term shutdowns. It recommends that purchasers consider these factors when selecting tube materials and thicknesses.

Tube diameters, thicknesses, and tube-hole drilling pitches. The minimum tube diameter recommended for power plant exchangers is ⅜-in (9.5-mm) OD. The standard covers tubes up to 2-in (50.8-mm) OD but permits larger diameters. It accepts average-wall tubes if the calculated thickness accounts for wall-thickness tolerance. It recommends the minimum tube wall thicknesses listed in Table 8.15 and the minimum drilling pitches of Table 8.16.

Tube-hole drilling. The sizes and tolerances for tube holes and ligament widths are essentially identical with those of the *TEMA Standards*.

Tube-to-tubesheet joints. The HEI PPS discusses requirements for the following kinds of tube-to-tubesheet joints: (1) those made by expanding tubes into ungrooved holes, (2) those made by expanding tubes into grooved holes, and (3) those made by welding and expanding.

The tubesheets of most exchangers used in power generation are carbon steel. Therefore, both the HEI PPS and the HEI CFHS recommend maximum joint temperatures for expanded-only joints of various tube metals expanded into carbon steel tubesheets. These are combined in Table 8.17.

The standard requires expansion for a depth of the lesser of 2 in (50.8 mm) or to within ⅛ in (3.18 mm) of the shellside tubesheet face.

TABLE 8.15   Minimum Tube Wall Thicknesses Recommended by the
HEI Power Plant Heat Exchanger Standards

Tube material	Wall thickness
Austenitic stainless steel	
Straight tubes	22-BWG average wall
U tubes	20-BWG average wall
Nickel alloy	18-BWG average wall
Copper and copper alloy	18-BWG average wall
Titanium: straight tubes	22-BWG average wall
Carbon steel	0.050-in (1.27-mm) average wall

TABLE 8.16   Minimum Recommended Tube-Hole Drilling Pitches of the *HEI Power Plant Heat Exchanger Standards*

Nominal tube OD		Nominal tube pitch	
in	mm	in	mm
3/8	9.5	1/2*	12.7*
1/2	12.7	5/8*	15.9*
5/8	15.9	13/16	20.6
3/4	19	15/16	23.8
7/8	22.2	13/32	27.8
1	25.4	11/4	31.8
11/4	31.8	19/16	39.7
11/2	38.1	17/8	47.6
2	50.8	21/2	63.5

*These pitches should be increased when the tube holes are double-grooved.

TABLE 8.17   Maximum Tube and Tube-to-Tubesheet Joint Temperatures

Tube material	Maximum tube metal temperature		Maximum joint temperature	
	°F	°C	°F	°C
Arsenical copper	400	204.4	350	176.7
Admiralty metal	500	260	350	176.7
90-10 cupronickel	600	315.6	400	204.4
80-20 cupronickel	700	371.1	450	232.2
70-30 cupronickel (annealed)	700	371.1	500	260
Nickel copper (annealed)	900	482.2	550	287.8
Nickel copper (stress-relieved)	800	426.7	550	287.8
Carbon steel	800	426.7	650	343.2
Stainless steel	800	426.7	500	260

It permits maximum tube-end protrusion of 1/4 in (6.4 mm) and tube-end recess of 1/16 in (1.6 mm), except that these must be flush with the top tubesheet of vertical exchangers.

The HEI PPS recommends two 1/8-in-wide × 1/64-in-deep (3.18-mm-wide × 0.40-mm-deep) grooves of rectangular or semicircular cross section for designs that require annular grooves in the tube holes for strength. It defines welded tube-to-tubesheet joints as seal-welded when the weld dimension parallel with the tube is less than the nominal tube thickness. It defines welded joints as strength-welded when the weld dimension parallel with the tube is equal to or more than the nominal tube thickness. Furthermore, the standard recommends supplementing strength welds by expanding the tubes into the holes when the weld length parallel with the tube is less than 1.4 times the nominal tube wall.

This standard has a typical construction and testing sequence for joints made by welding and expanding. It has criteria for determining how much of the axial tube load a joint may be allowed to carry when its strength has not been determined by testing for the following: (1) joints made by expanding only into bare holes, (2) joints made by expanding only into grooved holes, (3) joints made by welding and expanding when the holes are bare, (4) joints made by welding and expanding when the holes are grooved, and (5) joints made by welding only.

Baffles and support plates. The basic HEI PPS recommendations for how much hole diameters should exceed tube diameters are identical with TEMA's. However, those of the *TEMA Standards* include an overtolerance of 0.01 in (0.25 mm) for 96 percent of the holes and 0.015 in (0.38 mm) for 4 percent of the holes, and they permit drilling baffle and support-plate holes smaller than the standard when pulsating conditions are anticipated.

The recommended cross-flow baffle and support-plate thicknesses are similar to TEMA B's. An exception is that for unsupported tube lengths greater than 60 in (1254 mm), in shells larger than 59-in (1499-mm) ID, the prescribed thickness is ¾ in (19 mm). A significant difference between the *TEMA Standards* and HEI PPS is that the latter requires adding ⅛ in (3.18 mm) to the tabulated thicknesses for carbon steel baffles or support plates. In effect, this adds a corrosion allowance of ⅛ in (3.18 mm) to carbon steel baffles. Another significant difference is that the HEI PPS maximum permitted unsupported tube length is substantially less than TEMA's for all tube sizes.

HEI Standards for Closed Feedwater Heaters

Chapter 1 has definitions that apply to closed feedwater heaters. Chapter 5 discusses their tubeside construction briefly, and Chap. 6 their shellside construction. These discussions are based upon and refer to the *Heat Exchange Institute Standards for Closed Feedwater Heaters*. Feedwater heater technology is extensive, and the standards cannot be fully covered here. However, some comments are offered.

Performance. The demand for power varies with the time of day, day of the week, month of the year, and the general level of economic activity. Moreover, as new power stations are built, older ones may be shifted from base-load to peaking service. Furthermore, it is very costly to shut down a whole string of feedwater heaters for maintenance of one heater in the string. Therefore, it is a common practice to bypass the one being worked on, which changes the conditions of operation of the rest. If two strings are operated in parallel and it becomes necessary to shut one down for maintenance, the feedwater and steam ordinarily carried by both strings may flow through the one that remains in operation. Consequently feedwater heaters must perform under a variety of conditions.

In establishing a design basis for heater performance, the HEI CFHS recommend designing for specific design-point conditions. However, specifications should always apprise the designer of anticipated overloads that result from the circumstances described above and require the heater or heaters to withstand the excessive flows that ensue.

The HEI CFHS have an extensive checklist of minimum data that purchasers must provide to manufacturers. As a guide, the standards recommend minimum fouling resistances for shellside and tubeside, minimum TTDs (terminal temperature differences) for heaters without desuperheating zones, closest drain-subcooling approach for units that have integral subcooling zones, maximum tubeside average linear velocity for various tube metals, and limits for shellside pressure loss.

They also suggest various precautions and recommend criteria for nozzle and line sizes. The standards have recommendations for steam nozzle locations and steam distribution and drain and control connections. They describe some possible overload and abnormal operating modes and their potential for causing trouble. Other recommendations cover provisions for operating and startup vents. The purchaser's attention is called to the effect on vent steam flows needed to maintain required oxygen levels in deaerating heaters.

Mechanical design standards. Unless the purchaser specifies variances, the HEI CFHS mechanical design standards require construction and stamping according to the *ASME Code*, Section VIII, Division 1. This division may not apply to high-pressure heaters that exceed its pressure limits. The mechanical standards require the purchaser to specify the design pressures and temperatures. They provide a guide for rationally establishing these conditions.

The HEI CFHS suggest what to consider when selecting tubes. These recommendations include the maximum tube metal temperatures for various metals. In addition, the standards suggest maximum temperatures for expanded-only tube-to-tubesheet joints of various tube materials in carbon steel tubesheets. (See Table 8.17.) The joint temperature is assumed to be the feedwater outlet temperature.

Other coverages of the HEI CFHS mechanical standards are:

1. Tube gauges and minimum wall thicknesses for nonferrous, stainless-steel, and carbon steel tubes.

2. Tube length and U-tube bending.

3. Bundle construction.

4. Tube layout on minimum pitch [= the greater of tube diameter plus 3/16 in (tube diameter plus 4.8 mm) or 1.25 × tube OD].

5. Baffles, support plates, shrouds, longitudinal baffles, and impingement baffles.

6. Tubesheets.

7. Channel covers with and without pass-partition seal covers.

8. Heater supports and installation in condenser necks.

9. Nozzles. For nozzle loads they have a simplification of the Welding Research Council (WRC) method of analysis. They also have standard tolerances for nozzle and support locations.

Guide to API Standard 660

This guide reviews requirements of API Standard 660, *Shell-and-Tube Heat Exchangers for General Refinery Service*, hereafter called API 660. It covers technical sections and appendixes which exceed or supplement the TEMA R standards. It does not discuss sections devoted to commercial matters and does not follow API 660's numerical order.

API 660 is a *purchaser*'s specification intended for removable-bundle floating-head or U-tube construction and compels other designs to conform with the standard. It requires exchangers to meet the requirements of *TEMA Standards*, sixth edition, Sections 1, 2, 3, 5 (Class R), and 8 and to be built to the *ASME Code*.* API 660 applies some restrictions to the *TEMA Standards* and adds requirements and tolerances that they do not include.

Its Appendix C tabulates process and geometry constraints that apply to an exchanger or a group of exchangers. The tabulation enables a purchaser to inform a vendor of the constraints in an orderly way.

API 660 lists options that buyers may elect and specifications that require buyers' decisions. It highlights the paragraphs that describe these options and specifications with bullets in the margin adjacent to the paragraph number. API 660's Appendix B is a purchaser's yes-no checklist for the optional paragraphs and items they describe. In thefollowing, purchaser's decision items will be similarly highlighted.

---

*Section 8 of the sixth edition of the *TEMA Standards* specified materials for use in TEMA standard heat exchangers. It has been replaced in the seventh edition by a section on vibration.

Design temperature

API 660 defines shellside design temperature as the design metal temperature of the shell and shell cover, including flanges. It defines tubeside design temperature as the design metal temperature of the channel, including flanges, and the channel cover. Design temperatures of shell-cover and channel-cover.flange gaskets and bolts are the same as for the flanges. Design temperature for shell-to-channel gaskets and bolts is the more severe of shellside or tubeside design temperatures.

In selecting design temperatures, API 660 requires considering clean and fouled operating conditions and any other operating conditions that the purchaser specifies. For multiple shells in series, the maximum or minimum temperature on each side of each shell in the clean and fouled conditions must be considered.

Materials

When the purchaser specifies that certain types of stress cracking are possible, internal bolting must be ASME SA-193, Grade B7M.

To minimize the possibility of brittle fracture, the purchaser may specify impact requirements more stringent than those of Section VIII, Division 1, of the *ASME Code*.

Option for corrosion allowance

Bonded cladding thickness may be used as a corrosion allowance. Weld overlaying is considered to be bonded cladding.

Tubes

U tubes may be formed only from single lengths with no circumferential welds. Integrally finned copper-alloy tubes must be furnished in the annealed temper. Stress relief is required after bending for integrally finned copper-alloy tubes. For all U bends, heat treatment must extend for at least 6 in (150 mm) beyond the bend tangent.

For other materials, the purchaser must specify post-U-bending heat treatment.

Tubesheets

There must be an allowance of at least $\frac{1}{16}$ in (1.6 mm) between tube holes and gasket grooves for expanded-only tube-to-tubesheet joints. For welded joints, there must be an allowance of at least $\frac{1}{8}$ in (3.2 mm). The tolerance on these allowances is +0, −0.02 in (+0, −0.5 mm).

Tube-hole grooves must be square-edged, concentric, and free from burrs.

The design of channel-down vertical units must provide for a suitable means of holding the bundle in place at the tubesheet when the channel is removed. If shoulder bolts or drilled and tapped holes are used, at least four must be provided and their locations identified.

Channels, bonnets, and stationary and floating heads

Floating heads must be designed so that the cover bolting is readily accessible when the cover is removed. Packed-floating-head and packed-floating-tubesheet designs may not be used.

For bonnet construction, the exchanger must be designed so that it can be tested with the bonnets removed. Staybolts may not be used to strengthen stationary heads. Channel and shell external joint flanges must be through-bolted unless the purchaser accepts a deviation.

Postweld heat treatment is required for the following fabricated carbon steel channels and bonnets:

1. Channels and bonnets with six or more tube passes
2. Two- or four-pass channels and bonnets which have a cylinder-to-nozzle diameter ratio of 2.0 or less
3. One-pass channels and bonnets with nonaxial nozzles that have a cylinder-to-nozzle-diameter ratio of 2.0 or less

Shells and shell covers

Except for U-tube and kettle-type units, covers must be removable. Except for kettle-type exchangers, all inner girth and longitudinal seams must be finished flush with the unit's contour. In kettle-type units, longitudinal and girth welds must be flush in the bottom quadrant.

API 660 limits shell out-of-roundness for removable-bundle exchangers. It requires passing a template completely through the shell without binding. The template consists of two rigid disks, each having a diameter equal to the transverse baffles or tube supports, mounted perpendicularly on a shaft 12 in (300 mm) apart.

Shell supports. API 660 adds the following to the TEMA requirements for supports:

1. Removable-bundle fixed shell supports must be able to withstand a longitudinal force, acting at the bundle centerline, equal to 150 percent of the bundle weight.

2. The maximum allowed support shear stress is 40 percent of the yield strength.

3. Saddles must bear on at least one-third of horizontal plate shells.

4. The lower shells of stacked removable-bundle units must be able to carry the superimposed loads without distorting so much that they could bind the bundles.

5. A shim allowance of ¼ in (6 mm) must be provided between faces of the intermediate supports.

Unless the purchaser specifically approves using transverse-baffle-to-shell clearances greater than indicated in TEMA Table R-4.3, they are not permitted.

Bundles

These are some of API 660's requirements for bundles:

Transverse baffles, support plates, and impingement baffles. API 660 supplements TEMA Table R-4.41 by requiring cross-flow baffles and support plates to be at least as thick as the specified shellside corrosion allowance. It adds these requirements for impingement baffles to those of TEMA R:

1. Impingement baffles must extend at least 1 in (25.4 mm) beyond the nozzle bore.

2. Unrestricted bundle entrance flow area must be at least as great as the inlet-nozzle flow area.

3. Minimum impingement-plate thickness is ¼ in (6 mm).

Bypass seals. Specific bypass sealing-device requirements illustrated in API 660 are as follows:

1. These requirements apply to bypass seals for U-tube bundles:
   a. When the distance between baffle-cut edges is six tube pitches or less, a single seal must be provided.
   b. When the distance between baffle-cut edges is more than six tube pitches, there must be a seal every five to seven tube pitches between the baffle cuts. The outermost seals must not be more than 3 in (76.2 mm) from each baffle-cut edge.
2. Inner edges of peripheral seals must be at least as close to a tube as the nominal clearance between tubes.
3. Nominal seal-strip thickness must be the thinner of ¼ in (25.4 mm) or the transverse-baffle thickness. Bypass seal strips must be attached to the baffles by continuous welds.
4. The buyer may specify the need for and location of bypass seals in

straight-tube units. The buyer may also specify that bypass seal locations minimize obstructions to cleaning lanes or that continuous cleaning lanes must be maintained.

Bundle skid bars. On removable bundles that weigh more than 20,000 lb (9080 kg), API 660 requires skid bars or other suitable means for forming a continuous sliding surface. Skid bars must be welded to the transverse baffles and support plates.

For pulling bundles, the standard requires lugs or holes tapped to receive eyebolts on the outer face of the stationary tubesheet. The lugs or holes must be designed for a pulling force of at least 150 percent of the bundle's weight. Tapped holes must be fitted with threaded plugs, at least 2 in (50.8 mm) long, made of the same materials as the tubesheet.

Nozzles and other connections

API 660 limits flanged connections to forged or centrifugally cast welding necks, forged or centrifugally cast welding-neck flanges welded to pipe necks, and slip-on flanges welded to pipe. It restricts slip-on flange and pipe construction to 300 lb/in^2 (2100-kPa) design pressure and 850°F (455°C) design temperature. Steel flanges must be in accordance with ANSI B16.5 or API Standard 605 when they fall within the scope of those standards.

Nozzles may not protrude beyond shell, channel, or head inside surfaces. Couplings installed in shell cylinders may not protrude beyond their inside surfaces.

The projection of flanged connections must permit removing through bolting from either side of the flange with insulation in place. The purchaser must specify the insulation thickness.

The buyer may require connections of nominal pipe size (NPS) 1½ and larger to be flanged or beveled for welding and smaller connections to be flanged or threaded.

When the buyer specifies chemical cleaning connections, the smallest size is NPS 2.

Flanged external girth joints, gaskets, and gasket surfaces

API 660 requires that when nubbins are provided on flange faces, they be located on the female flange. After assembly, the standard requires a nominal clearance between flanges of ⅛ in (3.2 mm), extending within the bolt circle. This is done to allow checking the flanges for distortion caused by excessive bolt loads.

Gaskets for hydrocarbon service must be double-jacketed asbestos-filled metal, solid metal, or spiral-wound metal. Spiral-wound gaskets must be provided with a means to prevent overcompression. Metal-jacketed and solid metal gaskets must be of a material at least as corrosion-resistant as the gasket contact surface material. Solid metal gaskets must be softer than the gasket contact surface, including welds. Compressed-asbestos gaskets must be graphited on both sides or contain an antistick release agent.

The manufacturer must supply a complete set of spare gaskets for each exchanger.

Other than for nozzle-flange facings, gasket contact surfaces must lie within roughness height finish limits of 125 and 80 root mean square (rms) or 139 and 89 arithmetic average (AA).

Except for special services, the maximum gasket surface deviation from flatness on a plane at peripheral contact surfaces, as measured by a straightedge, is $\frac{1}{32}$ in (0.8 mm).

For special applications (for example, high-pressure–high-temperature or hydrogen service) the purchaser may specify the following tolerances:

Nominal exchanger diameter		Tolerance	
in	mm	in	mm
≤15	381	0.003	0.08
>15–30	381–762 inclusive	0.006	0.15
>30–45	762–1143 inclusive	0.009	0.23
>45	1143	0.012	0.30

Flatness must be measured with a dial indicator. For special services, when the channel is not designed with a channel cover, the flatness tolerance on individual pass-partition grooves is $\frac{1}{32}$ in (0.8 mm).

Flanges for external girth joints must be the forged welding-neck type, but for design conditions that do not exceed Class 150 pressure-temperature ratings governed in ANSI B16.5, forged slip-on welding flanges may be used. API 660 also permits using forged slip-on or other forged-welding-type flanges when the purchaser approves them.

Spiral-wound metal gasket windings must be made of 18 percent chromium–8 percent nickel unless the purchaser specifies otherwise.

Assembly

Match marking or doweling is required to prevent misassembling the following joints: (1) multipass floating-head cover-to-tubesheet joints, (2) multipass channel-to-tubesheet joints, (3) grooved channel cover-to-channel joints, and (4) stationary tubesheet-to-shell joints. The threads of external studs and nuts must be coated with a lubricant suitable for preventing galling.

Inspection and testing

The API 660 standard provides for the purchaser's inspection of heat exchanger materials, fabrication, conformity with mechanical design, and testing. The purchaser, purchaser's representative, or both may inspect. The standard requires a release for shipment by one of these individuals.

A purchaser who specifies inspection by a designated inspector must provide a description of inspection details beyond those that the *ASME Code* authorized inspector makes. The description specifies details of nondestructive examinations and pressure testing. It states how and where to attach nameplates and requires the manufacturer's serial number to be stamped on the following parts: (1) shell flange, (2) shell-cover flange, (3) channel or bonnet flange, (4) channel cover, (5) stationary tubesheet, (6) floating tubesheet, (7) floating-head cover flange, (8) floating-head backing device, and (9) test-ring flange and gland.

Supplemental requirements

The supplemental requirements section discusses additional design, fabrication, and examination requirements that apply only when the purchaser specifies them. Its requirements are intended for construction for critical services and whenever a cylindrical exchanger component's thickness exceeds 2 in (50.8 mm).

Suggested Reading

Mase, John R., and Alfred M. Smolen: "ASME Pressure Vessel Code: Which Division to Choose," *Chem. Eng.*, Jan. 11, 1982, pp. 133–136.
"Special Report of Worldwide Pressure Vessel Codes," *Hydrocarbon Process.*, December 1978.
Yokell, S.: "Design and Fabrication of Heat Exchangers," *Practical Aspects of Heat Transfer*, a CEP technical manual based upon proceedings of the 1976 fall lecture series of the New Jersey and North Jersey sections of the AIChE.

References

1. *ASME Boiler and Pressure Vessel Code*, American Society of Mechanical Engineers, New York. (New editions are published at 3-year intervals.)
2. *National Board Inspection Code*, The National Board of Boiler and Pressure Vessel Inspectors, Columbus, Ohio. (New editions of the *National Board Code* are issued at about the same time as new editions of the *ASME Code*.)
3. *Pressure Vessel Inspection Code*, API 510, 3d ed., The American Petroleum Institute, Washington, 1983.

4. *Standards of the Tubular Exchanger Manufacturers Association*, 7th ed., The Tubular Exchanger Manufacturers Association, Tarrytown, N.Y., 1989.
5. *Standard for Power Plant Heat Exchangers*, 1st ed., The Heat Exchange Institute, Cleveland, 1980; Addendum 1, 1984.
6. *Standards for Closed Feedwater Heaters*, The Heat Exchange Institute, Cleveland, 1984.
7. *Shell-and-Tube Exchangers for General Refinery Services*, API Standard 660, 4th ed., The American Petroleum Institute, Washington, September 1982.
8. "Mechanical Design Codes," *Heat Exchanger Design Handbook*, vol. 4, Hemisphere Publishing, New York, 1983. (This publication is intended to be revised annually.)
9. *Regels voor Toesellen onder Druck*, Government Printing Office, The Hague, Netherlands.
10. A. I. Soler and K. P. Singh, *Mechanical Design of Heat Exchangers and Pressure Vessels*, Arcturus Publishers, Cherry Hill, N.J., 1984.
11. *Synopsis of Boiler and Pressure Vessel Laws, Rules and Regulations by States, Cities, Counties and Provinces (United States and Canada)*, Uniform Boiler and Pressure Vessel Laws Society, Long Island City, N.Y. (Updated regularly.)

9

Troubleshooting

Introduction

Trouble in a heat exchanger seems to show up as either a process or a mechanical problem. However, thermal performance depends upon the construction of the exchanger, and mechanical functioning depends upon how the thermal regime affects the structure. Therefore, problems of mechanical failure and inadequate performance cannot be treated separately. This chapter is a guide to finding the causes of mechanical problems in tubular exchangers and the "fixes" necessary to restore them to service.

General Symptoms

The most frequent complaints are that (1) the unit does not perform as required and (2) it leaks. Performance deficiency is obvious when duty or pressure-drop requirements are not met, but there are more obscure problems. For example, a refrigerated condenser may adequately remove latent heat without exceeding the permissible pressure drop. Yet if the tube-wall temperature is too low, condensate may freeze on the tubes. This can lead to progressive loss of capacity, increase in pressure drop, or uneven operation. The frozen condensate may cause mechanical damage to the tubes or tube-to-tubesheet joints. Another example is an exchanger that transfers heat at both the design rate and pressure drop but, because of high tube-wall temperature, causes unacceptable stream degradation.

Similarly, a leak to the atmosphere is obvious, but one between the shellside and the tubeside may not be discovered until a gross mixing of the streams is discovered or there is a drastic decline in performance. Small leaks may lead to the erroneous conclusion that the tubes are progressively fouling.

Underlying Causes of General Symptoms

Performance usually deteriorates from deposits on the tube surfaces. However, a multipass exchanger's capacity to transfer heat may decline because of internal leakage between the passes. Such a leak slowly increases as the gasket surface erodes. The resulting capacity loss may also appear to be due to fouling. Often the problem will remain hidden until the channel and cover are removed in preparation for tube cleaning. Pass-partition and tubesheet erosion, as illustrated in Fig. 9.1, may then be discovered. Because erosion and corrosion interact, it may not be possible to determine which caused the damage.

Performance deteriorates when the clearance between the shell and the cross-flow baffles increases, but this structural ailment is not obvious. The cause may be baffle corrosion or damage during reassembly of a unit. Exchanger capacity also declines with increases in the clearance between baffle or support holes and the tubes due to corrosion. The increased annular clearance affects performance by allowing increased shell-fluid leakage, but it may also contribute to vibration damage to the tubes.

Mechanical problems such as tube damage and baffle wear may be caused by vibration forcing by the fluid regime, excessive baffle-hole–tube clearance, or failure to remove sharp upset material due to drilling from the back side of the baffles or tube supports.

The trouble may be the result of faulty thermal or mechanical design, poor construction, or misuse of the equipment.[1,2] Defects in thermal design show up quickly, but the effects of mechanical misdesign and shoddy work usually appear after the manufacturer's guarantee has expired.

Determining that an exchanger has been abused or misused may make you unpopular. Nevertheless, you must diagnose the problem dispassionately. You may have to get information from the specifier, the designer, the manufacturer, the installer, the user, and the maintainer. Each has a legitimate interest in the diagnosis. Of course, the information provided is colored by its source.

Assembling the Facts

Before starting to analyze the problem, collect as much of the following information as possible:

1. The process flowsheet

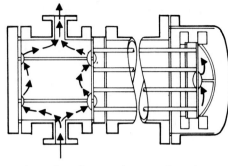

Bypassing at channel cover and
channel-to-tubesheet joint
due to erosion/corrosion

Bypassing at
return cover

Figure 9.1 Effects of tubesheet and pass-partition erosion-corrosion. (*Courtesy of* Chemical Engineering.)

2. The purchaser's original exchanger specification with all subsequent revisions

3. The manufacturer's original exchanger specification sheet with all subsequent revisions

4. All correspondence about the thermal and mechanical design

5. Thermal design calculations

6. Mechanical design calculations

7. Setting plan and assembly and detail drawings

8. Shop and field inspection reports

9. Radiographs, nondestructive examination reports, and records of hydrostatic and leak tests

10. Startup and shutdown procedures and procedures for dealing with upsets

11. Operating logs and temperature- and pressure-recorder charts

12. Maintenance records

Often it helps to visit the installation and to interview the operating and maintenance personnel. Frequently these people make changes that improve the way a heat exchanger functions or that reduce maintenance costs and downtime, but because they rarely have time and may not be trained to consider side effects, their actions may cause problems.

The following illustrates how an apparently innocent modification to a procedure may seriously damage an exchanger.

A pharmaceutical plant had several long-tube fixed-tubesheet evaporators built with bellows-type shell expansion joints. After each run, the specified procedure was to brush the inside of the tubes to remove organic matter, then to sterilize. Sterilization was accomplished by filling the tubes with water and then blowing them down with dry steam.

After a period of uneventful operation, the evaporators began to exhibit buckled tubes and leaks in the tube-to-tubesheet joints. The leaks and tube failures were randomly distributed in the tube field. Examining the available information led nowhere. It was obvious that the differences in tube metal temperatures within the bundle were causing the failures. However, the reason for the differences was unknown.

Interviewing the shift operators and maintainers shed no light, nor did examining many time-versus-temperature charts. However, on a plant visit the heat exchanger specialist noticed a neatly stowed steam hose with a pipe inserted into its outlet end. Screwed to the end of the pipe was a reducing bushing that appeared to have been turned down to fit into the evaporator tube ends. It was immediately surmised that the tubes had been individually steam-cleaned. This was confirmed by the operator's reply when he was asked what the hose was used for. "Oh," he said, "we save the brushing, boil-out, and blowdown steps by shooting live steam down each tube. And we don't have to worry about the difference in expansion between the shell and tubes because we have these great expansion joints." Unfortunately, the operator had also not worried about the difference in expansion between steamed tubes and adjacent cold ones.

Examining the flowsheet and specifications may provide an explanation of why there are differences between specified and measured design-point terminal conditions. Subtle modifications may have been made to the stated requirements in order to reduce exchanger size and cost. By reading the technical correspondence, a design compromise that led to the present problem may be spotted.

Misuse of computer design programs

Most exchanger calculations are made by computers, using thoroughly debugged and tested programs. Well-written programs warn the user of undesirable or unworkable aspects, as illustrated in Fig. 9.2.* However, the user usually has the option of ignoring the warnings and allowing program execution to continue; unheeded warnings may be the source of the trouble.

On the other hand, the program designer may have assumed that construction would follow the physical model upon which the program was based. Warnings that certain construction features are essential may therefore have been omitted. The program user may have had a

---

*Courtesy of B-Jac Computer Services, Inc., Midlothian, Virginia.

```
ERROR-COOLANT TEMPERATURE APPROACH TOO CLOSE FOR MULTIPASS CONDENSER
TRY COUNTER-CURRENT FLOW USING CHANGE CODE TPMX =1:
ARE THERE ANY CHANGES-Y N OR L? L = LIST OF CHANGE CODES
> SEMN = 2

WARNING-WMTO BASED ON COUNTER-CURRENT FLOW

WARNING-NUMBER OF TUBES SPECIFIED MAY NOT FIT IN SHELL
NUMBER OF TUBES CALCULATED = 992

I   ID   TLE   TLC   POS    POT     BS      BN   TP   TN     P   S    PRICE
1   44   19.6  19.1  0.990  10.371  16.800  14   6    1044   1   2    102996

WARNING-TWO OR MORE SEALING STRIPS MUST BE PROVIDED ON EACH SIDE TUBE BUNDLE
        WITH MAXIMUM SPACING OF 12 IN.

WARNING-BAFFLE NUMBER INCLUDES ONE FULL SUPPORT

ARE DETAILS DESIRED ON THIS DESIGN-Y N OR ALL?  (ALL = WITH HEADINGS)
> N
ARE THERE ANY CHANGES-Y N OR L?  (L = LIST OF CHANGE CODES)
> LO1A = 1 SIZE = 45:

WARNING-WMTO BASED ON COUNTER-CURRENT FLOW

WARNING-WMTO BASED ON COUNTER CURRENT FLOW

I   ID   TLE   TLC   POS    POT     BS      BN   TP   TN     P   S    PRICE
1   45   19.6  19.3  0.977  10.371  16.800  14   6    1044   1   2    105096

WARNING-TWO OR MORE SEALING STRIPS MUST BE PROVIDED ON EACH SIDE TUBE BUNDLE
        WITH MAXIMUM SPACING OF 12 in.

WARNING-BAFFLE NUMBER INCLUDES ONE FULL SUPPORT

WARNING-BYPASS LANES SHOULD BE ELIMINATED BY DUMMY TUBES OR TIES RODS
```

Figure 9.2 Computer program output showing warnings. (*Courtesy of* Chemical Engineering.)

different mental image and not provided the necessary features. For example, a program designer might assume that the user would employ seal strips or dummy tubes in any U-tube or multipass design to prevent fluid bypassing, but the exchanger designer omitted them because they were not shown on the computer output.

Most programs repeat input data in an orderly arrangement. Here is where to look for conceptual errors by examining the data fed to the machine. In addition, computer programs provide far more output information than is available on standard manufacturer's heat exchanger specification sheets. Finding out what is wrong may be simplified by having access to calculated film rates for each zone, the amount of excess surface provided, and the calculated interpass and metal wall temperatures. Rubin has pointed out the importance of tabulating design data by zones in multizonal condensers.[3]

Reviewing mechanical design calculations

Reviewing mechanical design calculations may be as important for what was not calculated as for what was. For example, the thickness calculation for the tubesheet may show that it is adequate to withstand the applied loads without exceeding the allowed stress levels. However, at the allowed stresses the tubesheet may deflect so much that there is pass-partition bypassing, as shown in Fig. 9.3. When the tubesheet deflection is severe, it may cause flanged-channel-to-tubesheet, shell-to-tubesheet, and channel-to-tubesheet-to-shell joints to leak.

Reviewing manufacturer's drawings

Flow arrows on the setting plan may flag incorrectly connected piping. By comparing assembly drawings with the installed exchanger, it may be found that the unit was put together incorrectly. A look at the construction details may disclose the mechanical source of a performance failure.

An example is a horizontal condenser in which the vapor condenses on the shellside, noncondensibles are present, and a shell vent is provided at one end, but there are no ears (see Fig. 9.4) on the baffles to prevent vapor bypassing. Such an omission may be very serious if the vapor inlet is large and if tubes have been eliminated from the layout to allow for providing impingement protection.

Use manufacturer's data reports and nameplate stamping to confirm information shown on the drawings. Read the installation, operating, and maintenance instructions for clues to what has gone wrong.

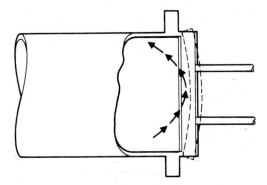

Figure 9.3 Bypassing due to tubesheet deflection. (*Courtesy of* Chemical Engineering.)

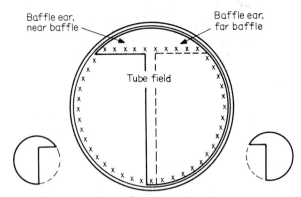

Figure 9.4 Ears required on baffles to prevent vapor bypassing. (*Courtesy of* Chemical Engineering.)

Examine inspection reports for notes of deviations from specifications and drawings for both those that were accepted and those that required correction. Either may have led to the malfunction. A study of radiographs and records of tests and nondestructive examinations may provide insight into what took place during fabrication.

Reviewing operating procedures and records

Scrutinize the procedures for startup, shutdown, and dealing with upsets to search out possible errors and omissions. Compare operating logs and charts with nominal values to pinpoint the onset of the disfunction. Search the maintenance logs for alterations or substitutions made in the hope of improving the equipment or of getting it back on line quickly after a shutdown.

Diagnosing Exchanger Ailments

When a problem occurs soon after starting up a new or recently overhauled exchanger, ask these questions:

1. What is the nature of the problem?

2. Did anything happen during transportation, handling, storing, installing, testing, or starting the unit that could have caused the trouble?

3. Were the manufacturer's installation and operating instructions followed?

4. Were specified startup and operating procedures followed?

5. Is the piping hooked up correctly?

6. Are the vents and drains connected and working?

7. Is the unit assembled correctly?

8. Is there a blockage or fouling resulting from inadequate cleaning after installation?

9. Was the trouble found when operating at the specified design-point conditions?

10. Are all needed controls and safety devices installed and operating?

When equipment that has been in satisfactory stable operation exhibits problems, the questions to ask are:

1. What is the nature of the problem?

2. Were any recent changes made to operating procedures?

3. Were any recent changes made to stream compositions, flow rates, or operating conditions?

4. Are the vents and drains working?

5. Are all controls and safety devices operating?

6. Are process-fluid plugged pressure-sensing instruments giving false readings?

7. Did an upset of any kind precede the onset of the problem?

8. Is the problem really with the exchanger, or is it elsewhere in the system?

Diagnostic techniques, instruments, and tools

The techniques for diagnosing heat exchanger ailments include looking, feeling, listening, and measuring. Most of what can be learned about a heat exchanger can be obtained by taking its temperatures and pressures, by metering its feeds and effluents, and by measuring it for dimensional changes.

Performance testing. The AIChE has published procedures for testing performance and the ASME for measuring temperature, pressure, and flow.[4,5] Full-fledged performance testing is costly and may not be practical, but it may be the only way to ascertain that the problem is with the exchanger and not elsewhere in the system.

It is self-evident that terminal conditions must be measured, but it may be equally important to measure intermediate temperatures. The cause of a condenser's not working as desired may be discovered by comparing a temperature profile with the assumed condensing curve. Examine horizontal units with shellside condensing for vapor and noncondensible maldistribution by measuring the temperature from the top to the bottom at intervals along the shell length. In a thermosiphon reboiler, estimate boiling-point elevation by comparing the liquid temperature with the temperature of the two-phase flow to the column. When condensing steam or other vapor is used in a heater that is acting erratically, the fault probably lies with ineffective condensate drainage. Install a recording flowmeter in the condensate drain line to detect wide swings in the condensate flow rate that indicate trap problems or the need for a condensate pump or barometric leg.

Searching for changes in process parameters.   Excessive acidity or alkalinity in the streams may cause unexpectedly high fouling and corrosion rates. Use a pH meter to monitor continuously for acidity-alkalinity.

A change in the composition of a gas mixture that contains a large percentage of hydrogen can affect the duty and heat transfer rate. Any dilution of hydrogen, used for cooling, with another gas may impair performance. Use a gas chromatograph to help unravel such problems.

Leaks of hydrocarbon vapors seldom are seen but usually are smelled. Because the olfactory sense tires quickly, operators may not become aware of a serious leak. When large hydrocarbon leaks are suspected, probe with a hydrocarbon-leak detector. Upon shutdown, locate the leaks by hydrostatic, bubble, halogen, or helium leak testing.

Examining for distortions.   The symptoms of many problems are distortion or deformation. Look for:

1. Bolts that are permanently stretched
2. Channel covers that are bowed
3. Extensions of tubesheets used as flanges that are cupped
4. Flanges that are bent, cupped, or distorted between bolt holes, giving a scalloped appearance
5. Ligaments between tube holes that are distorted or extruded
6. Nozzles and supports that are bent
7. Pass partitions that are bent or crippled

8. Tubes that are bowed

9. Tubesheets at the stationary or inlet end and return or outlet end that are not parallel with each other

10. Tubesheets that are rotated about the longitudinal axis

11. Tubesheets that are not flat or are wavy

12. Shell expansion joints that are deflected angularly or squirmed

Look also for deflections and deformations in supporting structures and in pipelines connected to the exchanger.

Use the instruments described in Chap. 7 as diagnostic tools. To measure the extent of corrosion without disassembling, scan ultrasonically or trepan and plug. To find out what lies under fouling or corrosion deposits, scrape the surface with an inspection scraper.

You can hear some of what goes on inside the exchanger by placing your ear or an industrial stethoscope against the shell, but interpreting what the sounds mean is difficult. Flashing liquids make characteristic sounds, as do gases and vapors flowing at sonic velocities and sand and silt flowing through a unit. In a closed feedwater heater, popping sounds heard in the vicinity of the subcooling zone indicate leaks in the subcooling-zone enclosure. Sometimes the degree of shellside fouling can be estimated by tapping the shell with an inspection hammer.

Heat Exchanger Illnesses

These are the kinds of troubles that may be encountered:

1. Overdesign

2. Underdesign

3. Maldistribution

4. Externally caused problems

5. Mechanical ailments

Overdesign and underdesign are discussed here for units in sensible-heat transfer and for process condensers and reboilers. Maldistribution, external factors, and mechanical difficulties are considered as they apply generally.

Overdesign

Many problems originate with the assumption that an overdesigned exchanger will work well at the design point. New and freshly cleaned exchangers are somewhat oversurfaced relative to design-point conditions because the designer has provided excess surface to allow for fouling. The resulting deviation from design-point outlet conditions is seldom objectionable because flow rates and inlet conditions can be adjusted somewhat. The fouling allowance is intended to permit operation at design conditions up to the point where the unit is normally shut down for cleaning.

However, the excess surface may be so great that it may not be possible to compensate enough to control the system. This may come about as follows: (1) Not enough is known about the fouling characteristics of the fluids. To be safe, excessive fouling resistances are specified. (2) The maintenance group specifies a very long interval between shutdowns for cleaning, and extrapolation from records of fouling rates results in the provision of a large fouling allowance. (3) A review committee has decided that more is better.

Very troublesome is the situation in which excess capacity has been arbitrarily specified. Here, the clean surface required at design-point conditions is first calculated. As is customary, additional surface is added to allow for dirt or scale buildup. Then the surface is increased as a percentage of the subtotal.

The best way to add such surface is to increase tube length (within the allowable pressure-drop limits) because it lets the fluid regime remain unchanged. However, if the purpose of the overdesign is to provide for future increases in flow rates, the tube count must be increased to carry the increased volume while staying within the pressure-drop limits. When this is done, the fluid regime at the original design point is not optimal. Hence the rate of fouling may exceed what was expected.

Overdesign in sensible-heat transfer. When a unit is designed for sensible-heat transfer on both sides, the cold-fluid outlet becomes hotter than designed. Tube metal temperature also is hotter at the cold-fluid inlet and colder at the hot-fluid outlet than anticipated. Interpass fluid and metal temperatures are similarly displaced.

As a result, the incoming cold fluid may be charred or the warm fluid frozen at their outlets. If the warm-fluid viscosity increases rapidly as temperature decreases, the pressure drop will be more than calculated. Tube metal temperature displacement is significant because it changes the assumptions that govern the design of fixed-tubesheet equipment. When the design is based on restraining the difference in expansion between the shell and the tubes, a substantial deviation can overstress the tubes, tube-to-tubesheet joints, and shell.

If an expansion joint is used to accommodate the difference, the deviation may cause more deflection than planned. This may reduce joint life.

Check for overdesign by measuring the flow rates, terminal temperatures, and pressures after startup. If a unit that is designed for cocurrent operation appears to be overdesigned, it likely was piped for countercurrent operation, permitting a temperature cross. Conversely, if too much surface in a countercurrent unit is causing charring or freezing, the cure may be to repipe for cocurrent flow.

When more tubes have been provided than are needed to carry the flow at optimum velocity, it may be possible to blank off some of them. Alternatively, the channel and return cover may be capable of being modified so as to bypass a pair of tube passes. Before deciding to do either, investigate what will happen to the tube metal temperatures as well as the effects on the structure of the exchanger.

A way to reduce effective heat transfer surface is to place long ferrules or inserts of inert insulating material in the inlet ends of each pass. The amount of effective surface can thus be controlled without materially changing the flow regime. (The ferrules also protect the tube ends from erosion.) To minimize the effects of turbulence at the exit from the ferrule bevel, insist on a long taper. (An angle of 15° is desirable but may not be practical to attain.) When considering using inserts, make sure that the tube material is not sensitive to crevice corrosion in the fluid handled.

If the flow cannot be turned down or the tubes or tube surface blanked off, effective surface may be reduced by relocating shell connections so as to create dead zones near the tubesheets. This is an extreme measure that will almost certainly reduce tube and tubesheet life because of corrosion in the dead zones. Leave the original shell connections in place, valved off, and drain the dead zones frequently.

Overdesign in process condensers. In a process condenser, the symptoms of overdesign are difficulty in balancing the column and reflux subcooling. To visualize what happens, consider a correctly sized condenser of area A, condensing a pure vapor of latent heat L at a rate W. Condensation takes place at temperature T and system pressure P. Cooling water flowing at rate w, having specific heat c, enters at temperature t_1 and leaves at temperature t_2. The condensing duty Q is established by the vapor flow rate and latent heat and is equal to the heat removed by the cooling water. This is shown in Eqs. (9.1) and (9.2).

$$Q = WL \qquad (9.1)$$

$$Q = wc(t_2 - t_1) \qquad (9.2)$$

The basic heat transfer relationship is

$$Q = UAT_m \tag{9.3}$$

The logarithmic mean temperature difference T_m is

$$T_m = \frac{(T - t_2) - (T - t_1)}{\ln\left[(T - t_2)/(T - t_1)\right]} \tag{9.4}$$

For simplicity, assume that the ideal-gas law holds true in the vapor supply and that L, c, and U remain constant. Now examine what will happen when condenser surface A is increased. The feed rate to the column, the reboiler surface, and the heat supply to the reboiler fix W. Therefore, by Eq. (9.1) Q is fixed. Because Q is fixed and U is constant, by Eq. (9.3) T_m must be reduced. This can be done by raising t_1 or t_2, or both. Operators are most likely to choke back on the water supply to reduce t_2. This reduces water velocity, which promotes organic fouling and inorganic scale deposition. If t_2 rises much above 120°F (49°C), dissolved inorganic salts may precipitate rapidly and form hard scale.

On the other hand, if w, t_1, and t_2 are maintained unchanged, the only way to reduce T_m is to reduce T. Because the vaporization rate fixes the vapor volume, P must be reduced to satisfy the ideal-gas law. This may affect column and reboiler operation. Excess condenser surface may subcool the condensate, thereby increasing the condenser duty. The subcooled reflux will cool the column, causing the controls to demand more heat from the reboiler. Not only is it wasteful to deliver excess heat to the reboiler and reject it in the condenser, but forcing the reboiler may lead to its operating at a higher heat flux than desirable. High reboiler heat flux may cause vapor binding and uneven operation, accompanied by rapid fouling. A better remedy is to limit t_2 to 120°F (49°C) and temper the cooling water to raise t_2.

The following horror story illustrates how costly it can be to overdesign a process condenser.

A fixed-tubesheet process condenser for corrosive vapor was designed for condensing inside 1-in-OD × 0.029-in-thick (25.4-mm-OD × 0.74-mm-thick) titanium Grade 2 tubes. The required shell size was 47-in (1194-mm) ID. The required tube length, including an allowance for fouling, was 11.6 ft (3.5 m). The designer selected 12-ft-long (3.7-m-long) tubes, but management decided arbitrarily to increase tube length to 16 ft (4.9 m) to provide for future increased capacity. No consideration was given to how the 39 percent oversize would affect column operation. The operators balanced the column by choking the cooling-water supply.

Some years later, column throughput was increased 30 percent, but the condenser could not handle the increase. Upon investigation, the shell was found to be filled with so much scale that cleaning was not practical.

Shortly thereafter, the condenser was scrapped.

If a process condenser is designed for horizontal operation, it may be possible to correct for overdesign by arranging the unit for vertical flow. Kern compared a vertical unit condensing n-propanol in the shell with a horizontal condenser of the same tube count and arrangement.[6] His calculations show a vertical clean overall coefficient that is 63 percent of the clean overall coefficient of the horizontal arrangement. For a specific problem, the difference may be more or less than in Kern's example. Therefore, calculate the vertical overall coefficient when considering such a change.

A way sometimes used to control overdesigned surface condensers is to reduce the overall coefficient by deliberately introducing air into the steam. The film of air, through which the steam must diffuse before it makes contact with the cold surface, may be considered an additional resistance in series with the original film and fouling resistances. Standiford reworked data of Meisenburg, Boates, and Badger to correlate their data in the form of an air-film resistance versus percent air in the steam.[7,8] These correlations are repeated here.

$$F = 0.00004C \tag{9.5}$$

$$F = 0.000065C' \tag{9.6}$$

$$F' = 0.00023C \tag{9.7}$$

$$F' = 0.00037C' \tag{9.8}$$

In these equations, F is fouling resistance in SI units, F' is the resistance in English units, C is weight percent air, and C' is mole percent air.

The air concentration increases as vapor traverses the condenser because vapor is condensed; condensing takes place over a range, reducing T_m. The fouling resistance of the air therefore increases from inlet to outlet, and the effective driving force decreases.

When vapor enters the tubes of a vertical downflow condenser, inert gas is swept through and separated in the bottom head by means of a funnel or baffle plate. This provides the option of controlling system pressure by controlling vent-gas pressure. If there is not enough inert gas in the system, some can be bled into the vapor inlet stream. For operation below atmospheric, pressure can be adjusted by bleeding air into the jet.

If the excess surface is causing the condensate to be subcooled too much, repipe the unit to bring coolant in at the top. This cocurrent-flow arrangement ensures that there will not be a temperature cross.

Another alternative is to loop-seal, to flood the bottom of the tubes. This is not a good choice because:

1. It may be difficult to achieve a desired amount of subcooling.

2. Noncondensibles cannot be gotten rid of.

3. System pressure control is indirect.

4. There is a possibility of hydraulic-hammer damage.

Overdesign in refrigerated condensers. In addition to the symptoms of oversurface already described for condenser overdesign, low suction and head pressures will be observed in oversized refrigeration equipment. Refrigerant vaporization temperature should have been chosen so that it is above the process-stream freezing point. If it was not, process fluid may freeze on the surfaces during startup. If the unit is sized correctly, the deposit may melt as the design flow is reached and the tube-wall temperature is raised above freezing. However, in overdesign, the coating will continue to build up.

Because pressure drop increases with the inverse of the square of the flow area, an early symptom of overdesign in refrigerated units may be an increasing process-side pressure drop. In refrigerated condensers, the pressure-drop rise raises the system pressure and boiling temperature in the vaporizer. Reboiler output decreases, further increasing relative condenser overdesign, which increases both the length of the condenser tubes coated with frozen condensate and the thickness of the deposit. This further increases pressure drop. The ratchet effect eventually leads to shutdown.

The overdesign may be remedied by using a higher-boiling refrigerant or by operating the refrigerant system at a higher pressure. In vertical refrigerated units, the refrigerant level can be controlled to reduce effective surface. In horizontal coolers, with refrigerant in the shell, the level may be reduced to expose tubes (if there is no adverse differential expansion between submerged and exposed tubes), but the exposed tubes would bypass uncondensed vapors to the vent. There would then be an overdesigned condenser that does not condense all the vapor that the surface is capable of condensing! These units may be corrected by (1) blanking tubes if pressure drop and differential expansion permit or (2) inserting sleeves of inert, low-thermal-conductivity material in the tube inlets. Sleeve length is set by how much excess surface is furnished. (The ends of the tubes may also be coated.)

Overdesign in reboilers.[9] The principal symptom of overdesign in horizontal thermosiphon reboilers is the phenomenon called *breathing*. It comes about as follows. Liquid enters the shell of the reboiler, where it meets the hot tubes and flashes. More liquid enters to replace the flashed material and cools the tubes. The fresh liquid remains briefly until it too flashes. Instead of even, continuous two-phase flow, puffs of vapor and entrained liquid leave the reboiler.

Ordinarily, there is a modest amount of excess surface (the difference between required clean and fouled surfaces, plus surface added by rounding calculations upward), and the temperature of the heating medium can be controlled to reduce the driving-temperature difference. But with gross overdesign the heat input may not be capable of being turned down enough to prevent more feed that enters from boiling up. This depletes the holdup volume, reduces the boiling point, and leads to breathing.

The problem can be mitigated by installing a restriction in the vapor outlet. This increases the pressure in the reboiler, elevating the boiling point. Doing so reduces the driving-temperature differential, at the same time causing some energy to be transferred by sensible heat at a lower rate than by nucleate boiling. The disadvantage is the flashing that takes place across the restriction. Always place the restriction directly at the reboiler outlet or provide a flash pot to ensure that the column is not used as a flash chamber.

When the configuration is a vertical thermosiphon with vaporizing in the tubes, excess surface can lead to drying out if the tubes are long. The low heat flux can also create insufficient pumping, making reboiler and column operation unstable. Reducing the temperature of the heating medium would seem to be the way to control the effects of the excess surface, but doing so further reduces pumping because the smaller temperature difference further reduces the heat flux.

Figure 9.5 shows a way often used to handle overdesign in this kind of reboiler. The vertical pipe leading from the condensate outlet causes the tube surface to be submerged in condensate to the height of the leg. Heat is transferred from the condensate by natural convection at a much lower rate than by vapor condensation. Therefore, the excess surface is rendered ineffective. When using this scheme, provide for blowdown at the inner surface of the bottom tubesheet (to avoid corrosion in the region of the stagnant condensate pool). Adjust the height of the leg to accommodate fouling buildup or operating variations. A level control may also be used.

The response time of this procedure is slow. A faster way to reduce the boiling rate is to introduce inerts into the heating medium. Although blanketing the surface is effective, it presents the problem of disposing of the inerts downstream.

If the boiling range is wide and heat is supplied in the sensible mode, effective temperature can be reduced by piping for cocurrent flow. If the range is small, piping cocurrently improves circulation because it generates more vapor at the bottom. Therefore, the inlet tem-

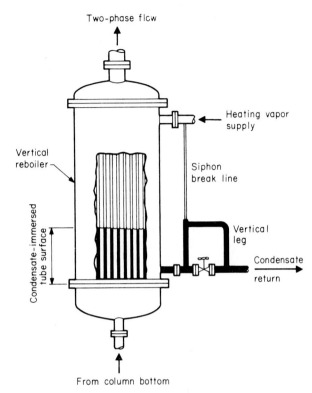

Two-phase flow

Heating vapor
supply

Vertical
reboiler

Siphon
break line

Vertical
leg

Condensate
return

Condensate-immersed
tube surface

From column bottom

Figure 9.5 Loop seal to flood excess surface in vertical reboiler. (*Courtesy of* Chemical Engineering.)

perature can be turned down to reduce temperature difference, with less decline in pumping than if heat were supplied by a condensing vapor.

Oversized kettle and internal-bundle reboilers unbalance the column. The overhead condenser may appear to be too small because of the volume of vapor generated. Here, too, column operation becomes unstable. Another problem that may be overlooked is that oversized kettles foul rapidly. For this reason, excessive allowance for fouling is self-defeating.

Because kettles operate well at both high and low temperature differences, overdesigned units can most easily be controlled by reducing the heating-medium temperature. When the heating mode is sensible, bring the hot fluid in at the bottom to reduce the effective temperature difference somewhat. For condensing vapors, a loop seal can be installed in the condensate to flood tubes in the outlet pass. Inert gas can also be introduced in the tubes to blanket some surface, but it will have to be disposed of later.

Forced-circulation reboilers essentially operate in the sensible-heat transfer mode in the tubes. When the unit is overdesigned, the symptoms at the reboiler itself are the same as for overdesign in a liquid heater. However, excessive vapor is flashed in the flash chamber, which both makes column operation unstable and overloads the condenser. There are no ill effects on the reboiler itself, and the rate of fouling does not increase when it is overdesigned.

The best way to control an overdesigned forced-circulation reboiler is to reduce the driving-temperature differential. A portion of the feed can be bypassed and remixed before the flash drum, but this may lead to more rapid fouling and some vaporization in the tubes. If the heating mode is a condensing vapor, some of the heating surface can be flooded by loop sealing, provided that the differential temperature between the tubes is not excessive. Inerts can also be introduced to blanket the surface; again the problem of downstream removal must be faced.

Underdesign

Underdesign is defined as inadequate surface to produce design outlet conditions when the fluids enter at design flow rates and conditions. It is probably the heat exchanger problem that occurs least frequently. In the author's 25 years of experience with two shops, not one of more than 6000 exchangers built had to be modified or replaced because of failure to perform.

Heater and cooler underdesign. Heater and cooler underdesign is signaled by failure of the stream outlet temperatures to reach design values. This may be accompanied by a pressure drop higher than allowed. Another kind of underdesign is excessive pressure loss when operating at design flows and temperatures. Underdesign may not be immediately apparent (unless the exchanger is tested for its clean performance rate) because the tubes are new and clean. But the unit appears to foul more rapidly than anticipated because the underdesign eliminates the fouling allowance.

Sometimes what seems to be a small deviation from design in the outlet temperature is symptomatic of substantial undersurface. The following shows how deviations of 1 or 2°F (approximately 0.6 to 1.1°C) can be associated with 10 or 15 percent less surface than required:

A 1-2 cooler is used to cool a volatile solvent from 120 to 80°F (48.9 to 26.7°C), with cooling water entering at 70° and leaving at 80°F (21.1 and 26.7°C). Table 9.1 shows that, with a constant overall coefficient and no change in cooling-water temperatures, 90.7 and 86.5 percent of the required surface has been provided when the solvent outlet temperature increased 1 or 2°F (0.6 to 1.1°C).

TABLE 9.1 Illustration of a Small Outlet Temperature Deviation Associated with Underdesign in a 1-2 Solvent Cooler

Solvent outlet temperature		Corrected LMTD		Actual LMTD as a percent of design LMTD	Percent of required surface provided
°F	°C	°F	°C		
80	26.7	17.31	9.6	100.0	100.0
81	27.2	19.09	10.6	110.3	90.7
82	27.8	20.00	11.1	115.4	86.5

NOTE: LMTD = logarithmic mean temperature difference.

In a liquid heater, when there is a large viscosity decrease with increasing temperature, failure of the outlet temperature to reach the design point may cause excessive pressure drop. Another situation in which pressure drop beyond design values may be observed occurs when the fluid circulated consists of a liquid and a gas phase. If the design basis was that of stratified or fully mixed flow but the actual regime is slug flow, there will be a substantial increase in pressure drop over the design value.

When gases are circulated, a decrease in system pressure can also cause excess pressure drop. The pressure loss varies inversely with gas density, which is a direct function of pressure. A possible remedy for excess pressure drop of gases that are flowing in the shell is to rearrange the piping and nozzles to an approximation of a divided-flow configuration.

Here a new inlet is relocated opposite the cutoff segment of a baffle in the middle of the bundle. The previous inlet becomes an outlet, manifolded to the original outlet. The scheme is shown in Fig. 9.6 for an even number of baffles, but it works equally well for an odd number.

Dividing the flow reduces shellside pressure drop to about one-eighth of the loss in a shell having the inlet at one end and the outlet at the other. It is necessary to provide impingement protection under the new inlet and do some surgery to the piping. Before proceeding with this change, analyze the thermal performance of the revised configuration.

Underdesign in process condensers. When a condenser seems to be too small, take into account that, in addition to the condenser's configuration, the system pressure, flow rate, and nature of the entering vapors determine its performance. The vapors may be generated from a pure liquid or from two pure immiscible liquids. For these conditions, condensing is isothermal. For all other combinations of phases and liq-

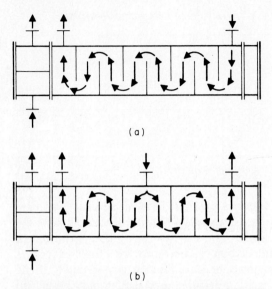

Figure 9.6 Reducing shellside pressure drop by converting to divided flow. (*a*) Original nozzle arrangement for conventional cross-flow. (*b*) Modification for approximations of divided flow. (*Courtesy of Chemical Engineering.*)

uid composition (e.g., vapors of miscible substances, pure vapors, and noncondensibles, vapors of miscible liquids with noncondensibles, vapors of miscible and immiscible liquids, and vapors of miscible and immiscible liquids in the presence of noncondensibles), vapor temperature decreases from vapor inlet to outlet.

A small change in system pressure, inward leakage of noncondensibles, or a difference in the entering-vapor composition can make a correctly sized condenser underperform. An unsuitable arrangement of vapor vent and condensate nozzles, poorly arranged internals, and inadequate venting can render an otherwise appropriate amount of surface area ineffective. And if a condenser designed for horizontal operation is installed in the vertical position, it will probably not be large enough. Therefore, to troubleshoot a malperforming condenser, investigate the vapor stream composition, system pressure, venting, possibility of vapor bypassing, noncondensible inleakage, and how the unit was installed relative to how it was designed.

Some indications that a condenser is underdesigned are:

1. Loss of volatile vapor out of the vent

2. High vent-gas temperature

3. An unusual temperature profile between vapor inlet and condensate outlet

4. Failure to reach design condensate-subcooling temperature in a condenser-subcooler

However, before concluding that the unit is too small, eliminate the possibility of a system pressure that deviates from design, excessive air inleakage, maldistributed vapor and dam baffle bypassing, or improperly arranged loop-seal piping.

Shellside condensing pressure drop is affected by total system pressure in the same way that gas-flow pressure drop is affected. Therefore, excessive shellside pressure drop in horizontal units can also be reduced by rearranging the connections to approximate divided flow. However, the vapor inlet is larger than the condensate outlet, and the change requires more modification. In addition, because gaseous inerts cannot be removed at the top of the shell, vent gases must exit from the sides of the condenser below the bundle centerline.

The principal reasons that divided-flow condensers underperform are maldistribution and inert-gas buildup. If the vapor is led directly to the bundle and the tube length is long, noncondensibles and more volatile material may accumulate near the tube ends, reducing effective surface and increasing pressure drop. Maldistribution can be rectified by replacing the single inlet with a vapor belt, thereby bringing the vapors into the bundle through several openings in the shell on either side of the divider baffle. Rectify accumulation of inerts by adding additional vents in the regions of the tube ends.

Adapted from surface condenser design, process condensers designed for pure cross-flow may be provided for services where the absolute pressure is below 0.5 lb/in^2 (3447 N/m^2), available pressure drop is below 0.15 lb/in^2 (1034 N/m^2), and the vapor condenses over a range of 20°F (11°C) or less.

In pure cross-flow, the ideal path for the vapor to follow as it flows into the bundle is a gradual transition from inlet nozzle to bundle of approximately 15° as shown in Fig. 9.7. But the construction is expensive and allowing space for a transition angle of even 20° is impractical for most units. As an alternative, condensers are sometimes built with the inlet nozzle entering a vapor dome. Such units underperform because of vapor maldistribution. The problem can be alleviated by providing additional vapor inlets near the tube ends, thereby splitting the vapor into three streams. Make sure that nearly equal quantities of vapor enter the inlets.

In vertical reflux and knock-back condensers that condense in the tubes, there is seldom inadequate surface to handle the duty. The overload is, instead, one of excess vapor velocity and consequent flood-

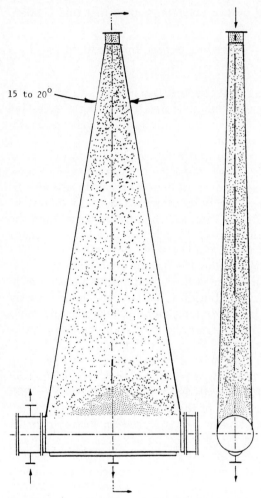

15 to 20°

Figure 9.7 Pure cross-flow condenser arrangement.

ing. This is described inelegantly as "puking." Reduce flooding by tilt-
ing the condenser 30 to 45° with the vertical.

Underdesign in reboilers.[9] The way a reboiler works on startup is the
clue to underdesign. Vapor output increases as the system heats up,
but before the design rate is reached, the output levels off and may
decrease. This results from excessive heat flux and consequent film
boiling. Considering reboiler overload in terms of heat flux enables
one to visualize how failing to control an overdesigned condenser can
make an adequate reboiler underperform. Heat removed in the condenser must be supplied by the reboiler. Excess removal overloads the
reboiler.

A thermosiphon reboiler may appear to be underdesigned when its static head is higher than planned for in design. Under this condition, the boiling point in the reboiler is elevated, narrowing the temperature difference between the reboiler contents and the heating medium. The excessive static head increases the circulation rate, driving the heat transfer mode toward sensible-heat transfer. Vaporization then occurs by flashing in the liquid rather than by nucleate boiling on the tubes. The rate in sensible-heat transfer is lower than in nucleate boiling. The combination of reduced driving force and poorer heat transfer rate lowers the effective capacity of the unit.

Excessive static head develops when the column liquid level is higher than planned for in design. A less frequent cause is higher bottoms-liquid density than estimated. Low piping friction losses result from larger-than-planned pipe diameters and shorter-than-estimated pipe lengths in the circulating loop.

Therefore, when a thermosiphon reboiler appears to be undersized, check for excessive circulation by installing a variable restriction between the column and the reboiler inlet. As flow is choked down, performance may reach the desired level. If variations in column feed rate and composition are small, install an orifice plate to assure constant metered flow.

Large horizontal thermosiphon reboilers underperform when the feed is not distributed uniformly along the length of the tubes. Before concluding that this kind of unit is too small, examine the feed entrance arrangements. If the boiling range is large and the design is not a split or double split arrangement, there may be a kind of internally generated maldistribution. What happens is that when the inlet stream strikes the hot tubes, the low-boiling liquids flash and travel to the outlet. This concentrates the high boilers in the ends, reducing the effective driving-temperature difference. If the bundle is a removable multipass one, to correct the situation convert to either split or double split flow.

Vertical thermosiphon units are usually unsuitable for operation under vacuum and at very high pressure. If you cannot balance a vacuum or high-pressure column in which vapor is supplied from a vertical thermosiphon, consider converting to forced circulation. Note that the size of the line between the column and the pump may have to be increased and the position of the reboiler adjusted because of net-positive-suction-head requirements.

In forced circulation, if the fluid being vaporized has several components with a wide spread of normal boiling points, an excessive circulation ratio may cause too much of the volatile components to boil off. This raises the overall boiling point, reducing the driving-temperature difference and thereby reducing performance. Thus, when a forced-circulation reboiler fails to perform, check the pump output volume. Correct excessive circulation by installing an orifice plate or other restriction in the pump discharge.

Insufficient circulation may also be the cause of low performance (as well as contributing to rapid fouling). In thermosiphons, the flow may be too small for the following reasons:

1. Insufficient static head

2. Excess friction in the piping

3. In tubeside flow, outlet-nozzle flow area smaller than tube flow area

4. In tubeside flow, inlet-nozzle flow area less than half of tube flow area

In these units, rapid fouling takes place if the rate of vaporization is more than 25 percent of the circulation rate. The units also foul rapidly when the weight rate of vaporization exceeds the weight rate of circulation.

If the pump characteristics have not been matched to the actual back pressure on the pump discharge, it may be necessary to install a restriction in the discharge to make it operate at the design rate. For example, a pump designed to deliver 2500 gal/min (9463 L/min) at a head of 20 lb/in^2 (137 kPa) may not be able to deliver the design volume at a head of 1 lb/in^2 (6.89 kPa), and the reboiler will underperform. Pump performance can be checked by shutting down and bypassing the pump. If there is no further decrease in performance, the unit has been operating in natural circulation.

Kettle reboilers are rarely underdesigned. In fact, if the fluid has a wide boiling range and the available driving-temperature difference is low, a reboiler will probably be oversized. This is so because the effective temperature difference will probably have been based on the vapor temperature. However, less volatile material tends to collect, depositing fouling and corrosion products that can reduce performance drastically. When this happens, improve arrangements for drawing off bottoms.

If you are convinced that the kettle is undersurfaced, consider the following alternatives: (1) Retube with low-fin tubes, and (2) replace the bundle with one that has low-fin tubes arranged on a spread pitch. (Spreading the pitch permits a higher heat flux.) Under most circumstances low-fin tubes do not foul more rapidly than bare tubes. For the right combination of heating and boiling materials, low-fin tubes provide a marked increase in effective surface in the available space.

The design of natural-circulation vaporizers for clean pure fluids, which are assumed not to leave a residue, is usually based on 100 percent vaporization. Inadequate performance in the form of surges is usually the result of failure to maintain a liquid level that will ensure submergence of all the tubes.

Corrective measures are (1) installation of a weir in the vaporizer shell, (2) installation of an internal or external standpipe, or (3) installation of a liquid-level control. However, if the tube ends of a vaporizer designed for full vaporization become fouled, the feed is not pure. To correct the fouling, rearrange the piping to provide a natural circulation rate of 3 times the vaporization rate. When working with forced-circulation equipment, double the pumping rate and recirculate half the flow.

Flow maldistribution

A major cause of underperformance in all kinds of exchangers is maldistributed flow.

Maldistribution in falling-film evaporators. A falling-film evaporator will not work as predicted if either there is uneven distribution of feed to the tubes or the liquid descending each tube does not wet the tube surfaces uniformly.

The causes of maldistribution to falling-film evaporator tubes are (1) an installation that is out of plumb, (2) inadequate calming of the feed to the top tubesheet, (3) variations in weir height and weir configuration from tube to tube, and (4) a combination of these factors. If the full circumference of each tube is not wet, the unit is probably out of plumb.

To reset the evaporator properly, insert a level in the tubes at the quarter and eighth points to verify their perpendicularity to the horizontal.

Maldistribution of tubeside flow. Maldistribution in heat exchanger tubes probably occurs under the following circumstances: (1) Axial nozzle entry velocity exceeds average tube velocity, and (2) radial nozzle entry velocity is 2 or more times average tube velocity. Indications of tubeside maldistribution are uneven tube-end erosion at the inlet-end tubesheet and underperformance.

When the fluid enters a bonnet axially, correct maldistribution by installing a distributor baffle (target plate). Alternatively, replace the bonnet with a conical enlarger. To be effective, the included angle must be quite small (somewhat less than 15°), and the construction may be impractical.

Some bonnets with axial inlets are made from truncated right cones having included angles as great as 60°. With this construction, anticipate some reduction in the calculated performance. Distribution can be improved somewhat by replacing the right cones with eccentric cones, as in the arrangement shown in Fig. 9.8. To estimate whether the cost is justified, compare the calculated overall coefficient with the measured coefficient of the clean unit. A quick way to assess the situation follows.

Assume that metal resistance of the clean unit is negligible compared with the sum of shellside and tubeside film resistances. Then U_c, the clean overall coefficient, in terms of the outside film coefficient related to the tube OD, h_{io}, is given by Eq. (9.9).

$$U_c = h_o h_i / (h_o + h_{io})$$
(9.9)

Define K as the ratio h_o/h_{io}, and substitute Eq. (9.9) to derive Eq. (9.10). Equation (9.10) relates the calculated clean overall coefficient to the calculated inside film coefficient:

$$h_{io} = \frac{(K + 1)}{K} U_c$$
(9.10)

By using the calculated values of h_o and h_{io} to evaluate K and the measured value of U_c in Eq. (9.10), estimate how much improvement of the inside film coefficient is required.

There is less likelihood of maldistribution when the fluid enters a channel radially. However, if there is maldistribution, correct it by using a distributor. There is better distribution in vertical units if fluid enters the bottom channel. For either axial or radial entry to the channel, distribution is more uniform in vertical bottom-fed units than in horizontal units.

Maldistribution of shellside flow. Maldistribution of shellside fluids may also cause exchangers to underperform. Condensing vapors may bypass available surface, traveling directly to the vent. Gases and liquids may flow parallel to the tubes in open channels created by the spreading of tube rows to accommodate U-tube bending and pass-partition location. Especially prone to shell-fluid maldistribution is the pull-through floating-head configuration.

Suspect shellside maldistribution as a cause of poor performance when (1) tubes have been dropped out of a full layout to accommodate impingement protection, (2) construction drawings show no seal strips or dummy tubes or very few distribution devices, and (3) temperature probes reveal temperature profiles different from those that were assumed.

The effects of shellside maldistribution may be dramatic. If tubes grouped at the periphery of a segment of a fixed-tubesheet unit are

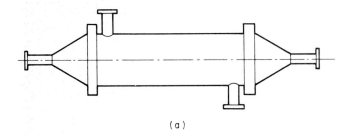

(a)

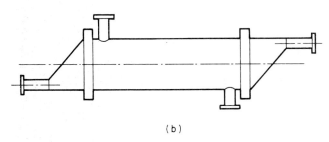

(b)

Figure 9.8   Improving tubeside distribution with eccentric conical bonnets. (*a*) Flow in tubes may not be distributed uniformly. (*b*) Using eccentric reducer bonnets distributes flow better. (*Courtesy of* Chemical Engineering.)

substantially hotter than the rest and if the shell is fitted with a bellows expansion joint, the unit may assume the shape of a banana. The bending may be seen, or cracked insulation and leaks in connections to the piping may be noticed. In floating-head equipment, the banana shape of the bundle is not visible but shows up as leaks in the tube-to-tubesheet connections, broken tubes, and bent baffles. A permanent set of the bundle into the banana shape can be revealed by shining an inspection light into one end of the tube nest and peering down the other.

This kind of distortion may be symptomatic of an excessive temperature range between the tubeside inlet and outlet of a multipass exchanger. However, in a horizontal unit that is cooling gas in the shell over a wide range—say, 1000 to 400°F (about 540 to 200°C)—when the gas is stratified into upper hot and lower cold layers, the bundle will also bend.

The most likely cause of stratification is location of both shellside connections on the top, combined with a baffle system that does not ensure complete gas mixing. Examine the baffle system for one or more of the following: (1) vertical cuts instead of horizontal ones, (2) location of a baffle where gas can bypass through the expansion joint (when a sleeve is not provided), (3) too few baffles, and (4) excessive clearance between baffles and shell.

To correct the situation may require the following surgery: (1) rotating the unit to change baffle-cut position to horizontal, providing an outlet 180° from the inlet, and blanking off the previous outlet; (2) rotating the unit and installing a distributor belt; (3) sealing the baffles to the shell; (4) installing seal strips; (5) installing a sleeve in the expansion joint; and (6) adding baffles. Some of these measures may require replacing or rebuilding the tube bundle.

Maldistribution of two-phase fluids. Maldistribution in horizontal two-phase flow can cause poorer heat transfer and higher pressure drop than anticipated. Instead of uniformly mixing, the liquid and gases stratify. When possible, overcome this problem by switching the position of the exchanger to vertical with the mixed stream entering at the bottom. Gas-liquid mixing may be improved by feeding gas and liquid coaxially, as shown in Fig. 9.9.

External causes of problems

Some troubles caused by factors external to heat exchanger design and construction have been discussed. An example is maldistribution in falling-film evaporator feed caused by not leveling the unit. A brief discussion of a few other external causes of difficulty follows.

Inerts in heating steam. When steam is used as a heating medium, the problems on the steam side are the same as for steam condensers. Noncondensibles may blanket the surface, thereby reducing capacity. In addition, unvented CO_2 or NH_3 may dissolve in the condensate and corrode the exchanger.

Condensate flooding. When heating vapor condenses, if condensate is not removed as it forms, the heat transfer surface is flooded with liquid. The lower rate of sensible-heat transfer at the flooded surfaces reduces capacity compared with latent-heat transfer. The retained condensate may be subcooled. If the vapor is supplied from a unit that is recovering heat elsewhere in the system, returning the subcooled condensate may unbalance the vaporizer.

Flooding results if the condensate discharge nozzle is too small or poorly placed or if condensate traps or seal-pot systems do not work as they should. To find the cause of flooding, check the condensate line to be sure that it has no bellies and slopes downward. Recalculate the nozzle size for the actual flow and pressure conditions. If these check out satisfactorily, look for dirt in the condensate trap. If the trap is

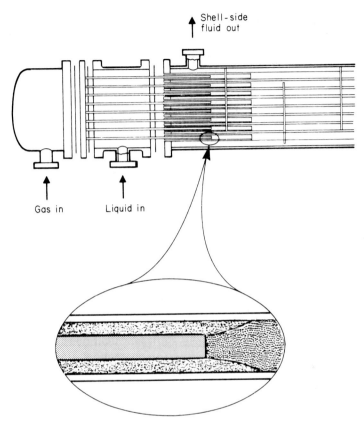

↑ Shell-side
fluid out

↑
Gas in

↑
Liquid in

Figure 9.9 Improving gas-liquid mixing by feeding gas and liquid coaxially. (*Courtesy of* Chemical Engineering.)

clean, it is probably too small or has not been selected properly for the service. Before coming to one of these conclusions, make sure that the trap has not been put in backward. Nonreturn traps will not work if the vapor supply pressure is lower than the pressure in the condensate receiver. When the receiver pressure is slightly higher, buildup of liquid head in the condensate pool may supply enough pressure to operate the trap. This uneven operation can make vaporizers and reboilers surge, unbalancing the downstream operation.

On startup, there may be insufficient pressure if the vapor demand is greater than the supply valve can accommodate. The remedy is to install a bypass and valve for manual startup or a different kind or capacity of control valve. Throttling the supply to bring the unit to temperature gradually may create a similar low-pressure situation.

Here flooding is not significant because only a temporary reduction in capacity is sought. However, when the exchanger is at temperature and the supply pressure is high enough to operate the trap, so much condensate may be backed up that the trap is temporarily overloaded. For this reason, there should be a manual condensate-trap bypass.

Inverted-bucket traps, because they have to be primed with condensate, may not work if they are insulated. If steam is not condensed in a trap, it may take a long time for the trap to become primed. Because most hot lines are insulated for safety and heat conservation, it is a common error to insulate inverted-bucket traps as well. Under these conditions, if such a trap is not performing well, strip the insulation and install a personnel guard.

Hydraulic hammer. Hydraulic hammer can damage condensate discharge lines and knock tubes loose from the joints to the tubesheets. The noise and shaking associated with steam hammer will occur if a steam trap is oversized and the pressure drop between the trap and the condensate receiver is large. Hydraulic hammer is an unsteady-state phenomenon that can be relieved with appropriate protective devices, such as air-cushioned domes in pipelines, but it is usually more desirable to install a correctly sized trap.

Instrument and control problems. Problems arising from instruments and controls are vexing because these devices are so reliable that they are the last to be suspected. Before a startup, check the calibration, zero point, and damping of the instruments used to measure and control level, flow, temperature, and pressure. When problems arise, look for condensate in sensing lines, plugging of inlets, or mechanical damage to sensing or transmitting elements. If an element is placed close to an inlet or is unprotected from fluid forces, anticipate a malfunction.

Correct condensation problems and some causes of plugging by insulating or steam-tracing lines. Avoid repeated mechanical damage by shielding or relocating elements. If the instruments and controls are not damaged and test out properly but operation is erratic, the sensing elements are probably located where a stream is not completely mixed or a constant flow regime has not been established.

Piping problems. A startling variety of foreign materials may be found in piping and equipment on startup. Typical are nuts, bolts, marking crayons, soapstone sticks, weld rod stubs and slag, crushed stone, sand and gravel, chunks of cinder block, pieces of construction blueprints, newspapers, twine, birds' nests, lunch bags, small tools, work gloves, articles of clothing and personal hygiene, small dead animals, etc.

When cooling water is drawn from ponds, rivers, or bays, salt, sand, and marine life may enter. When cooling-tower water is used, look for silt deposits in the heat exchanger's return end. It is a good practice to install a dual strainer in the cooling-water feed. This permits keeping foreign matter out and cleaning the strainer without interrupting production. However, single strainers with bypasses are frequently installed, and it is usual to provide a bypass around dual strainers. In the course of operation, the strainer may become plugged, starving the exchanger of cooling water. Instead of cleaning the strainer, the operator opens the bypass. After some time, the exchanger fails to perform, necessitating an unplanned shutdown.

A piping problem peculiar to kettle-type vaporizers is the manometer effect of connecting the column bottom to the kettle bottom. If the pipe leading the two-phase material from the reboiler to the column is too small or too long, the back pressure may depress the kettle's liquid level below the column's liquid level. Kettle designs assume that the liquid surfaces are at the same height, and the kettles are positioned accordingly. Because of the manometer effect, top tubes may be exposed when the kettle level is depressed. This is insidious because the operators may not become aware of the problem until there is product degradation or mechanical difficulty with the bundle.

Mechanical ailments

The symptoms associated with leakage between the shellside and the tubeside vary with the process parameters. Generally the fluid from the higher-pressure side appears downstream in the lower-pressure stream. But a leak in a distillation-column reboiler may cause steam distillation of some high boilers and thus alter the overhead-product composition; a leak in a condenser may be indicated by water in the product and reduced condenser performance, and rapid corrosion may be symptomatic of acid-cooler leaks.

Most leaks occur in the region of the tubesheets. This list of possible causes is long and includes the following:

1. Erosion-corrosion at the tube inlets
2. Cavitation damage at the tube outlets
3. Tubesheet erosion
4. Ligament cracking in one or both tubesheets
5. Tube-end fatigue
6. Tube-end stress-corrosion cracking

7. Tube-end crevice corrosion

8. Corrosion of the tubes in the regions between the tubesheets and adjacent baffles

9. Tube pullout or pushout

10. Relaxation of residual stress required for tightness in expanded joints

11. Root cracking in welded joints

12. Improper tube-hole finish; e.g., axial scores in hole surfaces

13. Tube-hole damage and ligament distortion occurring during tube installation (most often during retubing)

14. Erosion damage at the shell inlet

15. Cavitation at the shell outlet

16. Inadequate bundle support at the floating end of a floating head unit or at the free end of a U-tube bundle

17. Various kinds of vibration damage

There may also be leaks throughout the length of the tubes. The causes of such leaks are (1) general corrosion, (2) improper tube fabrication, and (3) vibration damage.

Erosion-corrosion at tube inlets. The evidence of erosion-corrosion at the tube inlets is thinning of the tube ends, usually on one side, and longitudinal rounded grooves. The cause may be maldistribution or excessive turbulence. If the inlet pass is free of erosion-corrosion but subsequent passes are not, the crossover area is probably too small. Rectify maldistribution as previously discussed. Tube ends may be protected with sleeves or with perforated plates drilled on the tubesheet pitch pattern to the tube ID. When the crossover area is inadequate, replace the channel and return cover. Partial retubing is justifiable for this kind of failure, provided that corrective steps are taken to prevent recurrence.

Impingement attack. This is a form of erosion characterized by sharply defined pits with smooth walls. The pits may be elongated in the direction of flow. They are usually concentrated in the inlet region but may extend throughout the tubes.

Cavitation damage at tube outlets. Cavitation damage at tube outlets appears as erosion and damage to the tube ends and tubesheet. Cavitation can be suppressed by installing a leg or standpipe in the outlet piping to make sure that the outlet chamber is full of liquid under hydrostatic head. Alternatively, install a wasting plate drilled on the tubesheet pitch pattern to the tube ID and fitted to the tubesheet. Partial retubing may also be justified for cavitation damage if the tubesheet can be repaired and prophylactic action is taken.

Tubesheet erosion. Tubesheet erosion may result from maldistribution, erosive particles in the tubeside inlet stream, leakage past pass partitions, and the wire drawing that occurs when tube-to-tubesheet joints leak. When high-pressure closed feedwater heater channel nozzles enter at an angle and there is insufficient distribution, the tubesheet and tube ends may be gouged out. These large and thick-walled nozzles are welded to the supply and discharge piping and therefore cannot easily be moved or realigned.

If suspended erosive particles in the inlet stream may not or cannot be removed and will not settle out at low flow velocities, increase the inlet-nozzle size. Otherwise, install an impact plate in the way of the inlet nozzle. The latter alternative is the most economical way to mitigate the effects of poorly placed feedwater inlet connections.

Leakage past pass partitions. For the most part, the effects on performance of modest amounts of pass-partition bypassing are not noticeable. When the effects are severe enough to manifest themselves as an apparent decline in thermal efficiency, erosion due to the bypassing will have taken its toll on the pass partitions and tubesheets. For this reason, whenever a multipass channel or bonnet is removed, examine the sealing surfaces of the pass partitions and tubesheet for corrosion and erosion. The causes of leakage past pass partitions are:

1. Bending of the pass partitions because of differential pressure

2. A permanently bowed tubesheet

3. Tubesheet deflection under pressure

4. Bowing due to the temperature difference between the channel face and the shell face

5. Insufficient bolting at the flange ring to seat the gasket at the pass-partition ribs

6. Flanges that are not rigid enough to transmit required gasket-rib seating force from the flange bolts to the pass partitions

7. Crevice corrosion followed by erosion as fluid leaks past the corroded surfaces

Bent pass partitions can be straightened and reinforced.

Repair corrosion and erosion by grinding to sound parent metal and depositing weld metal. The loss of gasket seal that results from a small amount of permanent set (dishing) may be overcome by changing the gasket material and thickness. Before electing this course, examine the flange calculations to make sure that the change is acceptable. If the tubesheets are too severely dished for a gasket change to make a difference and if they are thick enough, field-mill the pass-partition surfaces flush with the gasket-ring surface.

Stationary tubesheets of multipass removable-bundle units that deflect excessively under pressure may be stiffened by welding a strongback (beam) across the shellside of the tubesheet. However, if in operation the tubesheets bend (under internal pressure or for thermal reasons) and if they cannot be stiffened, the problem will recur.

Wire-drawing damage. Wire-drawing damage to tube holes when the joints leak is also called *wormholing* (to describe its appearance). It is most prevalent when the joints are front-face-welded only and there is a high pressure difference between the shell and the tubes. Thus this kind of damage is often found in feedwater heaters. It may be possible to repair the damage, but it is essential to find out why the joint leaked.

Ligament cracking. The main causes of ligament cracks are excessive heat flux through the tubesheet, thermal shock (an extreme case of excessive heat flux), corrosion from the shellside, and vibration. The heat flux through the tubesheet thickness is excessive when thermally induced forces in the ligaments combine with pressure forces to create a condition of overstress. Temperatures in tubesheets have been discussed in Chap. 3.

If a tubesheet is thick and the temperatures of the fluids in contact with the tubesheet faces are far apart, cracking found in ligaments has probably resulted from high heat flux. If the inlet tube pass temperature is very far from the outlet pass temperature and if ligament cracks are confined to the tube field at the inner edges of the passes, the heat flux between passes is probably too high. Other than redesigning the exchanger or changing the operating parameters, little can be done to correct this situation.

In vertical units, ligaments in the top tubesheet may crack because the underside of the tubesheet is not thoroughly washed by the shellside fluids. As a result, the tubesheet metal temperature may exceed the design basis temperature. After repairs, rectify inadequate tubesheet venting by installing vents, as discussed in Chap. 3.

Ligament failures in bottom tubesheets are due mostly to corrosion initiated by failure to blow down sediment. Such a tubesheet failure is usually preceded by tube failures near the bottom. However, cracks in the bottom tubesheet of a unit used to generate vapors (a waste-heat boiler, for example) are probably caused by thermal shock. Typically this results from not providing means to ensure that the bottom tubesheet will always be immersed in shell fluid. Fresh feed falling on the bottom surface cools it so rapidly that the tubesheet is shocked. The effect is equivalent to impact loading.

Another cause of heat shock on the bottom tubesheet is fluctuation on the surface between vapor binding and nucleate boiling. To investigate such thermally caused problems, calculate the tubesheet metal temperatures, the boiling coefficient on the tubesheet surface, and heat flux in the metal and boiling liquid.

The tubes and ligaments of vertical steam generators and similar devices may fail when there is insufficient cross-flow velocity to wipe away flocculent deposits from the feedwater. A rule of thumb for avoiding this problem is to design so that the average linear velocity across the top face of the tubesheet is no less than 3.3 ft/s (1 m/s).

Tube-end fatigue.   Tube-end fatigue often occurs in the rolled regions of joints of tubes that work-harden rapidly. Vibration-caused tube fatigue usually appears as breaks where the tubes emerge from the tubesheet. If the joint is front-face-welded only, vibration may cause the tube-to-tubesheet welds to crack. As illustrated in Chap. 6, fatigue cracks in welds usually start in the root and propagate by tearing the tube and tubesheet.

Little can be done to repair fatigue failures. However, one organization in the United States now offers a tubesheet repair service for thick tubesheets in which the damaged part of the tubesheet is gouged out and puddled with weld. Although this is intended as a temporary repair, closed feedwater heaters have been operated in the repaired condition for periods as long as a year.

Tube-end fatigue failures can be avoided in replacement bundles by eliminating the causes of vibration, using a different expanding method, or both. Similar to fatigue failure in appearance is tearing of the outer edges of the tube ends that may occur when a rolling-tool collar burnishes and hardens the tube edge. As the tube is expanded, the edge tears or is sensitized to tearing.

Crevice corrosions. Crevice corrosion causes tube failures within the tubesheet. Minimize the problem by expanding the tube end to make full contact with the depth of the tubesheet.

Stress-corrosion cracking. Stress-corrosion cracking (SCC) takes place in the transition between the expanded and unexpanded sections of the tubes and in zones fore and aft of the transition where the tube metal is in tension. To reduce stress corrosion in replacement tubes, use equipment and techniques that will produce a tight, strong joint with the least possible wall reduction and adequate interfacial pressure. It is also advisable to substitute a material less sensitive to SCC. Note that tube vibration amplifies the stresses that cause stress-corrosion cracking.

Tube-end corrosion behind the tubesheets. When a search reveals that the cause of stream mixing is tube leaks between the tubesheets and adjacent baffles, it is likely that the tubes corroded because there was little or no circulation in that region. There may also be inner-face tubesheet corrosion behind the inlet pass, which indicates that there is acceleration of the corrosion rate due to a higher temperature in that part of the tubesheet.

Smith has described the principal causes of dead spots:[10]

1. Assembling the bundles to the shells upside down.
2. Construction in which the distance between the tubesheets and adjacent baffles is greater than the baffle pitch in the body of the unit. (This is done to accommodate inlet and outlet nozzles larger in diameter than the desired baffle pitch.)

The need to blow down condensate from the shells of vertical units in which a liquid level is maintained has already been discussed.

In addition to creating dead spots (which reduce performance) upside-down assembly eliminates impingement protection, leading to tube erosion at the inlet and cavitation damage at the outlet. Therefore, when there is reduced performance, tube erosion at the tubes in the way of the inlet nozzle, and tube corrosion at the end regions, check for incorrect assembly.

Little can be done to correct dead spots due to baffle arrangement. But when ordering replacement bundles, consider some means of ensuring that flow sweeps the end compartments, as in the arrangement shown in Fig. 9.10.

Tube pullout or pushout. Leaks between the exchanger sides may occur if the tubes pull or push out of the tube holes. High tube loads are as apt to stretch or collapse the tubes as they are to pull them or push

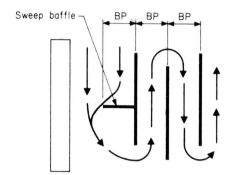

Sweep baffle

BP BP BP

Figure 9.10 Sweep baffle to eliminate dead spot at tubesheet. (*Courtesy of* Chemical Engineering.)

them out of the tubesheets. Therefore, on discovering tubes that protrude beyond or are positioned below their original position relative to the tubesheet face, look for accompanying tube damage.

Applying design pressure will not cause tubes to pull or push out of the tubesheets if the exchanger meets TEMA or HEI standards and satisfies the *ASME Code* requirements.[11–13] To investigate, map the positions of the affected tubes, indicating which pulled loose and which pulled out.

Unidirectional failures, located roughly in the center region, indicate that excessive pressure may have been applied. This may be due to a pressure-relief-valve malfunction, storing in the sun a shutdown unit filled with liquid and sealed, or failing to drain water from a shutdown unit when the temperature is below freezing. Overpressure may bend the tubesheets permanently. When it results from fluid expansion or freezing, overpressure may split tubes and damage flanges and bolting. Therefore, examine these parts of the unit too.

As explained in Chap. 3, if the design of the tubesheet assumed that the shell and/or channel would provide fixed support but they are not thick enough, the support may be less than fixed. This can also lead to tube pullout or pushout. Since tubesheet rotation due to insufficient shell support bends the shell at the end where the tubesheet is attached and since that is where small vent and drain nozzles are usually located, the joints of the vent and drain connections to the shell may also fail.

Unidirectional failures located mostly in the periphery of the tube field of a fixed-tubesheet exchanger, built without a shell expansion joint, indicate differential expansion that the tube joints are not strong enough to restrain. When there are failures in this region, reexamine the calculations of tube and shell metal temperatures and the tubesheet, tube-joint, and tube strength calculations.

When tubes in the hot-pass area of a multipass straight-tube unit push out and those in the cold-pass field pull out, the cause is too great a temperature range. Other indications are the bundle's assuming a banana shape in floating units and tube buckling in the hot pass.

Randomly distributed pulled-out tubes in straight-tube flue-gas–air exchangers indicate that some tubes are becoming fouled more rapidly than others. Flue gas ordinarily flows inside the tubes; therefore, the metal temperatures of the fouled tubes are closer to the cool-air temperature than the temperatures of the clean tubes, and the tubes pull loose.

The duration of residual stress in expanded joints is a function of the tube and tubesheet creep behavior during service. Long-term operation at high temperatures may relieve the locked-in stresses upon which expanded joints rely for strength and tightness. When residual stress relaxes after a substantial period of successful operation, the tube-to-tubesheet joints usually leak well before joint strength is seriously reduced. If inspection shows the tube ends and tubesheets to be in good condition, reexpand to restore tightness.

Failures in welded tube-to-tubesheet joints. When welded tube-to-tubesheet joints leak, the temptation is to make a quick fix by chipping or grinding out the crack, cleaning the area, and rewelding. But if the mechanism and cause of the failures are not determined, the repairs will solve the problem only temporarily. Repeated fixes will eventually make the tube joints incapable of being repaired.

Failures found soon after an exchanger goes into service are usually due to improper fabrication, but they may be due to faulty joint design. The kinds of trouble to expect are subsurface porosity and wormholing (used here to describe spiral leak paths in the weld), burn-throughs in the tubes, and weld root cracks.

Failures after a period of successful service can usually be traced to weld root cracking and propagation in the following locations, listed in the order of frequency: (1) through the weld, (2) through the weld and tube wall, and (3) through the weld, tube wall, and tubesheet.

Visual, radiographic, or other nondestructive examinations will probably not reveal how or why root-bead tearing originated. For a complete analysis, subject samples of failed joints to chemical and metallurgical study. The knowledge gained may enable prescribing appropriate repairs and measures to prevent recurrence.

Improper tube-hole finish. Tubes can hardly ever be expanded tightly into holes when the contact surfaces are axially scored. If a tight joint is made, it will probably leak soon after it goes into service. It is frustrating to find a few joints in the tube field that cannot be sealed by moderate increases in hydraulic expanding pressure or rolling torque. Because the tube or hole damage is hidden, it cannot be known that the problem stems from a scratched hole or tube. A frustrated worker may be tempted to increase pressure or torque enough to deform the ligaments to the point of loosening adjacent tube joints.

During construction, axial damage incidental to drilling may escape detection. The tool used for machining annular grooves into the holes may upset the groove-edge metal. If the upset material is not removed, the tube will be scratched during insertion. In addition to the joint-sealing problem, tube life may be reduced by premature corrosion along the scratches. (This is why it is prudent to require tube holes to be finish-reamed after grooving. However, it is even possible for the reamer to score the hole slightly.)

The symptom of improper finish is randomly located leaks that persist after expanding and reexpanding. The remedy is to extract the tubes from the leaking holes, refinish the holes, and install new tubes.

Tube-hole damage. During retubing, the holes may be scored when the old tubes are removed. The edges of annular grooves may be upset as tubes are pulled, subsequently scratching the new tubes as they are inserted. The conditions under which field retubing is done are frequently difficult, and axial scoring and upset metal may go unnoticed. The symptoms and treatment of this problem are the same as above.

Ligament distortion during retubing. During retubing the tendency is to assume that, in order to get the joints tight, it is necessary to apply higher rolling torque or expanding pressure than for building a new unit. If the hole finish has not been damaged or damage has been repaired, the assumption is not justifiable. Excessive rolling can misshape holes along the lines of the pitch pattern. Detect this kind of damage by rotating a tube micrometer inside the tube end rolled into the tubesheet. Little can be done to correct this situation. Depending upon the service conditions, it may be satisfactory to pull the tube, ream the distorted holes oversize, and expand a replacement tube and interposed ferrule together into the hole.

Erosion damage at the shell inlet. The symptoms of erosion damage at the shell inlet are pits, similar to tubeside impingement attack, and leaks in the tubes at the inlet region of the shell. Some causes are (1) lacking or inadequate impingement protection, (2) unforeseen flow conditions, (3) insufficient escape area around the impingement plate, and (4) insufficient calming length when there is an increase from the supply-pipe diameter to the inlet-pipe size.

Chapter 6 discussed requirements for impingement protection. There it was noted that for appropriate fluids and flow conditions no special provision for impingement protection is required. If there is erosion damage and no impingement protection, compare the actual impact factor (density × square of velocity) with the impact factors assumed in the design for the nozzle and inlet to the bundle.

If impingement protection has been omitted but is now required, there will probably not be enough room to install a plate that allows an adequate fluid escape area, one large enough so that the impact factor in the escape region does not exceed 4000 lb/(s · s) [approximately 1815 kg/(s · s)].

Alternatives are (1) to snap commercially available tube protectors over the first two or three tube rows in the way of the inlet, (2) to shield the tubes with formed half cylinders or angles, and (3) to install a dome, diffuser-reducer, or distributor belt. Refer to Chap. 6 for information about these devices.

When there is erosion despite the use of an impingement plate, either the impingement plate is too small or there is not enough escape area. As stated in Chap. 6, the edges of the plate should extend about 1 in (about 25 mm) beyond the trace of a 15° included-angle cone that is tangent to the nozzle bore where it pierces the shell. It may be necessary to install a larger plate or make the changes described above.

It is a reasonable design option to omit impingement plates by using large inlet nozzles to hold impact factors below the threshold values. This may be done when the available pressure drop is very small and the turbulence created by an impingement plate cannot be tolerated. But if the supply pipe to the shell is smaller than the inlet, anticipate erosion unless the enlargement reducer is placed 10 to 20 inlet-nozzle diameters before the inlet or a long-radius elbow, provided with a flow straightener, leads the supply to the inlet.

Cavitation at the shell outlet.   Cavitation may occur when the shell discharge flushes down a vertical pipe without restriction and the resulting reduced pressure induces bubbles of vapor to form in the fluid. In addition to cavitation, there is usually vortexing. After repairing the damage, install a vortex breaker in the outlet and a trap in the outlet piping.

Inadequate bundle support.   When a floating tubesheet overhangs, the tubes may sag. This permits the floating assembly to drag along the shell during bundle installation and pulling. If the unit is a packed type, the sealing surface (which requires a 63-rms finish to seal properly) is marred. No amount of extra packing or gland follower pressure will cure the leak that results. In all types of floating-tubesheet equipment, failure to provide a support at the floating end can lead to tube damage in the regions of the last baffle and floating tubesheet.

It is not practical to install a drilled support plate to correct rear-end bundle support deficiency. Geometry permitting, a shoe may be fastened to the inner face or bottom of the floating tubesheet to provide some support.

Vibration damage. Vibration damage was described in Chap. 6. Its symptoms are (1) tube leaks at baffle penetrations (this may also indicate crevice corrosion), (2) a pattern of leaks midway between baffles or between the baffles and adjacent tubesheets, (3) leaks at U bends, (4) excessive noise, and (5) cracks in tubes where they emerge from the tubesheets. If there are indications of vibration damage, it will probably be necessary to perform a complete vibration analysis to determine what to do about it.

Some remedies are:

1. Installing deresonating baffles to reduce excessive noise (when the vibration-forcing mechanism is acoustical coupling)
2. Lacing the tubes with wire between the baffles
3. Fitting flat bars or other devices between the tubes at locations between the baffles (staking the tubes)
4. Changing the shellside flow arrangement to divided flow, split flow, or cross-flow when thermally possible
5. Altering the character of the shellside stream
6. Retubing with tubes that have a natural frequency in a safe range
7. Replacing the bundle with one designed to be free of vibration damage

Improper tube fabrication. After an exchanger has been in service, it is hard to determine that a tube has failed because of improper manufacture. The starting point of the investigation is tube cleaning, followed by borescope examination. To confirm the suspicion of faulty manufacture, the tube must be extracted without further damaging it. In U-tube bundles only tubes in the outer row can be pulled. It is unpalatable to extract tubes because it shuts down production. The common practice is to plug the ends when one or more tubes leak and return the unit to service until a scheduled maintenance shutdown period. (Remember that if you operate the exchanger subsequent to installing plugs, evidence of faulty manufacture may be destroyed.)

When examining tube failures in welded tubes, look for incomplete fusion, inclusions, and burn-throughs. In seamless and welded-

and-drawn tubes, look for die and mandrel scratches. These are longitudinal gouges in the tube wall. Tubes may also fail because of the mill straightening operation or improper heat treatment. The innermost bends of U-tube bundles are the most severely stretched and compressed of all the tubes in the assembly. Improper bend fabrication in the inner rows appears as tube flattening and crimping.

In addition to the troubles symptomized by leakage between the sides, the following conditions may have to be dealt with.

Leaking gasketed joints.   If the force required to seal the gaskets at the pass-partition ribs was neglected in the design, the bolting may be insufficient (the bolts being overstressed), or the flanges (or rims of tubesheets extended as flanges) may bend excessively, or both. This condition is evidenced by stretched bolts, cupped flanges, and uncompressed gasket ribs. Short of modifying the flanges and bolting, all that can be done is to substitute a more easily compressed gasket after truing the parts.

Most flanges designed to the *ASME Code*'s rules, modified for gasket-rib compression and tubesheets extended as flanges, have adequate bolting and are suitably tight and strong. However, if during bolt-up they bend too much before the gasket is adequately yielded, the joint will leak after a period of operation. Further tightening of the bolts does not stop the leak because it increases the bending. Frustrated maintenance personnel may pull up on the bolts until the rims make contact without stopping the leak.

One prescription is to reexamine the flange and tubesheet design assumptions and to replace the gasket with one that is more easily yielded if the design is borderline. Another is to install a peripheral split limit ring. If the flange and tubesheet have taken a permanent set, they must first be remachined.

Weld shrinkage tends to cup ring flanges and fixed tubesheets at their joints to the shell. Joining the tubes by expanding tends to bow the tubesheets. Because of these tendencies, the ring of gasket that seals the mating parts may be pinched at its outer or inner edge. A small relaxation of bolt stress or gasket compression permits leakage. Leaks may be stopped by retightening but will probably recur. If too much torque is applied to the bolts, the flanges may be deformed beyond repair. The cure is to machine the gasket surfaces flat. If the unit cannot be shut down to find the cause of the leak, insert a split-ring spacer between the flange and the tubesheet at the edge beyond the bolt holes to avoid bending during retightening.

When a unit that has been disassembled for cleaning cannot be gotten tight upon reassembly, the obvious suspicion is that the gasket surface has been scratched or is dirty. However, the most frequent cause is flange warping caused by an improper unbolting procedure. If flanged joints are unbolted consecutively around the bolt circle, the flanges are very likely to bend. To prevent the bending, unbolt in the crisscross pattern recommended in the TEMA and HEI standards for bolting up. Loosen the bolts in several passes through the pattern, never completely unbolting a bolt on the first or second pass.

Unexplained stream mixing when the tubes and tube-to-tubesheet connections are tight may be due to leakage through the flanged joint at the floating end. In split-ring units, see if the split ring has twisted or if the bolts have been bent. These conditions reduce the force available to hold the return cover tightly to the tubesheet. Recurrence of split-ring bending can be prevented by machining the tubesheet and split ring to the configuration as in Fig. 5.14 of Chap. 5.

When flanged joints leak in high-temperature service, the bolts, gaskets, or both have probably relaxed. If the leaks are found early enough, the gasket may not be damaged; the leak can usually be sealed by carefully retorquing all the bolts in the original bolting sequence. To prevent flange damage during retorquing, insert the previously described split-ring spacer between the flange edges. The required interval between retorquing bolts may be increased by installing spring washers under the nuts. But remember that the spring washers are intended to take up bolt thermal expansion and will not eliminate the need to retighten. The least bolt relaxation will occur if all the bolts are loaded identically. Therefore, consider using a hydraulic bolt tensioner and ultrasonic bolt stress measurement.

Flanged joints may leak because the effect of differential expansion between the mating parts and bolts has been overlooked. Consider, for example, an insulated flanged joint operating at 650°F (343.3°C) that consists of a 2-in-thick (50.8-mm-thick) austenitic tubesheet bolted to a 2-in-thick (50.8-mm-thick) hub flange ring with SA-193 Gr. B7 stud bolts. The thermal coefficients of expansion at the operating temperature are 9.9×10^{-6} in/(in · °F) [5.5×10^{-6} mm/(mm · °C)] for austenitic steel and 7.3×10^{-6} in/(in · °F) [4.06×10^{-6} mm/(mm · °C)] for carbon steel. When heated, the studs will therefore expand by 0.018 in (0.46 mm); the tubesheet-flange combination will expand by 0.021 in (0.53 mm). If the whole structure were rigid, the additional stress on the bolts imposed by the differential thermal expansion would be about 21,750 lb/in^2 (about 150,000 kPa) more than the bolt-up stress. Of course the structure is not rigid; the flanges and tubesheet bend, and the gasket yields. Although the bolt-up stress was well below the bolt yield stress, it is likely that because of the thermally imposed load the gasket may be crushed and the joint may leak upon startup after a shutdown.

The simple fix for this problem is to increase the stud length by a total of $\frac{7}{16}$ in (11.1 mm) and to install carbon steel washers under the nuts to take up the additional length. Good results may also be obtained by using an equivalent thickness of fully compressed spring washers.

Failures in shell expansion joints. Expansion joints fail because of corrosion, fatigue, overpressure, larger-than-design axial deflections, unanticipated angular deflections and offsets, or some combinations of these causes. The elements of bellows expansion joints (thin-walled joints) are thin: 0.035 to 0.093 in (0.89 to 2.36 mm). Furthermore, most configurations cannot be fitted with vents and drains. Therefore, liquids flowing through horizontal shells are entrapped in the bottom of the joint and noncondensibles in the top.

The changes of direction of pressure and deflection stresses and the entrapment of process fluid create optimum conditions for stress-corrosion cracking of the austenitic steels from which bellows are ordinarily fabricated. Fluids high in chloride ion content cause stress-corrosion cracking. Therefore, in running down the source of failure, investigate the fluid composition and the bellows material.

Thick expansion joints made from flanged-only heads, flanged-only heads with flue holes, or similar construction are ⅛ in (3.18 mm) or thicker. There is usually room in the straight flanged section for vents and drains without impairing joint life. Furthermore, thick joint elements are often made of carbon steel, which is less sensitive. Therefore, stress-corrosion cracking is seldom seen in this kind of element. Corrosion in thick joints usually results from not piping up the vents and drains.

Both the *ASME Code* appendix for thin-walled joints and the *Standards of the Expansion Joint Manufacturers Association* (EJMA) require consideration of cycle life and testing.[14] For this reason, fatigue failures in bellows joints are improbable if the directions and amplitudes of deflections do not exceed design specifications and cycle life has not expired. However, a small discontinuity, such as a dent or weld drag, can drastically reduce cycle life.

With some restrictions, bellows expansion joints may be stamped for *ASME Code* construction. The joint manufacturer is not required to hydrostatically test the joint; the responsibility falls on the heat exchanger manufacturer who installs it. A leak in a bellows joint can be disastrous because there may be no acceptable way to repair it. Most bellows expansion-joint manufacturers will hydrostatically test on demand.

Thick-walled joints built to the rules of the *ASME Code* appendix for such joints require the user to specify cycle life and deflections and the manufacturer to demonstrate safe design and construction. The analytical procedures used are within the manufacturer's discretion. Therefore, when a thick-walled joint fails, part of the effort to discover the cause is a review of the manufacturer's design analysis, with emphasis on how cycle life was established. As stated in Chap. 6, most thick-walled-joint fatigue failures occur in the knuckles. Joints in which the knuckle radii are less than three metal thicknesses are candidates for low cycle life.

The probability of fatigue failure is increased when deflections are imposed that the design did not anticipate. Examples are (1) shop precompression or extension during fit-up; (2) offsets in installation; (3) anchoring supports on either side of the joint, which prevents free movement and causes angular deflection; and (4) twists imposed by nozzle loads.

When thin-walled joints are overpressured, the sidewall may be permanently bulged, and if the joint is multiconvoluted, it may squirm. These troubles are visible: in sidewall bulge there is a permanent reduction in the space between the sidewalls of adjacent corrugations of 7 percent, and in in-plane squirm the change of the pitch between adjacent convolutions is 15 percent at any measurement location. Within these limits, failure is not catastrophic, but joint life is severely reduced. Beyond this point, the root of the joint bulges, and there is general and continued deformation of the bellows with small increases in pressure until the joint bursts. After an episode of overpressure, it is essential to inspect the bellows for damage.

The most highly stressed areas of thick-walled joints are at the outer knuckle or edge and at the connection to the shell. Overstress may relieve itself by yielding at these localities. Nevertheless, that is where to look for signs of overpressure damage.

When investigating why a joint was fatigued, bear in mind that not only the frequency of deflection but also the amplitude, direction, and number of changes of direction affect joint life. It may not be possible to measure the actual deflection to compare it with the assumed deflection. Therefore, review the calculated deflection based on design conditions, and compare it with deflection calculated for actual operations. Look for the possibility that the free end is restrained. This can bend the unit at the expansion joint, thereby reducing joint life.

What can be done about a broken shell expansion joint? It is futile to try to repair bellows joints and nearly so to repair thick joints. However, some repairs that can be made to extend the exchanger's useful life are discussed in Chap. 7.

Packed-floating-head problems. Packed joints are *supposed* to leak slightly during operation. Trying to eliminate the last vestige of a leak creates problems. Squeezing the packing too tightly against the floating-tubesheet barrel restrains the bundle from moving relative to the shell. The restraint of movement may show up either as tube-joint leaks or as bent tubes.

If a packed joint leaks excessively (more than 5 to 10 drops a minute), tighten the nuts on the gland-follower bolts uniformly. If a moderate amount of tightening does not correct the problem, replace the packing. Simply shoving another ring of packing into the packing box may jam the inner hardened rings into the barrel and score it. Once the barrel has been scratched or scraped along its length, the joint will always leak (unless the barrel is refinished).

Packing problems often stem from cocking the gland follower as it is tightened against the packing. If a follower is cocked, back it off, loosen the packing, and retighten uniformly.

Summary

In troubleshooting exchanger problems, consider the interactions of thermal and mechanical design. Gather as much design, construction, and operating information as possible. Consider the nature of the problem and the possibility that the trouble lies elsewhere in the system.

Compare design assumptions with actual operating conditions. Search for upsets and flow regimes that deviate from those anticipated. Look into how clean conditions and excess surface affect system pressure and heat exchanger structure. When overcapacity has been provided, find out how the excess surface was furnished and determine its effect on normal operation.

Before concluding that equipment is underdesigned, determine if the piping and mechanical arrangements are suitable. Examine equilibrium relationships, heat release curves, effects of noncondensibles and venting, and boiling-point elevation. Search also for incorrect channel or bundle assembly, fluid bypassing around channel pass partitions, short-circuiting on the shellside, leakage between baffles and shells and tubes and baffle holes, and inadequate seal strips or dummy-tube placement.

Use instruments and nondestructive testing techniques to extend ability to sense what is wrong and detect the causes of symptoms. To troubleshoot leaks between the shellside and the tubeside, scrutinize the regions near the tubesheets for corrosion, erosion, fatigue, and vibration damage. Locate the positions of tube perforations relative to baffle positions for vibration indications. Examine the tubes for possible manufacturing flaws, and look into floating-head closure integrity.

When flanged joints leak, examine flange calculations. Determine if pass-partition gasket compression was considered. Look also for deformations resulting from weld shrinkage and improper bolting and unbolting procedures. Examine differential expansion between the flange-tubesheet sandwich and the stud bolting.

In troubleshooting expansion-joint failures, consider how drainage and venting affect the corrosion resistance of the material of construction. Examine the amplitude, direction, and frequency of changes of direction and deflections. Inspect joints after excursions of excess pressure.

Packed-floating-head problems arise from overtightening gland followers, scoring floating-head barrels, and cocking gland followers. When joints leak, replace hardened packing in preference to adding rings.

References

1. C. H. Gilmour, "Troubleshooting Heat-Exchanger Design," *Chem. Eng.*, June 19, 1967, p. 22.
2. "Discrepancies between Design and Operation of Heat Transfer Equipment," *Chem. Eng. Prog.*, January 1961, p. 71.
3. F. L. Rubin, "Multistage Condensers: Tabulate Design Data to Prevent Errors," *Hydrocarbon Process.*, June 1982, pp. 133–135.
4. *Equipment Testing Procedure, Heat Exchangers*, Section 1: *Vaporization, Condensation and Sensible Heat Transfer in Shell-and-Tube and Double Pipe Heat Exchangers*, 2d ed., American Institute of Chemical Engineers, New York.
5. *ASME Performance Test Code*, PTC 19.2, *Pressure Measurements*, American Society of Mechanical Engineers, New York, 1972.
6. D. Q. Kern, *Process Heat Transfer*, McGraw-Hill Book Company, New York, 1950.
7. F. Standiford, "Effect of Non-Condensibles on Condenser Design and Heat Transfer," *Chem. Eng. Prog.*, July 1979, pp. 59–62.
8. S. J. Meisenberg and others, *Trans. AIChE*, vol. 31, 1935, pp. 622–638; vol. 32, 1950, pp. 100–104, 449–450.
9. G. C. Shah, "Troublesome Reboiler Systems," *Chem. Eng. Prog.*, July 1979, pp. 53–58.
10. H. E. Smith, "The Interrelationships between Codes, Standards and Customer Specifications for Process Heat Exchangers—A User's Standpoint," presented at ASME winter annual meeting, New York, Dec. 2–7, 1979.
11. *Standards of the Tubular Exchanger Manufacturers Association*, 7th ed., The Tubular Exchanger Manufacturers Association, Tarrytown, N.Y., 1989.
12. *Standard for Power Plant Heat Exchangers*, 1st ed., The Heat Exchange Institute, Cleveland, 1980; Addendum 1, 1984.
13. *ASME Boiler and Pressure Vessel Code*, Section VIII, Division 1, Appendix AA, American Society of Mechanical Engineers, New York, 1986.
14. *Standards of the Expansion Joint Manufacturers Association*, 5th ed., Expansion Joint Manufacturers Association, Tarrytown, N.Y., 1980.

10

Writing and Interpreting Specifications

Introduction

This chapter discusses how to write and interpret heat exchanger specifications. It guides the purchaser in describing required performance and quality and in interpreting the seller's offering. It guides the seller in interpreting the buyer's requirements and in describing offers in response to buyers' inquiries.

The purpose of specifications is to communicate about general and structural requirements, procedures, dimensions, materials, and performance. The best way to achieve this goal is to make them concise, specific, and unambiguous. Pitfalls to avoid are elegant language, technical jargon, and legalistic phraseology. You will communicate most effectively by using the plainest possible language and, whenever possible, using tables, charts, drawings, and photographs.[1]

How to write specifications depends upon whether your purpose is to present design and quality requirements to be met or to describe how you propose to fulfill such requirements. Specifications for purchase requirements should set clear limits of acceptability. In responding to an inquiry or making an unsolicited proposal, specify unambiguously the limits of performance that will be fulfilled and the minimum standards of quality that will be provided.

How to interpret specifications depends upon whether your purpose is to learn what is required of you or to understand someone's offer.

Several types of specifications apply to heat exchangers. Some of their elements are common; some are unique to the type of specification. It is convenient to divide heat exchanger specifications arbitrarily into these four categories:

1. *General specifications.*   These apply to all the exchangers of a project, plant, group of plants, or organization.

2. *Performance specifications.*   These are concerned only with the fluid-flow, energy, and heat transfer requirements of individual units.

3. *Mechanical specifications.*   These are used to delineate the design and construction of heat exchangers and heat exchanger components.

4. *Procedure specifications.*   These specify how work on exchangers or parts of exchangers is to be done.

These classifications provide a framework for writing and interpreting technical specifications. They do not deal with commercial matters. However, there is an interface between technical and legal requirements because purchase specifications and suppliers' exceptions accepted by the purchaser are usually incorporated in purchase orders or contracts.

Elements Common to All Heat Exchanger Specifications

These elements are common to all categories of heat exchanger specifications: (1) documentation, (2) pagination, (3) caption numbering, (4) dual units* (when the situation requires such units), (5) order-of-governance statement, (6) intent statement, (6) scope statement, (7) definitions, (8) data sources, (9) list of subsidiary specifications that apply, and (10) list of applicable standards. The following discusses these elements.

Documentation

Document all specifications on a cover sheet to provide a trail of timeliness and accountability. Include the following:

1. Names, titles, and addresses of originators and authorizers of the specification

2. Specification number and title

3. Dates of original issue and revisions accompanied by the issuer's handwritten signature or initials

4. Approval or authorization signatures accompanied by dates

---

*For current practice in using dual units see ASME Guide SI-1, *ASME Orientation and Guide for Use of SI (Metric) Units*, 8th ed., The American Society of Mechanical Engineers, New York, 1978.

5. Statements of restrictions on copying and using the specification

Pagination

Number all pages serially. If many similar specifications are to be written, it may avoid confusion to prefix each page number with the specification number. For two-sided printing, it is convenient to number outer corners of facing pages.

Paragraph caption numbering

Numbered captions help readers to follow specifications. They also facilitate making tables of contents. Three systems in common use are described below. They are generally available in word-processing programs.

Traditional outline system. The traditional outline, also called the Harvard outline system, looks like this:

TITLE

I. FIRST-LEVEL HEADING
   A. Second-Level Heading
      1. Third-level heading
         a. fourth-level heading
            (1) fifth-level heading
               (a) sixth-level heading
               (b) sixth-level heading
            (2) fifth-level heading
         b. fourth-level heading
      2. Third-level heading
   B. Second-Level Heading
II. FIRST-LEVEL HEADING

Century-decade-unit system. The century-decade-unit system looks like this:

TITLE

100 FIRST-LEVEL HEADING
   110 Second-Level Heading
      111 Third-level heading
      112 Third-level heading
   120 Second-Level Heading
200 FIRST-LEVEL HEADING

Multiple-decimal system. This system and the Harvard outline are widely used. The multiple-decimal system looks like this:

1. FIRST-LEVEL HEADING
   1.1. Second-Level Heading
      1.1.1. Third-level heading
         1.1.1.1. fourth-level heading
            1.1.1.1.1. fifth-level heading
               1.1.1.1.1.1 sixth-level heading
               1.1.1.1.1.2 sixth-level heading
            1.1.1.1.2. fifth-level heading
         1.1.1.2. fourth-level heading
      1.1.2. Third-level heading
   1.2. Second-Level Heading
2. FIRST-LEVEL HEADING

Note that capitalization follows the levels, with all capitals at the first level, the first letter of each word capitalized at the second level, the first letter of the first word of the caption capitalized at the third level, and no capitals at subsequent levels. Boldface, underlining, double underlining, and combinations of boldface and double underlining may be used to enhance clarity.

These systems can accommodate an infinite number of subheadings. The century-decade system can be started with any desired power of 10 for the first level in the hierarchy; the traditional outline system can be further subheaded by using double, triple, etc., parentheses and alternating arabic numbers and lowercase letters; and the multiple-decimal system by using smaller and smaller decimal fractions. However, captions beyond the fourth level tend to confuse the reader.

Dual units

Use dual units under these conditions: (1) the specification will be used in both the United States and nations that use metric units; and (2) the specifications are intended for long-term use in the United States.*

Order-of-governance statement

Most heat exchanger specification packages contain the following documents:

1. General specifications for pressure vessels
2. General specifications for heat exchangers

---

*This assumes that the United States will eventually adopt the metric system.

3. Performance, mechanical, and procedure specifications

4. Outline or detail drawings

In addition to this list, project specifications may contain flowsheets that locate the exchangers in the process train and that show heat and materials flows and inlet and outlet pressures and temperatures at each exchanger.

Provisions of the several specifications often contradict each other. The drawings may conflict with the specifications. Information in the performance specifications may not agree with process flowsheets. Frequently, architect-engineer (AE) firms' requests for proposals (RFPs) have overlapping sets of specifications and documents that disagree with each other and with their clients' specifications and documents. Sometimes, division or plant specifications, drawings, and other documents differ from corporate specifications, but all are submitted to heat exchanger manufacturers with RFPs.

An order-of-governance statement is necessary to sort out which documents apply and to resolve conflicts between them. It establishes a hierarchical order of applicability when there are conflicts in provisions of specifications in a package. When analyzing a specifications package, the first thing to do is to look for the text that establishes the order of governance. If there is none and if several specifications conflict, find out from the issuer which governs. If this effort is unsuccessful, state your assumptions about the priorities in your response. Following is a typical hierarchy:

1. Owners' specifications supersede those of AEs unless transmittal documents state otherwise.

2. Plant specifications supersede division specifications, which supersede corporate specifications.

3. Flowsheet data take precedence over data listed on performance specifications.

4. Performance, mechanical, and procedure specifications supersede general specifications.

5. General heat exchanger specifications supersede general pressure vessel specifications.

Intent statement

Make an intent statement to avoid having to specify trivial details and to make sure that omissions, errors, and obscure phraseology do not negate the specification. In interpreting specifications, the intent statement should alert you to what the specifier is trying to communicate.

Scope statement

The scope statement defines the limits of applicability of the specification. It is (or should be) commensurate with the document's generality. Set the general boundaries of the specification by describing in the scope statement what it covers. However, list items that are specifically excluded. Use simple declarative sentences. Here is an example:

> This specification applies to shell-and-tube heat exchangers that have rolled-plate shells $\frac{3}{16}$ in to $1\frac{1}{4}$ in thick inclusive. Pipe shell exchangers are excluded.

Definitions

Define only words that have uncommon or special meanings. Listing definitions of names and terms in common use may obscure the meanings of special nomenclature and terminology.

Data sources

Cite only those sources of data not readily available in handbooks, manuals, texts, and trade literature. However, when data from several sources conflict, specify the source to be used. Furnish proprietary data in graphic form when possible. Preserve confidentiality by assigning code names or symbols to process fluids instead of their actual names.

List of subsidiary specifications

Refer to subsidiary specifications by number and source. Do not refer to other specifications unless they apply to the exchanger. In interpreting specifications, make sure that all referenced ones are relevant. Take exception to those that are not.

General specifications may refer to performance, mechanical, and procedure specifications as subsidiary specifications. In turn, mechanical specifications may refer to specifications for materials of construction as subsidiary documents.

List of standards

List all standards to be used, any exceptions, and permissible deviations.

Elements of General Specifications

In addition to the previously listed specification elements, include the following in general specifications.

Requirements for compliance with codes and regulations

Include the facts of publication about codes and regulations that govern the design, construction, and use of the exchanger in the location where it will be installed. Specify the edition or date of issue, or state that the most recent issues, addenda, or amendments apply.

Specifications that require manufacturers to comply with all local, state, and federal regulations put the burden on the supplier to discover the state and local ones that apply. However, they do not relieve the buyer or user from responsibility for the safety of persons and property at the site. Therefore, in writing purchase specifications, it is prudent to direct the manufacturer's attention to the applicable regulations. If all exchangers must comply with the requirements of the Occupational Safety and Health Act of 1970 (OSHA) as published in the *Federal Register* or with similar national, state, and local laws, this is the place to say so. If all units must conform with the requirements of the *ASME Boiler and Pressure Vessel Code (ASME Code)*, cite it in the general specifications.[2] State which sections and divisions apply unless subsidiary specifications make this clear.

Requirements for drawing and design review

Manufacturers and buyers often have different views about drawing and design review requirements. The *TEMA Standards* fairly present the general views of heat exchanger manufacturers.[3] At one extreme a manufacturer may be willing to provide only outline drawings or setting plans and tabulated performance characteristics. The manufacturer does not submit to the buyer drawings for approval or subsequent use and does not disclose design details. Replacements and repair parts can be procured only from the original manufacturer unless the equipment is disassembled and measured. Maintenance is impeded by virtue of the maintenance force's not knowing how the equipment is constructed.

At the other extreme, the buyer may insist on examining and approving all thermal and mechanical design calculations, construction details, and procedures and on the right to copy and use construction drawings without restraint. Some buyers may demand that fabrication drawings be made on their stationery, with the originals surrendered after shipment.

Buyers' specifications may contain a statement that their approval of drawings and calculations does not relieve the manufacturers from full responsibility for the performance and safety of their products. Such disclaimers belong in commercial terms and conditions and are best prepared by legal counsel. The *TEMA Standards* have disclaimer phraseology that is usually acceptable to manufacturers. It recognizes only that the buyer's approval does not relieve the manufacturer from having to conform with the *TEMA Standards* and *ASME Code* requirements.

Purchasers usually require early submission of an outline drawing and setting plan, followed by assembly and detail drawings. Setting plans have the information needed for work to go forward on foundations and piping. Assembly drawings provide general information and show how the exchanger is put together. Detail drawings have the dimensions of parts and subassemblies. They are useful to buyers for examining structural adequacy and for procuring repair parts.

In general, specifications specify that all drawings show the following information:

1. Manufacturer's name, address, and location of the shop producing the exchanger
2. Drawing title, drawing number, date drawn, revision numbers, revision dates, and revision descriptions
3. Reference drawing numbers and titles
4. Purchaser's name, location, purchase order number, and item number
5. Manufacturer's serial number
6. Pressure vessel code registration number corresponding with buyer's item number
7. Main centerlines of all views
8. Quadrant positions of the main centerlines (0°, 90°, 180°, and 270°) on all end and plan views of bonnets, channels, channel covers, re-

turn and floating-head covers, tubesheets, baffles and support plates, and shells

9. Note showing whether bolt holes are on the main centerlines or straddle them

10. Identification of working points that are not self-evident

Information to be shown on setting plans. Specify setting plans to show the following:

1. Overall dimensions.

2. Clearance needed for removing and reinstalling removable bundles and the tubes of fixed-tubesheet units.

3. Working points from which the dimensions are measured. These must coincide with the working points of the assembly and detail drawings.

4. Axial distances from the main working point to the nozzle centerlines, to the centers of bolt holes or slots in the supports, between adjacent nozzles, and between bolt-hole and slot centerlines in supports.

5. Support bolting pattern and allowance for expansion and contraction of the free end.

6. Distances from the main axial centerline to the centers of all nozzle faces and to the support bases.

7. Distances between the main axial centerline and nozzle centerlines of nozzles offset from the axial centerline.

8. Pitch angles of all pitched nozzles and supports.

9. Shimming allowances for stacked shells.

10. Dry and flooded weights of the assembled exchanger and the weight of the bundle alone if it is removable.

11. Arrows that indicate inlet and outlet flow direction for shellside and tubeside connections.

Information to be shown on assembly drawings. On assembly drawings specify that the following information is to be provided:

1. Design and test conditions

2. Construction code, stamping, and registration requirements

3. Manufacturers' standards that are to be followed; for example,

TEMA Mechanical Standards, C, B, or R, or an applicable HEI standard

4. Gross and net or effective surfaces

5. Cautionary notes about maximum and minimum permissible coincident shell-and-tube metal temperatures in fixed-tubesheet exchangers

6. Heat treatment specifications

7. Surface finishes and coating specifications

8. Nondestructive examinations to be performed

9. Corrosion and erosion allowances

Some manufacturers make one drawing to serve as both setting plan and assembly drawing. They submit the outline for preliminary approval. Upon completion, they submit the drawing for final approval. The advantages are that they (1) eliminate discrepancies between the setting plan and assembly, (2) require preparation of fewer drawings, (3) reduce response time, and (4) reduce drafting cost. The disadvantage is that the field crew may be confused because the drawing has more information than it needs to set the exchanger.

It may be necessary to itemize the design temperatures of individual parts rather than just those of the shellside and tubeside. It is acceptable for the manufacturer to specify compliance with more than one construction code only if these have no mutually exclusive provisions. The manufacturer should be required to use material specifications numbers from the applicable construction code to specify materials of pressure parts rather than trade names or common designations.

The assembly drawings should indicate not only the positions of the parts after assembly but also the sequence and manner of assembly and disassembly. Notes should list all procedure specifications to be used for construction and nondestructive examination.

Information to be shown on detail drawings.   Users need detail drawings to make an adequate review before construction begins. After units are in operation, detail drawings are a great help in maintaining and repairing a unit and in troubleshooting.

Manufacturers prefer to make only the detail drawings they need for production. They may rely on shop practice for some details and not show them on drawings. However, to enable a preconstruction review specify that all details are to be provided or that shop practices for undisclosed details be documented.

These are the details that are needed for a complete review:

Bundle drawings

1. Materials of construction
2. Tubesheet thicknesses; outside diameters; bolt circles; number, location, and diameter of bolt holes; tubesheet outer-tube-limit (OTL) circle or outer-tube-center (OTC) circle
3. Tubesheet-hole drilling, showing total number of holes, number of holes in each pass, pitch pattern, hole diameter, and drilling tolerances
4. Tubesheet-hole grooving; preparation for tube-to-tubesheet welding if the tubes are to be welded to the tubesheets
5. Tubesheet and baffle machining
6. Location of pass-partition grooves
7. Location on the stationary or front-end tubesheet of tie rods, dummy tubes, and seal-strip attachments
8. Back side of the tubesheets, showing details of their attachment to the shell (where welded)
9. Attachment details of barrels and pass partitions to TEMA C and N channels
10. Stationary tubesheet bundle-handling and pulling-attachment locations
11. Skirt and attachment details of packed floating tubesheets
12. Cross-flow baffle and support-plate dimensions, details of dam baffles, hole drilling, and finish, baffle spacings, cutoff positions, notches, slides for rails and skid bars
13. Construction and assembly details of special baffle systems
14. Longitudinal baffles, showing how they are attached to the back side of the stationary or front-end tubesheet, and baffle-to-shell sealing devices
15. Shrouding and separators for desuperheating and subcooling zones of feedwater heaters
16. Special tube bending for accommodating differential expansion between adjacent tubes and between passes
17. U-tube schedule, showing row number, number of tubes in each

row, centerline bend radii, straight length or lengths, tube diameter, gauge, and material specification

18. Impingement protection attached to the bundle in sufficient detail to permit calculating inlet and escape areas

19. Center-of-gravity and lift points

Shells

1. Materials of construction

2. Diameters, thicknesses, transition section angles, and head dimensions

3. Vapor-belt and expansion-joint details, including shrouding, external protection, and alignment devices

4. Impingement protection attached to the shell in sufficient detail to permit calculating inlet and escape areas

5. Main body flange details, showing ring and hub dimensions, drilling template, machining and attachment details, and gasket details

6. Nozzle constructions, showing penetrations, reinforcements, vent details of reinforcement pads, and instrument connections

7. Locations of weld seams

8. Details of weirs, dams, and flow control devices

9. Positions of cut lines for maintenance and repair

10. Details of stuffing boxes of packed-floating-head units, complete with lantern-ring and packing details

11. Internal entrainment separation and vortex control devices

12. Separator vessels for chillers

13. Supports, showing welding, attachments, and vent and drain holes

14. Attachments of nameplates, insulation clips, and other appurtenances

Channels, bonnets, return covers, and shell covers

1. Materials of construction

2. Diameters, thicknesses, transition section angles and head dimensions, and turnaround flow areas

3. Erosion protection

4. Flanges and closures showing ring and hub dimensions, snap rings, split rings, special clamping, lantern rings, packing, and gaskets

5. Nozzle constructions, showing penetrations, reinforcements, vent details of reinforcement pads, and instrument connections

6. Locations of weld seams

7. Details of diaphragm seals

8. Pass-partition dimensions, locations, attachments, and machining

To be able to evaluate the designs of parts built under most pressure vessel code rules, the extent of nondestructive examinations and heat treatments must be known. If it has not been shown on the assembly drawings, specify that it be listed on the details. When fatigue analysis is performed or when design methods not described in the code are used, specify that the basis of design be provided with the calculations.

Specifications for inspection requirements

Design, materials, and quality of work determine the quality of a heat exchanger. Inspection is a tool for controlling quality but cannot produce it. Inspectors can only observe and compare materials and work with standards. Their acceptance or rejection of a unit must be based upon clearly specified criteria.

The relationships of inspection, quality assurance, and quality control are frequently confused. The following digression is intended to clarify the differences to enable specifications for inspection to be written properly.

Quality assurance is the process of (1) assessing the risks and consequences of failure and establishing commensurate reliability levels; (2) determining that the design and construction needed to meet the reliability level have been set; (3) evaluating available design methods, construction materials, and manufacturing techniques and deciding which are acceptable; (4) establishing the amount of inspection and the acceptance criteria required to control the quality of the product; (5) surveying manufacturing facilities and evaluating production capabilities; and (6) documenting and tracking design calculations, materials that were used, procedures that have been followed, worker qualifications, and nondestructive examinations.

Quality control is making sure that the design, materials, and work comply with the specifications. This is achieved as follows: (1) verifying that proper design calculations have been made; (2) inspecting raw materials and accompanying mill-test reports for conformity with specifications and ascertaining that permanently marked heat numbers on the parts correspond with the mill-test report heat numbers; (3) determining that qualified procedures are used to build, examine, and test the exchangers; (4) determining that workers on the unit are qualified and that qualified welders stamp their identifying symbols adjacent to pressure welds; (5) inspecting the work for conformity with drawings and specifications; and (6) accepting units that meet the acceptance criteria and rejecting those that do not.

The amount and kinds of inspections to be specified vary with the degree of reliability established in the quality assurance review. It would be absurd to specify the same kind of inspection for a commercial hot-water heater as for a nuclear steam generator. Therefore, in general specifications state that inspection is required. Refer to the inspection brief or specification for the inspection that applies.

Here are some typical specification statements:

1. All exchangers are subject to inspection unless inspection is waived in writing.

2. Inspections will be performed as described in the accompanying mechanical specifications or inspection briefs.

3. Inspectors shall be permitted free access to all places concerned with the supply or manufacture of materials, parts, and exchangers at all times that work is to be done on such materials, parts, and exchangers.

4. The supplier or company on whose premises inspection is to take place shall furnish equipment, materials, facilities, and assistance needed for inspection, checking, and testing.

5. The inspector's safety shall be safeguarded by the operator of the facility where inspection is to be performed. Shields, guards, barriers, test pits or blockhouses, protective clothing, and safety personnel required to avoid injury or harm to the inspector shall be provided.

It is tempting to rely on the inspections that pressure vessel safety codes and manufacturers' standards require. However, pressure vessel codes are concerned only with safety, and manufacturers' standards set minimum requirements. A heat exchanger built to the *ASME Code*'s rules and stamped may have mislocated and misaligned connections and supports and improperly located pass partitions that permit bypassing. A unit may meet all the TEMA R mechanical standards and yet be very hard to assemble and disassemble.

Specifications for inspection should recognize these facts. However, they should not imply a confrontational relationship between shop personnel and buyers' inspectors. Inspectors who cooperate with shops often help in solving problems.

Specifications for nameplates and tags

Pressure vessel codes specify requirements for stamping and marking nameplates. Therefore, it is adequate to specify that stamping must conform with the code's requirements. Deviations that alter the code's specified data arrangement are usually unacceptable. However, if the required data are complete and arranged to conform with the code's requirements, it is usually acceptable to add supplementary information. Items sometimes added to code-required nameplates and stampings are as follows:

1. The authorized inspection agency's symbol or mark
2. The purchaser's order number
3. The purchaser's tag or item number
4. The weights of the shell and bundle empty and flooded and the weight of the bundle alone
5. Dual units for pressures and temperatures
6. Additional values of maximum allowable working pressures (MAWPs) for temperatures other than the design temperatures

When large amounts of supplementary data must be presented, specify that it be stamped on separate tag plates. For large units and for units where installation may make access to the official nameplate difficult, it is advantageous to specify installation of duplicate nameplates and tag plates. Specify that these are to be stamped "DUPLICATE" and that no pressure vessel code symbols are to be stamped on the duplicate nameplate.

In general specifications, state that the nameplates are to be permanently mounted on brackets that accommodate the insulation thickness. In the mechanical specifications or standards, specify the amount of protrusion and how the nameplate brackets must be joined to the unit. The general specifications should state that removable parts—for example, bundles, channels, and channel covers—must be stamped with the serial number of the unit to which they belong. Uniformity can be achieved by making nameplate and nameplate location sketches part of the general specifications.

Specifications for warning tags are extremely important. To be effective, warning tags must be located as close as possible to the hazard and be attention-getting and unambiguous. Describe warning-tag locations, size, and format in the general specifications. Include their text in the mechanical specifications. This is an example of a caution-tag statement:

> If heat treatment or stress relief has been performed, paint the following on the shell in capital letters, 3 in high:
> DO NOT WELD OR BURN—HEAT-TREATED MATERIAL

Specifications for preparation for shipment

Specify the locations, size, and type of lettering to be used in marking the exchanger for shipping, receiving, and installing it. Also require lift points to be indicated by text and arrows. State that marking paint, ink, or crayon must be harmless to the metal surfaces, wet or dry.

The manufacturers' standards have general provisions for cleaning and draining, protecting connections, and guarding against damage during shipment. However, they use vague and undefined terms such as "readily removable by hand or power brushing," "suitably plugged," and "suitably protected." Therefore, when manufacturers' standards are incorporated into specifications by reference, some modification may be required. The simplest is to specify who decides what is suitable. More detailed modifications may alter, add, or delete phraseology. Sometimes it may be necessary to write very detailed specifications for preparation for shipment.

Following are some items to modify or supplement. Judgment must be used in modifying or supplementing the manufacturers' standards.

1. Specify acceptance criteria for internal and external cleanliness.

2. Describe the required surface treatment and protection. Include acceptance criteria (for example, surface profiles of sandblasted or grit-blasted surfaces and thicknesses of coatings).

3. Refer to subsidiary specifications for surface treatments and coatings.

4. Provide a list of acceptable coatings for flange-face protection, such as "Exxon Corp.—Rust Ban 326" or "Ashland Oil—No-Rust 3."

5. Describe in detail how flanges and threaded and welding-end connections are to be protected.

6. Provide for identifying the need for unusual protection, reviewing containment, loading, and bracing plans, inspecting the loading before releasing for travel, and recording impacts during shipment.

7. Specify requirements for special drying and inerting for shipment.

It is more effective to write subsidiary specifications for preparing exchangers for export shipment than to include them in general specifications.

Elements of Performance Specifications

In specifying performance requirements, provide enough information to permit the rating engineer to do the design. Exchanger raters who respond to an RFP should specify what is being offered in enough detail to permit independent checking.

How a unit performs depends not only upon fluid temperatures, pressures, and properties but also upon its configuration and construction. The mechanical design depends not only upon the stated design conditions but also upon how performance affects the structure. Heat exchanger specification sheets (Figs. 10.1 and 10.2) of the *TEMA Standards* and *HEI Power Plant Standards* juxtapose performance and construction to emphasize the interdependence.[4]

The specification sheets in the manufacturers' standards are designed to present proposed service and construction (Fig. 10.1). With little modification, they can be made suitable for specifying requirements (Fig. 10.2). Although their tabular form is not suitable for specifying all possible offerings or requirements, use it as much as possible along with supplementary text and graphics.

Manufacturers' specification sheets are not adequate for describing batch operations. For this purpose, use supplementary sheets and sketches to specify a need or to offer to fulfill one. Following is a review of how to use the various parts of manufacturers' heat exchanger specification sheets.

Service description

Tersely describe how the unit fits into the flowsheet and what it does. Use the service description to flag unsteady-state service. Table 10.1 has examples of typical service descriptions for refining, processing, and power-generating equipment.

Size, type, operating position, and bundle orientation

Use the TEMA recommended practice to designate the size of equipment that you have rated. If you are specifying requirements, omit the size. When examining a response to an RFP, verify that the proposed size of the offered unit follows the accepted size-numbering system.

Generally, use the TEMA system to indicate the type of unit. How-

#						
1				Job No.		
2	Customer	Example Customer		Reference No. RFP 051		
3	Address	200 Valley Road, Smalltown, NJ 07006		Proposal No. QH 1260		
4	Plant Location Same			Date	Rev.	
5	Service of Unit Column #1 Forced Circulation Reboiler			Item No. F-1		
6	Size 33-144　Type AEL　(Hor/Vert)			Connected In	Parallel	Series
7	Surf/Unit (Gross/Eff.) 2355　Sq Ft; Shells/Unit 1			Surf/Shell (Gross/Eff.) 2320		Sq Ft

PERFORMANCE OF ONE UNIT

#			Shell Side		Tube Side	
9	Fluid Allocation					
10	Fluid Name		Col. 3 Ov'hd. (a)		Col. 1 Bottoms (b)	
11	Fluid Quantity, Total	Lb/Hr	14900		101160	
12	Vapor (In/Out)		14900			10658
13	Liquid			14900		90502
14	Steam					
15	Water					
16	Noncondensable					
17	Temperature (In/Out)	°F	214	96.5	184.4	188
18	Specific Gravity Density #/CuFt		0.199	46.3	49.3	0.9
19	Viscosity, Liquid	Cp	0.011 (V)	267 (L)	0.357 (L)	0.011 (V)
20	Molecular Weight, Vapor		40.5			12
21	Molecular Weight, Noncondensable					
22	Specific Heat	Btu/Lb °F	0.402 (V)	0.731 (L)	0.824 (L)	0.425 (V)
23	Thermal Conductivity	Btu Ft/Hr Sq Ft °F	0.132 (L)		0.179 (L)	
24	Latent Heat	Btu/Lb @ °F		381		533
25	Inlet Pressure	Psig		21		5
26	Velocity	Ft/S		NA		NA
27	Pressure Drop, Allow./Calc.	Psi	1	0.20	1	0.63
28	Fouling Resistance (Min.)		See line 30		See line 30	
29	Heat Exchanged 556 620		Btu/Hr; MTD (Corrected) (Weighted) 17.3			°F
30	Transfer Rate, Service 139.3 Dirty 145.1		Clean 214		Btu/Hr Sq Ft °F	

CONSTRUCTION OF ONE SHELL

#			Shell Side	Tube Side	Sketch (Bundle/Nozzle Orientation)	
32						
33	Design/Test Pressure	Psig	75 / 115	75 / 115		
34	Design Temperature	°F	300	300		
35	No. Passes per Shell		1			
36	Corrosion Allowance	In.	0	0		
37	Connections	In	8"-150# LJ	4" D, 2" V-150# LJ		
38	Size &	Out	3"-150# LJ	12"-150# LJ		
39	Rating	Intermediate				
40	Tube No. 1000 OD 0.75 In.;Thk (Min/Avg) 0.065 In.; Length 12 Ft Pitch 0.9375 ¼×30 ◇ 60 ◇×90×◇×◇					
41	Tube Type SA-249 W & D 10% Min Red			Material TP 316L		
42	Shell SA240TP316L ID 33		OD 33.5 In.	Shell Cover NA		(Integ.) (Remov.)
43	Channel or Bonnet SA240TP316L			Channel Cover SA240TP316L Throughout		
44	Tubesheet-Stationary SA240TP316L			Tubesheet-Floating NA		
45	Floating Head Cover NA			Impingement Protection In Shell on Bundle		
46	Baffles-Cross SA240TP316L Type Vert. cut seg			% Cut (Diam/Area) 25 Spacing: c/c 22.9 Inlet 21.5 In.		
47	Baffles-Long NA			Seal Type NA		
48	Supports-Tube NA		U-Bend NA	Type NA		
49	Bypass Seal Arrangement NA			Tube-Tubesheet Joint Str. Wld. & Hydroexp.		
50	Expansion Joint Inconel 625			Type Proc. Eng. w/cvr. 15000 cycles		
51	ρv²-Inlet Nozzle 1113		Bundle Entrance No vib. ind.	Bundle Exit No vib. ind.		
52	Gaskets-Shell Side NA			Tube Side Tef. Jcktd. Asb 1/8" tk.		
53	-Floating Head NA					
54	Code Requirements ASME Sec. VIII Div. I NB stmp.			TEMA Class B		
55	Weight/Shell		Filled with Water 11,200 lbs	Bundle		Lb
56	Remarks (a) Wt. % 1 CHCl; 45.8 Acetone; 33.2 Ethanol; 3.6 Mesityl Oxide;					
57	Balance water. (b) ³Wt% 1,2 CHCl; 5.6 Acetone; 6.3 Mesityl Oxide;					
58	Balance water. Av. Metal Temp. 3 Shell 205 Tubes 194 (Operating fl)					
59	Davits provided for channel covers 205 195 (Operating cl)					
60				20	128 (Inst. start)	
61	Expansion joint case		25	184 (Shell off)		

Figure 10.1 TEMA exchanger specification sheet applied to a reboiler by a manufacturer.

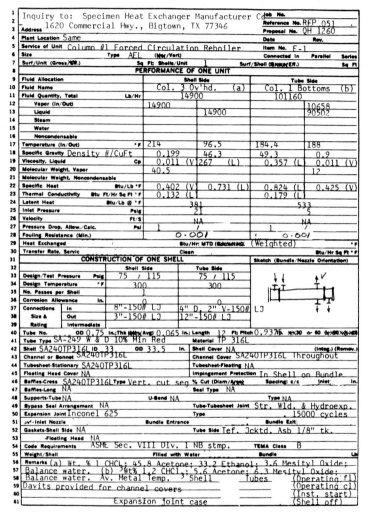

Figure 10.2   TEMA heat exchanger specification sheet applied to a reboiler by a purchaser.

TABLE 10.1   Typical Service Descriptions

C-1 column feed preheater

C-2 column feed–bottoms heat exchanger

C-2 column side-cut condenser

Stream 42 to stream 3 heat interchanger

Acetone-recovery-column thermosiphon reboiler

Vent-collection-tank T-8 refrigerated vent condenser

Resin reactor no. 3 batch reflux condenser

Thinning-tank no. 2 batch knock-back condenser

Product-holding-tank T-4 batch cooler

Formalin reactor-condenser no. 1

Solvent-recovery-column condenser-subcooler

Drains cooler no. 1

No. 2 engine-jacket water cooler

Train no. 1 stage no. 3 feedwater heater

Boiler blowdown cooler no. 1

Batch-thinning-tank recirculating cooler

ever, for power plant exchangers, if you judge it to be necessary, use the *HEI Power Plant Standards* system. For closed feedwater heaters, use the TEMA size system and refer to the construction and arrangement sketches of the *HEI Closed Feedwater Heater Standards* in the remarks section of the specification sheet.[5]

The operating position is the position of the axis of the tubes. Show it as horizontal (H), vertical (V), or pitched (P). Specify the pitch angle of pitched units relative to the horizontal or vertical centerline. Use a line sketch to show the angle unambiguously. Describe the position of the channels or bonnets of vertical U-tube units as "head up" or "head down."

Surfaces

Distinguish between gross, or total, surface and effective, or net, surface. Conventionally, tube surfaces are based upon the outside tube diameter. If this convention is not followed, note in the remarks that the reported or required surface is the inside surface. The net, or effective, surface is that part of the tube surface active in heat transfer. Exclude tubing within the tubesheets, within the gaps between inner and outer double tubesheets, and in U bends. In vertical shellside condensers, exclude the part of the tubes flooded with condensate. In evaluating surface offered by a vendor, verify the net and gross surfaces.

To verify condenser and feedwater heater ratings, it is necessary to know the surfaces that the thermal designer assigned to desuperheating, condensing, and subcooling. For vaporizers, one must know the preheating and boiling surfaces. In requesting proposals, require this information to be shown in the proposal specifications. Require the gross and effective surfaces and sensible and latent heat transfer surface distributions to be shown for each unit and for the individual shells of which it is composed. Provide this information when responding to an RFP.

Fluid allocations, fluid states, and flow quantities

The fluids need not be named, but there must be enough information about their properties to define their behavior. Safeguard proprietary information by using symbolic designations and listing the properties.

In allocating flows, it is usually desirable for smaller and more viscous streams to flow in the shell. However, fouling and corrosive fluids are best handled in the tubes. Within these constraints, allow the rater freedom to allocate the shellside and tubeside fluids to use the available pressure drops most economically.

Describe the physical states of the fluids as "vapor," "liquid," "steam," "water, well water, cooling-tower water, brackish water, seawater, or brine," and "noncondensibles." Enter the total steady-state weights flowing per hour through the shell and the tubes. Also, show the weights per hour of each component entering and leaving as vapor, liquid, steam, water, and noncondensibles and the weights per hour vaporized or condensed. When two or more liquid phases are present, state their flow rates separately.

Design point, terminal conditions, and duty and transfer rates

The design point applies to steady-state conditions. It is the set of coincident inlet and outlet fluid states, flow quantities, and inlet and outlet temperatures and pressures when the heat and materials flows are balanced. It determines the exchanger's size, fixes the amount of heat and materials to be transferred per unit time, and the temperature difference between the shellside and tubeside fluids.

If neither fluid changes state or if either changes state isothermally without accompanying preheating, desuperheating, or subcooling, the mean temperature difference (MTD) is determined from the four terminal temperatures. Ordinarily it is calculated as the logarithmic mean temperature difference (LMTD). If the flow is multipass, the MTD is corrected for the effects of reheating. However, when the duty is divided between sensible and latent heat and when multicomponent mixtures are being condensed, the temperature difference is reported as weighted MTD. The weighting reflects the allocation of surfaces and heat transfer rates in the heat transfer path from inlet to outlet of each fluid.

In specifying requirements, omit the MTD from the exchanger specification sheet. If you intend to check a proposed rating, require the rater to break the duty into its sensible-heat and latent-heat components.

For specifications that describe purchase requirements, present terminal pressures as an inlet pressure and minimum outlet pressure or as an inlet pressure and allowable pressure loss. For thermosiphon reboilers, state the available elevation of reboiler liquid surface and the height of column inlet and return connections. Also provide an estimate of the length of pipe to and from the reboiler and any flow restrictions in either line. Raters should state the elevations and line sizes assumed if this information was omitted from the RFP.

Fluid properties

List the fluid properties at inlet and outlet conditions. If the variation of properties with temperature and pressure is not linear, provide a table of data points or curves of the variation of properties with temperature and pressure. Note, however, that rating specifications customarily state only average property values.

Velocities, fouling resistances, and cleanliness factors

Two assumptions are made in calculating tubeside velocity: (1) The number of tubes per pass is the total tube count divided by the number of passes, and (2) the velocity per tube is the volumetric flow divided by the total tube-flow cross-sectional area per pass. These assumptions disregard the facts that there may be more tubes in some passes than in others and that the velocity within a tube is not constant across its flow area. (Turbulent-flow velocity at the center of a tube may be 20 percent higher than the velocity based upon the assumptions described above; viscous-flow velocity may be twice as high.)

Nevertheless, the velocity reported as feet per second (meters per second) is used to indicate the tendency to foul and the likelihood of erosion and corrosion. Therefore, in preparing a design specification, list the minimum and maximum permissible velocities but with awareness of the convention used in the industry. When examining a proposal, check to see that it is within the specified limits.

The calculation basis of reported velocity is not always self-evident. In sensible-heat transfer, if the density variation with temperature is small, it hardly matters whether the velocity is reported at inlet, outlet, or average conditions. However, for process heat exchangers, the practice is to calculate the velocity at the average temperature. In the feedwater heater industry, the convention is to report the velocity at 60°F (15.6°C). To use the velocity reported on the feedwater heater specification sheet, correct it to the velocity at the average operating temperature.

When there is a large density change from inlet to outlet in single-phase streams and when phase changes occur, a more detailed description is required. For single-phase flow, state the velocity at the tubeside inlet and outlet. When vaporization or condensation is taking place, report the individual liquid and vapor inlet and outlet velocities. A report of average inlet and outlet velocities of the average of the two-phase densities is meaningless.

The velocity at pass turnarounds affects tubeside pressure drop. Excessive interpass-flow velocity may cause pass-partition erosion and erosion-corrosion. On the other hand, sediment or slurry particles may be deposited if the turnaround velocity is too low. The *TEMA Standards* specify maximum turnaround velocities (calculated as illustrated in Chap. 5). It is necessary to check turnaround velocities when checking drawings to verify that the velocities are within the permissible limits of the standards. If nonstandard velocities are required because of the nature of the fluid, they should be specified in the inquiry specification and checked when the proposal is received.

Linear and mass velocities vary continuously in the shell because the flow areas and flow paths continually change. A stream entering the shell divides into streams that flow across the bundle, through the space between the shell and the baffles, and through the spaces between the tubes and the baffle holes. As the mass progresses from inlet to outlet, the stream quantities and flow directions vary, coming together at the outlet.

Historically, in thermal design the flow area used to calculate mass velocity was estimated as the distance not occupied by tubes in a fully tubed center row, multiplied by the space between adjacent baffles or tube supports. The reported shellside linear velocity was the total inlet volume divided by this flow area. This is not a good indicator of the shell fluid's tendency to foul, erode, or corrode the tube exteriors. It may be used to obtain conservative results in vibration analyses.

Current computer shellside design programs are based upon stream analysis. For vibration analysis, the flows are calculated at critical locations in the bundle. Film coefficients may also be based upon correlations with stream analysis. Standard exchanger specification sheets were developed before stream analysis technology. They are not set up to recognize or report the flows of the various streams and the stream velocities at critical locations. Specifications for reporting such information must be worked out between sellers and buyers.

As stated previously, fluid flows through exchangers may deviate substantially from design-point flows. Removing from service one shell of a unit arranged for parallel flow without throttling the flow through each side doubles the flow. Bypassing a feedwater heater in a train changes the extraction-steam flow and the terminal temperatures of the downstream heaters. Unregulated pumping without an intervening restriction between the pump and the exchanger may produce higher-than-anticipated flows. Reduced shellside pressures with constant gas or vapor flows may induce tube vibration. In preparing design specifications, specify the percentage of excess flow that the unit must be able to withstand or advise the manufacturer of the mode of operation that will produce the highest and lowest flow velocities. Whenever possible, indicate when the flows will be pulsating. Specify the anticipated worst-case coincident condition of pressure and flow.

In inquiry specifications, list either the shellside and tubeside fouling resistances or the minimum cleanliness factor. In reporting, show either the guaranteed service and clean overall rates or the service rate and cleanliness factor. The practice in the process industries is to specify fouling resistances and to report service and clean overall rates. In power generation it is to specify minimum cleanliness factors and report guaranteed ones. The relationships among service rate, clean rate, and overall fouling resistances are as follows:

$$1/U_s = 1/U_c + F_r \qquad (10.1)$$

$$F_r = (U_c - U_s)/U_c U_s \qquad (10.2)$$

$$U_s = U_c/(1 + F_r U_c) \qquad (10.3)$$

where F_r = total fouling resistance, $(h \cdot ft^2 \cdot °F)/Btu$ $[(h \cdot m^2 \cdot °C)/J]$
U_c = clean overall rate, $Btu/(h \cdot ft^2 \cdot °F)$ $[J/(h \cdot m^2 \cdot °C)]$
U_s = service overall rate, $Btu/(h \cdot ft^2 \cdot °F)$ $[J/(h \cdot m^2 \cdot °C)]$

It is seldom possible to design an exchanger with just enough surface to provide the specified fouling resistances. Consequently, the area provided usually exceeds the required area. Figure 10.3 shows in

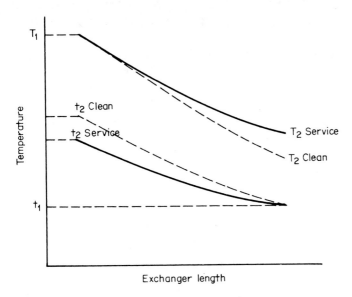

Figure 10.3   Variation of temperature with fouling.

a general way the difference between operation clean and operation fouled. The hot-fluid temperatures are indicated by the symbol T and the cold-fluid temperatures by the symbol t. To reveal the oversurface, some designers redefine U_s as U_d as shown in Eq. (10.4), where U_d takes the place of U_s as the calculated fouled rate.

$$U_d = Q/A\delta T \tag{10.4}$$

where A = effective area supplied, ft^2 (m^2)
Q = duty, Btu/h (J/h)
δT = corrected logarithmic mean temperature difference or weighted mean temperature difference, °F (°C)

With this method of reporting, U_s is less than U_d whenever excess area is supplied. It makes it easier to examine the effect of excess surface than the conventional way of reporting.

Cleanliness factor C is expressed as a fraction. The relationship between U_c, U_d, and C is shown in Eq. (10.5):

$$CU_c = U_d \tag{10.5}$$

The overall fouling resistance can be calculated from the overall service rate and cleanliness factor from Eq. (10.6):

$$F_r = (1-C)/U_s \tag{10.6}$$

Heat exchanger manufacturers rarely know as much about the fouling nature of fluids as users do.* They seldom know how frequently units will be cleaned or the condition of tube surfaces after cleaning. Furthermore, the manufacturer does not usually have enough information to evaluate economic factors that affect how long a unit must be operated between shutdowns for cleaning. Therefore, in process heat transfer the user should specify the fouling resistances or minimum cleanliness factor to be applied. The HEI standards for feedwater heaters and power plant exchangers have minimum fouling resistances and cleanliness factors based upon the collective experience of the power industry with boiler feedwater and steam.

Excess capacity

A remark often found in requirements specifications is "Provide X percent excess capacity." This is ambiguous because it may be interpreted to mean any of the following:

1. Increase the duty by X percent. Adjust the design-point conditions, but keep the flow quantities constant.

2. Design the unit for flows X percent greater than those specified, but keep the design-point conditions constant. This increases the duty by X percent.

3. Arbitrarily provide X percent more surface than is required by the thermal design, either by increasing the required tube length X percent or by increasing the required tube count X percent.

These alternatives have been discussed in Chap. 9.

In specifying excess surface, consider its effects on normal operation. Then state the basis of the requirement. It is prudent to require the offerer to analyze how the excess surface will affect normal operation. Unless this is specified (and negotiated with the offerer), it will probably not be done. The manufacturer cannot be expected to examine how excess heat exchanger surface will affect an entire system of which the heat exchanger is but a part.

Construction

In addition to the process parameters, performance depends upon the

---

*For a discussion of what is involved in selecting fouling factors, see J. Taborek et al., "Fouling—The Major Unresolved Problem in Heat Transfer," *Chem. Eng. Prog.*, vol. 68, no. 2, February 1972; vol. 68, no. 7, July 1972.

details of construction discussed in previous chapters. Following is some guidance in specifying construction.

Allow the rater maximum freedom to select pass arrangements consistent with piping and maintenance needs. In specifications for exchangers with large temperature ranges, require the rater to provide the average tube metal temperature for each pass in the clean and fouled conditions. This will permit analysis of the loads that result from interpass differential temperatures on the tubes, tubesheets, and tube-to-tubesheet joints. If the loads exceed acceptable maxima, it may be necessary to change the configuration to multipass shellside flow or to design with two or more shells in series.

Most of the time, the smallest, least expensive unit is one in which the permitted pressure drops are consumed. Multipass construction provides long flow paths that use up available pressure differentials at some expense of surface expended on reheating. The construction problems that arise with increasing numbers of tubeside passes have been discussed in Chap. 5 and the difficulties with multipass shellside construction in Chap. 6. In writing specifications, state the maximum number of tubeside passes that is acceptable. State also whether multipass shell construction is acceptable and your requirements for baffle-to-shell seals and insulation against thermal leakage. Examine manufacturers' specifications for details of shellside pass-partition construction.

The shellside film coefficient of heat transfer and pressure drop are related to the mass velocity and character of the flow. The segmental cross-flow baffle type, spacing, cut, and fit to the shell control both. Therefore, it is essential to know the baffle system details to evaluate performance specifications. This information is also necessary to evaluate the risk of shell-flow-induced vibration. Therefore, require it to be clearly described on manufacturers' exchanger specification sheets.

To minimize vibration and wear at inlet and outlet nozzles, specify minimum permissible sizes. Specify criteria for maximum allowable impact values only when there is a reason, unknown to the manufacturer, to deviate from the ones in the manufacturers' standard specified for the exchanger. Offerers' specifications should report the calculated impact values. For two-phase flow, they should describe the basis of the density calculation.

Performance specifications should clearly indicate agreement between the user and the manufacturer about the character of two-phase flow and the basis for establishing it. This requires a mutual understanding of the effects on heat transfer and pressure drop of the two-phase flow modes of mixed flow, layered flow, and slug flow.

In requirements specifications, indicate to the manufacturer the acceptability or requirement for transition section, vapor belts, and inlet domes and any special impingement-plate requirements. Manufacturers should detail what they propose for impingement protection in their proposal specifications.

Ordinarily the only physical restriction on shell size is space. Except for kettle-type reboilers and shellside condensers that operate at low pressure, it is thermally and economically desirable to pack the shell with tubes. In reviewing proposal performance specifications, verify that the TEMA or HEI manufacturers' standards have been complied with.

Remarks

Use the remarks section of exchanger specification sheets to communicate information that cannot be readily tabulated in the form. Typically, remarks are made about the following:

1. References to process-flow diagrams
2. References to supplementary tables or plots of variation of properties or heat content with temperature and pressure
3. References to supplementary data curves
4. References to computer printouts of calculated overall heat transfer coefficients when they vary markedly through the unit
5. Descriptions of excess-capacity requirements or provisions for excess capacity
6. Requirements for designing for extreme conditions, upsets, and runaways
7. Requirements for considering seasonal changes in operating conditions
8. Presence of solids in the fluids
9. Presence of dispersed gases in liquids
10. Proposed cleaning methods and frequency of cleaning
11. References to computer simulations
12. Information about cyclical operations
13. Frequency of startups and shutdowns

Specifying batch performance

Batch heat exchangers do not operate at steady-state conditions. Here is the information needed to specify an exchanger for batch service:

1. Batch size
2. Initial batch temperature
3. Final batch temperature
4. Time allowed for the batch to undergo the temperature change
5. Circulation rates and temperatures of feed and draw-off streams
6. Properties of the feed and draw-off streams over the batch temperature range
7. Inlet and outlet temperatures of the fluid used to cool or heat the batch (the second fluid)
8. Properties of the second fluid at the inlet and outlet temperatures

The batch circulation rate and the time allowed for its change from the initial to the final temperature are interdependent. If the characteristics and terminal temperatures of the second fluid are fixed, the time allowed for batch heating or cooling determines the required batch circulation rate. Therefore, specify the desired time and the maximum available circulation rate.

The rater will determine whether the temperature change can be achieved in the specified time and will optimize the circulation rate. If the batch temperature change cannot take place in the desired period with the available circulation rate, some of these steps may have to be taken: Increase the allowed time, increase the batch circulation rate, or increase the thermal driving force by changing the terminal temperatures of the second fluid.

Elements of Mechanical Specifications

Mechanical specifications define construction and structural-strength requirements. The following is a guide to preparing and interpreting mechanical specifications.

Design conditions: maximum allowable working pressure (MAWP)

Specifying design pressures and temperatures is the user's obligation. Here is what to consider:

1. The most severe coincident pressures and temperatures anticipated in the shellside and tubeside fluids

2. The possibility of pressure surges

3. The required tightness margin for pressure-relief devices

4. The effects of relieving excess pressure in process fluids

5. The limitations of the prevailing pressure vessel code

In the *ASME Code*, the minimum design temperature is the mean metal temperature through a part. The temperature at the surface may not exceed the maximum temperature for which the *ASME Code* lists an allowable stress. To estimate a part's mean metal temperature, thermal designers consider the following: (1) relative heat transfer rates, (2) temperatures on each side of the part, (3) the thickness of the part and its thermal conductivity, and (4) the area exposed to each fluid.

Of these data, the designer knows only the thermal conductivity beforehand. To estimate the rest requires trial designs. Therefore, the practice is to select the design metal temperature above the highest surface temperature. The penalty is that allowable stress is reduced. The *TEMA Standards* require the minimum design temperatures to be the *estimated maximum* metal temperatures at the specified operating conditions.

For high-pressure, high-temperature exchangers, it may be economical to estimate the mean metal temperatures. If a proposal specification uses this method, scrutinize the mean metal temperature calculations.

When design temperatures are chosen arbitrarily, they are only the temperatures at which maximum allowable stress values are selected. They are not the actual metal temperatures that will occur in operation. However, users should take note of the fact that the structure is designed only to withstand the thermal stresses at the specified worst-case conditions of startup, shutdown, or upset. Many exchangers cannot be safely operated at the design temperatures shown on drawings and manufacturers' data reports and stamped on nameplates. Other combinations of shell metal and tube metal temperatures may also be unsafe. Unfavorable combinations of interpass tube metal temperatures and combinations of tube and shell metal temperatures may cause bundles to distort, collapse, or stretch tubes and destroy tube-to-tubesheet joints.

If it is necessary to operate in a range of coincident tube and shell metal temperatures, specify the range to the manufacturer. Require the manufacturer to provide curves of the highest and lowest permissible coincident shell and tube metal temperatures throughout the range.

You may specify that each side of an exchanger be designed and stamped for sets of permissible coincident pressure-temperature conditions rather than for one design pressure at one temperature. This allows a unit to be used for multiple services. However, pressure-relief valves must be set to accommodate the design pressure-temperature combination in use. The maximum pressure difference between the sides determines the severity of pressure effects. If pressure and vacuum may be applied alternately without a change in design temperature, use this format: "###/FULL VAC." Here, ### represents the positive pressure. The pressure that the mechanical designer uses in computing thickness requirements will be the absolute pressure to which the part is subjected. For example, if the tubeside design pressure is full-vacuum and the shellside 150 psig, calculations for the shellside of the tubesheet and external pressure on the tubes will be based upon 165 psia.

Users customarily specify design conditions that permit the full design pressure to be applied to each side with the other side at atmospheric pressure (or full-vacuum, when vacuum operation is specified for the other side). Manufacturers will assume that this ordinary practice is to be followed unless the user specifies differential-pressure design.

In selecting design pressures, consider that in normal operation there may be pressure surges or fluctuations. Moreover, spring-loaded pressure-relief valves cannot be expected to open suddenly and fully when they reach the set pressure; they may leak first. Therefore, select design pressures that allow margins between normal operating pressures and safety-relief-valve set pressures. Be aware that the design pressure shown on TEMA and HEI exchanger specification sheets will usually be the MAWP that the manufacturer stamps on the nameplate and shows on the manufacturer's data report form. This means that the operating pressures must be lower than the design pressures shown on the exchanger specification sheet. Otherwise, there will not be margins between the normal operating pressures and the design pressures that will avoid pressure-relief-device leakage.

Note also that noxious, lethal, or radioactive fluids under excess pressure may not be relieved to the atmosphere. Relieving to containment vessels may be very costly.

The design pressures may determine which pressure vessel code or code section or paragraphs apply. In Chap. 8, it was pointed out that the rules of Section VIII, Division 1, are based upon design principles and practices that apply to pressures no higher than 3000 lb/in^2

(20,680 kPa). Units designed to operate above the limit may not be stamped under Division 1 unless they comply with all of its requirements. Additions to the rules and deviations from them may be necessary for higher-pressure designs. Division 2 applies without a pressure limit. However, the analytical methods used must be justified.

For each side of an exchanger, the MAWP stamped on the nameplate and given on the manufacturer's data report is the highest permissible pressure coincident with the operating temperature at which one pressure-relief device may be set. It is measured at the top of the unit in the normal operating position. When more than one pressure-relief device is used, Division 1 permits the second device to be set to relieve at 105 percent of MAWP for process-generated pressure and to 110 percent of MAWP for pressure caused by external heat.

Manufacturers can seldom procure materials of the exact thicknesses required by the design conditions and corrosion-erosion allowances. They buy materials of the next larger nominal thicknesses. Advantage may be taken of the actual thicknesses by fully reinforcing nozzle penetrations and back-calculating the maximum pressure, including static head, at the specified operating temperature that each part can withstand. The exchanger may then be stamped on each side with the MAWP equal to the back-calculated pressure of its weakest part. Manufacturers will not perform such back calculations or provide reinforcement beyond that required by the design pressure unless the mechanical specifications require it. If back-calculated MAWPs are higher than the specified design pressure, it may be possible to operate near or at the specified design pressure and yet have a margin for relief.

When specifying this requirement, also require the manufacturer to identify the limiting part on each side. As with design pressures, MAWPs may be determined for various design temperatures.

Test conditions

The standard hydrostatic-test pressure is 1½ times the MAWP multiplied by the lowest ratio of allowable stress at test temperature to allowable stress at design temperature. The usual test medium is water, but most codes permit other liquids. The manufacturer will use water unless the mechanical specifications require that another liquid is to be used. The *ASME Code* permits pneumatic testing at 1.25 times the temperature-stress-adjusted MAWP if a unit cannot be safely supported when filled with liquid or if it cannot be readily dried and traces of test liquid cannot be tolerated. The user must specify when other test media are to be used and when traces of test liquid are intolerable.

Except for heat exchangers, most newly built pressure vessels constructed with corrosion allowances are hydrostatically tested at 1½ times the pressure that is back-calculated from the nominal thicknesses, including corrosion and erosion allowances. The allowable stress values used in the back calculations are the ones that apply at the test temperature instead of the design temperature. This should not be permitted or specified for heat exchangers. The reason is that corrosion allowance is not usually specified for the tubes, which may collapse under excessive external pressure, and that the higher test pressure may damage the tubesheets.

The purpose of the *ASME Code*'s hydrostatic test is to stress parts under *internal* pressure. The code has no requirement for external-pressure testing. However, when the shell is tested, the tubes are subjected to external pressure equal to the shell test pressure. This may cause them to collapse and must be considered when specifying tube thickness.

Materials of construction

Except in unusual cases, the user is responsible for specifying materials of construction. It is not adequate to use generalities such as SS Type 304. Instead, use the material specification numbers of the applicable pressure vessel code or manufacturers' standards, and specify the acceptable product forms (cast, rolled or forged, plate, tubing), for example, SA-240-TP 304 plate.

Danger or hazard category

The user is responsible for specifying the hazard category of the exchanger. An example is the specification of lethal service in Section VIII of the *ASME Code*. Although the service description on the exchanger specification sheet and the names of the fluids flowing may alert the manufacturer to the requirement for designing to a specific danger category, the pressure vessel codes put the burden of making a definitive statement on the user.

Corrosion and erosion allowances

The user is responsible for specifying allowances for corrosion and erosion beyond those incorporated in the governing pressure safety code. In specifying these allowances, state the amount of metal to be provided on each side of pressure-containing parts. The manufacturers' standards allow the depth of the groove in grooved covers and tubesheets to be considered as corrosion-erosion allowance. The thickness of grooved covers and tubesheets for pressure resistance is that measured to the bottom of pass-partition grooves.

Chapter 8 pointed out that the *ASME Code* and manufacturers' standards generally limit the manufacturer's requirement to provide wasting allowances to pressure parts. It suggested additional allowances or alternatives for nonpressure parts. A practical way to prevent premature loss of effectiveness of nonpressure parts is to specify that they be at least as thick as a multiple of the metal thickness allowed for corrosion in the pressure envelope. Alternatives are to specify thicknesses greater than those of the manufacturers' standards and to specify the use of corrosion-resistant material for nonpressure parts.

It is not practical to provide as much additional metal for corrosion and wear of the tubes as it is for other pressure parts. Furthermore, corroded or worn tubes may be more readily replaced than other main pressure components. However, always specify a tube thickness greater than that required just for structural strength and to resist pressure. This may be as little as 10 percent for high-strength, high-alloy materials and as much as 100 percent for carbon steel tubes. Take into account that the approximate difference between minimum and average wall is one gauge and that the thickness of nominal wall tubes varies ±10 percent from the specified nominal thickness.

If there is a possibility of electrolytic corrosion, consider specifying the installation of wasting plugs or plates that will be preferentially attacked. The size, contact area, and surface area to be exposed must be shown in the specification.

Heat treatment

Exchangers and parts of exchangers may be heat-treated for any or all of these reasons:

1. To relieve unacceptably high residual forming stresses. This is usually a pressure vessel code requirement.

2. To relieve excessive weld shrinkage stresses. This may also be a pressure vessel code requirement.

3. To prevent cracking in weld deposits and adjacent parent metal. This is usually a pressure vessel code requirement.

4. To refine metal grain structure. This may be a pressure vessel code requirement.

5. To restore corrosion resistance of metals after welding.

6. To restore the strength of metals affected by welding and forming. This is generally a pressure vessel code requirement.

7. To enhance the strength of metals.

8. To enhance machinability.

9. To reduce postfabrication distortion that might result from slow

self–stress relief of formed or welded components.

Heat treatment specifications are best produced by the joint efforts of users, manufacturers, and metal producers. These should be separate subsidiary specifications referred to in the mechanical specifications.

Nondestructive examination and testing

It is a quality assurance function to determine the kinds and degrees of nondestructive tests and examinations of the various components covered in mechanical specifications. The quality requirements must be set to make sure that the strength of the materials and joints of the pressure parts are within the design assumptions and to verify that the exchanger will conform with expectations of trouble-free operation and life.

Include requirements for performing nondestructive examinations in components and parts specifications. Describe procedures for performing nondestructive examinations and acceptance criteria in procedure specifications.

For pressure vessel code purposes, the function of mandatory nondestructive examinations is to reveal internal and surface discontinuities. These are some of the nondestructive methods that may be used:

1. Radiographic examination

2. Ultrasonic examination

3. Magnetic-particle examination

4. Fluid-penetrant examination

5. Eddy-current and other electrical examinations

6. Various leak tests

It is not satisfactory to specify that nondestructive testing is to conform with pressure vessel code requirements. The codes permit various options; for example, within certain limits Section VIII, Division 1, of the *ASME Code* allows (1) no weld radiography, (2) spot radiography of pressure welds, (3) partial radiography of pressure welds, or (4) full radiography of these welds. In specifying radiography requirements, it is helpful to know their differences. These are explained in the following digression.

In the *ASME Code*, the purpose of spot radiography is to verify the skill of the welders. The extent of radiography is one radiograph for each 50 ft (15.2 m) or less for each welder. The spot that is chosen to be radiographed is selected by the authorized inspector (see Chap. 8) after the welding is complete. Because welders do not know which spots will be examined, they are expected to exercise care in all their welding. Shops are expected to control weld quality by performing spot radiography as the work proceeds. Manufacturers may discard spot radiographs after the authorized inspector has accepted the work. The *ASME Code* allows higher joint efficiencies for spot-radiographed welds than for welds that are not examined.

The purpose of specifying full and partial radiography is to verify the quality of the work rather than the skill of the welders. The *ASME Code* allows the same stresses in partial and fully radiographed welds as in the parent metals by considering the joints to be 100 percent efficient. In partial radiography, at least 6 in (152.4 mm) of welds and an intersection in one weld of a specified category are fully radiographed. Partial radiography might be specified when an inlet channel of a single-pass exchanger operates at a far higher temperature than that of the outlet channel. The higher allowable joint efficiency makes up for the lower allowable stress in the high-temperature part. The manufacturer must keep partial and full radiographs as long as it is mandatory to keep other records of the exchanger.

After establishing requirements for eddy-current or ultrasonic examinations, specify the parts to be examined and the percentage of scanning. For example, because even small discontinuities in the bonds of cladding metals to base metals in tubesheets cannot be tolerated, specify 100 percent ultrasonic scanning. Because eddy-current and ultrasonic examination reveal different kinds of flaws, it may be desirable to specify dual examination for critical services.

Specify liquid-penetrant examinations to reveal surface conditions that may indicate subsurface flaws. Liquid-penetrant examination reveals surface cracks and porosity. Magnetic-particle examination of parts that can be magnetized reveals surface flaws and flaws somewhat under the surface.

Parts specifications

Write parts specifications to describe requirements that apply to the major parts. Build the specifications on the manufacturers' standards. Some guidelines follow.

Tubing. To achieve a desired level of quality, it may be necessary to specify requirements beyond those specified in the pressure vessel code. For example, welded austenitic steel tubes may be within the tolerances of ASME specifications SA-249 and SA-450 yet have a weld bead so high that it damages expander rolls and makes it impossible to seal hydraulic-expanding mandrels.

Pressure vessel code tubing specifications permit using various manufacturing methods for producing tubes. They also allow for purchasers' needs by permitting them to specify special requirements. An example is Paragraph 5.2 of ASME specification SA-249:

> Subsequent to welding and prior to final heat treatment, the tubes shall be cold worked either in both weld and base metal or in base metal only. *The method of cold working may be specified by the purchaser. When cold drawn, the purchaser may specify the minimum amount of reduction in cross-sectional area or wall thickness or both.* [Italics added.]

In specifying tubing, use the pressure vessel code designations and add any special requirements and restrictions.

Tubesheets. In specifying tubesheet materials, designate the material of construction and acceptable product form. Use the pressure vessel code's specification number. As with tubing, add special requirements and limits. If the code does not mandate the stress analysis method for design and you favor a specific one other than that of the manufacturers' standard, include the requirement in the tubesheet specification.

Chapter 3 discussed the TEMA and HEI drilling tolerances for standard and special close fits. Specify special close fits for tubes to be expanded into tubesheets under these conditions:

1. The tube material is subject to stress corrosion-cracking in the environment to which it is exposed.

2. The tube material work-hardens.

3. The tube material has a low elastic modulus (because of springback).

The tables of drilling tolerances and maximum recommended tube gauges for expanded joints in manufacturer's standards are based upon ligament thickness, which is fixed by the selection of tube diameter and pitch. For tube thicknesses that exceed the recommended limits, consider specifying a spread pitch on the exchanger specification sheet or a minimum pitch.

The specified minimum standard ligament width is based upon a width tolerance of not more than twice the drill-drift tolerance plus 0.02 in (0.51 mm) for tubes smaller than ⅝-in (15.9-mm) OD and twice the drill-drift tolerance plus 0.03 in (0.76 mm) for tubes of ⅝-in (15.9-mm) OD and larger. The permissible drill-drift tolerance in inches is 0.0016 times the tubesheet thickness divided by the tube diameter (in millimeters, 0.041 times the tubesheet thickness divided by the tube diameter).

Include in tubesheet specifications any supplements to manufacturer's standards required to achieve a desired standard of quality. Examples of supplementary statements are: "Stationary tubesheets of vertical, channel-down removable-bundle units shall be provided with at least four (4) equally spaced collar bolts"; and "The distance between the edges of tube holes and gasket grooves shall be at least 0.0625 in (1.6 mm) for tubesheets into which tubes are to be expanded and 0.125 in (3.18 mm) for tubesheets to which tubes are to be welded."

Tube-to-tubesheet joining.   In preparing inquiry specifications, include any special requirements for tube-to-tubesheet joining. To evaluate the joining quality that will be offered, require proposal specifications to include the joining-procedure specification. Knowledgeable purchasers may also specify that they must approve the joining procedure.

Baffles and tube supports, tie rods and spacers, dummy tubes, and seal strips.   The manufacturer's standards and other applicable standards are generally adequate for baffles, supports, tie rods and spacers, dummy tubes, and seal strips. They may be supplemented from the following list:

1. When shell fluids undergo sensible-heat transfer, baffle cuts shall be over and under in horizontal units unless otherwise specified. Baffle cuts shall be vertical in horizontal exchangers for condensing and vaporizing shell fluids.

2. Baffles shall not be notched for draining when the shell fluid is single-phase unless the viscosity exceeds _____ centipoise. (Fill in the blank.)

3. The bottom segmental baffles in horizontal units that handle sulfuric acid in the shell shall be provided with semicircular drainage notches that have a 1/4-in (6.4-mm) radius.

4. Baffle holes for tantalum, titanium, and zirconium tubes shall be drilled 1/64 in (0.4 mm) larger than the tube OD. The hole edges shall be relieved on both sides of the baffles.

5. The baffles shall be the thicker of 2 times the shell corrosion allowance or the TEMA (or HEI) tabulated thickness plus 1/16 in (1.6 mm), 1/8 in (3.2 mm), etc.

6. The first and last baffles shall be located at least 1/2 in (12.7 mm) away from the inlet and outlet shell connections.

7. Baffles shall be provided with ears to prevent fluid bypassing.

8. The minimum tie-rod diameter shall be 3/8 in (9.5 mm).

9. Each baffle or support plate in shell sizes 33 in (838 mm) and smaller shall be pierced by at least four tie rods suitably spaced to stabilize the baffle. For shells 34 to 48 in (864 to 1219 mm) inclusive, each plate shall be pierced by at least five tie rods. Larger baffles or support plates shall be pierced by at least six tie rods. Four tie rods shall be located 90° apart as close as possible to the OTC.

10. Tie rods shall not be welded to the baffles or tube supports.

11. When protective cladding is supplied on the shellside of the tubesheet, alloy plugs shall be welded into the tubesheet to receive the threaded tie-rod end.

13. In shells that carry single-phase fluids, sealing devices shall be used whenever the space between the shell ID and the OTL exceeds 3/4 in (19 mm).

14. Sealing devices shall be provided in symmetrical pairs and shall not extend beyond the baffle edges. When sealing devices are required, at least one pair shall be provided for shells up to 23-in (584-mm) nominal ID. Larger shells shall be fitted with at least two pairs.

15. Tie rods and spacers may be used as sealing devices, provided that the spacers are permanently centered on the tie rods.

16. The attachment details of dummy tubes shall be subject to approval.

17. Minimum seal-strip thickness shall be 1/4 in (6.4 mm). Seal strips shall not be thicker than the larger of 1/4 in (6.4 mm) or the transverse-baffle thickness.

Longitudinal baffles.   Specify the methods that are acceptable for minimizing thermal and fluid leakage of longitudinal baffles, including the manner of baffle-to-shell sealing. For air-gap baffles, require the manufacturer to specify the thicknesses of the parallel plates and the method of sealing the edges.

Shells and shell covers.   The manufacturer's standards specify minimum cylinder and formed-head thicknesses for shells and shell covers. You may wish to supersede the tabulated thicknesses with a table that more closely fits your requirements.

Rolled-plate shells.   Neither HEI nor TEMA standards address the required roundness of rolled-plate shells. Adding requirements to the mechanical specifications may forestall problems. Examples are:

1. Completed shells shall allow a metal template to pass completely through the shell without binding. The template shall consist of two rigid disks, rigidly centered perpendicularly on a shaft 12 in (305 mm) apart.

2. Except for U-tube exchangers and kettle-type reboilers, shell covers shall be removable.

Vapor belts and expansion joints.   The TEMA, HEI, and API standards do not cover vapor belts. The *TEMA Standards* cover thick-walled expansion joints and refer the purchaser to the EJMA standards for thin-walled ones. The HEI and API standards do not cover expansion joints. Therefore, it is necessary to provide the details of your requirements in parts specifications. (See Chap. 6.)

Channels, bonnets, and return covers.   For these parts, it is adequate to specify conformity with the manufacturers' standards. Consider specifying that all welds of pass partitions to channel barrels and tubesheets be fully penetrating. Also consider specifying that welded multipass channels and bonnets must be stress-relieved before machining.

Closures, bolting flanges, and quick-opening covers.   Specify the acceptability of or requirement for welded closures and bolting flanges. Describe the kinds of quick-opening closures that are acceptable in terms of safety and effectiveness. It is essential to require a safety mechanism to be provided that will prevent opening a quick-opening closure when there is pressure in the tubes or shell.

Here is a checklist of flange specification options:

1. Flange type
    a. Welding-neck
    b. Slip-on
    c. Lap-joint (and several modifications)
    d. Loose-ring (optional type)
    e. Integral-ring
2. Flange facing
    a. Fully confined
    b. Tongue-and-groove
    c. Semiconfined (rabbet)
    d. Raised-face
    e. Flat-face

Gaskets.   In specifying gaskets, state the material, thickness, and minimum ring and rib widths. Bear in mind that the *ASME Code*'s recommended values for yield and tightness multiplier (y and m) are not mandatory, and state any deviations from its tabulated values that must be used in design. State whether gaskets used in hydrostatic testing are to remain in place and whether or not it is permissible to use gasket dope or sealant. Also specify the number of spare gaskets that the manufacturer must provide.

Bolting.   Use the material specifications from the applicable pressure vessel code to specify bolting material. Provide sketches of acceptable shoulder-bolt configurations, or require sketches to be submitted for ones that are proposed. Specify the fraction of the total number of bolts that are required to be shoulder bolts. Other items to specify are minimum and maximum permissible sizes, requirements for special washers, such as conically shaped spring washers, and the impermissibility of using studs threaded into tapped holes.

Flanged connections.   Specify flanged connections by listing the nominal pipe size of the neck, the material specification and thickness of the neck, the flange rating and standards, flange facing, and type. This is a typical abbreviated description:

12-in SA 106 × ½-in wall with 300-lb ANSI SA 105 RTJ WN

This describes a 12-in pipe neck of steel to ASME Code specification SA 106 that is ½ in thick and to which is welded a 300-lb American National Standards welding-neck flange. The flange is forged to specification SA-105 and has a ring-joint facing. Use similar descriptions for long welding necks and slip-on and ring-flange connections. More generally, specify the types of flanges and facings and the materials that are required or permissible for different services and operating conditions.

To avoid limiting the shellside or tubeside MAWP to what the nozzle reinforcement will permit, specify 100 percent reinforcement for all nozzles. To minimize turbulence where nozzles pierce shells and channels and to make maintenance easier, specify that nozzles are to be flush with inside surfaces. However, specify also that weld shrinkage deformations shall not be corrected by grinding into the metal of the inner surfaces.

Include minimum sizes for fabricated flanged nozzles by specifying that long welding necks must be used below the minimum size. Specify any restrictions on using axial and tangential connections and nozzle location requirements at shell inlets and outlets. Detail requirements for eliminating dead spaces near inlet and outlet shell nozzles.

Screwed connections.   Screwed connections are used mostly for vents, drains, and instrument connections. The *TEMA Standards* for couplings were discussed in Chap. 8. The common American standards for couplings are 150 lb, 3000 lb, and 6000 lb. Of these, the 150-lb standard should be used only in exchangers that are used in noncritical low-pressure services and are constructed of high-alloy materials.

Couplings are made as half couplings and full couplings. Variations include socket-welding couplings and threadolets. Specify the size, type, material of construction, and rating. You may cite the manufacturer's standard for requirements for threaded vents, drains, and instrument connections. However, it is clearer to list the number, location, and service of these connections and chemical cleaning connections or special vent nozzle arrangements on sketches.

Supports. To obtain adequate supports, include wind loads, earthquake zones, externally applied loads, and bundle-pulling force in mechanical specifications. To minimize corrosion, require all attachment welds of supports and handling fixtures to be continuous except where they cross main seams. At seam-crossing points, require attachments to be ground to a radius that will permit their clearing the weld.

Lifting fixtures and attachments. Use a sketch to specify the sling arrangement on which lifting fixtures are to be or have been designed. Sketches are also useful in specifying lifting davits, channel-cover hinges, and bundle-pulling attachments.

Elements of Procedure Specifications

Procedure specifications should be written for fabrication, nondestructive examination and testing, inspection, maintenance, and repairs. Pressure vessel codes require qualified written procedures for work on pressure parts, as do codes that govern inspection, alteration, and repairs. They also require workers who do the work to be qualified in using the procedures. The codes distinguish between the parameters that may be varied without requalifying the procedures and workers and those for which a change requires requalification. Noncode procedure specifications should parallel the form of code procedures.

Write procedures in terse, simple language. Include the following:

1. A title that describes the work

2. Specifications of the materials or parts involved

3. A description of the limits of the procedure's applicability

4. Specifications of the materials, supplies, and services to be used

5. Specifications of the machines and tools to be used

6. A description of parameters and techniques to be used and their acceptable ranges of variation

Combine the specification number and job description in the title. Examples are:

1. Procedure Specification No. W-201. Gas-tungsten arc-welding (GTAW) austenitic stainless-steel tubes to austenitic stainless-steel tubesheets.

2. Procedure Specification No. F-121. Roller-expanding heat exchanger tubes into tubesheets.

3. Procedure Specification No. NDE-30. Fluid-penetrant examination of tube-to-tubesheet welds.

4. Procedure Specification No. T-4. Hydrostatic-testing shell-and-tube heat exchangers.

State the specification numbers of the materials upon which the work is to be done and the thicknesses and material forms that define the limits of the procedure's applicability. This abstract from a procedure specification for welding tubes to tubesheets shows how:

Tube materials. The tubing shall conform with ASME specification no. SA-249-TP304, which is found in materials group no. P-8 of QW-422, *P-Numbers Grouping of Base Metals for Qualifications* of Section IX of the *ASME Boiler and Pressure Vessel Code.*

Tubesheet material. The tubesheet material shall conform with ASME specification no. SA-240-TP304 for plate, which is found in materials group no. P-8 of QW-422, *P-Numbers Grouping of Base Metals for Qualifications* of Section IX of the *ASME Boiler and Pressure Vessel Code.*

Base-metal description. This procedure is for welding ¾-in-OD × 0.049-in-thick tubes to a 2-in-thick tubesheet in which the ligament between the holes is ³⁄₁₆ in nominal.

Filler metal. No filler metal shall be used.

The continuation of the welding procedure abstract illustrates how to describe materials and services.

Shielding gas. Shielding gas shall be pure argon, flowing at a rate of 15 ft^3/h.

Cleaning materials. The solvent for cleaning the tube ends and tubesheet shall be acetone. A volatile nonchlorinated solvent may be used when it is not safe to use acetone, provided that it leaves no residue upon evaporation.

Air for drying the solvent-washed parts shall be provided in sufficient volume to dry the parts. The air supply shall be filtered dry air with a dew point of −20°F. Drying-air temperature shall be no less than 100°F.

When machines and tools may affect the quality and character of the work, specify them in detail. Rolling equipment might be described as follows:

Tube-rolling equipment.   The tube-rolling machine shall be an Airetool Division of Dresser Industries model no. 966, 725 r/min electric rolling motor, with torque control model no. 113-25-A or Airetool Airtrol air-driven model no. 950, 1250 r/min rolling motor with automatic torque-sensing cam. Equivalent motors and torque controls manufactured by Elliott Company or Wilson Manufacturing Co. are acceptable.

Airetool tool no. 1229, stock no. 5027100, having three rolls no. R-11, stock no. 58820, and mandrel no. M-59, stock no. 2528300, supplied by Airetool shall be used.

The torque analyzer to be used for verifying torque settings shall be a Cleco model DWTS-150 torque analyzer as manufactured by Dresser Industries.

Describe the parameters and techniques in language familiar to people who do the work. This tube-to-tubesheet welding procedure is typical:

Preparation of base metal.   The tubesheet face shall be machined to 125 rms or smoother. Hole edges on the front face shall be prepared for welding by chamfering to a 45° angle with ⅛-in legs. The surface to be welded shall be wire-brushed with fine austenitic steel wire brushes and solvent-washed and air-dried immediately before welding. No rust, oil, grease, or other foreign matter shall remain on the surfaces to be welded.

Subsequent to cleaning, the tube ends shall be positioned to project not less than ¹⁄₁₆ in or more than ⅛ in beyond the tubesheet face. The tube position shall be fixed by locking in place with a Haskel HydroSwage and tube-lock tool as supplied by Torque and Tension Equipment Inc. of Santa Clara, California. No lubricant shall be used in tube locking.

The tube position shall not be fixed by roller expanding.

Preheating.   No preheating shall be done.

Minimum welding temperature.   No welding shall be performed when the temperature of the parts is less than 60°F.

Postweld heat treatment.   No postweld heat treatment shall be done.

Welding process.   The welding shall be done by the gas-tungsten arc-welding process using a nonconsumable, thoriated tungsten electrode and manual equipment. Filler metal shall not be used. Shielding gas shall flow around the electrode at a rate of 15 ft³/h.

Electrical characteristics.   The welding current shall be direct, high-frequency, straight-polarity with the base metal on the positive side of the line. Voltage shall be 12 V. Current flow shall be 90 to 110 A.

Electrode and shielding cup.   The electrode shall be ⅛ in in diameter, shielded by a cup having a ⅜-in-diameter orifice.

Position.   The tubesheet shall be in the vertical plane. Welding shall be upward backhand and downward forehand.

Number of passes.   Welding shall be completed in one pass with an overlap of approximately ¼ in beyond the starting point of the weld. The weld shall be faired smooth at the stopping point. Excess weld metal shall be removed from the tube opening.

Defects and repairs.   Any cracks, blowholes, or porosity disclosed by visual or nondestructive examination shall be filed to sound metal or to the root of the weld, solvent-cleaned, air-dried, and rewelded. If required, bare filler metal ¹⁄₁₆ in in diameter may be used to replace metal lost in filing. The analysis of the filler metal and weld deposit shall be compatible with that of the base metal.

When you examine procedure specifications for joining tubes to tubesheets, be sure that these items are covered:

1. Tube-hole and tube-end cleaning.
2. Measures to be taken to maintain the tubesheet perpendicular to the longitudinal axis of the exchanger and the tube holes aligned end to end.
3. The sequence in which the tubes are to be joined to the tubesheets.
4. The surface condition required after the joining is completed.
5. For roller expanding:
    a. Minimum and maximum wall reduction and torque cutoff setting.
    b. Frequency of checking torque cutoff setting with a torque analyzer.
    c. Lubrication to be used.
    d. Technique, including depth of rolling, method of feeding, and retraction. For thick tubesheets, depth is to be rolled in one pass, rolling progression, and overlap.
    e. For hydroexpanding, the hydraulic pressure and mandrel insertion depth.
    f. For welding, the welding procedure specification.
    g. The specimen size to be used in qualification testing and the qualification tests to be performed.
    h. Repair procedures for joints that fail the tightness test on the finished exchanger.

References

1. Kenneth W. Houp and Thomas E. Pearsall, *Reporting Technical Information*, 4th ed., Glencoe Publishing Co., Encino, Calif., 1980.
2. *ASME Boiler and Pressure Vessel Code*, American Society of Mechanical Engineers, New York. (New editions are published at 3-year intervals.)
3. *Standards of the Tubular Exchanger Manufacturers Association*, 8th ed., The Tubular Exchanger Manufacturers Association, Tarrytown, N.Y., 1989.
4. *Standard for Power Plant Heat Exchangers*, 1st ed., The Heat Exchange Institute, Cleveland, 1980; Addendum 1, 1984.
5. *Standards for Closed Feedwater Heaters*, 4th ed., The Heat Exchange Institute, Cleveland, 1984.

Index

Page numbers in *italic* type indicate illustrations.

Crossover area (turnaround space)
(*Cont.*):
TEMA Standards requirements for,
242

Dam baffle, 35
Danger category, 449, 599
Dead spot between tubesheet and first
flow baffle, 308, 554, *555*
Deburring tubing, 79
Degreasing of tubing, 75
Derating, 386
Design agency, 465
Design agent, 468
(*See also* User: designated agent of)
Design conditions, specifying, 595
Design maximum working pressure, 35,
465, 597
Design metal temperature, 465, 466
Design point, 504, 509, 587
Design specification, 461, 462
Design temperature, 465, 510
Destructive testing of tubing, 81
Desuperheating zone in feedwater
heater, 23, 35, 318–321
Details and drawings, specifying
requirements for, 574, 576
on bundle drawings, 577
for channels, bonnets, return covers,
and shell covers, 578
for shells, 578
Detector-probe testing methods, 149
Detnaformed tube-to-tubesheet joints, 171
Diagnosing exchanger ailments, 525–565
Diaphragm, 35, 245, 246, 252
(*See also* External-bolted-cover
manway)
Differential-pressure design, 344–346,
597
Diffuser plate, 263
Dishing of tubesheets due to tube
expanding, 169, 364
Disk-and-doughnut baffles, 23, 35
Distortions, examining exchanger for, 527
Distribution belt, 296, *297*, 298
adding to existing shells, 443
(*See also* Vapor belt)
Divided flow, 12, 14
Dome space, 319
Double-block valves for isolating
in-service exchangers, 375, 412
Double grooves, 36
Double-segmental baffles, 23, 36, 319,
326, 327
Double split flow, 12
Double tubesheets, 36, 127, 144, 229,
233, 235, 236
conventional, construction of, 127, 129,
130, 132, 135, 170
integral, 133–136, 229
Drain, tubesheet, of vertical exchanger,
141

Drains and draining:
cascading, 33
feedwater heater, 315, 509
flashing, protection for, 29
of heads, 220, 221
location of in shell, 314
of straight-tube exchangers, 228
Drains cooler, 24, 29
Drains inlet, 29
(*See also* Subcooling zone in feedwater
heaters)
Drains outlet, 24
Drains subcooling-zone bypass, 25
Drawings, 573, 574
Drill drift, 125, 362, 603
Drill-type external cleaners, 397, 398
brushes, cutters, and heads for use
with, 398, *399, 400,* 401
drives for, 400, *401, 402*
(*See also* Internal cleaners)
Drilling, 123–127, 330–331
baffles and supports, 330, 364
BTA: gun drills for, 126
manual laying out prior to, *124*
multiple-spindle, 125
numerically controlled, 331
post-and-beam drilling machines for, 125
radial drills for, 123
stack, *124,* 330, 331
of tubesheets, 123–127, 363, 506, 556
twist drills for, 126
Drilling pitch distance, 224, 225, 257
for HEI power plant exchangers, 224,
506, 507
minimum, specifying, 603
for *TEMA Standards* exchangers, 224,
495
Drilling pitch patterns, 46, 223, 225, 323
accessibility for cleaning with, 224
ligament widths with, 224, 225
on-center, 226
radial, 224
rotated square, 224
rotated triangular, 223, 317
spread, 224
square, 223, 224, 317
straddling centerlines, 226
triangular, 223, 317
Drips, 315
Dual-gauge tubes, 37, 87, *88*
Dual units, use of in specifications, 570
Dummy tube, 37
(*See also* Sealing devices)

Eddy-current testing, 76, 91, 228, 413, 427
specifying requirement for, 602
Effective surface, 37
Egg-crate baffles and supports, 38, 331
EJMA (Expansion Joint Manufacturers
Association), 305, 562
Elliptical-head low-pressure manway
access channel, 19, 250

NTIW (*see* No tubes in window)
Nuclear Board, 451

Off-line cleaning methods, 395
   (*See also* Chemical cleaning; Hydraulic
     cleaning; Mechanical cleaning)
Offset bend lines, 45
   (*See also* U-tube bundle)
Offset nozzle, 45
On-stream (on-line) cleaning, 409, 410
One-pass shell, 12, 14
Operating pressure, 45
Order-of-governance statement, 570
Orientation, specifying, 583
Orifice baffles, 45
Outer tube center (OTC), 45, 225
Outer tube limit (OTL), 45, 225, 226
Outside-packed floating head: TEMA
   Type P, 235, 236
Overdesign, 528–536
Owner's responsibilities, 461
   (*See also* User: responsibilities of)

Packaging:
   of tubing, 82
   of U tubes, 89
Packed floating-head problems, 563–565
Packed tube-to-tubesheet joints, 155, 156
Packing ring, 45
Packingbox, 45, 235, 236
Paragraph numbering of specifications,
   569–570
Partial-pass, full-length subcooler, 320
Partial retubing, 433, 439
Parting line [*see* Burn (parting) line in
   feedwater heater shell]
Parts specifications, 602
Pass arrangements, tubeside, 215,
   220–221
   in fixed-tubesheet exchangers, 229
   layouts, schematic of, 220
   for mixed flow, 222
   number of passes in, 215–217
   for pie flow, 222
   for quadrant flow, 220
   for ribbon flow, 47, 219
   for U-tube exchangers, 237, 239
Pass-partition cover, 46, 244, 245
   bolting ring and bolts for, 246, 258
   (*See also* Channels)
Pass-partition groove, 19, 511
Pass partitions, shellside, 332–335, *336,*
   337, 593
   hollow core, 332, 335
   insulated, 332, 335
   packed, *338*
   plug-welded to shell, *336*
   for removable bundles, 335
   single and multiflex, *338*
   for two-pass construction, *335*
   uninsulated, 332, 335
   welded, 332

Pass partitions, tubeside, 215–222
   API Standard 660 requirements for
     welding of, 218
   bending of, 253, 254
   bolting rings for, 246
   bypassing of, 45, 219, 366
   construction of, 253–260
   for converting single- to two-pass
     construction, 257
   erosion of due to bypassing, 520
   for feedwater heaters, 246
   floating, construction of, 259
   fluted, 258
   inspection of, 366
   minimum thicknesses in manufactur-
     ers' standards, 253–254
   sealing to tubesheets of, 216
   space for, 216, 217
   in TEMA C and N and D construction,
     218, 219, 258
   thick, suggested modifications of, 257
   tightness of gasketed channel-
     to-tubesheet and welds of to
     tubesheets, 218
   in U-tube construction, 237
   welded, 258
Passivating of heat-treated tubing, 76
Patches, 380
Performance, specifying, 568, 583–595
Performance index, 394
Performance qualifications, 461, 484
Performance testing, 526
Pickling of heat-treated tubing, 76
Pie-flow layouts, 222
Pipe shells, 281, 282, 290
   range of sizes of thick-walled extruded
     pipe for, table of, 290
   TEMA shell sizes and permissible pipe
     sizes available in the United
     States, table of, 283–289
Pipe tolerances, 282, 291
Piping causes of trouble, 548
Pitch (*see* Drilling pitch patterns)
   (*See also* Baffle pitch; Drilling pitch
     distance)
Pitch pattern (*see* Drilling pitch patterns)
Plain-face tubesheet confinements, 46, 106
Plasma cladding, 201
Plate shell (*see* Shells)
Plug (*see* Tube plug)
Plug mandrel, 71, 74
Plug welding, 46
Pneumatic testing, 598
Poisson effect in tube expanding, 165
Pop-a-Plug (*see* Breakaway plug)
Position:
   channel down, 33
   channel up, 33
   designating, 15
   of feedwater heaters, 25, *28*
   inclined, 41
   specifying, 583, 586